Winc

Fanta
available fo

Conferences, Civil Ceremonies, Christenings, Dinners, Dances, Filming, 'Fun Days', Marquee Events, Meetings, Seminars, Team Building,Wedding Receptions, Xmas Parties, Wakes

A viewing is strongly recommended!
For further information
or arrange an appointment to view please call:-
AM & PM CATERING
020 8789 4447

info@winchesterhouse.co.uk www.winchesterhouse.co.uk

londonlaunch

London's Events Community

Every year over 1million event planners turn to Londonlaunch.com to find the venues and suppliers they need. Imagine what your presence on Londonlaunch.com could do to your sales? No don't imagine, let someone who knows tell you...

"Since joining Londonlaunch.com, we have shot up in Google rankings – the system works brilliantly."

Katie Soutar, Sales & Marketing – Owen Brown Ltd.

"We've had great fun with the new features on Londonlaunch! With the content of our own Londonlaunch profile and venue pages changing on a regular basis, the easy-to-use content management system is a huge asset of the website. Well done Londonlaunch.com!"

Julian Saipe, Managing Director – Zafferano Catering

the facts speak for themselves

- 103,000 event buyers source from the site every month
- 1000's of £'s in e-commerce put through the site
- Over 250 enquiry forms completed every month, in addition to telephone enquiries
- £1.77 average cost-per-lead
- 210 impressions per featured business / month on average
- Top of the search engines for key London event-related terms
- The most popular events portal in the world
- The entire events industry is covered

Call our Team **NOW** to find out more

+44 (0)20 7471 2600 | www.londonlaunch.com
enquiries@londonlaunch.com

◎Harden's

PARTY, CONFERENCE & EVENT GUIDE

2010|11

Venue and Services for Corporate and Social Events

hardens.com/party

in association with

HotelMap.com™

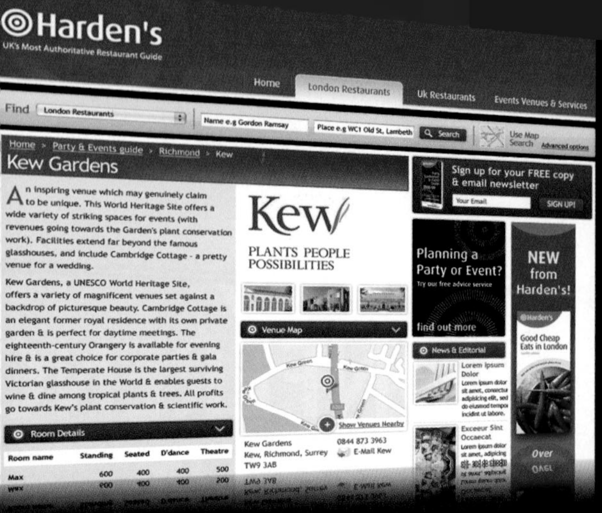

Search online
www.hardens.com/party

Sales & Marketing Manager: Ellie Roberts
Sales Executive: Samara Burke
Production Manager: Julie Pallot
Cover design: Margaret Vanschaemelhout
Research Assistants: Lacara Barnes-Rowe, Gaz Kllokoqi

ISBN 978-1-873721-92-6

British Library Cataloguing-in-Publication data:
A catalogue record for this book is available from the British Library.

Printed and bound in Spain by Graphy Cems, Navarra

Harden's Limited
14 Buckingham Street
London WC2N 6DF

CONTENTS

INTRODUCTION

Some people are occasionally kind enough to describe this guide – now in its eleventh edition – as the 'bible' of the party and events world. It is certainly true that – so far as we know – this is the only regularly-published annual guide solely concerned with the huge range of venues and services which are available for events in and around London.

This year we are delighted to be publishing the guide in association with HotelMap. Through its unique booking technology, HotelMap enables venues and event bookers to accommodate their clients with enormous ease. Its free to install and can earn the user substantial commissions.

Some first-time users of this guide may assume that this publication is like our restaurant guides, so it's perhaps worth noting that it is very different. Publication of this guide is largely paid for by its advertisers, and this guide seeks to make no subjective judgements that any venue or service is any 'better' than another.

This is just as well, as whether you have a good experience at any particular venue is likely to have much to do with what you personally make of it.

In the same way as our restaurant information, the content of this guide is available in more dynamic format on our website (at www.hardens.com/party). Please visit that address for regularly updated information.

We hope you'll find this book – and our website – a handy resource throughout the coming year. If you have any suggestions for improvements to this guide, please let us know at party@hardens.com.

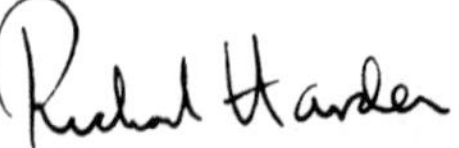

kingsplace
EVENTS

LOCATED JUST 5 MINUTES WALK FROM ST PANCRAS STATION, KINGS PLACE IS A STUNNING NEW EVENTS VENUE

With the emphasis on technology, this amazing venue has seen the lights of some of the most high profile events in London • Versatile for day time or evening events, the several different spaces set the tone to deliver great experiences • Water views onto Regent's Canal, two fantastic art galleries, concert halls, café, restaurant and bar complete this exciting building.

90 York Way London N1 9AG **event bookings: 020 7014 2838**
events@kingsplaceevents.co.uk www.kingsplaceevents.co.uk

HOW TO USE

Price bands

The price bands indicate, in the most general terms, the overall minimum level of expenditure per head you are likely to incur in giving a party at a particular venue.

£B – Budget
It should be possible to organise a drinks party for about the same cost per head as an evening in a wine bar, or a party with food and drink for about the same cost as eating in a modestly priced restaurant.

£M – Medium
The costs of a party with wine and food will generally run at, or a little above, those of providing similar catering in a middle to high class restaurant. Drinks parties will probably cost as much per head as a meal in a modestly priced restaurant.

£E – Expensive
Outside the budget of most private individuals and mainly, therefore, used for corporate events.

Where two levels are shown (eg £B-M), the likely range of expenditure straddles two bands.

Capacities - e.g. (150,100,–,125)

The maximum normal capacity of the venue for a private function is given in bold type at the beginning of each entry.

Individual room capacities are given in the small print. This list of rooms may not be exhaustive – details are given only for the more important or interesting rooms, or, in some cases, rooms which are representative of other similar rooms.

We list capacities of which we are aware in the following format:
(Standing, Seated, Cabaret, Theatre-style)

Where we do not hold information to intimate suitability in the relevant configuration a dash (–) appears – this does not necessarily mean that the room is unsuitable for that purpose.

Alcohol, amplified music and dancing

Permitted, unless otherwise indicated. The fact that no restrictions are noted does not imply that 'anything goes'.

HOW TO USE

Restrictions on use

Any explicit restrictions upon hirers or types of function are noted. The absence of such a note does not, of course, mean that the venue may not be selective about the functions and hirers which it will accept.

Catering

Restaurants, hotels, wine bars and pubs will generally expect to provide all the food and drink for any event on their premises.

For other venues, we give a guide to stipulations concerning catering arrangements, as follows:

"in-house catering" – there is a resident caterer, the use of which (unless an alternative is stated) is generally obligatory.

"xco catering" – using the specified caterer is obligatory.

"list of caterers" – one of a list of approved outside caterers must be used.

"hirer's choice of caterer" – you can, in principle, bring in the caterer of your choice (though some venues may wish to vet your proposed arrangements).

Even where there is no obligation to use a particular caterer, you may find that there is a resident caterer which is able to offer keener prices than an outsider.

Finishing times

There are venues where the finishing time for functions is not at all open to negotiation, and others which are almost completely flexible. For many, the question is a grey area – you may find that there is a 'preferred' finishing time, but that, for an extra payment, a later conclusion is perfectly feasible. For venues which have a meaningful general rule about the finishing time for events, we give the time in the small print – we must emphasise, however, that this can be no more than a broad indication. In some cases, the time given is subject to a licensing extension being obtained, but this will generally be dealt with by the venue.

Days and times available annual closures

Except as indicated (immediately after the finishing time, where applicable), venues are generally available daily throughout the year for day and evening functions. Many venues, however, close around Christmas and the New Year, and many City venues have an August holiday.

Private Venues

The Academy WC1
£M-E, (40,15,–,30)
21 Gower St
Ⓣ 020 7631 4115
Ⓕ 020 7636 3442
Ⓦ hardens.com/party/academy
Ⓔ resacademy@theetoncollection.com
Intimate spaces for a variety of functions, in a Bloomsbury hotel consisting of five Georgian townhouses. Its amenities include a small garden. / 11pm; in-house caterers; no amplified music; Boardroom (20,15,–,–).

Adam Street WC2
£M, (350,80,120,60)
9 Adam St
Ⓣ 020 7379 8000
Ⓕ 020 7520 9356
Ⓦ hardens.com/party/adamstreet
Ⓔ neda@adamstreet.co.uk
Intriguingly located in c18 vaults beneath the Strand, this fashionable members club comprises a restaurant, a club bar, a dance floor and private dining rooms. Non-members hire individual rooms or the whole space on special occasions. / 3am; not available Sundays; in-house caterers; Gallery (100,60,–,60); Rehearsal Rm (80,–,–,50); Dining Rm (–,12,–,–).

Addington Palace CR0
£M, (750,750,750,600)
Gravel Hill
Ⓣ 020 8662 5060
Ⓕ 020 8662 5026
Ⓦ hardens.com/party/addington
Ⓔ info@addington-palace.co.uk
Imposing, listed Palladian building, once the country retreat of the Archbishops of Canterbury, set in 163 acres of grounds landscaped by Capability Brown. The bright and airy Winter Garden is licensed for weddings. / midnight; hirer's choice of caterer (in-house available); Winter Garden (100,60,50,90); Great Hall (200,120,–,150); Dining Room (50,40,–,40); Robing Room (80,–,–,40); Empire Room (40,30,–,30); Wellington Room (50,40,–,35); Chadwick Healey (20,20,–,–); Marquee (–,750,–,600).

Admiral Coddrington SW3
£M, (60,50,–,–)
17 Mossop St
Ⓣ 020 7581 0005
Ⓦ hardens.com/party/cod
A well-known, characterful Chelsea pub, which also boasts a major restaurant operation nowadays. The upstairs function room is a handy size for many private events. / midnight; in-house caterers; Restaurant (–,50,–,–); Bar (60,50,–,–); Garden (30,20,–,–); Function Room (60,30,–,–).

Alain Ducasse at the Dorchester W1
£M-E, (–,18,–,–)
Park Ln
Ⓣ 020 7629 8866
Ⓕ 020 7629 8686
Ⓦ hardens.com/party/ducasse
Ⓔ alainducasse@thedorchester.com
The Park Lane outpost of one of the world's starriest chefs. Its most interesting private dining facility is the Table Lumière – a lavishly dressed dining table within the main restaurant, but cut off from general view by a spangly curtain which wouldn't look out of place on Star Trek. / 10pm; Tue-Sat, available from noon; in-house caterers; no amplified music; Salon Prive (–,12,–,–); Salon Park Lane (–,30,–,–); Table Lumiere (–,7,–,–).

Albannach WC2
£M, (400,45,–,–)
66 Trafalgar Sq
Ⓣ 020 7930 0066
Ⓕ 020 7389 9800
Ⓦ hardens.com/party/albannach
Ⓔ info@albannach.co.uk
The location is hard to beat for centrality, and when this (modestly) Scottish-themed, modern bar/restaurant is taken over in its entirety, it has a good capacity for medium-size events. / 1am, Fri & Sat 3am; not available Sun, Sat L; in-house caterers; no amplified music; no dancing; Private Rm (–,20,–,–).

Aldwych Theatre WC2

£M, (200,–,–,1163)
Aldwych
T 020 7836 5537
F 020 7240 0633
W hardens.com/party/aldwychtheatre
E email@aldwychtheatre.co.uk

A large theatre (opened in 1905), available for hire subject to the constraints of the current production. / very restricted availability; 1am; hirer's choice of caterer; no dancing; Bar (200,–,–,–).

Alexandra Palace & Park N22

£M, (10250,5000,5000,7250)
Alexandra Palace Way
T 020 8365 2121
W hardens.com/party/alexandrapalacepark
E info@alexandrapalace.com

Set within 196 acres of parkland, this enormous Victorian pile enjoys splendid panoramic views of London. Is it the most flexible venue in town? In its selection of distinctive halls and rooms you could comfortably seat events ranging from 10-5,000 people. On-site parking for 2,000 cars. / in-house caterers; Great Hall (10250,5000,5000,7250); West Hall (2500,2000,2000,2500); Palace Restaurant (400,360,360,360); Londesborough Rm (200,156,156,170); Palm Court 5 (75,–,–,50); Palm Court 1 (25,–,–,–); Palm Court 2/3 (40,–,–,30); Palm Court 4 (30,–,–,25).

Alexandra Palace Ice Rink N22

£M, (1750,–,–,–)
Alexandra Palace Way
T 020 8365 4381
F 020 8883 3999
W hardens.com/party/alexandrapalaceicerink
E icerink@alexandrapalace.com

You can take over the whole Ally Pally rink by the hour – ideal for a skating birthday party. They have even hosted a wedding reception. Between mid 2010 and June 2011 it is undergoing complete refurbishment, and – though a temporary rink will be in operation – availability is uncertain. / 8pm; weekends available from 5pm; hirer's choice of caterer (in-house available); no alcohol.

All Hallows EC3

£M, (120,70,–,65)
Byward Street
T 0845 618 7274
W hardens.com/party/allhallows
E info@beyondboyle.com

A contemporary building next to an ancient church by the Tower of London well-suited to meetings, workshops, parties and dinners. / 11.30pm.

All Star Lanes (Brick Lane) E1

£M, (500,200,400,50)
95 Brick Lane
T 020 7426 9205
W hardens.com/party/allstarbricklane
E sally@allstarlanes.co.uk

Set on a mezzanine floor, the private room, Penthouse, is available for hire. The space is ideal for corporate events and client entertainment or for screenings, conferences and private dining. Penthouse boasts 3 bowling lanes, its own cocktail bar, canapé menu, a 42" plasma screen (with karaoke!) and room for dancing. / Mon-Thu 11.30pm, Fri-Sat 12.30am, Sun 10.30pm; in-house caterers; Main Hall (350,200,200,–); Private Room (130,30,–,–); Private Room (120,–,–,–); Private Room (100,–,–,–); Private Room (80,–,–,–); Private Room (60,–,–,–); Private Room (50,–,–,–); Private Room (40,–,–,–); Private Room (30,–,–,–).

Alma SW18

£B, (80,60,–,–)
499 Old York Rd
T 020 8870 2537
W hardens.com/party/alma
E alma@youngs.co.uk

A popular Wandsworth pub, with an upstairs parlour available for presentations, dinners and drinks and – perhaps rather surprisingly – also for weddings. / midnight; in-house caterers.

Altitude 360 SW1
£M-E, (1200,350,–,400)
29th Floor
T 0843 309 4461
F 020 7627 4271
W www.altitudelondon.com
E events@altitudelondon.com

Altitude 360° is London's premier venue in the sky, located on the 29th floor of the Millbank Tower in Westminster. With a contemporary setting and panoramic views, Altitude 360° is an iconic space for any corporate or private event. / 2am; in-house caterers; River Room (600,300,–,300); Millbank Media Center (300,–,–,300); Altitude 360° (600,350,–,400).

Amadeus Centre W9
£M, (250,180,150,80)
50 Shirland Rd
T 020 7286 1686
F 020 7226 1225
W hardens.com/party/amadeuscentre
E info@amadeuscentre.co.uk
This converted c19 century chapel in Little Venice offers a characterful space, with good natural light for receptions, parties and private events. / Fri- Sat 2am; otherwise 6pm; not available Mon, Wed, Thu & Sun evenings; list of caterers; Lower Hall (250,80,40,80).

Amaya SW1
£M, (–,14,–,–)
Halkin Arc
T 020 7823 1166
F 020 7259 6464
W hardens.com/party/amaya
E amaya@realindianfood.com
This stylish 'nouvelle Indian' restaurant in Belgravia is one of London's best subcontinental eateries. Its private dining room is called The Silver Room, and is available for meetings as well as meals. / midnight; in-house caterers; no music; no dancing; Silver Room (–,14,–,–).

Ambassadors Bloomsbury WC1
£M, (250,210,180,250)
12 Upper Woburn Place
T 020 7693 5402
W hardens.com/party/ambassadorsbloomsbury
E meetings@ambassadors.co.uk
Close to Euston, and, five minutes from King's Cross – an 100-bedroom hotel, with eight contemporary meeting rooms, maximum capacity 250. / no pets; midnight, late licence 1am; in-house caterers; Vision (30,18,–,35); Think (40,18,–,39); Innovate (100,63,54,100); Enterprise (250,180,162,250); Prosper (180,108,90,175); Create (40,18,–,39).

Ambassadors Theatre WC2
£M, (–,–,–,403)
West St
T 020 7828 0600
F 020 7828 6882
W hardens.com/party/ambassadorstheatre
Completed in 1913, the original home of 'The Mousetrap' can be hired for presentations and conferences, subject to the constraints of the current production. / restricted availability; available subject to constraints of current production ; hirer's choice of caterer.

America Square Conference Centre EC3
£M-E, (300,200,140,230)
17 Crosswall
T 020 7706 7700
W hardens.com/party/americasquare
Billing itself as 'A Contemporary, Funky Meeting Space in the City' – this purpose-built venue, one minute's walk from Tower Hill is well-suited to business training and conferences. London's original Roman wall runs through the building, adding interest to a number of the spaces. / 11pm; in-house caterers; no live music or discos; no dancing; Ludgate Suite (300,200,140,230); Walbrook Suite (70,60,30,50); Aldgate & Bishopsgate Suites (130,60,–,100); Aldgate Suite (50,–,20,30); Newgate Suite (90,40,40,80); Fleet Suite (140,60,50,90); Bishopsgate Suite (80,–,30,60).

Andaz EC2

£M-E, (700,230,170,250)
Liverpool St
Ⓣ 020 7618 5000
Ⓕ 020 7618 5055
Ⓦ hardens.com/party/andaz
Ⓔ info.londonliv@andaz.com
Formerly called the 'Great Eastern', this was the City's first grand hotel of recent times. It offers a wide range of accommodation with options to suit many types of function. / 1am; Private Dining & Events; Great Eastern (400,220,170,250); Bishopsgate & Chancery (160,94,70,110); Moorgate & Monument (30,26,–,30); Gallery (300,–,–,–); Fenchurch (100,70,–,60).

L'Anima EC2

£M-E, (–,14,–,–)
1 Snowden Street
Ⓣ 020 7422 7000
Ⓦ hardens.com/party/anima
Ⓔ info@lanima.co.uk
This slick City Italian has been one of the best new restaurants to arrive in the City of London in recent years, and is decorated to an unusually high specification. At the rear, it has a very swish, marbled private room.

Annabel's W1

£E, (220,160,–,–)
44 Berkeley Sq
Ⓣ 020 7629 1096
Ⓕ 020 7491 1860
Ⓦ hardens.com/party/annabels
This grand and comfortable Mayfair nightclub has been a legend for decades. It makes an ideal venue for a small to medium-sized party, but the active involvement of a member will be required. / members club; 3am; in-house caterers.

The Antelope SW1

£B-M, (60,30,–,–)
22 Eaton Ter
Ⓣ 020 7824 8512
Ⓦ hardens.com/party/antelope
Ⓔ antelope@fullers.co.uk
A well-known pub, whose character is strongly defined by its pukka location, just off Eaton Square. A pleasant upstairs room is available for receptions and dinners. / 11pm; not available Sun; in-house caterers; no amplified music; no dancing.

AOP Gallery (The Association of Photographers) EC2

£M, (200,100,–,100)
81 Leonard St
Ⓣ 020 7739 6669
Ⓕ 020 7739 8707
Ⓦ hardens.com/party/aop
Ⓔ gallery@aophoto.co.uk
In a warehouse in the heart of trendy Shoreditch, a contemporary photographic gallery available for private events and parties. / midnight; hirer's choice of caterer; no cash bar.

Apartment 195 SW3

£B-M, (100,60,60,55)
195 Kings Rd
Ⓣ 020 7349 4468
Ⓕ 020 7349 4450
Ⓦ hardens.com/party/apartment
Ⓔ events@kornicis.co.uk
This Chelsea bar offers a choice of cosy, clubby spaces for private events, or you can take the whole place. / 11pm; hirer's choice of caterer (in-house available); Cellar (25,15,–,55).

Apex City of London Hotel EC3

£M-E, (100,60,–,80)
1 Seething Ln, Tower Hill
Ⓣ 020 7702 2020
Ⓕ 020 7702 2217
Ⓦ hardens.com/party/apexcityoflondonhotel
Ⓔ london.events@apexhotels.co.uk
A rather businesslike modern hotel. It has a good range of high-spec function accommodation, all of it on a relatively small scale. / 1am; in-house caterers; no amplified music; no dancing; Geneva (50,32,–,50); City Suite (80,60,–,80); New York (40,24,–,40).

Apothecaries' Hall EC4
£M-E, (250,130,–,–)
Blackfriars Ln
Ⓣ 020 7236 1189
Ⓕ 020 7329 3177
Ⓦ hardens.com/party/apothecarieshall
Ⓔ beadle@apothecaries.org
With its lovely approach (through a small, cream-coloured courtyard, off a cobbled lane), its charming hall, its sober Court Room and its Parlour decorated with apothecaries' jars through the centuries, this ancient building offers one of London's most delightful settings. / no paper confetti; 11pm; not weekends; list of caterers; no dancing; Parlour (50,40,–,–); Courtroom (50,40,–,–).

Aqua London W1
£M-E, (800,240,–,–)
240 Regent St
Ⓣ 020 7478 0540
Ⓦ hardens.com/party/aqualondon
Near Oxford Circus, this fifth-floor venue is decked out in glamorous style, has extensive roof terraces and two separate restaurants (Nueva – Spanish, and Kyoto – Japanese). You can hire out the whole place for a big stand-up, or a section, or sections-within-each-section for smaller events. / 1am; in-house caterers; Nueva (400,140,–,–); Nueva Private Glass Dining Room (–,16,–,–); Nueva Private Area With Terrace (60,40,–,–); Kyoto (180,100,–,–); Kyoto Private Glass Dining Room (–,10,–,–).

Aquarium EC1
£M, (500,–,–,–)
Aquarium: 256-260 Old St, EC1V
Ⓣ 020 7251 6136
Ⓕ 020 7253 6999
Ⓦ hardens.com/party/clubaquarium
Ⓔ oj@clubaquarium.co.uk
London's only nightclub with integral swimming pool and Jacuzzi (towels provided) can be booked in its entirety in the early days of the week / Mon-Wed 3am, Thu 6am, Fri 6am, Sat & Sun 24 hour; hirer's choice of caterer; Shark Bar (150,–,–,–); Lounge Bar (100,–,–,–).

Aragon House SW6
£B-M, (220,55,55,–)
247-249 New King's Rd
Ⓣ 020 7731 7313
Ⓦ hardens.com/party/aragonhouse
Ⓔ info@aragonhouse.net
Part of the British Legion building overlooking Parson's Green has been converted into this trendy-looking lounge bar. There's a function room – 'The Blue Room' – available for weddings, parties and events – plus a basement bar opening onto a patio for a drinks party. / midnight; catering in bar is in-house; Function Rm (220,–,–,–).

Armourers' & Braisers' Hall EC2
£M-E, (125,100,–,–)
81 Coleman St
Ⓣ 020 7374 4000
Ⓕ 020 7606 7481
Ⓦ hardens.com/party/armourersbraisershall
Ⓔ info@armourersandbrasiers.co.uk
This grand livery hall (1840s) is notable for its distinctive decoration. Guests are generally received in the rich comfort of the gilt-walled Drawing Room and proceed to the armour-lined, vaulted hall, lit by the candles of the impressive c18 chandeliers. / midnight; list of caterers; Court Rm (–,20,–,–).

Arndale House WC2
£M-E, (250,80,75,180)
13-15 Arundel St
Ⓣ 020 7395 9162
Ⓕ 020 7395 9182
Ⓦ hardens.com/party/arndalehouse
Ⓔ bustillo@iiss.org
The home of the International Institute for Strategic Studies is a remodelled Victorian building by Temple tube. It boasts state-of-the-art conference and presentation facilities, with river views. / no non-IISS events dealing with conflict; 11pm; in-house caterers; 4th Floor Conference Rm (40,24,–,40).

Artesian Well SW8
£B-M, (500,–,–,–)
693 Wandsworth Rd
T 020 7627 3353
F 020 7627 2850
W hardens.com/party/artesianwell
E artesianwell@btconnect.com
A popular Clapham bar part owned by the man who designed Beach Blanket Babylon and whose similarly lavish style suits it well as a venue. There are four rooms over three floors (each with a full bar). The Moody Room boasts a glass dance floor. / 3am; in-house caterers.

Arts Club W1
£M-E, (200,160,120,80)
40 Dover St
T 020 7290 3554
F 020 7409 0913
W www.theartsclub.co.uk
E eventsales@theartsclub.co.uk

"London home of the Muse and the Amuse" - an elegant but unstuffy Mayfair address, whose manageable size and layout make for conviviality, and where the mixed traditional and modern styles of the rooms produce an atmosphere of easy going charm. A paved garden leads off the dining room. / 2am; dining & drawing rms not available Wed eve; hirer's choice of caterer (in-house available); music until 1am; dancing restricted in certain areas; Dining Rm (200,150,120,–); Bar & Conservatory (100,–,–,–); Drawing Rm (80,26,–,–); Garden Rm (100,60,60,80); Board Rm (30,12,–,30).

Arts Depot N12
£B-M, (500,240,160,400)
Tally Ho Corner
T 020 8369 5471
W hardens.com/party/artsdepot
E events@artsdepot.co.uk
A North Finchley arts centre, offering a state-of-the art auditorium, gallery, café and bar. / 11pm; in-house caterers; Main Auditorium (500,240,160,400); Studio Theatre (–,–,–,150); Dance Space (50,72,–,50).

Artworkers Guild, The WC1
£B-M, (70,16,–,100)
6 Queen Sq
T 020 7278 3009
F 020 7833 1828
W hardens.com/party/artworkersguild
E elspeth@artworkersguild.org
An unaltered early-c18 Bloomsbury house, mainly used for lectures with an artistic leaning, but also available for hire for social and business events. / 10pm; closed Sun; hirer's choice of caterer; no amplified music; no dancing; Lecture Hall (–,–,–,100); Master's Room (reception Hall) (50,–,–,–); Gradidge Room (70,16,–,30).

Ascot Racecourse SL5
£M, (1550,1100,900,–)
Ascot
T 01344 878572
F 01344 878569
W hardens.com/party/ascot
E businessandevents@ascot.co.uk
The recently redeveloped Ascot racecourse comes complete with a striking state-of-the-art stand, complete with many modern facilities. / midnight, late licence available; Sodexho.

Athenaeum Hotel W1
£M, (100,50,–,55)
116 Piccadilly
T 020 7499 3464
F 020 7493 0644
W hardens.com/party/athenaeumhotel
E ievents@athenaeumhotel.com
A comfortable modern Mayfair hotel, some of whose smaller function rooms have views of Green Park. For a small and discreet gathering, consider one of the hotel's apartments, located in converted Edwardian townhouses. / 1am; in house or hirer's choice of kosher catering; no amplified music; Ardmore (20,12,–,–); Apartments (–,6,–,–).

The Atlas SW6
£B, (120,40,40,–)
16 Seagrave Rd
T 020 7385 9129
W hardens.com/party/atlas
E theatlas@btconnect.com
A popular gastropub, near Earl's Court, with a good reputation for its cooking. It has two private party rooms (not available independently), one with its own bar. / 11pm (late license till midnight in function room); in-house caterers.

Audley W1
£M, (120,–,–,–)
41-43 Mount St
T 020 7499 1843
F 020 7355 1478
W hardens.com/party/audley
A grand and opulent boozer, in a very smart corner of Mayfair. The private hire possibilities are the cellar bar (cheaper at the weekend) and the upstairs dining room. / Mon-Sat 11pm, Sun 10.30pm; in-house caterers; Upstairs Dining Room (40,–,–,–).

Aura SW1
£M, (210,90,200,–)
48-49 St. James Street
T 020 7499 9999
F 020 7499 8383
W hardens.com/party/aura
E info@the-aura.com
This cool St James's basement venue features classic films projected on the wall over the bar, hydraulically adjustable tables (for cocktails or dining), and tinted mirrors. Generally a bar/restaurant, it's a natural for taking over in its entirety for events. / age 18+; 3.30am; in-house caterers.

Auriol Kensington Rowing Club W6
£M, (110,80,–,–)
14 Lower Mall
T 07931 755946
W hardens.com/party/akrowing
E phil@philtaylor.org.uk
This long-established rowing club, enjoying a splendid location on the paved towpath just upstream of Hammersmith Bridge. A two-storey function suite comes complete with south-facing balcony and terrace, plus a fully equipped commercial kitchen. / 11pm, Fri & Sat, midnight; list of caterers.

Automat W1
£M, (200,110,–,–)
33 Dover St
T 020 7499 3033
F 020 7499 2682
W hardens.com/party/automat
E info@automat-london.com
In a Mayfair side street, this American restaurant has become an international in-crowd destination. Its long and thin configuration – with three very different dining areas – makes taking the whole place the best private dining option. / 1am; in-house caterers; no music; no dancing; Conservatory (–,60,–,–).

Avenue Restaurant & Bar SW1
£M-E, (300,160,–,–)
7-9 St James's St
T 020 7321 2111
F 020 7321 2500
W hardens.com/party/avenuerestaurant
E sarahb@danddlondon.com
Situated in the heart of St James' in Mayfair, the grand, contemporary venue has lofty ceilings and fabulous lighting which will ensure a wonderful experience for your guests. Avenue can seat up to 150 guests or up to 300 standing. The separate private dining room can seat up to 20 guests. / list of kosher food suppliers available; Mon-Sat 1am, Sun 11pm.; in-house caterers.

Avenue House N3
£M, (90,70,60,80)
17 East End Rd
T 020 8346 7812
F 020 8346 3702
W www.avenuehouse.org.uke
E info@avenuehouse.org.uk
A Victorian villa in Finchley, partly rebuilt in recent times, offering a variety of function rooms for 5-90 people. Some are definitely suitable only for business meetings, but others, such as the Drawing Room (the largest) are licensed for weddings. / 11pm, Sat & Sun 11.30pm; hirer's choice of caterer (in-house available); Drawing Rm (90,70,70,80); Stephens Rm (90,69,–,69); Salon (45,35,–,35); Dining Rm (30,–,–,25); Balcony Rm (–,15,–,–); Study Rm (–,–,–,20).

Aviator GU14
£M-E, (150,50,70,90)
Farnborough Road
Ⓣ 01252 555 892
Ⓕ 01252 555 899
Ⓦ hardens.com/party/aviatorfarnborough
Ⓔ meetings@aviatorfarnborough.co.uk
Located near the M3 and M25, and 30 minutes from Heathrow and London – a 4-star with meeting facilities, Sky Bar and brasserie. / 12am, late license available; in-house caterers; 1 (40,20,30,35); 2 (40,20,30,35); 1 & 2 (100,50,70,90); 3 (15,12,12,16); 4 /5 (20,12,12,16); 4 & 5 (50,25,30,45); 6 (15,12,12,16); Boardroom (–,14,18,–); Sky Lounge (80,50,70,50); Deli (40,14,36,30).

Axis WC2
£M, (200,100,–,–)
One Aldwych
Ⓣ 020 7300 0300
Ⓕ 020 7300 0301
Ⓦ hardens.com/party/axisrestaurant
Ⓔ axis@onealdwych.com
Handy for business or gatherings, this unusually-styled basement restaurant is conveniently located on the fringe of Covent Garden. The whole restaurant is available for hire, or there's a choice of six contemporary private rooms for meetings, private dining and receptions. / midnight; in-house caterers; no amplified music; Private Rooms 1 & 2 (100,50,–,–); Private Room 3 (50,30,–,–).

Babalou SW2
£B-M, (2000,–,–,–)
The Crypt
Ⓣ 020 7738 3366
Ⓕ 020 738 3345
Ⓦ hardens.com/party/babalou
Ⓔ info@babalou.net
St Matthew's Church dominates Brixton's main traffic junction, and its crypt – usually a bar – provides a flexible space for private events for 300+. / 6am; in-house caterers; Private Rm X 4 (100,–,–,–).

Babble W1
£B-M, (350,–,–,–)
59 Berkeley Sq
Ⓣ 020 7758 8255
Ⓕ 020 7758 8254
Ⓦ hardens.com/party/babble
Ⓔ info@babble-bar.co.uk
A large bar in a smart Mayfair location. You can hire the whole place – for smaller events (up to 40), you can take your own booth. / in-house caterers.

Babylon W8
£M-E, (150,110,–,–)
99 Kensington High St
Ⓣ 020 7368 3993
Ⓕ 020 7938 2774
Ⓦ hardens.com/party/babylon
Ⓔ babylon@roofgardens.virgin.co.uk
If you want altitude (and are prepared to pay for it), the restaurant above Kensington's amazing Roof Gardens (see also) offers an intriguing venue. / midnight, Sun 5pm; in-house caterers; no amplified music; no dancing; Private Rm (–,12,–,–).

BAC SW11
£B-M, (600,400,400,550)
Lavender Hill
Ⓣ 020 7326 8211
Ⓕ 020 7978 5207
Ⓦ hardens.com/party/bac
Ⓔ venues@bac.org.uk
This impressive Victorian building in Battersea is best known as an arts centre, but it also does big business in the form of weddings and other events. It claims the largest sprung dance floor in the country. / midnight Main Hall, 11pm Lower Hall; hirer's choice of caterer; Lower Hall (200,140,120,180).

BAFTA, 195 Piccadilly W1
£M, (350,204,180,227)
195 Piccadilly
Ⓣ 020 7292 5801
Ⓕ 020 7734 1009
Ⓦ www.195piccadilly.co.uk
Ⓔ events@195piccadilly.co.uk
With its auditorium, state-of-the-art screening rooms and BAFTA's private members bar, this extremely central venue can host private parties, weddings, conferences, launches and board meetings. / 1am;

In-house by The Capital Group; David Lean Room (350,204,180,200); Princess Anne Theatre (–,–,–,227); Run Run Shaw (50,30,–,40); Run Run Shaw/Mezzanine (180,50,–,60); Boardroom (–,20,–,–); Gallery (50,25,–,30).

Baglioni Hotel SW7

£M-E, (100,50,–,60)
60 Hyde Park Gate
T 020 7368 5802
F 020 7368 5701
W hardens.com/party/baglioni
E l.marshall@baglionihotels.com
An Italian-owned boutique hotel overlooking Kensington Gardens, almost Miami-kitsch in décor, with some accommodation for private dinners and receptions. / 2am; in-house caterers.

Bakers' Hall EC3

£B-M, (100,77,–,80)
9 Harp Ln
T 020 7623 2223
F 020 7621 1924
W hardens.com/party/bakershall
E beadle@bakers.co.uk
Located a short step from the Tower, this modern livery hall, lightly wood-panelled, stands at the foot of the company's own office block. / 11pm; weekdays only; list of caterers; no music; no dancing; no cash bar; Court Rm (60,26,–,60).

Balls Brothers SE1

£B, (150,100,100,–)
Balls Brothers: Hays Galleria, SE1
T 020 7407 4301
W www.ballsbrothers.co.uk
E haysgal@ballsbrothers.co.uk
Handy for the City, a traditional-style South Bank wine bar that's available for exclusive hire at weekends.

BALLS BROTHERS
RESTAURANTS BARS & FUNCTION ROOMS

/ 1am; in-house caterers; Bar (150,60,–,–)The Fish Restaurant (–,100,–,–), Terrace Bar (150,80,–,–).

Balls Brothers Lime Street EC3
£B-M, (450,–,–,–)
52 Lime Street
Ⓣ 020 7283 0841
Ⓦ www.ballsbrothers.co.uk
Ⓔ limest@ballsbrothers.co.uk

Classic City Wine Bar Restaurant in great location next to the iconic Lloyds Building and close to all major transport links offers stylish food, great wines and fantastic hospitality. All events catered for with exclusive hire possible in the evenings and weekends. / *11pm; all day; in-house caterers; Bar (350,–,–,–); Restaurant (100,–,–,–); Private Room 1 (–,–,–,–); Private Room 2 (–,–,–,–).*

Balls Brothers Minster Pavement EC3
£B-M, (500,180,180,230)
Minster Court
Ⓣ 020 7283 2838
Ⓕ 0870 243 9763
Ⓦ www.ballsbrothers.co.uk
Ⓔ minster@ballsbrothers.co.uk

At Balls Brothers Minster Pavement we can help you painlessly plan your party or event within our three self-contained private function rooms that can be hired individually or as one. You can be sure that our experienced team will assist you in planning, right from the early stages to the day of that all important occasion. / *1am; all day; in-house caterers; St Margaret's (75,40,40,60); St Giles (100,60,60,90); St Claves (75,40,40,60); Minster Suite (300,180,180,220).*

Baltic SE1
£M, (560,140,–,–)
74 Blackfriars Rd
Ⓣ 020 7928 1111
Ⓕ 020 7928 8487
Ⓦ hardens.com/party/baltic
Ⓔ info@balticrestaurant.co.uk

A dramatic conversion of ex-industrial premises near Tate Modern has helped make a great success of this Eastern European restaurant and cocktail bar. There's a private room overlooking the main eating area, or you can hire the venue in its entirety. / *11.15pm; in-house caterers; no amplified music; no dancing; Private Rm (–,30,–,–).*

Baltic Exchange EC3
£M-E, (120,40,–,80)
38 St Mary Axe
Ⓣ 020 7623 5501
Ⓕ 020 7369 1623
Ⓦ hardens.com/party/balticexchange
Ⓔ c.eccleston@balticexchange.com

The "new" Baltic Exchange has, since 1995, occupied an the impressive Art Deco building, which offers a number of options for businesslike gatherings. / *smart casual dress code; midnight (flexible); Balls Brothers; Boardroom (–,26,–,–).*

Bam-Bou W1
£M-E, (60,150,–,–)
1 Percy St
Ⓣ 020 7323 9130
Ⓕ 020 7323 9140
Ⓦ hardens.com/party/bam-bou
Ⓔ reservations@bam-bou.co.uk

This clubby Fitzrovia Vietnamese restaurant has been lavishly furnished. Several private areas available for hire. / *11pm, bar 1am; not available Sun or Sat lunch; in-house caterers; no dancing; Red Bar (60,–,–,–); Main Restaurant (–,150,–,–).*

Bank of England Sports Centre SW15

£M, (400,270,270,400)
Priory Ln
Ⓣ 020 8876 8417
Ⓕ 020 8878 7007
Ⓦ www.bankofengland.co.uk
Ⓔ events@bankofengland.co.uk

The Bank of England Sports Centre, situated in 32 acres of sporting fields and woodland, is a stunning venue for your party. A taste of the country just moments from Richmond Park and 18 mins from Waterloo. Whether you are planning a conference, wedding, cocktail party, barbecue, banquet or dinner dance, we have the perfect setting. / *1am; until 12.30 am; Restaurant Associates; Terrace Room (400,270,270,400); Green Room (100,48,–,60); Balcony Bar (100,48,48,50).*

Bank Restaurant & Zander Bar, Westminster SW1

£M, (250,150,140,–)
45 Buckingham Gt
Ⓣ 020 7630 6644
Ⓕ 020 7630 5665
Ⓦ www.bankrestaurants.com
Ⓔ westminster.reservations@bankrestaurants.com

BANK
RESTAURANTS & BARS

Situated in the midst of St James Bank Restaurant & Zander Bar mixes style and sophistication with a lively atmosphere. With two Private Dining Rooms available which offer an intimate dining experience whilst allowing guests to feel part of the restaurant buzz. The restaurant is available for exclusive hire. / *11pm, late license available; no restrictions; in-house caterers; no amplified music; dancing for exclusive hire only; Private Rms (combined) (–,40,–,–); Private Rms (x2) (–,20,–,–); Mezzanine (semi-private) (–,10,–,–).*

Bankside Gallery SE1

£B-M, (200,70,–,–)
48 Hopton St
Ⓣ 020 7928 7521
Ⓕ 020 7928 2820
Ⓦ hardens.com/party/bankside
Ⓔ info@banksidegallery.com

A pleasant gallery, near Tate Modern. Home to the Royal Watercolour Society and Royal Society of Painter-Printmakers, it is situated at the foot of a modern block, set back from the river. / *10.30pm; available from 6pm; hirer's choice of caterer; no amplified music; no dancing.*

Banqueting House SW1

£M-E, (500,380,350,–)
Whitehall
Ⓣ 020 3166 6157
Ⓕ 020 3166 6159
Ⓦ www.hrp.org.uk
Ⓔ James.Harkin@hrp.org.uk

The sole remaining fragment of the Palace of Whitehall, Inigo Jones's stately c17 hall (with Rubens ceiling) offers just the venue if you're setting out to impress. The undercroft is an elegant space, available separately. / *1am; list of caterers; Main Hall (500,380,350,–); Undercroft (375,150,–,–).*

Bar Kick E1

£B, (300,50,150,–)
127 Shoreditch High St
Ⓣ 020 7739 8700
Ⓕ 020 7613 2509
Ⓦ hardens.com/party/barkick
Ⓔ admin@cafekick.co.uk

A Shoreditch bar where you can have a football tournament? Table football, admittedly, but it would certainly make a change. / *Mon-Wed 11pm, Thur-Sat midnight, Sun 10.30pm; in-house caterers; no amplified music.*

Bar Soho W1

£B, (300,85,–,–)
23-25 Old Compton St
T 020 7439 4089
F 020 7255 8610
W hardens.com/party/barsoho
E events@barsoho.co.uk
The name does not lie – this buzzing candlelit bar really is in the heart of Soho. For a central get-together, you can hire the first floor private room, or, for a bigger event, you may be able to hire the whole place. / 18+; 3am, Sun 12.30am; in-house caterers; Private Room (100,–,–,–); Ground Floor (200,–,–,–).

Barber-Surgeons' Hall EC2

£M, (250,120,–,150)
Monkwell Sq
T 020 7334 3980
W hardens.com/party/barbersurgeonshall
E katie.jayson-morgan@kudoshospitality.co.uk
This light, panelled livery hall, near the Barbican, was remodelled in the '60s in traditional style. It is available primarily for business and livery functions. / no filming ; 10.30pm; Kudos Hospitality; no amplified music; no dancing; Reception Rm (100,–,–,55).

Barbican Art Gallery EC2

£M, (450,350,96,2000)
Barbican
T 020 7382 7093
F 020 7382 7237
W hardens.com/party/barbicanartgallery
E conference@barbican.org.uk
This twin-level gallery is quite reasonably priced by City standards, and is a popular venue (especially in the summer). Depending on the layout of the current exhibition, access to the external Sculpture Court may be possible. / midnight; Searcy's; no amplified music in Conservatory.

Barbican Centre EC2

£M-E, (450,288,156,–)
Barbican Centre
T 020 7382 7043
F 020 7382 7237
W hardens.com/party/barbicancentre
E banquetingevents@barbican.org.uk
The huge, jungle-like Conservatory would not seem out of place in Kew Gardens and makes a dramatic setting for a grand event. It can be used in combination with the Barbican Art Gallery. / 11.30pm; available evenings & weekends; Searcy's; music volume restrictions apply; Garden Rm (300,288,156,–); Conservatory Terrace (150,–,–,–).

Barnard's Inn Hall EC1

£M-E, (–,90,50,–)
Holborn
T 020 7831 0575
F 020 7831 5268
W hardens.com/party/barnardsinn
E enquiries@gresham.ac.uk
As a walk-on rôle in 'Great Expectations' confirms, this Inn of Chancery – a hall with c14 origins – has quite a history. Substantially refurbished by owners the Mercers' Company, it has only in recent years been made available for hire (for more sedate events). / 11pm; weekdays only; hirer's choice of caterer.

The Battersea Barge SW8

£B-M, (250,80,80,–)
Nine Elms Ln
T 020 7498 0004
F 020 7622 9729
W hardens.com/party/batterseabarge
E mail@batterseabarge.com
The Battersea Barge, is tucked away in an away-from-it-all location near New Covent Garden market. It has a cosy interior, and the upper deck has great river views. There's an integral sound system and large dance floor. / strictly over 21's, no stag nights; 2am; in-house caterers.

Battersea Evolution SW11

£E, (2500,2500,2500,–)
Chelsea Bridge Entrance
T 020 7836 1035
F 020 7836 1044
W hardens.com/party/batterseaevolution
E info@batterseaevolution.co.uk
For ten months of the year, a private company takes over the 15,000 sqm hard-standing area of Battersea Park, and offers "a myriad of possibilities for event and production companies". If you're

looking for somewhere to stage a larger-scale event this is an attractive, and fairly central, space. / *2am; in-house caterers.*

Battersea Park SW11
£M, (5000,2000,2000,–)
Battersea Park
T 020 8871 7534
F 020 7223 7919
W hardens.com/party/batterseapark
E asmith@wandsworth.gov.uk
The only one of the more central parks to enjoy a river frontage offers some useful spaces for the erection of marquees, especially large ones. For the park's only permanent party venue, see Pump House Gallery. See also Battersea Evolution. / *no glass, no fireworks; hirer's choice of caterer; some restrictions on music.*

Beach Blanket Babylon W11
£M, (200,60,–,–)
45 Ledbury Rd
T 020 7229 2907
F 020 7313 9525
W hardens.com/party/beachblanketW11
E bookings@beachblanket.co.uk
A Notting Hill bar whose neo-Gothic interior has some claim to modern-classic status. For private hire, you can only take the whole place (or, at less busy times, just the bar), but there's a curtained-off bar area available on all but the busiest days. / *midnight; in-house caterers; Bar Area (200,45,–,–); Private Room (120,60,–,–).*

Beach Blanket Babylon E1
£M, (800,250,250,–)
19-23 Bethnal Green Rd
T 020 7749 3540
F 020 7739 6680
W hardens.com/party/beachblanketE1
E bookings@beachblanket.co.uk
The new, much larger Shoreditch offshoot of the Notting Hill bar/restaurant of the same name. The eye-catching design here is no less baroque. / *1am; in-house caterers; Restaurant (–,200,–,–); Cocktail Bar (300,–,–,–).*

Beauberry House SE21
£M, (500,400,–,–)
Gallery Rd
T 020 8299 9788
F 020 8299 96793
W hardens.com/party/beauberry
E info@beauberryhouse.co.uk
Formerly known as Belair House, this imposing Georgian building by Dulwich Park hosts a restaurant of some ambition, with facilities for civil weddings and private dining. / *in-house caterers; Function Rm/Balcony (150,62,–,–); Bar (80,33,–,–).*

Beaufort House SW3
£M, (350,110,–,–)
354 Kings Road
T 020 7352 282
W hardens.com/party/beaufort
E info@beauforthousechelsea.com
A bar/brasserie in the heart of Chelsea, over which there's an attractive, modern private member's club incorporating a small private room for dining and screenings, and above that a penthouse champagne bar (which has maintained the original pitched roof). By negotiation, all sections are available for events. / *Champagne Bar (110,–,–,–); Private Dining (50,22,–,–); Bar & Brasserie (100,50,–,–).*

Bedford SW12
£M, (200,–,–,250)
77 Bedford Hill
T 020 8682 8940
F 020 8582 8959
W hardens.com/party/bedford
E info@thebedford.co.uk
A vast Victorian pub in Balham. The building incorporates numerous venues-within-a-venue, including "Shakespeare's Globe", which is a two-tier theatre, and a ballroom. Various rooms can accommodate parties from 16 people upwards. / *Ballroom available only Fri and every other Sun; in-house caterers; Ballroom (200,–,–,–); Theatre Room (–,–,–,250); Tavistock Room (75,–,–,–).*

Bedroom Bar EC2

£B-M, (150,–,–,–)
62 Rivington St
T 020 7613 5637
F 020 7256 1242
W hardens.com/party/bedroombar
E info@comedycafe.co.uk

In fashionable Hoxton, a warehouse-conversion with a NYC-loft-apartment look. It's a hip bar most of the time, but you can also hire it for private parties and events. / 2am, Sat 3am; in-house caterers; Function Room (80,–,–,–).

Bel Canto W2

£M, (–,120,–,–)
Corus Hotel Hyde Park
T 020 7262 1678
F 020 7444 0001
W hardens.com/party/belcanto
E reservations@lebelcanto.co.uk

French cuisine coupled with operatic entertainment – waiters are trained opera singers. You can hire out this restaurant in its entirety (with or without the singers). / 2am, Sat & Sun 3am; hirer's choice of caterer (in-house available).

HMS Belfast SE1

£M, (450,144,96,50)
Morgans Lane
T 020 7403 6246
F 020 7404 0708
W www.hmsbelfast.iwm.org.uk
E hms.belfast@sodexho-uk.com

This WWII cruiser, permanently moored by Tower Bridge, offers a range of possibilities for medium-sized events, including weddings (and a recent refurbishment has provided much built-in AV equipment). The decks afford a very central location for a summer drinks party. / 1am; Sodexho Prestige; no amplified music on deck; Quarter Deck (Summer Evenings) (350,–,–,–); Ship Co's Dining Hall (240,132,96,–); Gun Rm (120,60,60,–); Admiral's Quarters (30,20,–,–); Wardroom and Anteroom (100,50,–,50).

Bellamy's W1

£M, (80,80,–,–)
18-18a Bruton Pl
T 020 7491 2727
F 020 7491 9990
W hardens.com/party/bellamys
E gavin@bellamysrestaurant.co.uk

A smart mews restaurant that's established itself as quite a fixture with the more discreet sort of Mayfair folk. It's available for private hire only in its entirety. / 10.30pm; not available Sun, Sat L; in-house caterers; no music; no dancing.

belowzero restaurant + lounge & ICEBAR LONDON W1

£M, (270,100,50,60)
31-33 Heddon St
T 020 7478 8917
F 020 7287 8844
W www.belowzerolondon.com
E events@belowzerolondon.com

belowzero is a stylish bar, lounge & restaurant and home to ICEBAR LONDON. London's 'coolest' event space offers a truly unique environment in which to host dinners, parties, product launches and teambuilding days. Comfortable atmospheric surroundings and outstanding hospitality help deliver outstanding events from 20 to 270 guests. / 1am; 9am - 1 am; in-house caterers; Wolf Bar (70,–,–,–); Moose Dining Room (90,70,50,60); Reindeer Lounge Bar (45,26,–,20); Moose & Reindeer (180,100,50,60); Whole Venue (180,100,50,60); ICEBAR LONDON (60,–,–,–).

Belvedere W8

£M-E, (250,140,–,–)
off Abbotsbury Rd
T 020 7734 7333
F 020 7734 0033
W hardens.com/party/belvedere
E sales@whitestarline.org.uk

With one of the prettiest locations in London – actually in the park –

this Holland Park restaurant is ideal for private hire in its entirety, perhaps most obviously for a wedding reception. / 1am; in-house caterers; no amplified music; no dancing; Top level (100,80,–,–).

Benares W1

£M, (400,140,–,–)
12a Berkeley Square House
Ⓣ 020 7629 8886
Ⓕ 020 7499 2430
Ⓦ hardens.com/party/benares
Ⓔ enquiries@benaresrestaurant.com

Atul Kochhar's acclaimed modern Indian restaurant recently emerged from a successful refurbishment in the wake of a fire. It's well-suited to hiring in its entirety, or there are a number of discrete spaces for private hire. / in-house caterers; Main Restaurant (400,140,–,–); Burton Room (40,22,–,–); Dover Room (–,14,–,–); The Berkeley Room (40,30,–,–); The Lounge (80,32,–,–).

Benjamin Franklin House WC2

£M, (40,34,–,25)
36 Craven Street
Ⓣ 020 7839 2008
Ⓦ www.benjaminfranklinhouse.org
Ⓔ sarah@benjaminfranklinhouse.org

Located in the heart of London, just steps from Trafalgar Square, this Georgian terraced townhouse plays host to both corporate and private events (including wedding receptions) in an elegant c18 setting. / nothing attached to walls/floors, no flames; 11.30pm; list of caterers; no dancing; Franklin's Parlour (40,34,–,25); Mrs Stevenson's Parlour (40,25,–,20); Seminar Room (30,–,–,20); Board Room (10,10,–,–); Outside Terrace (20,–,–,–).

The Bentley Hotel SW7

£M-E, (150,70,–,70)
Harrington Gardens
Ⓣ 020 7244 5378
Ⓕ 020 7244 5566
Ⓦ hardens.com/party/bentley
Ⓔ info@thebentley-hotel.com

Opulent, much-marbled five-star Hotel in South Kensington which has three private dining rooms suited to events such as cocktail parties, wedding breakfasts, and meetings. The largest overlooks the garden square. / 11.30pm; in-house caterers; no amplified music; Daniel (–,12,–,–).

Bentleys Oyster Bar and Grill W1

£M, (100,60,60,–)
11-15 Swallow St
Ⓣ 020 7734 4756
Ⓕ 020 7758 4140
Ⓦ www.bentleys.org
Ⓔ reservations@bentleys.org

Now in its ninth decade, Bentley's Oyster Bar and Grill first opened its doors in 1916 in the same beautiful historic building it occupies today. In addition to the Oyster Bar, The Grill Room and the Alfresco Terrace, Bentley's also benefits from two private dining rooms, accommodating up to 60 guests for dining with no hire fees. / 11.30pm; midday; in-house caterers; 3am Licence - (Private Hire); Crustacea Room (–,14,–,–); Jameson Room (100,60,60,–).

The Berkeley SW1
£M-E, (400,200,160,–)
Wilton Pl
T 020 7235 6000
F 020 7201 1660
W hardens.com/party/theberkeley
E info@the-berkeley.co.uk

A modern Maybourne (formerly Savoy) Group hotel in Knightsbridge. Styling is generally fairly conventional, although the Mulberry Room is decorated in subdued contemporary style. See also Marcus Wareing at the Berkeley. / 1am; in-house caterers; Mulberry (40,18,–,–); Knightsbridge (–,10,–,–); Tattersalls (–,22,–,–).

Bermondsey Square SE1
£M-E, (300,80,80,110)
The Bermondsey Square Hotel
T 020 7378 2450
F 020 7378 2460
W hardens.com/party/bermondseysq
E reservation@bermondseysquarehotel.co.uk

The outside terrace is the biggest events attraction at this boutique hotel in Bermondsey, which can hold a drinks reception or BBQ for up to 250 people. Screenings for up to 50 can be accommodated in partnership with a neighbouring cinema. / 2am; in-house caterers; Terrace (100,–,–,–).

Berry Bros. & Rudd SW1
£M-E, (100,60,–,–)
3 St James's St
T 020 7396 9600
F 020 7396 9619
W hardens.com/party/berrybrosrudd
E thecellars@bbr.com

A section of the extensive cellars of this famous wine merchant by St James's Palace – owned by the same family for three centuries – has been tastefully converted into a pair of dining (or tasting) rooms. / 10.30pm; in-house caterers; no dancing; The Cellars (100,60,–,–); Townhouse (–,14,–,–).

BFI IMAX SE1
£M-E, (400,450,–,450)
1 Charlie Chaplin Walk
T 0844 873 4966
F 020 7960 3112
W www.bfi.org.uk/venuehire
E imax.hire@bfi.org.uk

The BFI IMAX consists of a 480-seat auditorium, and boasts the largest cinema screen in the UK (20m by 26m). An advanced digital stereo system creates a complex sound world around you, perfectly complementing the film, PowerPoint or video images on screen. We are the ideal venue for conferences. / 10.30pm; list of caterers; alcohol only in plastic containers in auditorium; Auditorium (–,450,–,450); 1st Floor Foyer (320,200,–,–); Ground Floor Foyer (400,200,–,–).

BFI Southbank SE1
£M-E, (200,–,–,450)
Belvedere Road
T 020 7815 1343
W www.bfi.org.uk/venuehire
E michelle.white@bfi.org.uk

BFI Southbank houses four auditoriums with state of the art projection equipment and outstanding presentation facilities. Located in the heart of London's South Bank, one of the world's most exciting cultural centres, BFI

Southbank is an inspiring location to stage an event and presents a unique alternative to traditional conferencing and reception venues. / 5pm; weekdays 9am-5pm; in-house caterers; NFT 1 (–,–,–,450); NFT2 (–,–,–,147); NFT 3 (–,–,–,134); Studio (–,–,–,38); Reception (250,–,80,80).

Bingham TW10

£M-E, (150,90,60,50)
61-63 Petersham Road
T 020 8940 0902
F 020 8948 8737
W www.thebingham.co.uk
E events@thebingham.co.uk

The perfect riverside location: its Garden Rooms offer three flexible interconnecting rooms that also make one breathtaking space. It has a private entrance, access to its own heated terrace and landscaped garden. Rooms are bathed in natural daylight, have state-of-the-art equipment and cater for up to 90 seated guests and 150 standing. / midnight; all day; in-house caterers; Some music restrictions; Garden Room 1 (–,20,24,30); Garden Room 2 (–,20,18,25); Garden Room 3 (–,20,30,50); The Garden Room Exclusive (150,90,60,–).

Bishopsgate Institute EC2

£B-M, (470,18,–,280)
230 Bishopsgate
T 020 7247 6844
F 020 7392 9250
W hardens.com/party/bishopsgateinstitute
E enquiries@bishopsgate.org.uk

A Victorian institute in a Grade II listed Arts & Crafts building by Liverpool Street station. With its large, wooden-floored main hall, and very high ceilings, it makes a very handy location for a corporate bash. / 11pm; list of caterers; Elleyne Room (–,–,–,30); Roseberry Room (–,18,–,–); Boardroom (55,–,–,18); Townsend Gallery (–,4,–,–); Upper Hall (260,–,–,260); Great Hall (500,–,–,320).

Bistro 1 W1

£B, (–,60,–,–)
75 Beak St
T 020 7287 1840
W hardens.com/party/bistro1
E b1@bistro1.co.uk

One of central London's truly budget bistros, handily located in Soho. For a private party, you can take the whole place. There is another branch not far away, in Frith Street, and also one in Southampton Street (Covent Garden). / 11.20pm; in-house caterers.

Bistrothèque E2

£B-M, (300,160,–,–)
23-27 Wadeson St
T 020 8983 7900
F 020 8880 6433
W hardens.com/party/bistrotheque
E info@bistrotheque.com

Strikingly located in its post-industrial setting, an East End restaurant that's established itself as a trendy destination for those in the know. On an exclusive-hire basis, it is well suited to use for private functions, or there are two rooms for smaller events. Cabaret can be arranged. / midnight; in-house caterers; no dancing; Cabaret Rm (80,60,–,–); Restaurant (–,150,–,–); Private Room (–,50,–,–).

Blackheath Concert Halls SE3

£M, (1000,600,200,600)
23 Lee Rd
T 020 8318 9758
F 020 8852 5154
W hardens.com/party/blackheathhalls
E programming@blackheathhalls.com

These characterful Victorian halls (claiming to be the first purpose-built concert halls in the country) are well appointed, and a local favourite for a whole range of events from concerts to wedding receptions. / 11pm-midnight; hirer's choice of caterer; Recital Rm (250,160,100,–).

Blakemore House Conference and Wedding Venue SG4

£M, (300,–,250,300)
Blakemore End Road
T 01438 728 203
F 01438 729 211
W www.blakemorehouse.co.uk
E sales@blakemorehouse.co.uk

Blakemore House in the beautiful village of Little Wymondley is just a short drive from Stevenage town centre and the A1(M) and only 30 minutes from central London. Set in 6 acres of beautifully landscaped gardens and comprises 6 stylish event spaces, all with views over the gardens. Various room sizes accommodate a wide range of events, from intimate dinners to award ceremonies and gala dinners for up to 300 guests. / Garden Room (300,–,250,300); Rosemary Room (200,–,150,150); Thyme Room (100,–,80,100); Marjoram Room (80,–,50,50); Sage Room (40,–,24,20); Bay Room (–,–,24,–).

Bleeding Heart EC1

£M, (–,120,–,–)
Bleeding Heart Yd
T 020 7242 8238
F 020 7831 1402
W www.bleedingheart.co.uk
E bookings@bleedingheart.co.uk

'Best Private Dining in Britain' said The Independent *of this hidden-away, collection of private dining rooms around a cobbled courtyard between Farringdon and Holborn Circus. Famed for 25 years for its "immaculate" service and "superb food", Bleeding Heart will ensure you have a truly memorable event for 12 or 120. / midnight; in-house caterers; music restricted; dancing restricted; Wine Cellar (No Seven) (–,30,–,–); The Parlour (No Seven) (–,18,–,–); Red Room (–,35,–,–); Terrace Room (–,44,–,–); Bleeding Heart (w/e Only) (–,140,–,–).*

Blenheim Palace OX20

£E, (500,300,300,120)
Woodstock
T 01993 813874
F 01993 810580
W hardens.com/party/blenheimpalace
E sales@blenheimhospitality.com

The home of the 11th Duke of Marlborough (and birthplace of Sir Winston Churchill) is one of the finest houses in England. A few miles north of Oxford, and set in 2,100 acres of Capability Brown gardens, its state rooms offer unparalleled opportunities to impress. / midnight; hirer's choice of caterer (in-house available); no red wine for standing receptions in palace state rooms;

Orangery (350,160,100,–); Marlborough (180,80,–,120).

Bloomsbury Ballroom WC1

£M, (850,250,200,400)

37-63 Bloomsbury Square

T 020 7404 7612

F 020 7404 0365

W hardens.com/party/bloomsburyballroom

E bloomsbury@vpmg.net

Claiming to be "London's most opulent Art Deco venue", this self-explanatory spot on a handsome square offers a number of spaces suited to events. / 2am; hirer's choice of caterer; no music before 7 pm Mon-Fri; Ballroom (550,–,–,–); Crush Bar (240,–,–,–); Long Bar (60,–,–,–).

Bloomsbury Theatre WC1

£B-M, (150,–,–,535)

15 Gordon St

T 020 7679 2777

F 020 7383 4080

W hardens.com/party/bloomsburytheatre

E admin@thebloomsbury.com

This modern theatre is a flexible space equipped to a high standard, and it's handy for the 'Midtown' area between the City and the West End. / 11pm; available subject to constraints of current production; in-house caterers; no dancing; Foyer (150,–,–,–).

Blue Elephant SW6

£M, (650,350,–,–)

3-6 Fulham Broadway

T 020 7385 6595

F 020 7386 5204

W hardens.com/party/blueelephant

E london@blueelephant.com

Handily located near Fulham Broadway tube, London's longest-established grand Thai restaurant has made itself quite a 'destination'. It's a venue on quite a scale, and its lush interior makes it a 'natural' for a larger-scale exotic-theme event. / 11.30pm, Sun 10.30pm; no Sat L; in-house caterers; no amplified music; no dancing.

Bluebird SW3

£M, (650,240,60,100)

350 King's Road

T 020 7559 1208

F 020 7559 1115

W www.bluebird-restaurant.com

E sarah.widdowson@danddlondon.com

Bluebird boasts 4 beautifully well appointed private dining rooms with impressive views of the restaurant, a bounty of natural daylight or a chic 1930's style space which make the perfect place to hold your own private event. The restaurant and bar's stylish space can be booked exclusively and accommodates 230 people for a seated event or up to 650 for a standing reception. / midnight; 8am - midnight; background music avaliable. DJ/band exclusive hire; Mezzanine (–,32,32,35); Beaufort Room (70,40,–,40); Gallery Room (120,66,60,100); Bluebird Room (50,30,–,30); Beaufort & Gallery Room (200,110,60,100).

BMA House WC1

£M-E, (320,200,200,300)

Tavistock Square

T 020 7874 7020

F 020 7383 6645

W www.bma.org.uk

E events@bma.org.uk

BMA House is a grade II listed building ideally located in fashionable Bloomsbury. The house underwent significant development in 2008 and is now available for corporate and private hire; boasting an impressive portfolio of 26 versatile rooms, a courtyard and garden offering important outdoor space so rarely found in London. / 11.30pm; in-house caterers; no music in garden area; Great Hall (320,200,160,300); Prince's Room (90,50,48,70); Snow Room (150,100,64,100); Lutyens (320,–,–,–); Paget Room (170,120,80,150); Garden Room (90,–,–,–); Council Chamber (–,–,–,97); Black

Suite (150,–,–,150); Harvey (100,–,–,100); Courtyard Suite (160,–,–,120).

Boisdale SW1
£M, (–,80,–,–)
15 Eccleston St
Ⓣ 020 7730 6922
Ⓕ 020 7730 0548
Ⓦ hardens.com/party/boisdale
Ⓔ info@boisdale.co.uk
This clubby Scottish restaurant near Victoria Station – celebrated for its steaks, whiskies and its cigars (outside) – has a number of areas available for private hire. Live jazz adds to the party atmosphere, and for smokers there's the benefit of a large 'Cigar Terrace'. / 1am; closed Sat L, all Sun; in-house caterers; no amplified music; no dancing; Back Bar (–,26,–,–); Jacobite Room (–,22,–,–).

The Book Club EC2
£B-M, (400,110,–,–)
100-106 Leonard Street
Ⓣ 020 7684 8618
Ⓕ 020 7684 1491
Ⓦ hardens.com/party/homebar
Ⓔ mail@homebar.co.uk
Formerly known as 'Home', this spacious bar/club/restaurant remains one of the most happening spots in the Shoreditch scene. You can hire the Basement Bar or, for a big event, the whole place (including the upstairs restaurant). / Thu-Sat 2am, Mon-Wed, midnight; not available Sun; in-house caterers; Basement Bar (250,–,–,–); Private Dining Rm (–,16,–,–).

Borscht & Tears SW3
£B, (–,100,–,–)
46 Beauchamp Pl
Ⓣ 020 7589 5003
Ⓦ hardens.com/party/borscht
This rowdy Russian restaurant of 40 years' standing in Knightsbridge seems oblivious to the whims of fashion, and remains a popular destination for the more boisterous sorts of parties. / 1am; in-house caterers.

Il Bottaccio SW1
£M-E, (400,200,180,250)
8/9 Grosvenor Place
Ⓣ 020 7235 9522
Ⓕ 020 7235 9577
Ⓦ hardens.com/party/bottaccio
Ⓔ info@bottaccio.co.uk
Occupying an impressive c19 building, this Italianate venue offers a very central location, and views over the gardens of Buckingham Palace. / 1am; hirer's choice of caterer (in-house available); no bands after midnight.

Boudin Blanc W1
£B-M, (–,20,–,–)
5 Trebeck St
Ⓣ 020 7499 3292
Ⓕ 020 7495 6973
Ⓦ hardens.com/party/boudinblanc
Ⓔ reservations@boudinblanc.co.uk
It's no longer the inexpensive bistro as which some may still remember it, but this rustic Shepherd Market restaurant remains very popular nonetheless. It has two cosy private rooms. / 1am; in-house caterers; no music; no dancing; Private Rm 2 (wine Cellar) (–,14,–,–).

Boujis SW7
£E, (250,–,–,–)
43 Thurloe Street
Ⓣ 020 7584 2000
Ⓕ 020 7589 4343
Ⓦ hardens.com/party/boujis
Ⓔ info@boujis.com
A South Kensington club whose profile was much enhanced by its popularity with the young princes. It is divided into several alcoves, with three private spaces. / 3am; hirer's choice of caterer (in-house available).

Boundary E2
£M, (200,136,–,–)
2-4 Boundary St
Ⓣ 020 7729 1051
Ⓦ hardens.com/party/boundary
Ⓔ info@theboundary.co.uk
Sir Terence Conran's new Shoreditch bar/restaurant/hotel offers a range of spaces for private entertainment. For appropriate events, you may even be able to arrange exclusive hire of the rooftop bar and dining

room. / *5.30pm; available from noon; in-house caterers; no amplified music.*

Bow Wine Vaults EC4

£B-M, (60,50,–,–)

10 Bow Church Yard

T 020 7248 1121

F 020 7248 2568

W hardens.com/party/bowwinevaults

E info@bowvinevaults.com

A City restaurant/wine bar, charmingly situated behind St Mary-le-Bow, with a basement restaurant. It makes a nice location for a low-key City get-together. / *11pm; available Mon-Fri evenings only; in-house caterers; no music; no dancing.*

Brasserie Roux SW1

£M, (180,140,–,–)

Sofitel St James London

T 020 7968 2900

F 020 7747 2242

W hardens.com/party/brasserieroux

E info@brasserieroux.com

Just off Trafalgar Square, this large brasserie has a private dining room, complete with reception area, which is available for small lunch and dinner parties, receptions and business meetings. / *1am (need to apply for a license); in-house caterers; no amplified music; Private Room (180,140,–,–).*

Brasserie St Jacques SW1

£M, (70,60,–,–)

33 St James's St

T 020 7839 1007

F 020 7839 3204

W hardens.com/party/brasseriestjacques

E brasseriestjacques@btconnect.com

An upmarket Gallic brasserie in St James's, offering an airy space for private dining. / *1am; available from noon; in-house caterers; no amplified music; Private Rooms (40,20,–,–).*

Brewers' Hall EC2

£M, (125,90,–,80)

Aldermanbury Sq

T 020 7600 1801

F 020 7776 8939

W hardens.com/party/brewershall

E courtsecretary@brewershall.co.uk

The Brewers' Company is reasonably flexible about the use of its elegant, panelled hall which – together with its adjoining rooms – suits a range of smaller functions. / *11pm; list of caterers.*

The Brewery EC1

£M, (1000,700,650,–)

Chiswell St

T 020 7638 8811

F 020 7638 5713

W hardens.com/party/thebrewery

E info@thebrewery.co.uk

This former brewery is now one of the City's most notable party and conference venues. The highlight is the Porter Tun – originally an c18 storehouse – that boasts an unobstructed floor space of 780 square metres and original king post timber roof. / *1am; in-house caterers; Porter Tun (1000,700,650,–); King George III (700,390,250,–); Queen Charlotte Rm (180,160,130,–); Sugar Rms (120,100,100,–).*

The Brickhouse E1

£M, (200,45,–,–)

The Old Truman Brewery

T 020 7247 0005

W hardens.com/party/brickhouse

E marta@thebrickhouse.co.uk

In Brick Lane, a restaurant with an intriguing three-story, balconied contemporary interior, and regular entertainment, which would offer quite a lot of possibilities for standing events (in particular). / *2am; in-house caterers; Ground Floor (–,35,–,–); Second Floor (–,45,–,–); Third (–,16,–,–).*

Brinkley's SW10

£M, (–,40,–,–)

47 Hollywood Rd

T 020 7351 1683

F 020 7376 5083

W hardens.com/party/brinkleys

E brinkleys@brinkleys.com

The appeal of this airy, modern British restaurant, off the Fulham Road, is wide-ranging, and this must be the nicest restaurant in London to be notorious for stag and hen parties. There are three private rooms. / *12.30am; garden only available Mon & Tue; no live bands; no dancing; Private Rm 2 (–,20,–,–); Private Rm 3 (–,18,–,–); Garden (–,30,–,–).*

Britannia W8

£M, (200,–,–,–)
1 Allen St
T 020 7937 6905
W hardens.com/party/britanniaw8
E britannia@youngs.co.uk
Always a superior boozer, this establishment just off Kensington High Street has been refurbished in recent times, and relaunched as a gastropub. You can hire it exclusively for a large party. / midnight; in-house caterers.

British Acadamy SW1

£M-E, (–,–,–,–)
10-11 Carlton House Terrace
T 020 7969 5200
F 020 7969 5300
10-11 Carlton House Terrace provides an exceptional venue for meetings, functions, corporate events, parties and weddings. From the grand sweeping black marble staircase of no.10 which flows into elegant rooms with richly ornate architecture; to the intricate and classically English design within Gladstone's former home, no.11, there is a space to suit every taste. / 1 am; 7 am - 11 pm; Lecture Hall (100,–,60,80); Council (125,80,60,36); Mall (100,60,–,80)Burlington & Cornwall (60,24,–,–); Marks (–,14,–,–); No. 11 Lobby (160,–,–,–);Wolfson Auditorium (200,100,56,140);Gallery (140,40,–,–); Music (100,60,35,60); Music & Council (120,–,–,–)

The British Library NW1

£M, (255,40,–,255)
Conference Office
T 020 7412 5528
F 020 7412 5530
W hardens.com/party/bl
E conferences@bl.uk
Given its scale, and its importance for the English-speaking world, it's perhaps surprising that this enormous building, by St Pancras, has relatively limited function and event facilities. / no candles; 9pm (flexible); available Wed-Sun; Peyton & Byrne.

British Museum WC1

£E, (329,–,–,323)
Great Russell St
T 020 7323 8136
F 020 7323 8137
W www.thebritishmuseum.org
E corporate@britishmuseum.org
The Clore Education Centre within the 'Great Court' comprises two technically-equipped tiered auditoria seating 142 and 323 delegates, several breakout rooms and two foyer areas, best suited to presentations, conferences and launches. / 10pm; in-house, plus list of approved caterers; no amplified music; no dancing; BP Theatre (–,–,–,323); Stevenson Theatre (–,–,–,142); Sackler Room A (–,–,–,45); Sackler Room B (–,–,–,45); Sackler Rooms combined (–,–,–,80); Claus Moser Room (–,–,–,35); Studio (–,–,–,35); East Foyer (329,–,–,–); West Foyer (329,–,–,–).

Broadgate Estates EC2

£M-E, (800,–,–,–)
Broadgate Centre
T 020 7505 4000
F 020 7382 9854
W hardens.com/party/broadgate
E arena@broadgateestates.co.uk
For a winter party in the City, why not hire the ice rink at this Manhattanite city complex by Liverpool Street. / 2.30pm; available Mon-Fri; no amplified music; no dancing; Arena (400,–,–,–).

Broadway House SW1

£M, (–,56,56,110)
Tothill Road
T 0844 824 6523
F 020 7222 2782
W hardens.com/party/broadwayhouse
Conference, meeting and training rooms at the heart of Westminster. 13 rooms featuring high speed broadband and the latest audio-visual and teleconferencing equipment. Conveniently located in central London, next to St. James's tube station. Various room sizes suitable for up to 110 delegates. In house chef and experienced technical support. / 5.50pm; in-house caterers; no music; no dancing; Abbey Room (–,30,–,40); Board Room (–,14,–,–); Brunel Room (–,12,–,–); Carteret Room /St James's Room (–,10,–,–); Council Chamber (–,56,–,110); Dartmouth

Room (–,16,–,–); The Whittle Room (–,22,–,32); Westminister Suite (–,56,–,100); Stevenson (–,46,56,–); Lawrence (–,21,16,35).

Brocket Hall AL8
£M-E, (200,150,60,150)
Welwyn
T 01707 335241
F 01707 333309
W hardens.com/party/brockethall
E events@brocket-hall.co.uk

"England's finest residential venue", set in 543 acres of parkland just 22 miles north of London, with comprehensive conference and incentive facilities for up to 150 guests (and 46 king-sized bedrooms). Events can be combined with golf on Championship courses and the Palmerston Golf Academy. / midnight, late licence available; in-house caterers; Ball Room (200,150,60,–); Dining Room (–,50,–,–); Family Dining Room (–,20,–,–).

Brompton Oratory SW7
£B-M, (140,100,–,–)
Brompton Rd
T 020 7808 0935
W hardens.com/party/bromptonoratory
E oratoryoffice@aol.com

St. Wilfrid's Hall is a gracious Victorian room in the outstanding peaceful setting of the Brompton Oratory church, suitable for wedding receptions, dinner & cocktail parties, recitals and lectures. Nearby St Joseph's Hall is a more functional room suited to children's parties, recitals, lectures and company presentations. / 10pm; not available Sun; hirer's choice of caterer; no amplified music; no dancing; St. Joseph's Hall (140,100,–,–).

Brown's Hotel W1
£M, (100,80,–,70)
Albemarle St
T 020 7493 6020
W hardens.com/party/brownshotel
E dpettifer@roccofortecollection.com

Re-launched by Rocco Forte, this Mayfair hotel maintains a rather traditional English charm. All the function accommodation is on a relatively small scale. / 1am; in-house caterers; no amplified music; no dancing; Clarendon (100,72,–,70); Niagara & Roosevelt combined (80,80,–,–); Graham Bell Rm (–,8,–,–).

Browns WC2
£M, (150,100,100,150)
Browns: 82-84 St Martin's Ln, WC2N
T 020 7395 6091
F 020 7497 5005
W hardens.com/party/browns
E courtrooms@mbplc.com

This Grade II listed building, near Covent Garden, boasts 4 attractively converted courtrooms, each complete with judges' bench. It can cater for conferences, meetings, lunches and receptions, using the chain's English brasserie menu, plus a wide range of wine and cocktails. / 11pm to 1am; in-house caterers; Courtroom 1 (150,100,100,150); Courtroom 2 (70,48,48,70); Courtroom 3 (50,40,40,50); Courtroom 4 (20,12,–,20).

Burgh House NW3
£B-M, (110,50,–,60)
New End Sq
T 020 7431 0144
F 020 7435 8817
W hardens.com/party/burghhouse

A charmingly-located Queen Anne house in Hampstead, with a very pretty ground floor music room which is especially suited to weddings and more sedate receptions. / 10.30pm; not available Mon & Tue; in-house caterers; no amplified music; no dance floor.

Bush Hall W12
£B-M, (350,200,150,200)
310 Uxbridge Road
T 020 8222 6955
F 020 8222 6933
W www.bushhallmusic.co.uk
E notes@bushhallmusic.co.uk

A stylish music & entertainment venue, previously an Edwardian dance hall, dressed with chandeliers and ornate plastered decor. Whether you're looking to host a corporate event, a wedding reception, a special birthday party, product launch, or a hip spot to showcase your latest signing, Bush Hall is the answer. / 1am; Available Mon- Sun till 1am; hirer's choice of caterer; live music must finish by 11pm, DJ thereafter..

The Business Design Centre N1
£M-E, (3000,2500,1200,2500)
52 Upper St
Ⓣ 020 7288 6225
Ⓕ 020 7288 6444
Ⓦ hardens.com/party/thebusinessdesigncentre
Ⓔ maxb@businessdesigncentre.co.uk
Modern exhibition premises in Islington, sometimes used for large-scale corporate events. / 1pm for banqueting dinner; The Good Eating Company; Gallery Hall (650,–,450,650).

Butchers' Hall EC1
£M, (250,160,90,180)
87 Bartholomew Close
Ⓣ 020 7251 7171
Ⓕ 020 7251 7170
Ⓦ hardens.com/party/butchers
Ⓔ enquire@chesterboyd.co.uk
This Smithfield livery hall in traditional style offers flexible accommodation which is much used both for business affairs and socially. / 11pm (1am possible); closes mid- August for two weeks; Chester Boyd; Taurus Suite (100,65,48,80).

Cable SE1
£B, (1000,–,–,–)
Bermondsey Street Tunnel
Ⓣ 0207 403 7730
Ⓦ hardens.com/party/cable
Ⓔ info@cable-london.com
Atmospheric arches and tunnels under London Bridge station provide the accommodation for this large club, whose sound and entertainment systems have been installed with both clubbers and corporate hirers in mind. / standard club nights 6am; 24 hour entertainment and drinking licence; hirer's choice of caterer.

Cactus Blue SW3
£M, (60,60,–,–)
86 Fulham Rd
Ⓣ 020 7823 7858
Ⓕ 020 7823 8577
Ⓦ hardens.com/party/cactusblue
Ⓔ renata@cactusblue.co.uk
This impressively-designed Chelsea bar and restaurant (southwest American) has a suite for private parties, the Blue Room. It's changing hands in autumn 2010, so change may be afoot. / midnight; in-house caterers; no amplified music; no dancing; Blue Room (60,40,–,–).

The Cadogan SW1
£M, (70,32,–,38)
75 Sloane St
Ⓣ 020 7201 6618
Ⓕ 020 7245 0994
Ⓦ hardens.com/party/thecadogan
Ⓔ mklavina@cadogan.com
The traditional interior of this fashionably-located Knightsbridge hotel has had a contemporary facelift in recent times. The Salon Lillie would make a nice venue for a smaller wedding or reception. / midnight; in-house caterers; Salon Oscar (20,12,–,–); Salon Lillie (50,32,–,38); Combined (70,–,–,–).

Café de Paris W1
£M-E, (715,220,180,180)
3 Coventry St
Ⓣ 020 7395 5807
Ⓕ 020 7117 4246
Ⓦ www.cafedeparis.com
Ⓔ Andrew@cafedeparis.com

In the heart of Piccadilly, Café de Paris is a dazzling and opulent venue superb for hosting all types of parties from lunches, dinners, canapé receptions and film premieres to product launches, awards ceremonies and Christmas celebrations. An expert events team is on hand to ensure that everything runs perfectly. / Mon-Sat 3am, Sun 12.30am; in-house caterers; VIP Rm (100,–,–,–); Red Bar (40,–,–,–); Blue Bar (75,–,–,–).

Café du Marché EC1
£M, (120,60,–,–)
22 Charterhouse Sq
T 020 7608 1609
F 020 7336 7459
W hardens.com/party/cafedumarche
A popular French restaurant, occupying a 'designer-rustic' warehouse conversion near Smithfield market. You can use the more intimate 'Rendezvous', or the whole of the upstairs. / midnight; not available Sun; in-house caterers; Rendezvous (80,35,–,–).

Café Emm W1
£B, (–,60,–,–)
17 Frith St
T 020 7437 0723
W hardens.com/party/cafeemm
It's only semi-private, but the rear area of this very popular budget bistro in the heart of Soho would make a good venue for a student-style dinner. / in-house caterers.

The Caledonian Club SW1
£M-E, (300,170,110,200)
9 Halkin St
T 020 7333 8722
F 020 7201 1500
W www.caledonianclub.com
E banqueting@caledonianclub.com
Adjacent to Hyde Park Corner, and with 8 private function rooms, available for leisure and business meetings, private dining and receptions. Membership is not a pre-requisite for holding meetings. The Terrace is an ideal setting for al-fresco entertaining. Accommodation is also available at the Club, designed with comfort in mind. / midnight; in-house caterers; Johnnie Walker Music Room (250,170,80,200); Selkirk Room (50,36,24,40); Stuart Room (60,54,32,50); Library (60,30,24,45); Morrison Room (–,8,–,–); Smoking Room (100,60,40,80); Oval Room & Terrace (100,–,–,–).

Callooh Callay EC2
£B, (150,70,–,–)
65 Rivington St
T 020 7739 4781
W hardens.com/party/calloohcallaybar
E info@calloohcallaybar.com
An eclectically-furnished, relatively recent arrival on the Shoreditch bar scene. For a private event, you can have any one of the three rooms, or take the whole place. / 1am; in-house caterers; Private Area (60,–,–,–); Private Area (50,–,–,–); Private Area (25,–,–,–).

Canal Café Theatre W2
£B-M, (–,–,–,60)
Bridge House
T 020 7289 6056
W hardens.com/party/canalcafetheatre
E mail@canalcafetheatre.com
"The longest-running live comedy show in Britain." For your party, perhaps you'd like to block-book one of their twice-nightly shows. / 9.30pm; in-house caterers.

Candid Arts Trust, The EC1
£B-M, (200,25,–,–)
3 Torrens St
T 020 7837 4237
F 020 7837 4123
W hardens.com/party/candidarts
E info@candidarts.com
The banquet room at this idiosyncratic art gallery and Goth hang-out, near Angel tube, makes an atmospheric party venue if you're on a budget. It offers flexible and reasonably priced accommodation for a whole range of functions. / midnight; hirer's choice of caterer (in-house available); certain floors no musc; Banquet Rm (50,25,–,–); First Floor (200,–,–,–); Basement (100,–,–,–).

Canning House SW1
£B-M, (200,80,–,120)
2 Belgrave Sq
T 020 7235 2303
F 020 7838 9258
W hardens.com/party/canninghouse
E pilar.socrras@canninghouse.org
The first-floor rooms of the Hispanic and Luso Brazilian Council, which overlook the square, are extremely popular for drinks parties. They offer

affordable grandeur at a very smart address, a stone's throw from Hyde Park Corner. / *no candles; midnight; hirer's choice of caterer; dancing on ground floor only; Library (80,–,–,70).*

Cannizaro House SW19

£M-E, (120,96,96,–)

West Side

T 020 8879 1464

F 020 8879 7338

W hardens.com/party/cannizarohouse

E experienceteam@cannizarohouse.com

This Georgian mansion-hotel, prettily situated in Cannizaro Park on the edge of Wimbledon Common, recently emerged from a comprehensive refurbishment. It offers a good range of function rooms of various sizes. / *11pm; in-house caterers; Viscount Melville Suite (120,96,70,–); Queen Elizabeth Rm (70,40,–,–).*

Cannon Bridge Roof Garden EC4

£M-E, (450,100,–,175)

25 Dowgate Hill

T 0845 230 3899

W hardens.com/party/cannonroofgarden

Great views of the river and City are a highlight at this unique roof garden and luxurious glass-front marquee over the station, built for summer entertaining by Diamond City Events. If it rains, there's cover for 150 guests. / *11pm; available June and July, from 6.30 pm.*

Canonbury Academy N1

£M-E, (120,30,–,95)

6 Canonbury Place

T 020 7359 6888

F 020 7704 1896

W hardens.com/party/canonburyacademy

E canonburyacademy@btinternet.com

A beautifully refurbished c16 Benedictine priory standing in its own gardens. Each individually decorated room – of which there are 25 – has antique furniture and overlooks the gardens. This is a venue best suited to quieter corporate events. / *companies only; 6pm; weekdays only; in-house caterers; no amplified music; no dancing; Queen Elizabeth (60,30,–,40).*

Cantaloupe EC2

£M, (350,–,–,–)

35-42 Charlotte Rd

T 020 7613 4411

W hardens.com/party/cantaloupe

E info@cantaloupegroup.co.uk

The original industrial-chic bar which helped make Shoreditch hip. For private hire, you can take over a particular area, or the whole place. / *midnight; in-house caterers.*

Cape - St. Katharine Docks E1

£B, (260,–,–,–)

Thomas More Square

T 020 7702 9222

W hardens.com/party/cape

Close to St. Katharine's Dock, a bar that's handy for after work drinks, or informal celebrations either in its entirety or book one of their booths.

The Capital SW3

£M-E, (40,24,–,–)

Basil St

T 020 7589 5171

F 020 7225 0011

W hardens.com/party/capitalhotel

E events@capitalhotel.co.uk

The private dining rooms of this chic, small hotel – right by Harrods – are in a fairly traditional style. Its restaurant has long enjoyed a reputation as offering some of the best cooking in town. / *11pm; in-house caterers; Eaton Suite (40,12,–,–); Cadogan (40,24,–,–); Sitting Room (24,10,–,–).*

Captain Kidd E1

£B, (65,40,–,–)

108 Wapping High St

T 020 7480 5759

W hardens.com/party/captainkidd

One of the most popular places for food and drink in Docklands, this olde worlde riverside pub has one function room – the second floor Observation Deck (which has large windows overlooking the river). Parties of up to 25 can take a corner of the Gallows restaurant. / *11pm; in-house caterers; no music; no dancing.*

Cargo EC2
£B, (500,50,–,–)
83 Rivington St
T 020 7739 3440
F 020 7739 3441
W hardens.com/party/cargo
E cargomanagers@cargo-london.com
Long a fixture of the Shoreditch scene, this railway-arch nightclub has a number of spaces suitable for events. Or, for a larger event, you could take the whole place. / Mon-Thur 1am, Fri-Sat 3am, Sun midnight; in-house caterers; Restaurant (80,50,–,–).

Carlton Club SW1
£M-E, (150,90,90,100)
69 St James's St
T 020 7399 0904
F 020 7399 4093
W hardens.com/party/carltonclub
E info@carltonclub.co.uk
The spiritual home of the Tory party, this elegant St James's club – which has a wonderful staircase – makes a very congenial venue for those of a rightwards persuasion. It has a range of rooms, the largest of which is the Churchill. All events require the sponsorship of a member. / members club; 11pm; weekdays only; in-house caterers; no music during week; Cabinet Rm (50,36,–,40).

The Carlton Mitre Hotel KT8
£M-E, (140,110,60,120)
Hampton Court
T 020 8979 9988
W hardens.com/party/carltonmitre
E gmmitre@carltonhotels.co.uk
Over three centuries old, this Thames-side hotel, whose entrance is opposite that of Hampton Court Palace, has pleasant function facilities overlooking the river. Should you choose to arrive or depart by boat, the Rivers Edge benefits from its own private mooring. / no 18ths, 21sts or stag nights; midnight; in-house caterers; no music after midnight and no music outside; Pavilion (140,90,50,120); Cardinal Wolsey (30,–,–,30).

Carpenters' Hall EC2
£M, (350,220,–,230)
Throgmorton Av
T 020 7382 1670
F 020 7382 1683
W hardens.com/party/carpentershall
E info@carpentersco.com
Forming the arch over the London Wall end of Throgmorton Avenue, this '60s livery hall makes an impressive venue. / no weddings; 11pm; weekdays only; hirer's choice of caterer; no amplified music; no dancing; Luncheon Rm (–,32,–,–).

Carvosso's W4 1
£M, (90,55,–,–)
210 Chiswick High Road
T 020 8995 9121
F 020 8995 9122
W hardens.com/party/carvossos
E enquiries@carvossosat210.co.uk
Chiswick's old police station has been attractively converted. It has a first-floor function space with private bar, and there are also three small private rooms. / Smaller Private Rooms X 3 (–,10,–,–).

The Casino at the Empire WC2
£M-E, (1800,80,90,120)
5-6 Leicester Sq
T 020 3014 1016
F 020 3014 1035
W hardens.com/party/thecasinoattheempire
E smccormack@london-clubs.co.uk
"Live entertainment, 5 vibrant bars, 2 restaurants and a state-of-the-art casino" – this West End venue, is available for hire for "parties, seminars, conferences, celebrations or even poker tournaments". / 24 hours licence; in-house caterers; Flame (120,75,–,–); Face 2 Face (150,80,90,120); FuLuShou (70,60,–,–); Icon Bar & Terrace (80,50,–,–); Shadow Bar (150,60,–,–); Upper Level (450,–,–,–); Whole Venue (1800,–,–,–).

Cavalry & Guards Club W1

£M, (300,120,–,–)
127 Piccadilly
T 020 7499 1261
F 020 7495 5956
W hardens.com/party/cavalryguardsclub
E functions@cavgds.co.uk
This carefully maintained Edwardian club, overlooking Green Park, has a number of charming traditional rooms, of which the largest is the Coffee Room. / 11pm; in-house caterers; Waterloo Rm (60,20,–,–).

Cavendish SW1

£M-E, (100,77,48,80)
81 Jermyn Street
T 020 7930 2111
F 020 7839 2125
W hardens.com/party/cavendish
E info@thecavendishlondon.com
This '60s four-star, 230-bedroom hotel has a great St James's position just off Piccadilly. It has a number of banqueting rooms on the first floor for smaller functions. / 1am; in-house caterers; Alto (100,77,48,80); Stratus (–,14,12,24); Nimbus (–,10,–,–); Cirrus (–,14,–,–); Electra (–,44,25,50).

The CBI Conference Centre WC1

£M, (250,80,116,200)
Centre Point 103 Oxford St
T 020 7395 8014
F 020 7395 8016
W hardens.com/party/cbi
E jpurcell@etcvenues.co.uk
On the first floor of the landmark Centre Point tower, a flexible suite of rooms suitable for conferences and for business entertaining generally. / 11pm; in-house caterers; Methven (–,80,–,200); Rms 1, 2 & 3 (48,48,–,80); Concourse (250,80,116,–).

Cecconi's W1

£B-M, (–,12,–,–)
5-5a Burlington Gdns
T 020 7434 1500
F 020 7434 2020
W hardens.com/party/cecconis
E reception@cecconis.co.uk
Constantly full of fashionable types, this Mayfair corner restaurant is never made available for private hire in its entirety. There is, however, a private room which can be used for intimate lunches or dinners. / Mon-Sat 11.30pm, Sun 10.30pm; in-house caterers; no amplified music; Private Room (–,12,–,–).

Cecil Sharp House NW1

£B-M, (500,300,300,–)
2 Regent's Park Rd
T 020 7485 2206
F 020 7284 0534
W hardens.com/party/cecilsharphouse
E hire@efdss.org
The Primrose Hill home of the English Folk Dance and Song Society has two panelled halls which are available for private receptions and dances (sprung floors). There is also a small but attractive walled garden (plus a small car park). / no wedding receptions or birthday parties; 11pm; in-house caterers; Trefusis Hall (150,140,100,–).

Central Hall Westminster SW1

£M, (1000,400,400,2160)
Storey's Gate
T 020 7222 8010
F 020 7222 6883
W www.c-h-w.co.ukl
E events@c-h-w.co.uk
If you're looking for a central meeting place, this vast Viennese Baroque confection opposite Westminster Abbey certainly lives up to its name, and it offers a number of options for events on quite a scale. Alcohol is nowadays allowed in the Great Hall (subject to moderate consumption). / 11pm; Kudos Hospitality; no alcohol in Great Hall - no open bars; Great Hall (1000,400,400,2160); Lecture Hall (500,200,200,450); Library (500,200,200,450); Aldars Gate (250,100,100,250); George Thomas (150,70,70,150); Dinsdale Young (60,30,30,60).

Century W1

£M, (250,85,85,120)

61-63 Shaftesbury Avenue

T 020 7534 3080

F 020 7534 3090

W www.centuryclub.co.uk

E events@centuryclub.co.uk

Century is a bright and spacious private members club overlooking St Anne's Gardens in Soho. The club has built a reputation for its bespoke approach to holding events and welcome non-members in their private hire areas. Century can accommodate up to 300 guests for events. / 1am; 8am; in-house caterers; Rose Langton Room (250,80,80,120); 4th Floor (100,85,85,–).

Le Cercle SW1

£B-M, (100,80,–,–)

1 Wilbraham Pl

T 020 7901 9999

F 020 7901 9111

W hardens.com/party/cercle

E info@lecercle.co.uk

An interesting space for an event if taken over in its entirety, this basement restaurant specialises in high-quality Gallic tapas. For smaller events, you can try out the mezzanine overlooking the restaurant. / midnight; available from noon; in-house caterers; no amplified music; Private Room (30,12,–,–).

Chandos House W1

£M-E, (150,100,–,80)

2 Queen Anne Street

T 020 7290 2951

F 020 7290 2959

W hardens.com/party/chandoshouse

E info.chandos@rsm.ac.uk

A choice of grand rooms, reception areas and a terrace provide accommodation for an intimate dinner for ten, or a grand wedding for 120. / 11pm; in-house caterers; no live bands or loud amplified music; dancing on ground floor only; Robert Adam Rm, Ground Floor (70,30,–,40); James Adam Rm, Ground Floor (40,20,–,32); Terrace Rm (–,30,–,–); Terrace (90,–,–,–); Duke Rm, First Floor (70,50,–,60); Duchess Rm, First Floor (40,40,–,32).

The Chapel Bar N1

£B-M, (200,80,–,50)

29a Penton St

T 020 7833 4090

W hardens.com/party/chapelbar

E info@thechapelbar.co.uk

Tucked away on Penton Street, this bar hosts corporate events, wedding receptions, product launches and so on, catering for groups of up to 300. / 3am, later licence available; available every day.; in-house caterers.

The Charles Dickens Museum WC1

£B-M, (120,50,–,–)

48 Doughty St

T 020 7405 2127

F 020 7831 5175

W hardens.com/party/dickensmuseum

E info@dickensmuseum.com

Oliver Twist's Bloomsbury birthplace is a four-floor c19 house, for the most part filled with display cabinets detailing his life and that of his creator. Entertaining takes place primarily in the atmospheric basement Library, whose period bookcases are filled with rare editions of the Great Novelist's work. / no flash photography; 11pm; hirer's choice of caterer (in-house available); some restrictions on music; no dancing; no red wine.

Charlotte Street Hotel W1
£M-E, (60,28,–,74)
15 Charlotte St
T 020 7287 4434
F 020 7806 2002
W hardens.com/party/charlottestreethotel
E events@firmdale.com
A boutique hotel in a street long famous for restaurants, just north of Soho. It offers a range of options for intimate gatherings, with a private screening room a particular feature. / midnight; in-house caterers; no amplified music; no dancing; Screening Rm (–,–,–,74); Rm1 (60,28,–,30); Rm 2 (25,12,–,12).

Chartered Institute of Public Finance & Accountancy WC2
£M, (60,45,–,60)
3 Robert St
T 020 7543 5612
F 020 7543 5700
W hardens.com/party/cipfa
E conference.centre@cipfa.org
Though a little institutional, this Adam house offers a fine view over the Embankment from its fourth-floor committee room. The Council Chamber can be used for dinners. There are lower-floor rooms, which are really only suited to business entertaining. Over 2010 there has been major upgrading to its AV facilities. / 10.30pm; Owen Bros Caterers; Conference Rm (60,40,–,60); Council Chamber (60,40,–,60); Room 4 (–,32,–,60); Room 5 (–,12,–,12).

Chatham Hall SW11
£B, (100,80,80,80)
152 Northcote Rd
T 020 8871 6394
F 020 8871 6391
W hardens.com/party/chathamhall
E publichalls@wandsworth.gov.uk
Former Battersea stables, available for events including children's parties (around 80 youngsters) or cocktail parties. / children under 8 only; 11pm; weekends only; hirer's choice of caterer; no amplified music.

The Chelsea Gardener SW3
£B-M, (350,150,–,–)
125 Sydney St
T 020 7352 5656
F 020 7352 3301
W hardens.com/party/chelseagardener
E victoria@chelseagardener.com
Handily located near Chelsea Old Town Hall, a garden centre which does quite a business as a venue for indoor and outdoor events. / 11pm; list of caterers; no dancing.

Chelsea Old Town Hall SW3
£B-M, (520,180,140,440)
King's Rd
T 020 7361 2220
F 020 7362 3442
W www.rbkc.gov.uk/venues
E hall-let@rbkc.gov.uk
Chelsea Old Town Hall, located on the King's Road is a unique venue that brings heritage and style to every event. The granite columned entrance, marble floors, ornately coved ceilings and well equipped meeting spaces offer a desirable and popular venue for all kinds of commercial, corporate and private event. / no naked flames; midnight; 8 am - Midnight; list of caterers; no amplified music after 11pm; Main Hall (400,180,140,440); Cadogan Suite (Only with Main Hall) (120,–,–,–); The Small Hall (150,100,70,150).

Chelsea Physic Garden SW3
£M, (550,325,–,400)
66 Royal Hospital Rd
T 020 7352 5646
F 020 7376 3910
W hardens.com/party/chelseaphysic
E hire@chelseaphysicgarden.co.uk
London's secret Garden in the heart of old Chelsea provides a magical setting for any occasion. A marquee or awning may be required for larger events. The venue boasts a newly-refurbished lecture room with full AV. / 10.30pm (extension possible); list of caterers; no amplified music, all music to finish by 10pm; Garden (550,325,–,400); Lecture Room (100,50,–,80); Reception Room (120,60,–,100).

Chelsea Football Club SW6

£M-E, (1500,750,700,950)
Stamford Bridge
T 0871 984 1955
F 020 7915 1914
W hardens.com/party/chelseavillage
E events@chelseafc.com
Huge modern Fulham venue, overlooking the Chelsea FC ground (and part of the same complex), offering 21 function spaces in all. / 1am; available on non-match days, mornings till 2pm; in-house caterers.

Chessington World of Adventures KT9

£M-E, (6000,100,–,–)
Chessington
T 01753 626 209
F 020 7465 0884
W hardens.com/party/chessington
E events@merlinvenues.com
With easy access to the M25, a theme park providing an adventurous setting for a (probably corporate) day out. / min requirement 100; 5pm; list of caterers.

Chesterfield Mayfair W1

£M-E, (200,100,60,130)
35 Charles Street
T 020 7491 2622
F + 44 (0) 20 7491 4793
W hardens.com/party/chesterfieldmayfair
A cosy, traditional hotel in a quiet corner of Mayfair. Options for entertaining include the Conservatory (best-suited to a stand-up), Royal Suite for larger events, or the panelled Library for a small private dinner. / 11pm; The Royal Suite (200,50,60,130); The Conservatory (80,28,25,60); The Library (40,18,–,30).

Cheyne Walk Brasserie SW3

£M, (120,74,–,–)
50 Cheyne Wk
T 020 7376 8787
F 020 7876 5878
W hardens.com/party/cheynewalk
E events@cheynewalkbrasserie.com
A chic Gallic restaurant, in the heart of old Chelsea. It has an upstairs bar, with river views, well suited to being taken over for a private dinner. / midnight; in-house caterers; no dancing; Salon/lounge/bar (70,–,–,–).

Chez Bruce SW17

£M, (–,75,–,–)
2 Bellevue Rd
T 020 8672 0114
F 020 8767 6648
W hardens.com/party/chezbruce
E enquiries@chezbruce.co.uk
This Wandsworth restaurant – unchallenged as the best in south London – has a pleasant room upstairs, overlooking the common. Or, for a larger event, you can hire the whole of the ground floor. / 1am; in-house caterers; no amplified music; no dancing; Private Rm (–,16,–,–).

Chez Gérard, Opera Terrace WC2

£B-M, (200,150,–,–)
The Market
T 020 7379 0666
F 020 7497 9060
W hardens.com/party/chezgerardopera
E opera@groupechezgerard.co.uk
The terrace of this branch of the Chez Gérard steak-frites chain overlooks the Royal Opera House, and offers one of the most central al fresco venues. / 11.30pm; in-house caterers; no amplified music; no dancing.

China Tang W1

£M-E, (–,180,–,–)
The Dorchester
T 020 7629 9988
F 020 7629 9595
W hardens.com/party/chinatang
E chinatang@dorchesterhotel.co.uk
The private dining facilities at David Tang's swanky Chinese restaurant, in the basement of the Dorchester Hotel, are very plush indeed (and come with a high level of equipment for business presentations). The dining room itself can also be hired, but its décor is arguably less attractive. / in-house caterers; no amplified music; no dancing; Private Rm 1 (–,18,–,–); Library, Private Rms 2/3 (–,18,–,–).

Chiswick House W4

£E, (350,250,150,50)
Burlington Ln
T 020 8742 2762
F 020 7973 3470
W hardens.com/party/chiswickhouse
E lisa.bevan@chgt.org.uk

The famous landscaped gardens and structure of this grand Palladian villa (1729) emerged in 2010 from a £12m revamp. As well as its suite of interconnecting first-floor rooms, event options now include a pavilion marquee, and architecturally striking new café in the grounds. / no 18ths, 21sts or childrens parties; 11pm; available summer from 6.30pm, winter from 4.30pm, weddings Fri & Sat; list of caterers; no red wine for standing receptions; First Floor (6 Rms) (150,96,80,–); Domed Saloon (100,48,–,50); Pavillion Marquee (350,250,–,–); Conservatory (80,–,–,–); Cafe (150,80,–,–).

Chiswick Moran Hotel W4

£M, (200,120,48,80)
626 Chiswick High Road
T 020 8996 5200
F 020 8996 5201
W hardens.com/party/chiswickmoranhotel
E chiswickc&b@moranhotels.com

'West Coast' chic twinned with Irish hospitality is the aim at this west London hotel, where event options include five private suites, the Napa restaurant and Globe Bar. / 24 hour licence; in-house caterers; Fairfax Room (110,60,48,80); Fairfax East (50,30,24,40); Fairfax West (50,30,24,40); Sunset Room (–,10,–,–); Beverley Room (–,10,–,–); Westwood (–,18,–,–).

Chor Bizarre W1

£M, (85,55,–,–)
16 Albermarle St
T 020 7629 9802
F 020 7493 7756
W hardens.com/party/chorbizarre
E chorbizarrelondon@oldworldhospitality.com

Mayfair Indian restaurant that aims to capture the spirit of the 'Chor bazzaar' (or thieves' market) with its kaleidoscopic interior: an Aladdin's cave of bric-a-brac and fascinating antiques sourced from various Indian bazaars. It serves regional dishes from different parts of the subcontinent. / midnight; available from noon; in-house caterers; no amplified music; Private Rm 1 (–,25,–,–).

Chowki W1

£B-M, (150,120,–,–)
2-3 Denman St
T 020 7439 1330
F 020 7287 5919
W hardens.com/party/chowki
E info@chowki.com

Just by Piccadilly Circus, a contemporary Indian restaurant which is very popular venue for home-style cuisine. If you're looking for a private party in as central a location as you could ever want, you're unlikely to do better than the private dining area here. Or you could hire the whole place. / Mon-Sat 11.30pm, Sun 10.30pm; in-house caterers; no music; no dancing; Private Dining Area (–,40,–,–).

Christ Church Spitalfields E1

£M, (600,250,250,400)
Fournier St
T 020 7377 6793
F 0870 066 7305
W www.spitalfieldsvenue.org
E info@spitalfieldsvenue.org

One of London's greatest Baroque churches provides the setting for this impressive new venue. The main space is the soaring nave. For more intimate affairs, the former vestry is available. / 11.30pm; list of caterers; red wine only at dinner with preferred caterer; Old Vestry Rm (40,25,–,–).

Christie's SW1

£M-E, (500,180,–,–)
8 King St
T 020 7389 2205
F 020 7839 2132
W hardens.com/party/christies
E ejames@christies.com

The Great Rooms of this St James's auctioneer are, subject to other requirements, sometimes made available for suitable functions. / midnight; available Mon-Fri from 6pm, limited availability.; list of caterers; no dancing.

Christopher's WC2
£M-E, (80,40,–,–)
18 Wellington St
- T 020 7240 4222
- F 020 7240 3357
- W hardens.com/party/christophers
- E events@christophersgrill.com

This upmarket American restaurant – which occupies a very impressive Victorian building in Covent Garden – has a fully private basement dining room. (There is also a 'Small' dining room – on the light and impressive 'piano nobile' – but it is rather less private.) / midnight; in-house caterers; no amplified music; no dancing; Small Dining Rm (–,26,–,–).

Chuen Cheng Ku W1
£B, (–,400,–,–)
17 Wardour St
- T 020 7437 1398
- F 020 7434 0533
- W hardens.com/party/cck

Vast, gaudy, Chinatown restaurant set in a characterful (if in some areas faded) building. Any of the rooms (for groups of 30 people and up) may be taken privately and if you want a fun, cheap celebration, the trolley dim sum here at weekend lunchtimes is a good bet. / midnight; in-house caterers; no amplified music; no dancing; Rm 1 (–,180,–,–); Rm 2 (–,100,–,–); Rm 3 (–,60,–,–); Rm 4 (–,40,–,–).

Church House SW1
£M, (650,372,264,664)
Dean's Yd
- T 020 7390 1590
- F 020 7390 1591
- W hardens.com/party/churchhouse
- E sales@churchhouseconf.co.uk

A conference centre near Westminster Abbey. As well as the main Assembly Hall, there is a wide range of function accommodation. / 1am; Kudos Hospitality; no amplified music; Harvey Goodwin Suite (240,160,120,180); Hoare Memorial Hall (230,150,120,230); Bishop Partridge Hall (120,90,–,130); Westminster (30,30,–,40); Jubilee (20,12,–,20); Assembly Hall (550,372,264,664).

Churchill Museum and Cabinet War Rooms SW1
£M-E, (400,130,100,150)
King Charles St
- T 020 7766 0134
- F 020 7930 5850
- W www.iwm.org.uk/churchill
- E cwr@sodexo.com

The intriguing underground bunker where Winston Churchill and his War Cabinet led Britain and her allies to victory during WWII. Recently re-jigged to provide more event space, it can accommodate functions for 10-400 people. / candles and indoor fireworks are not permitted; 11pm (1am with additional charge); Sodexo ; HCA Auditorium (250,130,80,150); Harmsworth Room (150,100,35,50); Switch Room (50,30,–,–); Learning Suite (40,50,–,40).

Chutney Mary SW10
£M, (50,110,70,70)
535 Kings Rd
- T 020 7351 3113
- F 020 7351 7694
- W hardens.com/party/chutneymary
- E chutneymary@realindianfood.com

One of London's oldest Indians known for gourmet cuisine and a stylish setting. The main restaurant can be hired for larger events (and is licensed for weddings), while the private room with natural daylight, is ideal for more intimate occasions. / midnight; in-house caterers; Private Room (50,32,–,–).

Cinnamon Club SW1
£M, (250,150,–,–)
The Old Westminster Library
- T 020 7222 2555
- F 020 7222 1333
- W hardens.com/party/cinnamonclub
- E reception@cinnamonclub.com

Hidden-away in Westminster, this lavish Indian restaurant – in a converted library, with some books still in situ – has made a major name for the quality of its cooking. It offers a good variety of rooms ideal for a range of events. / midnight; 10am; in-house caterers; no amplified music; Private Room (70,60,–,–).

Cinnamon Kitchen EC2
£B, (450,130,–,–)
9 Devonshire Sq
T 020 7626 5000
F 020 7397 9611
W hardens.com/party/anise
E info@cinnamonclub.com
This swanky Indian restaurant near Liverpool Street is an impressive space, with various areas that can be hired independently for events. These include the 'outside' terrace (under a large glass canopy), a private dining room and the bar (Anise). A wedding license has been applied for. / midnight; available from noon; in-house caterers; Restaurant (300,130,–,–); Anise (bar) (160,70,–,–); Terrace (100,60,–,–); Private Dining Room (–,12,–,–).

Circus Space N1
£M-E, (400,300,300,350)
Coronet St
T 020 7613 4141
F 020 7729 9422
W hardens.com/party/circusspace
E alex@thecircusspace.co.uk
This huge, high-ceilinged City-fringe venue is a training area for circus acts. It can be hired for corporate events (when a certain amount of theming will almost certainly be required). / restricted availability; midnight; available on 6 occasions annually, for a maximum of 4 days at a time; hirer's choice of caterer.

Cirque De Soir W1
£B, (180,30,–,–)
12 New Burlington Street
T 020 7734 6766
W hardens.com/party/cirquedesoir
E ryan@cirquedusoir.com
This Mayfair bar/member's club is known for its boudoir-esque decor and its regular weekly circus acts, and as a private hire might be just the job if you're looking to have an event with a decadent atmosphere. / 3am; VIP (30,30,–,–); Basement (70,–,–,–).

Cittie of Yorke WC1
£M, (300,100,–,–)
22 High Holborn
T 020 7242 7670
F 020 7405 6371
W hardens.com/party/cittieyork
This large pub by the entrance to Gray's Inn is one of the largest and most characterful of any traditional pub in London – with brass pipes, wooden alcoves and a high wooden ceiling. It has a long, thin, white-walled Cellar Bar which is available for private hire. / 11pm; in-house caterers; no music; no dancing; Cellar Bar (120,65,–,–).

City Hall - London's Living Room SE1
£M-E, (250,100,–,120)
The Queens Walk
T 020 7983 4088
F 020 7983 4137
W hardens.com/party/cityhall
E living.room@london.gov.uk
London's Living Room is situated on the top floor of City Hall (the 'headlamp') and offers stunning panoramic views of the London skyline. Organisations will need permission from Mr Mayor. / very restricted availability; 11pm (flexible); in-house caterers, hirer's choice in some circumstances; some restrictions on music; no dancing.

City Hotel E1
£B-M, (350,250,140,140)
12-20 Osborn Street
T 020 7247 3313
F 020 7377 5998
W hardens.com/party/cityhotellondon
E d.lynch@rcadirect.co.uk
Conveniently located (Brick Lane, 5 min walk from Liverpool Street station), this City-fringe property has three venues (Lane Bar, Café Suki, Temple Rooms), and can provide in house/external catering, events/wedding packages including discounted hotel rooms. / 3am; hirer's choice of caterer (in-house available); Lane Suite Rm 3 (50,35,–,35).

City Inn Westminster SW1

£M, (200,130,96,130)

30 John Islip St

Ⓣ 020 7932 4803

Ⓕ 020 7233 7575

Ⓦ hardens.com/party/cityinnwestminster

Ⓔ westminster.events@cityinn.com

The Sky Lounge, with its impressive views, is the highlight attraction at this large modern hotel, near Tate Britain. / midnight; in-house caterers; no music outside; Private Dining (200,130,130,150); Sky Lounge (–,12,–,–).

City of London Club EC2

£M, (300,120,90,100)

19 Old Broad St

Ⓣ 020 7588 8558

Ⓕ 020 7374 2020

Ⓦ www.cityclub.uk.com

Ⓔ events@cityclub.uk.com

A charming, Palladian club building, whose first-floor drawing room is one of a number of fine period rooms for entertaining. There are also a number of more modern rooms around a terrace garden which are suitable for meetings presentations etc. and the Club also has a licence for civil wedding ceremonies. / 1am; in-house caterers; dancing only on ground floor; Main Dining Rm (300,110,90,100); Drawing Rm (200,–,–,–); Garden Rm (100,50,–,80); Salisbury Rm (50,40,–,–); Masterman/Wellington Rms (20,14,–,–); Salisbury Rm (50,40,–,–); Hardwick Rm (–,10,–,–); City Room (40,20,–,30); Bar (50,–,–,–).

The City Presentation Centre EC1

£M, (250,–,–,130)

4 Chiswell St

Ⓣ 020 7628 5646

Ⓕ 020 7628 6776

Ⓦ hardens.com/party/citypresentation

Ⓔ info@citypresentationcentre.co.uk

The name says it all – a venue mainly used for financial world presentations. / 7pm; in-house caterers; no dancing; no spirits; Theatre (80,–,–,120).

City University EC1

£B-M, (300,424,–,500)

Event Management Service

Ⓣ 020 7040 8037

Ⓕ 020 7040 8592

Ⓦ hardens.com/party/cityuniversity

Ⓔ events@city.ac.uk

The university has a number of theatres, meeting rooms and large flexible spaces for hire. Most of the facilities – but not the Level Six Suite – are only available out of term. / restricted availability; 9pm; in-house caterers; no amplified music; no dancing; Northampton Suite (160,184,–,–); Great Hall (–,–,–,500); Oliver Thompson Lecture Theatre (–,–,–,360); Cass main auditorium (–,–,–,180).

Clapham Grand SW11

£B-M, (1500,500,–,–)

21-25 St John's Hill

Ⓣ 020 7223 6523

Ⓕ 020 7223 7838

Ⓦ hardens.com/party/claphamgrand

Ⓔ info@claphamgrand.com

This large former theatre is home to one of the longer-lasting nightclubs in the capital, complete with the UK's largest flashing dance floor! Its seating has three tiers which can be sectioned off for individual use. / 3am; hirer's choice of caterer.

Claridge's W1

£M-E, (450,240,192,–)

Brook St

Ⓣ 020 7629 8860

Ⓦ hardens.com/party/claridges

Ⓔ banqueting@claridges.co.uk

This Mayfair dowager has in recent years become one of London's most consistently successful grand hotels, and it has some very elegant

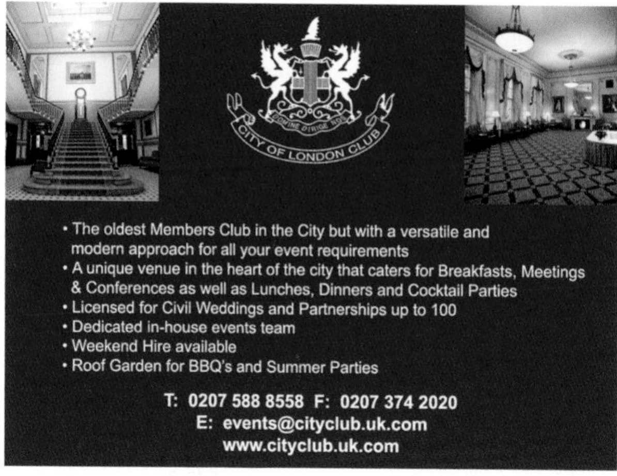

function facilities, especially the Ballroom. Gordon Ramsay's restaurant in the hotel is managed separately. / *midnight; in-house caterers; no music in certain rooms; no dancing in certain rooms; Ballroom (450,240,192,–); Drawing Rm, French Salon (200,96,–,–); Kensington (60,50,–,–); St James's (25,14,–,–); Board Rm (25,14,–,–); French Salon (120,84,84,–); Mirror Room (120,96,–,–).*

Clerkenwell House EC1
£B, (330,43,–,–)
23-27 Hatton Wall
T 020 7404 1113
W hardens.com/party/clerkenwellhouse
E office@clerkenwellhouse.com

An attractive, comfy Clerkenwell lounge bar that's worth considering for private and office parties, and is also licensed for weddings. Both basement venue and ground floor have DJ booths – sit down meals generally happen upstairs. / *midnight, Thu-Sat 2am; in-house caterers; Ground Floor (160,–,–,–); Upstairs (80,43,–,–); Basement (100,–,–,–); VIP Room (–,10,–,–).*

The Clink SE1
£B-M, (40,–,–,–)
1 Clink St
T 020 7403 0900
F 020 7403 5813
W hardens.com/party/clink
E events@clink.co.uk

Near London Bridge, this former prison (yes, the original) and erstwhile brothel is now a tourist attraction. They no longer have access to a larger space – events are now mainly canapé receptions lasting a couple of hours, and follow a tour of the exhibitions following prostitution through the ages. / *12am; not available 10am-6pm; in-house caterers.*

Cliveden SL6
£E, (150,120,–,40)
Taplow
T 01628 668561
F 01628 668561
W hardens.com/party/cliveden
E special.events@clivedenhouse.co.uk

The Astors' Thames-side palazzo, set in National Trust grounds, is now a luxurious hotel. You could take the whole place over for a house party, but, for more 'modest' events, the French Dining Room (with panelling from Madame de Pompadour's hunting lodge) is a particular attraction. / *11pm; in-house caterers; no amplified music; no dancing; Great Hall (150,–,–,–); Terraced Dining Rm (–,120,–,–); French Dining Rm (75,60,–,–); Macmillan Boardroom (–,20,–,–); Churchill Boardroom (–,24,–,40); Boudoir (–,24,–,–).*

Clos Maggiore WC2
£M-E, (40,23,–,–)
33 King St
T 020 7379 9696
W hardens.com/party/closm
E events@closmaggiore.com

A pretty and ambitious restaurant, among the tourist traps of Covent Garden, which has an elegant upstairs private room. The wine list is extraordinary. / midnight; in-house caterers; no dancing.

Clothworkers' Hall EC3
£M-E, (350,200,–,–)
Dunster Court
T 020 7623 7041
F 020 7397 0107
W hardens.com/party/clothworkershall
E enquiries@clothworkers.co.uk

One of the grandest halls in the City – it is made available on a limited basis, primarily for business, livery and charity functions. Guests proceed from a contemporary hall up to the elegant first-floor Reception Room. Off this opens the Livery Hall – a '50s chamber, decorated on traditional lines. / no weddings; 11pm; not available Fri-Sun; in-house caterers; no amplified music; no dancing; Reception Rm (150,–,–,–).

Club 49 Soho W1
£M-E, (225,–,–,–)
Greek Street
T 020 7439 4159
W hardens.com/party/club49soho
E info@club49soho.com

This centrally located nightclub is spread over two levels. For exclusive hire, the obvious option is to take the whole place, but areas of the club can be taken for less private types of event. / age 21+ only, smart casual; 3am; in-house caterers.

The Cobden Club W10
£M, (470,120,80,100)
170-172 Kensal Rd
T 020 8960 4222
F 020 8968 4386
W hardens.com/party/cobden
E info@thecobden.co.uk

Ever-fashionable North Kensington hang-out, housed above a still-functioning working men's club. The main party space is the 'retro-baroque' Grand Hall – like all the facilities, it may be made available to non-members at 'off-peak' times. / 1.30am; in-house caterers; Ground Floor (120,100,–,70); First Floor (150,120,–,75); Second Floor (200,100,–,100).

Cochrane Theatre WC1
£B-M, (308,–,–,308)
Southampton Row
T 020 7269 1600
F 020 7831 5476
W hardens.com/party/cochranetheatre
E info@cochranetheatre.co.uk

A modern Bloomsbury theatre, well suited to presentations, but – of course – subject to the constraints of the current shows. / restricted availability; 11pm; available subject to constraints of current production; hirer's choice of caterer; Auditorium (–,–,–,308); Bar (308,–,–,–).

Cocoon W1
£M-E, (450,170,–,–)
65 Regent St
T 020 7494 7600
F 020 7494 7607
W hardens.com/party/cocoon
E reservations@cocoon-restaurants.com

In first-floor premises, looking down on Regent Street, a bar/restaurant whose 'Blade-Runner-esque' decor is ideal for a hipper kind of event. / Mon-Fri 1am, Sat 3am, late license on request; in-house caterers; Restaurant (450,156,–,–); Private Dining Room (–,14,–,–).

Coin Street Neighbourhood Centre SE1
£M, (250,78,90,150)
108 Stamford Street
T 020 7021 1600
F 020 7021 1699
W hardens.com/party/coinstreetneighbourhoodcentre
E helpdesk@coinstreet.org

In the South Bank's landmark Oxo Tower, a flexible venue for indoor and outdoor events. / 9.30pm; list of caterers; no alcohol; Max Nasatyr Room (250,78,–,150); Fred Miller 1&2 (40,24,–,35); Lil Patrick 1&2 (30,–,–,25); Neighbourhood Room (250,78,–,150); Rooftop Garden (75,–,–,–).

The Coliseum WC2
£M, (400,130,–,2400)
St Martin's Ln
T 020 7845 9203
F 020 7836 6910
W hardens.com/party/eno
E events@eno.org

Europe's largest lyric theatre,

restored in recent years to its full Edwardian splendour. It offers a selection of rooms for smaller-scale entertaining. The largest room, the Sky Bar, gives you a close-up view of the famous globe. / very restricted availability; midnight; in-house caterers; no dancing; Royal Retiring Room (26,8,–,–); Harewood (6,4,–,–); Sky Bar (320,90,–,–); Balcony (200,40,–,–).

The Collection SW3

£M-E, (400,180,180,130)
264 Brompton Rd
T 020 7225 1212
F 020 7225 1050
W hardens.com/party/collection
E elly@the-collection.co.uk

With its wonderfully posey catwalk entrance, this glossy South Kensington address is ideally suited as a private venue for 'look-at-me' events. You can hire the whole place, or just the mezzanine dining space overlooking the large bar. / midnight, Sun 11pm; in-house caterers; no amplified music; no dancing; Mezzanine (300,180,–,130).

Le Colombier SW3

£M, (–,30,–,–)
145 Dovehouse St
T 020 7351 1155
F 020 7351 5124
W hardens.com/party/colombier
E lecolombier1998@aol.com

A well-reputed mid-range traditional French restaurant in Chelsea, which benefits from a light and unusually well-proportioned first-floor private room. / 1am; in-house caterers; no music; no dancing.

The Comedy Store SW1

£M, (–,–,–,400)
1a Oxendon St
T 020 7930 2949
F 020 7930 2951
W hardens.com/party/comedystore
E london@thecomedystore.co.uk

A well-known comics' venue, near Piccadilly Circus, available for private hire on a limited basis. / age 18+; 5.30pm; available Mon, all day & Tue-Fri, 10am-5.30pm; in-house caterers.

Comedy Theatre SW1

£M, (–,–,–,790)
Panton St
T 020 7420 4800
F 020 7321 5311
W hardens.com/party/comedytheatre
E comedymanager@theambassadors.com

A Victorian theatre, last reconstructed in the 1950s, available for hire subject to the constraints of the current production. / restricted availability; 11pm; available subject to constraints of current production; list of caterers.

Common Ground Cafe & Bar SW18

£M, (120,120,120,–)
Wandsworth Common
T 020 8874 9386
W hardens.com/party/nealslodge
E info@commongroundcafe.org.uk

Formerly called 'Neal's Lodge', this former farmhouse, right on Wandsworth Common has recently undergone a complete refurbishment. Natural light, lots of plants, and French windows opening onto a terrace impart to it a countrified feeling. Seating is in the Conservatory, with the Maple Room available for dancing. / 1am; in-house caterers.

The Commonwealth Club WC2

£M-E, (400,224,100,220)
25 Northumberland Ave
T 020 7766 9200
F 020 7766 9222
W hardens.com/party/commonwealthclub
E eventscoordinator@rcsint.org

A suspended glass dining room – unique in London, apparently – is one of the features of the extensive function facilities at this modern club building, just off Trafalgar Square. / midnight; in-house caterers; Reception Area (250,120,100,–); Thorne Rm (70,40,–,55); Seminar Room (110,64,–,80); Craven Room (70,60,–,60); Glass Dining Rm (–,16,–,–); Auditorium (250,144,100,220); Conference Room (100,80,–,110); Restaurant Level (400,224,–,–); Boardroom (–,14,–,–).

Concrete E1

£M, (275,80,–,–)
Lower Ground Floor
T 020 7749 1883
W hardens.com/party/concrete
E josh@concretespace.co.uk

Underneath trendy Pizza East, this descriptively-named bunker is managed by the Soho House group and – complete with bar, DJ booth and sound system – provides a useful space for parties or launches. / midnight; in-house caterers.

Congress Centre WC1

£M, (850,300,250,500)
23-28 Gt Russell St
T 020 7467 1318
F 020 7467 1313
W hardens.com/party/congresscentre
E congress.centre@tuc.org.uk

It's not just champagne socialists who can party at the TUC's fine '50s building, in Bloomsbury. The glass-walled Marble Hall, overlooked by a huge Epstein statue, is an elegant modern reception space. You can even get married here. / 7pm; in-house caterers.

Connaught W1

£M-E, (200,120,–,–)
Carlos Pl
T 020 7107 8894
W hardens.com/party/connaught
E straudt@the-connaught.co.uk

This very grand Mayfair hotel has undergone a number of refurbishments in recent years with the latest £70m addition completed in May 2010, including Mayfair's first ballroom for 80 years. A number of private rooms have been added, as well as a Sommelier's table – 3 floors below ground in the wine cellars. / midnight; in-house caterers; no amplified music; no dancing; Regency Room (40,24,–,–); Georgian Room (–,10,–,–); Ball Room (200,120,–,–).

Conservatory at Chelsea SW3

£M, (500,400,400,–)
Royal Hospital Gardens
T 0870 423 3567
F 0870 220 6325
W hardens.com/party/conservatorysw3
E info@the-ultimate.co.uk

A marquee within the grounds of The Royal Hospital, offered for a six-week season each summer, capable of housing barbecues for up to 600 guests. / midnight; Create; no amplified music, live music must stop 10.30 pm.

The Conservatory at Painshill Park KT11

£M-E, (400,320,320,320)
Portsmouth Road
T 01932 584 283
F 01932 868 001
W hardens.com/party/painshill
E events@painshillevents.co.uk

If you're looking for a large marquee site of more than usual charm and historical interest, this recently restored c18 garden – whose points of interest include a Gothic temple, a Chinese bridge, a ruined abbey and a remarkable grotto – has much to recommend it. There is also a Conservatory. / midnight; Touch of Taste or Create (hirer's choice also avai.

Conway Hall WC1

£B-M, (400,185,185,400)
25 Red Lion Sq
T 020 7242 8032
F 020 7242 8036
W hardens.com/party/conwayhall
E conwayhall@ethicalsoc.org.uk

On the corner of Red Lion square, the South Place Ethical Society (the UK's largest humanist group) occupies a 1920s Art Deco hall, with a range of characterful, if not especially smart, accommodation. / 11pm, Sat midnight; hirer's choice of caterer.

Coopers Arms SW3
£M, (60,40,–,–)
87 Flood St
T 020 7376 3120
F 020 7352 9187
W hardens.com/party/coopersarmssw3
E coopersarms@youngs.co.uk
An attractive Young's pub in Chelsea with a pleasant party room upstairs, where for a sit-down two dozen people can sit around a ship's dining table.(Undergoing refurbishment in mid 2010 – some changes to the room's layout may be afoot). / 11pm; in-house caterers.

Coopers' Hall EC2
£M, (90,32,–,25)
13 Devonshire Sq
T 020 7247 9577
F 020 7377 8061
W hardens.com/party/coopershall
E enquire@chesterboyd.co.uk
Livery hall – Georgian in origin – used for some business functions as well as livery dinners. It is available primarily to an established circle of former users but applications from newcomers will be considered. / 10.30pm; Chester Boyd; no amplified music; no dancing; Court Rm (60,–,–,25); Dining Rm (45,32,–,–).

Coq d'Argent EC2
£M-E, (300,150,–,–)
1 Poultry
T 020 7395 5006
F 020 7395 5050
W hardens.com/party/coqdargent
E anabelh@conran-restaurants.co.uk
The D&D (fka Conran) group's grand top-floor restaurant boasts views and an impressive garden, overlooking the Bank of England, and striking outdoor terraces. It has no private dining as such, but the whole place would make quite a spectacular venue for a (City boy and girl's) wedding reception. / midnight; in-house caterers.

Coram's Fields WC1
£M-E, (50,–,–,–)
93 Guilford Street
T 020 7837 6138
W hardens.com/party/coramsfields
E info@coramsfields.org.uk
'Adults may enter accompanied by a child' at this large green in Bloomsbury, bequeathed to the capital's kids by a Victorian philanthropist. For a big event for juniors it's just the place, but they don't do adult events (and there's no alcohol allowed on-site). / no political party or religious groups; 12.30am; hirer's choice of caterer; Venue 1 (50,–,–,–); Venue 2 (30,–,–,–).

The Coronet SE1
£M, (2160,350,300,570)
28 New Kent Rd
T 020 7701 1500
F 020 7701 1300
W hardens.com/party/coronettheatre
E info@coronettheatre.co.uk
Near Elephant & Castle, a stylishly restored '20s cinema with Art Deco features. It is now a dedicated function space. / Mon-Wed 3am Thurs-Sun 7am; hirer's choice of caterer; no RnB, basement or garage music.

Corrigan's Mayfair W1
£M-E, (50,70,70,–)
28 Upper Grosvenor Street
T 020 7499 9943
F 020 7758 4140
W www.corrigansmayfair.com
E reservations@corrigansmayfair.com
AA London Restaurant of the Year, Corrigan's Mayfair redefines the concept of quintessential British cuisine. In addition to the stylish cocktail bar and stunning restaurant, there are two private dining rooms with no hire fees. The exclusive Chef's Table seats up to 12 and the Lindsay Room seats up to 30. / no; 11.30pm; midday; in-house caterers; no; Chef's Table (–,12,–,–); Lindsay Room (50,30,–,–); Exclusive Use (–,70,70,–).

Courtauld Gallery WC2
£E, (200,50,–,–)
Somerset House
T 020 7845 4618
F 020 7836 7613
W hardens.com/party/courtauld
E events@somersethouse.org.uk
England's finest collection of Impressionist paintings provides an impressive backdrop for entertaining in this world-famous gallery. / 11pm; list of caterers; no amplified music; no dancing; no red wine.

Courthouse Hotel Kempinski W1
£M, (200,100,70,150)
19-21 Great Marlborough Street
T 020 7297 5516
F 020 7297 5599
W hardens.com/party/courthousehotel
E vanessa@courthouse-hotel.com
A very central hotel incorporating what till recently was the principal court house in central London. It has a set of banqueting rooms (The Chambers), and also a 5th-floor Roof Terrace. / 11pm; in-house caterers; Private Cinema (–,–,–,94).

Covent Garden Hotel WC2
£M-E, (50,28,–,47)
10 Monmouth St
T 020 7806 1000
F 020 7287 5551
W hardens.com/party/coventgardenhotel
E events@firmdale.com
The private dining facilities at this elegant boutique hotel on the fringe of Covent Garden are ideal for smaller gatherings. Or give your own film show in the screening room. / 11.30pm; in-house caterers; no amplified music; no dancing; Screening Rm (–,–,–,47).

Covent Garden Market WC2
£M, (500,–,–,–)
Covent Gdn
T 020 7227 3700
F 020 7222 5949
W hardens.com/party/brandspace
E info@brandspace.co.uk
For a gathering on a summer evening, you might like to consider this famous central marketplace. Entertainment by the market's own street-performers can be arranged. / restricted availability; 7pm-8pm; hirer's choice of caterer.

Crazy Bear (Restaurant) W1
£M-E, (–,70,–,–)
26-28 Whitfield Street
T 020 7631 0088
W hardens.com/party/crazybear
Near Goodge Street tube, this lavishly decorated Thai restaurant comprises a glam' basement bar (complete with amazing blingy toilets) and a swish ground floor dining room.

Crazy Bear (Member's Club) WC2
£M-E, (150,130,–,–)
17 Mercer Street
T 020 7520 5450
F 020 7836 6435
W hardens.com/party/crazybearclub
E enquiries@crazybear-membersclub.co.uk
In a quiet corner of Covent Garden, this recently launched members' club features the wildly opulent decor that's been such a feature of the group's restaurants. You can hire the venue in its entirety, or there are a couple of smaller private spaces. / Private Lounge or Dining Room (40,40,–,–).

Crazy Larry's SW10
£B-M, (700,400,–,–)
533 King's Rd
T 020 7376 5555
W hardens.com/party/crazylarrys
E info@crazylarrys.co.uk
Long-established younger-scene Chelsea/Fulham border nightclub, available seven days a week for exclusive hire. / 3am; hirer's choice of caterer, alcohol in-house.

Criterion Restaurant W1
£M, (250,150,100,–)
224 Piccadilly
T 020 7839 0100
F 020 7930 8380
W www.criterionrestaurant.com
E events@criterionrestaurant.com

The Criterion Restaurant is the only culinary destination in the capital blessed with the romance, grandeur and charisma of a neo-Byzantine design, and is soaked in fascinating history. A perfect venue for an unforgettable event whether it be a gathering of friends/family, an exclusive party or a wedding reception. / lunch 4pm, dinner 1am; lunch and dinner; in-house caterers; live music until 1am; license till 1am; Semi Private Terrace (100,70,–,–).

Cross Keys SW3
£B-M, (240,70,–,–)
1 Lawrence St
T 020 7349 9111
F 020 7349 9333
W hardens.com/party/crosskeys
E xkeys.nicole@hotmail.co.uk
Nicely located in Old Chelsea, this impressively renovated pub/restaurant has a first floor gallery which is a popular drinks party venue, and a top floor suited to private dinners. Or hire the whole place. / midnight, Sun 11.30pm; in-house caterers; Gallery (120,–,–,–); Room At The Top (60,35,–,–); Restaurant (–,60,–,–).

Crown & Greyhound SE21
£B, (100,70,–,–)
73 Dulwich Village
T 020 8299 4976
F 020 8693 8959
W hardens.com/party/crowngreyhound
The only pub in Dulwich Village has a second-floor private room with its own entrance. It boasts a dance floor, a PA system and a large TV, as well as overhead projectors. You can even get married here. / 11pm, Thu-Sat midnight; closed Sun; in-house caterers; no live bands; Private Rm (large) (100,70,–,–).

Crown Moran Hotel NW2
£M, (300,300,250,300)
142-152 Cricklewood Broadway
T 020 8452 4175
F 020 8452 0952
W hardens.com/party/crownmoranhotel
E crowncb@moranhotels.com
Behind an eye-catching Victorian facade in Cricklewood, this north west London hotel offers five different event spaces. Extensive leisure facilities too, if you're organising something of a residential nature. / Sun-Wed midnight, Thu 1am, Fri-Sat 2am; in-house caterers; no live music; Sala Rm (150,120,100,120); Barnet Rm (60,60,60,60); Brent/Camden Rm (–,12,12,–).

Crown Tavern EC1
£B, (100,–,–,–)
43 Clerkenwell Gn
T 020 7253 4973
W hardens.com/party/crowntavern
At weekends, this pleasant pub, peacefully situated north of Smithfield, can be taken over in its entirety if you have sufficient numbers. For the rest of the week, a function room is available. / midnight; in-house caterers; no dancing; Function Rm (50,–,–,–).

Crowne Plaza London - The City EC4
£M, (250,140,100,160)
19 New Bridge Street
T 0871 942 9190
F 020 7438 8088
W hardens.com/party/crowneplazacity
E loncy.conference@ihg.com
A stylish modern hotel – located right in the City heartlands, by Blackfriars station – which is particularly suited to the business functions for which it comes well equipped. It offers a good selection of flexible accommodation for smaller and medium-size events. / midnight; in-house caterers; Bridewell Room (250,140,100,160); Bridewell 1 (150,80,60,80); The Board Room (–,16,–,–).

Crypt EC1
£M, (200,120,120,–)
14 Ely Pl
T 020 7242 8238
F 020 7831 1402
W www.bleedingheart.co.uk
E thecrypt@bleedingheart.co.uk

As the scene of the wedding feast of Henry VIII and Catherine of Aragon, this atmospheric stone-walled space boasts a long and colourful entertaining history. Today the magical medieval Crypt offers corporate and private banqueting and wonderful wedding receptions with restaurant - quality food from the adjoining Bleeding Heart Restaurant. / midnight; Bleeding Heart Restaurant.

Cumberland Hotel W1
£M-E, (400,240,170,350)
Marble Arch
T 0871 376 9014
W hardens.com/party/cumberlandhotel
E mandesales.cumberland@guorman.co.uk
A large contemporary-style hotel at the end of Oxford Street, with 26 function and meeting rooms decked out in the high-tech style that now characterises the whole building.
/ 1am; in-house caterers; Blue 3&4 Combined (150,120,96,150).

Cutty Sark SE10
£M-E, (300,300,300,–)
The Cutty Sark Trust
T 020 8858 2698
F 020 8858 6976
W www.uniquevenuesoflondon.co.uk/cutty_sark/index.html
E enquiries@cuttysark.org.uk
Cutty Sark is undergoing a £25m conservation programme – aiming to transform it into a splendid 21st century venue – and will again be available for private hire in 2011. The vessel will be suspended allowing visitors to walk, dine or dance under her. A glass apron will give year round protection to visitors. / in-house caterers.

Da Mario SW7
£B-M, (130,130,130,–)
15 Gloucester Rd
T 020 7584 9078
F 020 7823 9026
W hardens.com/party/damario
E enquiries@damario.co.uk
This long-established pizzeria near the Albert Hall has a late-night disco basement, with the option of individual tables to sit differing sizes of party (from 8 to 30 or 40). Or you can take over the whole cellar.
/ 1am; in-house caterers.

Dali Universe SE1
£M-E, (–,–,–,–)
County Hall
T 020 7450 7600
F 020 7450 7639
W www.thedaliuniverse.com
E events@thedaliuniverse.com
Dali Universe presents a collection of works by Spanish Surrealist Salvador Dali (plus Picasso and Chagall). It's old space by 'The Eye' has now closed and (as of July 2010) its new location – 'A stunning new exhibition space in the heart of central London' – had yet to be announced. / in-house or preferred caterers.

Dans Le Noir EC1
£M-E, (–,60,–,–)
30-31 Clerkenwell Green
T 020 7253 1100
F 020 3217 2072
W hardens.com/party/danslenoir
E booking@danslenoir.com
For an event with a difference – you can't see! – take over this City-fringe restaurant where you dine in pitch black, and service is by blind waiters. It's an amazing experience… if not a culinary one.

Dartmouth House W1
£M, (350,140,140,120)
37 Charles St
T 020 7529 1554
F 020 7495 1886
W hardens.com/party/dartmouthhouse
E dartmouthhouse@compass-group.co.uk
The imposing Georgian HQ of the English Speaking Union, in Mayfair, offers some characterful rooms, particularly suitable for weddings and for receptions. The marbled courtyard makes an impressive setting for summer events. / 11.30pm; Leith's; music outside until 8.30pm; Courtyard (100,–,–,–); Churchill Rm (100,80,48,100); Small Drawing Rm (60,50,24,50).

Dean Street Townhouse W1
£M, (–,12,–,–)
69-71 Dean Street
T 020 7434 1775
W hardens.com/party/deanstreettownhouse
E info@deanstreettownhouse.com
Attached to a new hotel, this Soho townhouse is currently one of the hotter venues in the West End – particularly for thirtysomethings – with a restaurant in posh diner style. Event options are limited to use of a private dining room.

Debut London SE1
£B-M, (2900,790,590,400)
Weston St
T 020 7407 1617
F 020 7378 7463
W hardens.com/party/bridgese1
E marcus@debutlondon.co.uk
Formerly called 'The Bridge SE1', this venue comprises six arches below London Bridge, and claims to be London's largest licensed nightclub. It follows that the space available is vast, but arches can be used together or individually to create numerous effects for many different types of event. / 1am; in-house caterers; Main (1200,390,–,400); Grey Arch (400,400,–,200); Red (400,200,–,200); Blue (600,370,–,350); Hide Out (300,160,–,50).

The Decorium N22
£M, (1000,650,466,826)
22 Western Rd
T 020 8888 4770
F 020 8888 6770
W hardens.com/party/decorium
E sales@decorium.co.uk
A stone's throw from Alexandra Park, a vaulted purpose-built function venue, in neo-classical/Regency style. It's licensed for civil weddings. / midnight; hirer's choice of caterer.

Del' Aziz (Bankside) SE1
£B, (250,95,–,–)
5 Canvey Street
T 020 7633 0033
W www.delaziz.co.uk
E bankside@delaziz.co.uk
A stylish, bustling Mediterranean brasserie and restaurant located behind the Tate Modern with 2 unique spaces and an outdoor terrace all available for private hire which can accommodate a wide range of meeting and event needs from intimate gatherings to corporate functions. / 2am; 8am; in-house caterers; Upstairs (100,45,–,–); Downstairs (150,80,–,–).

Del' Aziz (Bermondsey) SE1
£B, (240,130,–,–)
11 Bermondsey Square
T 020 7407 2991
W www.delaziz.co.uk
E Bermondsey@delaziz.co.uk
The newest and swankiest addition, this branch combines a sultry Moroccan lounge bar and bohemian brasserie with an open plan bakery to create a unique spot for intimate gatherings to corporate functions. With an outdoor terrace this is a sought after venue in central London's new up and coming area. / 2am; 7am; in-house caterers; Deli (50,30,–,–); Bar (70,30,–,–); Restaurant (120,70,–,–).

Del' Aziz (Fulham) SW6
£B, (200,145,–,–)
24-32 Vanston Place
T 020 7386 0086
F 020 7610 1661
W www.delaziz.co.uk
E fulham@delaziz.co.uk

A popular hidden gem offering an eastern Mediterranean experience with a modern twist. The Fulham branch has 2 unique environments with its bustling bohemian brasserie to one side and stylish-Moroccan lounge to the other, this location makes a great venue for small or large groups looking for something a bit different. / 7am; in-house caterers; Deli (80,70,–,–); Aziz (120,75,–,–).

Del' Aziz (Swiss Cottage) NW3
£B, (250,180,–,–)
Ground Floor
T 020 7586 3338
W www.delaziz.co.uk
E swisscottage@delaziz.co.uk

A family friendly venue with an eclectic eastern Mediterranean vibe this branch is cozy spot to enjoy any type of event, offering a large space that can be arranged to suit your needs. / 10pm; 8.30am; in-house caterers; no dancing.

Del' Aziz (Westfield) W12
£B, (120,90,–,–)
Westfield Shopping Centre
T 020 8740 0666
W www.delaziz.co.uk
E westfield@delaziz.co.uk

An oasis set in Europe's largest shopping centre, the Westfield branch with its stylish Mediterranean market place vibe is a great venue, offering a lush outdoor terrace and fountain to delight your senses. / midnight; 8am; in-house caterers.

Delfina Galleries SE1
£M, (500,260,260,250)
50 Bermondsey St
T 020 7564 2400
F 020 7357 0250
W hardens.com/party/delfinagalleries
E events@thedelfina.co.uk

This bright and spacious South Bank gallery has become well known as a stylish venue that's well suited to both social occasions and corporate events. It has an interesting location near Bermondsey Antiques Market, but is also very convenient for the City. / midnight; Café Gallery not available until 4.30pm Mon-Fri; in-house caterers; bands only in exhibition gallery; Exhibition Gallery (350,250,250,250); Café Gallery (200,130,100,100).

Depot SW14
£B-M, (–,120,–,–)
Mortlake High St
T 020 8878 9462
F 020 8392 1361
W hardens.com/party/depotbrasserie
E info@depotbrasserie.co.uk

By the water, on a bend of the river, this Barnes restaurant has an especially charming location. You can take it over in its entirety for suitable events. / 11pm, Sun 4pm; in-house caterers; no amplified music; no dancing; Outside Area (–,40,–,–).

Design Museum SE1
£M, (250,150,80,150)
28 Shad Thames
T 020 7940 8766/8262/8766
F 0870 909 1909
W www.designmuseum.org
E specialevents@designmuseum.org

Located in an elegant modernist building on the River Thames by Tower Bridge, the Design Museum has magnificent views of the City of London, Tower Bridge and Canary Wharf, and a large outside terrace from which to enjoy them on a warm day. / Contemporary Design Gallery subject to exhibition; 11pm; list of caterers; no red wine in the Contemporary Design Gallery; Riverside Hall (250,120,80,–);

Contemporary Design Gallery (180,–,–,–); Design Museum Space (200,70,50,150).

Detroit WC2
£B-M, (200,80,–,–)
35 Earlham St
T 020 7240 2662
F 020 7240 8084
W hardens.com/party/detroit
E mail@detroit-bar.com
This sci-fi-cave-style bar in Covent Garden makes an unusual setting for a drinks party. It's available in the early part of the week or (less frequently) at weekends. For smaller parties, the bar subdivides into smaller areas. / midnight; not available Sun; in-house caterers; no dancing; Long Room, Crypt (35,35,–,–).

Devonport House SE10
£M-E, (120,84,84,120)
King William Walk
T 020 8269 5400
F 020 8269 5401
W hardens.com/party/devonporthouse
E devreception@deverevenues.co.uk
Smartly-traditional (and some more modern) function facilities – part of the Maritime Greenwich World Heritage Site. Business use predominates. / midnight; in-house caterers; music must end at midnight.

Dickens Inn E1
£B-M, (150,120,160,–)
St Katherine's Wy
T 020 7488 2208
F 020 7702 3610
W hardens.com/party/dickensinn
E dickensinn@btopenworld.com
Prettily located, at the edge of St Katherine's Dock, this large inn has a warehouse-conversion function room used for discos and wedding receptions. / midnight; in-house caterers.

Dock Kitchen W10
£M, (–,80,–,–)
Portobello Dock
T 020 8962 1610
W hardens.com/party/dockkitchen
Next to Regent's Canal at the north end of Ladbroke Grove, this restaurant occupies a redeveloped Victorian building that was once one of Virgin's recording studios. As well as a private room, you could hire the venue for a meal preceded by drinks on the waterside terrace. / Private Room (–,24,–,–).

Docklands Sailing & Watersports Centre E14
£B-M, (2000,130,130,130)
235a Westferry Rd
T 020 7537 2626
F 020 7537 7774
W hardens.com/party/docklandssailing
E clare@dswc.org
Purpose-built Docklands premises with one large and one smaller room on the first floor for hire. The main hall is very bright and has huge windows and a balcony overlooking Millwall Dock. There are also sailing and dragon boat racing possibilities. / midnight; in-house caterers.

$ EC1
£M, (120,75,–,–)
2 Exmouth Mkt
T 020 7278 0077
W hardens.com/party/dollar
E brett@dollargrills.com
For our money, it's the cosy basement Martini bar which is the best feature of this Clerkenwell bar/brasserie, but both sections are available for private hire. / in-house caterers; Lounge (120,–,–,–).

Dolphin House SW1
£M, (200,30,–,–)
Dolphin House
T 020 7798 8000
W hardens.com/party/dolphinhouse
E dh@dolphinsquare.co.uk
The bar and restaurant of this large 1930s apartment complex can be made available for events, both private and corporate (with accommodation available from amongst over 100 serviced apartments). / 1am; Restaurant (–,30,–,–); Bar (200,–,–,–).

Dominion Theatre W1
£M, (200,120,120,2100)
269 Tottenham Court Rd
Ⓣ 020 7927 0900
Ⓕ 020 7580 0246
Ⓦ hardens.com/party/dominion
Ⓔ dominionevents@nederlander.co.uk

If you're looking for a venue with more than a hint of Deco, the facilities of this enormous West End theatre may be worth checking out. / *10pm; in-house caterers; The Garland Suite (40,15,–,20); The Studio (200,120,120,200); The Gallery (100,100,100,100); The Chaplin Suite (75,40,–,50); The Milburn Suite (20,8,–,–).*

The Don EC4
£M, (75,45,–,–)
20 St Swithin's Ln
Ⓣ 020 7626 2606
Ⓕ 020 7626 2616
Ⓦ www.thedonrestaurant.co.uk
Ⓔ bookings@thedonrestaurant.co.uk

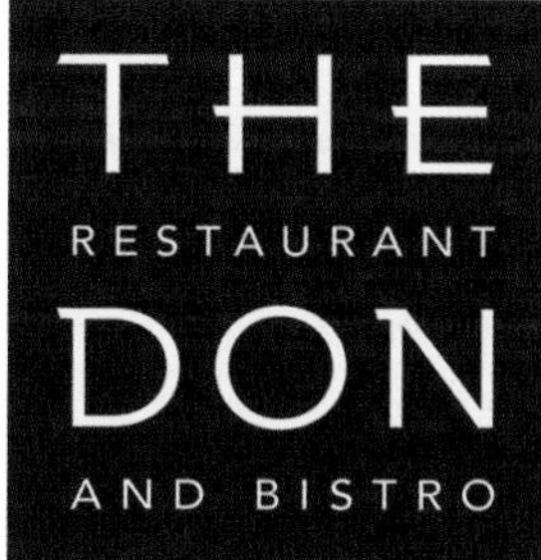

Voted "Best Restaurant for Business in The City", and famed for "excellent and attentive" service, The Don is where the original Sandeman Company bottled their ports and sherries for 200 years. Private Dining is available in the medieval Cellar, the cosy Bistro, airy White Room and intimate Wine Study. / *midnight; evenings only; in-house caterers; no amplified music; no dancing; Restaurant (50,35,–,–); Bistro (60,40,–,–); Private Rm (30,24,–,–); White Room (75,45,–,–); Wine Study (–,16,–,–).*

The Dorchester W1
£M-E, (1000,500,–,500)
53 Park Ln
Ⓣ 020 7629 8888
Ⓕ 020 7319 7117
Ⓦ hardens.com/party/thedorchester
Ⓔ banqueting@thedorchester.com

Glamorous opulence distinguishes the banqueting rooms at this Mayfair hotel – they all have real style, from the subtly-mirrored Ballroom down (or rather up) to the extraordinary fairy-tale setting of the eighth floor penthouse with terrace, fountain and spectacular view. / *1am; in-house caterers; no amplified music on bedroom floors; Ballroom (1000,500,–,500); Orchid (250,140,–,120); Penthouse (40,16,–,–); Boardroom (–,12,–,–); Pavilion (60,34,–,–); Park Suite (100,60,–,60); Crystal (120,60,–,40).*

Dover Street Restaurant & Bar W1
£M-E, (400,250,400,–)
8-10 Dover St
Ⓣ 020 7491 7509
Ⓕ 020 7491 2958
Ⓦ hardens.com/party/doverst
Ⓔ bookings@doverst.co.uk

A large and long-established Mayfair dine-and-dance venue. It offers alcoves and spaces (non-exclusively) for various size of party, or you can exclusively hire one of the bars or the whole venue (in which case they will advise on bands and music accordingly). / *3am; in-house caterers; Upper Bar (65,50,–,–); Lower Bar (150,120,–,–); Alcove (–,24,–,–).*

Dr Johnsons' House EC4
£B-M, (100,30,–,–)
17 Gough Sq
Ⓣ 020 7353 3745
Ⓕ 020 7353 3745
Ⓦ hardens.com/party/drjohnsonshouse
Ⓔ curator@drjohnsonshouse.org

Apart from its literary associations, the charm of this four-storey house is that it is a plain Georgian building – authentically neutral in décor – hidden away just off Fleet Street. The house is generally available only for early evening receptions, but occasionally for wedding receptions and the like. / 9pm/9.30pm; available from 6pm, Sun by arrangement; list of caterers; no amplified music; no dancing.

Drapers' Hall EC2
£M-E, (450,224,–,320)
Throgmorton St
T 020 7588 5001
F 020 7448 1307
W hardens.com/party/drapershall
E banqueting@thedrapers.co.uk
Behind the Bank of England, this livery hall, remodelled in Victoria's day, is one of the City's finest. / midnight; closed late July-Sep; in-house caterers; Court Dining (120,96,–,100).

DreamBagsJaguarShoes E2
£M, (250,–,–,–)
34-36 Kingsland Rd
T 020 7729 5830
W hardens.com/party/dbjs
E manager@dreambagsjaguarshoes.com
If you want an event setting that's almost a parody of urban-trendiness, how about hiring part of this ever-evolving Shoreditch bar? / 1am; in-house caterers; no dancing; Basement (150,–,–,–).

The Driver N1
£B, (150,–,–,–)
2-4 Wharfdale Road
T 020 7278 8827
W hardens.com/party/driver
E info@blondeproductions.co.uk
A stylish King's Cross bar, whose 'designer-y' upper floors, restaurant and roof terrace provide a flexible space for different types of event, complete with sounds systems, projection and DJ booths. / Sun-Thu 12pm-12am, weekends 12pm-4am; in-house caterers; Ground Floor (150,–,–,–); 1st Floor (150,–,–,–); 2nd Floor (120,–,–,–); 3rd Floor (120,–,–,–); Roof Terrace (80,–,–,–).

Duchess Theatre WC2
£M, (50,–,–,470)
Catherine St
T 020 7395 0780
F 020 7240 4540
W hardens.com/party/duchesstheatre
E nicola.seed@nimaxtheatres.com
Designed in 1929 in a vaguely Tudor style, a theatre available for presentations and so on, subject to the dictates of the current production. / 5pm; available subject to constraints of current production; hirer's choice of caterer; Bar (50,–,–,–).

Dukes Hotel SW1
£M-E, (100,60,45,80)
35 St James's Place
T 020 7491 4840
F 020 7493 1264
W hardens.com/party/dukeshotel
E bookings@dukeshotel.com
A late-Victorian St James's hotel with two conventional private rooms, which suit intimate dinners or perhaps a wedding. / midnight; in-house caterers; Marlborough Suite (100,60,45,80); Sheridan Rm (20,12,–,15).

Dulwich College SE21
£B-M, (400,300,–,180)
Dulwich Common
T 020 8299 9284
F 020 8299 9262
W hardens.com/party/dulwichcollege
E enterprise@dulwich.org.uk
An impressively equipped Victorian school – in extensive and leafy grounds – which offers a variety of possibilities for functions and entertainments (especially sports-related). Moderate prices are helped by a no-corkage policy – as long as catering is in-house. The Old Library has a wedding licence. / no candles, no helium balloons; midnight; not available during the day in term; list of caterers; no dancing in great hall or old library; Old Library (80,–,–,120); Great Hall (–,200,–,380); Lower Hall (150,90,–,120); South Cloister (200,120,–,–).

Dulwich Picture Gallery SE21
£M-E, (350,120,–,109)
Gallery Rd
T 020 8299 8713
F 020 8299 8700
W www.dulwichpicturegallery.org.uk
E events@dulwichpicturegallery.org.uk
England's oldest, purpose-built picture gallery houses a magnificent collection of old masters (and a mausoleum for its founders). It is set in five acres of gardens and has

undergone extensive refurbishment in recent years, including the installation of an elegant glazed cloister. / midnight; list of caterers; no red wine; Garden & Gallery (350,120,–,–); Linbury Rm (76,50,–,109); Gallery Cafe (90,50,–,–).

Dyers' Hall EC4

£M-E, (–,57,–,–)
10 Dowgate Hill
T 020 7236 7197
F 020 72480774
W hardens.com/party/dyershall

A small, early-Victorian hall, available to suitable hirers for luncheons and dinners only. / 11pm; in-house caterers; no amplified music; no dancing.

The E Rejuvenation Centre E1

£M-E, (300,100,–,150)
132 Commercial St
T 020 7650 0718
F 020 7650 0719
W hardens.com/party/erejuvenation
E info@erejuvenation.co.uk

Feng Shui looms large at this Shoreditch venue, which is divided into five areas, each decorated according to a different elemental theme (and with appropriate music). It seems to have a surprisingly wide appeal, with many clients seeming to have nothing obviously New Agey about them at all! / 11pm; hirer's choice of caterer (in-house available).

E&O W11

£M, (–,84,–,–)
14 Blenheim Cr
T 020 7229 5454
F 020 7229 5522
W hardens.com/party/eando
E eando@rickarrestaurants.com

Perennially hip and happening, this Notting Hill bar/restaurant offers an interesting oriental tapas menu. They sometimes make the whole place available for hire, and there's also the option of a basement private room. / 10.45pm, Sun 10.15pm; in-house caterers; no amplified music; no dancing; Private Dining Room (–,20,–,–).

Ealing Town Hall W5

£M, (450,250,150,500)
14-16 Uxbridge Rd
T 020 8825 6060
F 020 8825 6066
W hardens.com/party/ealingth
E halls@ealing.gov.uk

An impressive Victorian town hall, well geared-up for function business, and offering a variety of settings – from the council chambers themselves to small meeting rooms. / 1.30am; list of caterers; no amplified music; Nelson Rm (80,75,–,80); Princes Room (220,180,–,–).

Earls Court & Olympia SW5

£M, (20000,8000,6000,17500)
Warwick Road
T 020 7385 1200
W hardens.com/party/eco
E vanessa.whybro@eco.co.uk

With nigh on 100,000 square metres of exhibition space, a maximum capacity of 20,000, and dedicated tube stations and parking, capacity is certainly not a problem at the largest function spaces within striking distance of the centre of town. Conferences centres attached to both venues can be used for smaller events. / Leith's & Creative Events; Earl's Court 1 (20000,8000,6000,17500); Earl's Court 2 (6000,5000,4000,6000); Olympia Conference Centre (500,200,150,250); Brompton Hall (2000,1500,1250,2000); Olympia Grand (7000,4000,3500,7000); Olympia National (4000,3000,2500,4000).

Earlsfield Library SW18

£B, (–,75,–,–)
276 Magdalen Rd
T 020 8871 6389
F 020 8944 6912
W hardens.com/party/earlsfield

A library with a pleasant barrel-vaulted room, available for social functions. / 11pm; hirer's choice of caterer; no ampl music; no alcohol licence.

East Hampstead Park Conference Centre RG40

£M, (250,110,90,180)
Wokingham
T 01189 747576
F 01189 793870
W hardens.com/party/easthampark
E sales@eastpark.co.uk

A Victorian house set in 60 acres of parkland, offering accommodation for everything from conferences to weddings. / midnight; in-house caterers; Windsor (–,20,–,30).

East India Club SW1

£M, (250,140,–,–)
16 St James's Sq
T 020 7930 1000
W hardens.com/party/eastindiaclub
E banqueting@eastindiaclub.co.uk

This imposing St James's club makes no efforts to market its facilities to non-members. However, if you can find one of their number (6,000 or so) to act as host (and be present), it offers a number of rooms which make convivial places for dinners and receptions. / members club; midnight; in-house caterers; no amplified music; no dancing.

East Wintergarden E14

£M-E, (1000,500,450,600)
43 Bank St
T 020 7418 2725
F 020 7512 9117
W hardens.com/party/eastwintergarden
E eastwintergarden@canarywharf.com

Part of Canary Wharf – a large, vaulted, glazed space, precisely in keeping with its name. (Former sibling venue Cabot Hall is now closed.) / midnight (flexible - but it costs £800 per hour plus VAT to hire the room after midnight); in-house caterers; Promenade Room (–,25,–,14); Hall (1000,500,450,600).

ecurie25 N1

£B-M, (350,–,–,–)
9 Railway Street
T 020 7278 3010
W hardens.com/party/ecurie25
E enquiries@ecurie25.co.uk

A party for petrol heads? Consider this club for supercar lovers, which occupies a large, converted print works right next to King's Cross station. There are about 30 cars on display at any time, a stage, and plenty of space for, say, a dance floor. / no music.

Egg N7

£B-M, (1000,–,–,278)
200 York Way
T 020 7609 8364
F 020 7619 6189
W hardens.com/party/egglondon
E info@egglondon.net

An impressive three-floor nightclub, near King's Cross. For events, its 'surprise' feature is a courtyard garden. / 24 hour licence; hirer's choice of caterer (in-house available).

Eight Over Eight SW3

£M, (–,95,–,–)
392 King's Rd
T 020 7349 9934
F 020 7351 5157
W hardens.com/party/eightovereight
E eightovereight@rickarrestaurants.com

Will "E&O" Ricker's trendy Chelsea restaurant is decked out in his hallmark, hip clean-lined style and provides similar oriental-inspired fare. It's to re-open in the second half of 2010, having been closed most of the year due to fire damage. / 11pm; not available Sun L; in-house caterers; no amplified music; no dancing; Private Room (–,14,–,–).

Electric Ballroom NW1

£B, (1200,–,–,–)
184 Camden High St
T 020 7485 9006
F 020 7284 0745
W hardens.com/party/electricballroom
E mags@electricballroom.co.uk

A rather nice, old-established Camden Town dance hall. It's located right by the tube station, and ideal for a large dance or major themed event. / 3am; not available Fri-Sun; hirer's choice of caterer, alcohol in-house.

Elena's L'Etoile W1

£M, (50,32,–,–)
30 Charlotte St
T 020 7636 7189
F 020 7637 0122
W hardens.com/party/elenasletoile
E elenas@corushotels.com

This old-fashioned Fitzrovia restaurant has a rare degree of period charm, and offers a choice of private rooms with character. / *midnight; in-house caterers; no music; no dancing; Oscar Room (50,32,–,–); Elena's Room (30,16,–,–); Lounge Room (20,16,–,–); Private Room (10,9,–,–).*

Elstree Film Studio WD6
£M, (400,250,250,–)
Shenley Rd
T 020 8953 1600
F 020 8905 1135
W hardens.com/party/elstreestudios
E info@elstreestudios.co.uk
A film studio usually offers a blank space in which you have the opportunity (and cost) of building your own set. The attraction here is precisely the opposite – it's a smart, conventional banqueting suite, offering the (unusual) option, if you must, of bringing in your own caterer. / *very restricted availability; 2am; in-house caterers generally preferred.*

Eltham Palace SE9
£E, (300,200,150,200)
Courtyard
T 020 8294 2577
F 020 8294 2621
W hardens.com/party/elthampalace
E emily.holl@english-heritage.org.uk
This intriguing building was the boyhood home of Henry VIII. The hall ultimately became the home of the Courtauld family, who made some celebrated Art Deco additions. / *no stilettos; midnight; available Sun-Thu evenings only, Fri & Sat 3pm-midnight; list of caterers; no red wine for standing receptions; Great Hall (300,200,150,200); Drawing Rm (100,60,–,80); Dining Rm (–,10,–,–).*

Embargo 59 SW10
£B-M, (300,70,–,–)
533b Kings Rd
T 020 7351 5038
W hardens.com/party/embargoclub
E enquiries@embargo59.com
In the early evening (till 11pm), you can hire this intimate Chelsea nightclub for a drinks or dinner party. Such of your guests as wish to can then stay on for the rest of the evening. / *3am; hirer's choice of caterer.*

Engineer NW1
£B-M, (–,100,–,–)
65 Gloucester Av
T 020 7722 0950
F 020 7483 0592
W hardens.com/party/engineer
E info@the-engineer.com
A fashionable Primrose Hill gastropub, with two private dining rooms upstairs, or you could hire the whole restaurant. / *midnight; in-house caterers; no amplified music; no dancing; Mirror Rm (–,20,–,–); Private Room 1 (–,32,–,–).*

Epsom Downs KT18
£M, (800,600,600,800)
Epsom
T 01372 726311
F 01372 748253
W hardens.com/party/epsomdowns
E epsom@jockeyclubracecourses.com
The racecourse has two separate multi-level buildings – the Queen's Stand and the recently built Duchess Stand – which together offer a huge number of options for anything from a small event to a wedding, conference or awards ceremony. / *1am; in-house caterers; Jockey Club Rm (150,140,120,–); Oaks Hall (1000,700,350,800); The Diomed Suit (400,300,200,450); Lammtarra Suit (170,100,60,100); The Gallops Suit (80,60,30,50); The Downs View Suit (110,90,80,150); The Blue Riband Room (400,350,150,250); The Board Room (100,60,40,60).*

L'Escargot W1
£M, (–,60,–,–)
48 Greek St
T 020 7734 7333
F 020 7734 0033
W hardens.com/party/escargot
E sales@whitestarline.org.uk
Long-established Soho restaurant, with two good-quality private rooms. The larger, barrel-vaulted room, is particularly distinctive. / *11.15pm; not available Sat L and Sun; in-house caterers; no amplified music; no dancing; Private Rm 2 (–,30,–,–).*

Estorick Collection N1
£M-E, (200,40,–,80)
39a Canonbury Sq
T 020 7704 9522
F 020 7704 9531
W hardens.com/party/estorick
E curator@estorickcollection.com
A collection of modern Italian art (including Modigliani, Morandi and the Futurists) is on display in this Georgian villa in Islington – an intimate but stylish setting for an event. / 9pm; available day Mon & Tue, otherwise evenings, except Thu; hirer's choice of caterer (in-house available); no dancing; no red wine.

Eton College (Dorney Lake) SL4
£M, (300,250,–,–)
Eton College Rowing Centre
T 01753 832756
F 01753 851767
W hardens.com/party/dorneylake
E info@dorneylake.co.uk
The school boathouse is available for external events and functions. The main room has a balcony overlooking the rowing lake. / midnight; in-house caterers.

ExCeL London E16
£B-M, (1125,–,800,1125)
London Docklands
T 020 7069 4602
F 020 7069 4747
W hardens.com/party/excel
E sales.enquiries@excel-london.co.uk
A "world-class, state-of-the-art" event venue, in Docklands. Apart from 65,000 square metres of exhibition space, in May 2010 a £165m extension opened, creating London's first ever International Convention Centre, incorporating the UK's largest fully-flexible auditorium (with 5,000 seats), London's largest banqueting hall, plus 17 further meeting rooms for 50-1,200. / 24 hour licence; Leith's; Platinum Suite (1125,–,800,1125); ICC Capital Suite (1190,–,640,1190); Gallery Meeting Rooms (90,–,48,90); ICC Auditorium (5000,–,–,–); ICC Capital Hall (–,–,–,5000).

Fabric EC1
£B-M, (1800,140,140,200)
77a Charterhouse St
T 020 7336 8898
F 020 7253 3932
W hardens.com/party/fabric
E events@fabriclondon.com
The enormous nightclub by Smithfield market is intriguingly laid out in a former cold store (for New Zealand lamb, if you're interested). Facilities include three dance floors, five sound systems, six bars and a VIP lounge. / no set time on weekdays, Fri 6am, Sat 8am, Sun 6am; available Mon-Thu; hirer's choice of caterer (in-house available).

Fan Museum SE10
£M-E, (80,30,–,40)
12 Crooms Hill
T 020 8305 1441
F 020 8293 1889
W www.fan-museum.org
E admin@fan-museum.org
The Orangery is well-suited to intimate dinners, receptions and away days. In the evening guests have exclusive use of the entire museum and can enjoy a private tour of the temporary exhibition. Capacity: 30 (dinners), 70 (reception). / 10.30pm; list of caterers; no amplified music; no dancing; Museum (70,–,–,–); Orangery (70,30,–,40).

Farmers' & Fletchers' Hall EC1
£M, (200,120,64,120)
3 Cloth St
T 020 7251 7171
F 020 7251 7170
W hardens.com/party/farmersfletchershall
E enquire@chesterboyd.co.uk
A modern livery hall, decorated in a traditional style. It's quite an adaptable venue for smaller and medium-sized events. / 1am; Chester Boyd; Court Rm (20,18,–,20).

The Fashion and Textile Museum SE1
£M, (240,50,50,90)
83 Bermondsey St
T 020 7407 8664
F 020 7403 5333
W hardens.com/party/fashionmuseum
The Fashion and Textile Museum lies at the heart of London's artistic Bermondsey Village. A remarkable

building designed by Mexican architect, Ricardo Legoretta, the FTM is now a part of Newham College and is being redeveloped to become an education, exhibition and visitor centre for contemporary fashion, textiles and jewellery. / 11pm ; list of caterers; noise volume limits apply.

Favela Chic EC2

£B-M, (250,80,–,–)
91-93 Great Eastern St
T 020 7613 5228
F 020 7613 4228
W hardens.com/party/favelachic
E booking@favelachic.com
This Brazilian-meets-Parisian restaurant-bar-club-performance space is not for the faint hearted, but if you're willing to let loose, Favela Chic may be the place to do it. / 2am; in-house caterers.

The Fellow N1

£B, (120,80,–,–)
24 York Way
T 020 7833 4395
W www.thefellow.co.uk
E natalie@thefellow.co.uk
The Fellow specialises in modern British cuisine with a European twist. We use locally sourced, seasonal produce and our menus change daily. We also feature a glamorous retro-styled cocktail bar & heated walled terrace as well as our intimate private room, perfect for dinners, meetings or parties. / late license available; all day; in-house caterers; no dancing; Black Door Cocktail Bar (100,–,–,–); Private Room (20,12,–,–).

15 Hatfields SE1

£M-E, (500,220,–,250)
15 Hatfields
T 020 7827 5920
W hardens.com/party/hatfields
A newly-built South Bank centre with the latest in conference and event technology. The venue is well suited for conferences, training, work-shops, awards parties, cocktail canapes, receptions, private parties and product launches. / 1am; list of caterers; Ground Floor (500,220,–,250); Boardroom (450,192,–,200); Earth, Water, Air (350,144,–,150); Earth, Water (175,72,–,96).

52-53 Russell Square WC1

£M-E, (90,–,–,70)
52-53 Russell Square
T 020 7631 6900
W hardens.com/party/32stjs
E info@cipr.co.uk
The CIPR have moved from 32 St James's Square and – though their new HQ is also Grade II listed – doesn't have as many event possibilities as the old location, especially for social functions. The current facilities would suit, say, a small conference followed by a drinks reception. / 10pm; in-house caterers; no loud music; Room 1 (90,–,–,70); Room 2 (60,–,–,40).

FireHouse SW7

£M-E, (200,60,–,–)
3 Cromwell Rd
T 020 7584 7258
F 020 7584 9768
W hardens.com/party/firehousesw7
E info@firehousesw7.com
Though it's a club, this townhouse opposite the Natural History Museum has a restaurant available to non-members, which would make an atmospheric venue for a small dinner (up to 12 people). Or hire the whole place. / members club; 3am; in-house caterers.

Firepower - The Royal Artillery Museum SE18

£M-E, (500,260,–,150)
Royal Arsenal Woolwich
T 020 8855 7755
F 020 8855 7100
W hardens.com/party/firepower
E info@firepower.org.uk
A Woolwich museum of the history of artillery, which provides a number of spaces suitable for corporate entertaining. / midnight; in-house, plus list of approved caterers.

First Bowl Queensway W2

£B, (1500,–,–,–)
17 Queensway
T 020 7229 0172
F 020 7229 5207
W hardens.com/party/firstbowl
E info@queensiceandbowl.co.uk

The action at Central London's only ice rink is no longer limited to falling over on a slippery, cold surface – you can hire the entire Bayswater centre and try Sega World, ten-pin bowling and pool too. / 11.30pm; hirer's choice of caterer (in-house available); Ice Rink (750,–,–,–); Bowling Alley (150,–,–,–); Karaoke Room 1 (30,–,–,–); Karaoke Room 2 (15,–,–,–).

First Floor Restaurant W11
£M, (100,75,–,–)
186 Portabello Rd
T 020 7243 0072
F 020 7221 9440
W hardens.com/party/firstfloorportobello
E info@firstfloorportobello.co.uk

Long a fixture of Notting Hill, this very atmospheric and spacious venue (in fact, a converted pub) incorporates a ground floor bar, a restaurant and two top-floor private dining rooms. / 1am; hirer's choice of caterer (in-house available); background music only; no dancing; Private Dining Rm 1 (30,28,–,–); Private Dining Rm 2 (70,43,–,–); Restaurant (100,75,–,–); Bar (100,–,–,–).

Fishmongers' Hall EC4
£E, (300,220,120,–)
London Bridge
T 020 7626 3531
F 020 7929 1389
W hardens.com/party/fishmongershall
E clerk@fishhall.org.uk

An august Thames-side livery hall, which has only in recent times become generally available for (suitable) event hire. / 11.30pm; weekdays only; in-house caterers; no dancing.

Fitzroy Square W1
£B-M, (150,80,–,70)
Fitzroy Sq
T 020 7529 8921
F 0871 750 2937
W hardens.com/party/fitzroysq
E roomhire@georgiangroup.org.uk

A Grade I listed Georgian House in a tranquil square just off Tottenham Court Road, suited to both corporate and private events. / no candles; 11pm; hirer's choice of caterer.

Floridita W1
£M, (411,360,–,–)
100 Wardour St
T 020 7314 4000
F 020 7314 4040
W www.floriditalondon.com
E info@floriditalondon.com

Floridita

Nestled within the heart of the bustling West End, Floridita London emulates the 1930s style of the legendary El Floridita, creating the perfect blend of glamour and decadence. Available to hire exclusively for up to 600 guests and with 3 exclusive areas Floridita is perfect for every event from film premieres to corporate functions. / 5.30pm - 2am Tue - Wed, 3am Thu - Sat; in-house caterers; Havana Lounge (90,68,–,–); Bar Constante (70,52,–,–); Salon Rojo (35,–,–,–).

Fluid EC1
£B-M, (250,–,–,–)
40 Charterhouse St
T 020 7253 3444
F 020 7608 2777
W hardens.com/party/fluidbar
E james@fluidbar.com

A neat retro-Japanesey theme (incorporating old arcade games) adds interest to this Smithfield bar, which can be hired in its entirety for a private party. / 4am; in-house caterers.

Forbes House SW1
£M-E, (200,120,120,150)
Halkin St
T 020 7344 9211
F 020 7235 5750
W hardens.com/party/forbeshouse
E events@forbeshouse.co.uk

This immense, late-Georgian Belgravia house has a number of rooms available for conferences, dinners and parties. Change is afoot at the end of 2010, after which time the venue may not be available. / midnight; in-house (day), list of caterers (eves); no amplified music outside.

Forge WC2
£B-M, (100,80,–,–)
14 Garrick St
T 020 7379 1531
F 020 7379 1530
W hardens.com/party/forge
E info@theforgerestaurant.co.uk

Occupying an interesting conversion of an old industrial building opposite the Garrick Club in Covent Garden, this traditional French restaurant has a range of options for parties. You can hire the whole place, a series of linked rooms, or smaller groups can take just one of the rooms. / *1am; available from noon; in-house caterers; no amplified music; Private Room (–,22,–,–).*

Forman's Fish Island E3
£M-E, (600,400,350,300)
Stour Rd
T 020 8525 2390
F 020 8525 2398
W hardens.com/party/formansfishisland
E info@formansfishisland.com

"The closest venue to London's Olympic stadium" – this new fish smokery-cum-conference centre (yes, really) occupies an intriguing and impressive new building, overlooking the 2012 event's centrepiece. / *in-house caterers; Floor 1 (220,90,–,90); Floor 2 (800,480,–,350).*

Fortnum & Mason W1
£M-E, (150,1000,–,70)
181 Piccadilly
T 020 7734 8040
F 020 7437 3278
W hardens.com/party/fortnum
E restaurants@fortnumandmason.co.uk

Recently emerged from a major wash and brush-up, the Queen's grocers offer a number of spaces suitable for events in their landmark St James's Restaurant. / *midnight; in-house caterers; Wine Bar (–,50,–,–); St James's Rm (150,120,–,–); Burlington Room (80,56,–,70); Gallery Restaurant (–,80,–,–); Ground Floor (–,500,–,–); Lower Ground Floor (–,500,–,–).*

Fortune Theatre WC2
£M, (80,–,–,432)
Russell St
T 020 7010 7901
F 020 7010 7911
W hardens.com/party/fortunetheatre
E fortunemanager@theambassadors.com

An Art Deco theatre in Covent Garden, available for presentations during the day. Event use is subject to the constraints of the resident show, but as 'The Woman in Black' has now been running for as long as anyone can remember, the pattern of likely availability is fairly well established! The bar has recently been refurbished. / *restricted availability; 5pm (available for longer on Sundays); not available Tue or Sat; in-house caterers; Bar (80,–,–,–).*

45 Millbank SW1
£M, (250,190,–,180)
Chelsea College of Art and Design
T 020 7514 8514
W hardens.com/party/millbank
E 45millbank@chelsea.arts.ac.uk

Right by Tate Britain, these impressively Edwardian premises – originally the HQ of the Royal Army Medical Corps – have been converted in modern times into the new home of the Chelsea College of Art and Design. Three grand rooms are available for private hire. / *midnight; list of caterers; no music (Red Room only); The Banqueting Hall (250,190,–,180); Red Room (100,80,–,–).*

Forty Hall EN2
£M, (250,180,160,180)
Enfield
T 020 8363 4774
F 020 8363 8252
W hardens.com/party/fortyhall
E info@fortyhallbanqueting.co.uk

A Grade I listed house set in a beautiful landscape garden. Banqueting takes place in the Tudor Barn. / *midnight; hirer's choice of caterer (in-house available).*

Founders' Hall EC1

£M, (100,75,–,80)

1 Cloth Fair

Ⓣ 0870 780 9639

Ⓕ 020 7251 7170

Ⓦ hardens.com/party/foundershall

Ⓔ enquire@chesterboyd.co.uk

This small, modern (1987) hall, in Smithfield, combines a large number of decorative styles into a surprisingly small space. The Livery Hall boasts striking contemporary décor. / 11pm; Chester Boyd; some restrictions on music; no dancing; Livery Hall (100,75,–,80); Parlour (20,–,–,25).

The Foundling Museum WC1

£M-E, (200,100,–,100)

40 Brunswick Square

Ⓣ 020 7841 3616

Ⓕ 020 7841 3601

Ⓦ www.foundlingmuseum.org.uk

Ⓔ events@foundlingmuseum.org.uk

One of London's hidden treasures - a stunning mix of 18th century interiors and contemporary spaces for receptions and dinners. The Foundling tells the poignant story of England's first home for abandoned children, contains Britain's first public art collection and holds the largest private collection of Handel memorabilia including his will. / 11pm; list of caterers; music must be appropriate to the venue; no dancing; no red wine unless seated; Picture Gallery option 1 (170,90,–,100); Picture Gallery option 2 (150,80,–,90); Picture Gallery option 3 (130,70,–,80); Picture Gallery option 4 (110,60,–,70); Picture Gallery option 5 (100,50,–,60); Picture Gallery option 6 (90,40,–,50); Court Room option 1 (–,30,–,50); Court Room option 2 (–,20,–,40); Court Room option 3 (–,10,–,30).

Four Seasons Canary Wharf E14

£M-E, (200,200,160,200)

Westferry Circus

Ⓣ 020 7510 1999

Ⓕ 020 7510 1998

Ⓦ hardens.com/party/fourseasonsE14

Ⓔ ewan.cheung@fourseasons.com

The grandest hotel in the environs of Canary Wharf offers a big range of function rooms. Contemporary in style, it does big business in weddings and bar mitzvahs (and also, of course, corporate events). / 1am; in-house caterers; Ballroom (200,200,160,200); River Rm (100,66,–,75); City Rm (55,30,–,36).

The Fox Club W1

£M-E, (70,27,32,–)

46 Clarges St

Ⓣ 020 7495 3656

Ⓕ 020 7495 3626

Ⓦ hardens.com/party/foxclublondon

Ⓔ bethan@foxclublondon.com

Less stuffy than many of Mayfair's traditional establishments, this small club aims to be a fun and friendly place for social entertaining. / midnight; in-house caterers; no live music; dancing restricted on ground floor; Restaurant (45,25,–,–); Drawing Room (20,10,–,–); Elizabeth Armistead Room (40,30,–,–).

Frederick's N1

£M, (200,120,120,–)

106 Camden Pas

Ⓣ 020 7359 3902

Ⓕ 020 7359 5173

Ⓦ hardens.com/party/fredericks

Ⓔ eat@fredericks.co.uk

A grand Islington restaurant with two private rooms. The Clarence Room is an elegant first floor room, which is a pleasant place for a dinner or small reception, and licensed for civil weddings. For larger events, it may be possible to use the whole restaurant, with its impressive conservatory. / 11.30pm; in-house caterers; Clarence Rm (–,32,–,–); Sussex Rm (–,16,–,–).

Freemasons' Hall WC2

£M, (120,300,200,–)

60 Great Queen Street

Ⓣ 020 7831 9811

Ⓕ 020 7831 6021

Ⓦ www.uniquevenuesoflondon.co.uk/freemasons_hall/index.html

Ⓔ khaigh@ugle.org.uk

An impressive space that's only relatively recently been opened for events and has hosted a number of big award ceremonies and film premiers; suited to conferences, launches, fashion shows, and a wide variety of different types of hospitality functions. / optional; hirer's choice of caterer; no music; no dancing; alcohol on first floor only.

Freud Museum NW3

£M, (90,35,–,–)
20 Maresfield Gdns
T 020 7435 2002
F 020 7431 5452
W hardens.com/party/freudmuseum
E info@freud.org.uk
Spacious '20s Hampstead villa in which the great man lived his last days and where his daughter, Anna, lived until the '80s. Its domestic ambience makes it ideal for intimate gatherings, especially in summer when the charming garden can be used. / 11pm; available Wed-Sun from 5pm, Mon & Tue all day; hirer's choice of caterer; no dancing; Marquee (40,35,–,–).

Froebel College SW15

£B-M, (160,100,–,–)
Roehampton Ln
T 020 8392 8100
F 020 8392 3746
W hardens.com/party/frobelcollege
E c.simmons@roehampton.ac.uk
The home of Froebel College, in leafy Roehampton, set in 25 acres of grounds and gardens (complete with a large lake). / midnight; list of caterers.

The Frontline Club W2

£M, (100,56,–,100)
13 Norfolk Place
T 020 7479 8960
W hardens.com/party/frontlineclub
E mail@frontlineclub.com
This club/restaurant in the thin area near St Mary's Paddington is named for the war reporters whose photography adorns its walls. The first-floor club room may be used for suitable events. / 11pm (flexible); in-house caterers.

Fulham House SW6

£B-M, (160,100,120,150)
87 Fulham High St
T 020 7384 4670
F 020 7384 4679
W hardens.com/party/fulhamhouse
E info@alv.mod.uk
This listed Georgian house – the oldest in Fulham – accommodates a branch of the TA, and is also a popular party venue. The main hall (an extension) is a flexible space with a glass-canopied ceiling. The Dining Room is formal. / very restricted availability; 11.30pm; not available Wed evening; list of caterers; Dining Rm (80,40,–,60).

Fulham Palace SW6

£M, (180,200,120,84)
Bishops Av
T 020 7736 8140
F 020 7751 0164
W hardens.com/party/fulhampalace
E functions@fulhampalace.org
A recently refurbished medieval palace, with courtyard, which makes a pleasant venue for weddings, receptions and the like. / 1am; list of caterers; Great Hall (150,90,–,90); Drawing Rm (50,50,–,–); Dining Rm (50,30,–,–); Marquee (250,200,–,–).

Fulham Town Hall SW6

£B-M, (420,400,200,400)
Fulham Broadway
T 0845 337 0314
F 020 8753 2380
W hardens.com/party/fulhamth
E events@lbhf.gov.uk
A grand Edwardian town hall, handily close to Fulham Broadway tube. The Concert Hall shares many of the attractions of the Great Hall, but on a smaller scale. Both halls are licensed for weddings. / no candles; 2am; hirer's choice of caterer; no amplified music in concert hall; Concert Hall (220,150,100,200).

Gallery Soho WC2

£M, (150,60,80,80)
The Gallery Soho
T 07841 374 735
W hardens.com/party/gallerysoho
E rene.andria@thegallerysoho.com
With its white walls and wood floors, this three-floor gallery space on the fringe of Soho is an ideal 'blank canvas' for an event. With its fully equipped bar and AV, it's particularly well-suited to launches and corporate functions. / 1am ; hirer's choice of caterer (in-house available); no music.

Galvin Bistrot de Luxe W1
£B-M, (30,22,–,–)
66 Baker St
T 020 7935 4007
F 020 7486 1735
W hardens.com/party/gbdl
E info@galvinuk.com
The bar at this elegant bistro is available for private hire (primarily, it seems, by wedding parties coming from the nearby Marylebone registry office, but suited to a range of events.) / midnight; available from noon; in-house caterers; no music; Private Room (30,22,–,–).

Galvin La Chapelle E1
£M-E, (–,12,–,–)
35 Spital Square
T 020 7299 0400
F 020 7299 0401
W hardens.com/party/galvinlachapelle
This stunningly converted chapel near Spitalfields Market has been one of the best restaurants to open in the City in recent years. It's not generally made available for full hire, but there is a gallery overlooking the main hall for private events.

Garden Bar and Grill W10
£B, (400,160,–,–)
41 Bramley Rd
T 020 7229 1111
W hardens.com/party/gardenbarandgrill
E JSwinscoe@aol.com
A contemporary pub near Latimer Road tube with one of the largest gardens in London eclectically decorated with booths and candles, and available for parties, corporate evenings and bespoke events for 20 to 400. In a previous life, the bar was a blues club, and there's a large stage. / midnight; in-house caterers; Inside (200,80,–,–); Outside (200,80,–,–); Deck (120,–,–,–).

Garden Café NW1
£B-M, (300,200,–,–)
Inner Circle
T 020 7930 8619
F 020 7930 8754
W hardens.com/party/gardencafe
E gardencafe@companyofcooks.com
An extraordinary '60s building, recently refurbished, with a special location, by the rose garden. It's in the heart of Regent's Park and when available for private hire offers dramatic autumnal and winter views. / availability based on park, seasonal (autumn & winter); dusk; in-house caterers.

The Garden Museum SE1
£M, (200,120,100,–)
Lambeth Palace Rd
T 020 7401 8865
F 020 7401 8869
W www.gardenmuseum.org.uk/venuehire/
E jess@gardenmuseum.org.uk
This deconsecrated church building has quite a handy location, by Lambeth Palace. It is used for wedding receptions, corporate events and press launches. / 1am; available from 5pm, Sat after 4pm; list of caterers; Garden (150,–,–,–).

Gate Street Barn GU5
£B, (200,130,130,150)
Gate Street
T 01483894362
Mob: 07787 153212
F 01483 892637
W hardens.com/party/gatestreetbarn
E info@gatestreetbarn.com
A handy venue for corporate events – summer BBQs, Christmas parties, Team Building days, wine tastings – in a rural setting. No in-house caterers or corkage. All weather car parking, less than 1 hour down the A3. / midnight; list of caterers; Meeting Room (–,8,–,–).

Gay Hussar W1
£M, (–,40,–,–)
2 Greek St
T 020 7437 0973
F 020 7437 4631
W hardens.com/party/gayhussar
E gayhussar@corushotels.com
The atmosphere of this venerable,

creaky Hungarian restaurant – long a haunt of Soho's socialist intelligentsia – permeates as far as the cosy upper-floor private rooms. / midnight; not available Sun; in-house caterers; no music; no dancing; Second Floor (–,12,–,–).

Geffrye Museum E2

£M-E, (250,70,–,60)
136 Kingsland Rd
T 020 7739 9893
F 020 7729 5647
W www.geffrye-museum.org.uk
E info@geffrye-museum.org.uk

Set in beautiful 18th century almshouses with attractive gardens just a mile from the City, the Geffrye Museum explores the home from 1600 to the present day. Its displays of period rooms provide an unusual and atmospheric backdrop for receptions, launches, lectures and meetings. / restricted availability; 10pm; main galleries: Tue-Thu evenings, Arts rooms and Lecture room, Tue-Fri all day; day-time hire in-house, evening hire outside caterers; no loud music; no dancing; Restaurant & Galleries (250,70,–,–); Art rooms (60,60,–,60); Lecture room (50,50,–,50).

gem W1

£B, (548,–,–,–)
10 Beak St
T 020 7437 0239
F 020 7494 2892
W hardens.com/party/gem
E info@gem-bar.co.uk

Formerly known as Pearl, this clubby two-floor Soho venue, has spaces to suit most size of stand-up party. / age 21+ only; 3am; available from noon; in-house caterers; Basement (208,–,–,–).

The Geological Society of London W1

£M, (172,172,–,172)
Burlington House
T 020 7434 9944
F 020 7494 0579
W hardens.com/party/geologicalsoc
E enquiries@geolsoc.org.uk

A central and impressively-housed Mayfair venue (adjacent to the Royal Academy), where a range of smaller-scale facilities come at relatively reasonable cost. / 5.30pm; weekdays only; in-house caterers; no music; no dancing; Arthur Homes Rm (16,16,–,–); Lecture Theatre (172,–,–,172); William Buckland (–,13,–,–); Council Room (–,25,–,–).

George Inn SE1

£B-M, (100,50,–,–)
77 Borough High St
T 020 7407 2056
F 020 7403 6956
W hardens.com/party/georgeinnse1
E 7781@greeneking.co.uk

National Trust pub, just south of London Bridge – the only remaining galleried coaching inn in town. It has two pleasant private rooms, but the restaurant, part of which may be taken privately, is more characterful. Best of all is the Old Bar. / 11pm; in-house caterers; no amplified music; no dancing; Old Bar (50,–,–,–); Function Rm (100,50,–,–); Function Rm 2 (50,30,–,–).

Gibson Hall EC2

£M, (500,300,182,450)
13 Bishopsgate
T 020 7334 3982
F 020 7334 3941
W www.uniquevenuesoflondon.co.uk/gibson_hall/index.html
E sales@gibsonhall.com

A sumptuous (going on garish) City hall, dominated by crystal chandeliers. The Garden Room is plain in comparison, but it does have lots of natural light and overlooks the secluded garden – ideal for summer receptions for up to 300. / no flames, no balloons; midnight; in-house caterers; Garden (400,–,–,–); Garden Rm (230,80,–,150).

Gilgamesh NW1
£M-E, (1000,500,–,–)
The Stables Camden Market
T 020 7482 5757
F 020 7482 5772
W hardens.com/party/gilgameshbar
E events@gilgameshbar.com
Boasting a 40-foot high retractable ceiling and an extraordinary carved bar, this massive Camden Town restaurant-cum-bar (and so on) can be hired in sections or, for a larger event, in its entirety. / 2.30am, Sun 1.30am; in-house caterers.

Glaziers' Hall SE1
£M, (500,240,170,260)
9 Montague Close
T 020 7403 3300
F 020 7407 6036
W hardens.com/party/glaziershall
E sales@glaziershall.co.uk
A modern South Bank livery hall, with views of the City and the Thames, offering conference and banqueting services. There are five flexible spaces that can be used separately or in conjunction with each other. / 1am; list of caterers; Master's Room (–,24,–,–).

The Golden Hinde SE1
£M, (120,40,–,–)
St Mary Overie Dock
T 020 7403 0123
F 020 7407 5908
W hardens.com/party/goldenhinde
E info@goldenhinde.com
Full-scale reconstruction of Sir Francis Drake's galleon, moored between Southwark and London Bridges. The rigging is floodlit at night enhancing the setting, and you can go out on deck in the summer. You can get married here too. / midnight (flexible); list of caterers; no amplified music.

The Golden Lion SW1
£B, (100,35,–,–)
25 King St
T 020 7925 0007
W hardens.com/party/goldenlion
E enquiries@goldenlionstjames.com
This St James's pub is usually closed for weekend evenings, but for parties of more than 80 it will open for you exclusively. There is a characterful upper room, the Theatre Bar, which is also available independently during the week for parties of 25-45 people. / 11pm; in-house caterers; no amplified music; Theatre Bar (50,35,–,–).

Goldsmiths College SE14
£B-M, (700,–,–,–)
Goldsmiths Students Union
T 020 8692 1406
F 020 8694 9789
W hardens.com/party/goldsmithscollege
E su@gold.ac.uk
One of London's finest art schools, unglamorously located in New Cross. The students' union has two bars with full nightclub facilities. / restricted availability; 3am; Fridays, Saturdays and Sundays; hirer's choice of caterer; Bar Revolution (300,–,–,–).

Goldsmiths' Hall EC2
£M-E, (700,232,–,300)
Foster Ln
T 020 7606 7010
F 020 7606 1511
W hardens.com/party/goldsmiths
E tony.bowen@thegoldsmiths.co.uk
The epitome of majestic, classically-styled grandeur, this gilded early c19 livery hall, a stone's throw from St Paul's, manages to be stately rather than stiff in atmosphere. It is available for hire primarily by an established circle of former users for special events, but applications from newcomers will always be considered. / 11pm; not available Fri-Sun; Kudos; no dancing; no cash bar; Drawing Rm & Exhibition Rm (150,70,–,80); Livery Hall (500,232,–,300); Court Luncheon Room (–,50,–,–); Exhibition Room (150,70,–,80).

Goodenough College WC1
£M, (250,220,120,250)
Mecklenburgh Square
T 020 7753 0578
F 020 7833 2632
W hardens.com/party/goodenough
E events@goodenough.ac.uk
In a leafy part of Bloomsbury, an academic institution with pleasant function facilities, including a characterful, panelled great hall (built in the 1930s). Most of the

facilities are in 'London House', with a couple of rooms across the square in 'William Goodenough House'. Accommodation is available at the 'Goodenough Club'. / 11pm; in-house caterers; Great Hall (250,220,120,250); Large Common Room (150,80,56,120).

The Goring SW1

£M, (250,200,–,–)

Beeston Pl

T 020 7396 9000

F 020 7592 9016

W hardens.com/party/thegoring

E privatedining@thegoring.com

Surprisingly tranquil for Victoria, this is one of the few family-owned quality hotels in town. It has some pretty rooms for entertaining, including two panelled dining rooms. The Garden is available for suitable functions. / midnight; in-house caterers; Archive Rm (100,44,–,–); Drawing Rm (25,12,–,–); Goring Garden (250,200,–,–).

Le Gothique SW18

£B-M, (–,140,–,–)

The Royal Victoria Patriotic Bldg

T 020 8870 6567

W hardens.com/party/gothique

E marklegothique@aol.com

The particular appeal of this French restaurant is its access to the very pretty cloister garden of its magnificently overwrought Victorian building, near Wandsworth Common. / midnight; Sun only in Summer(May- Sept); in-house caterers; music inside only; dancing inside only.

Gow's Restaurant and Oyster Bar EC2

£B-M, (230,100,100,–)

81 Old Broad Street

T 020 7920 9645

W www.ballsbrothers.co.uk

E gows@ballsbrothers.co.uk

Gow's Restaurant and Oyster Bar, located next to Liverpool St station in the City of London, serves the finest, freshest seafood accompanied by an extensive wine and champagne list. The stylish Oyster Bar is perfect for watching the world go by, with a great range of drinks and lighter dishes / 11pm; in-house caterers; Oyster Bar (80,50,50,–); Restaurant (150,100,100,–).

Grand Connaught Rooms WC2

£M, (1000,550,400,750)

61-65 Gt Queen St

T 020 7405 7811

F 020 7831 1851

W hardens.com/party/newconnaughtrooms

E events@newconnaughtrooms.co.uk

One of London's oldest sets of banqueting suites, two centuries old, is now mainly used by business and the Masons – this was once an annexe of the neighbouring Temple. The Grand Hall, with three huge chandeliers, is particularly impressive. Formerly known as the 'New Connaught Rooms' – it benefited from a £7m refurbishment in summer 2009. / 3am (24 hrs concierge); in-house caterers, but hirer's choice at weekends; Edinburgh (500,250,170,300); Grand Hall (1000,550,400,750); Durham (60,50,–,60); Penthouse (80,50,–,40).

Grand Trafalgar Square WC2

£M-E, (2000,1000,256,1000)
8 Northumberland Avenue
T 020 7839 8877
F 020 7451 5500
W hardens.com/party/grandtrafalgarsquare
E info@TGatTS.com
For sheer grandeur – if of a slightly institutional kind – it's hard to beat this suite of grand Victorian rooms, originally built as a hotel (The Victoria Hotel), and in their time part of the MOD, the LSE, and now once again a hotel. / 24 hours; in-house caterers; Ballroom (600,420,256,518); Old Billiard Room (500,240,224,404); Annex (200,140,56,105); Salon (100,40,21,75); Entrance Hall (40,–,32,40); Victoria (100,40,38,45); Westminster (–,20,30,35); Smaller Meeting Rooms (20,–,16,20).

Grange Holborn WC1

£M-E, (300,160,70,300)
50-60 Southampton Row
T 020 7242 1800
F 020 7404 1641
W hardens.com/party/grangeholborn
There's a purpose-built conference & event centre at this large hotel north of Holborn tube, with six banqueting suites (details for largest shown). / midnight, but it is possible to aply for a late licence; self-catering, alcohol in-house; Orion Suite (130,140,70,220); Orion A-D (60,30,15,50).

Grange St Paul's EC4

£M-E, (1000,550,304,800)
10 Godliman Street
T 020 7074 1000
F 020 7074 1100
W hardens.com/party/grangestpauls
A roof terrace with wonderful views of St Paul's is the top attraction at this large, modern, 430-room City hotel, which is capable of handling conferences for up to 2,000 delegates. / midnight; in-house caterers.

Gray's Inn WC1

£M-E, (350,150,60,120)
8 South Square
T 020 7458 7830
F 020 7458 7935
W hardens.com/party/graysinn
E banqueting.functions@graysinn.org.uk
The attractive and quiet squares surrounding this Inn of Court provide a wonderful setting for business and social events. In addition to the tranquil interiors, with six principal rooms, the Inn has five acres of private gardens and a marquee available in the summer months. / no fireworks, funfairs or confetti; 11.30pm; Hall available from 5pm weekdays, all day weekend; in-house caterers; no dancing in LPR; Large Pension Rm (150,70,45,120); Small Pension Rm (30,15,–,–); Seminar Rm (–,9,–,–); Spy Room (150,–,45,100).

Great Eastern Dining Rooms EC2

£M, (200,60,–,–)
54 Great Eastern Street
T 020 7613 4545
F 020 7613 4137
W hardens.com/party/greateasterndining
With its mix of cocktail and pan-Asian 'tapas', Will Ricker's sleek corner bar/restaurant was one of the pioneers that helped put Shoreditch on the map. It used to have a party space called 'Below 54', but that's now GloGlo's (see also). / midnight, Fri & Sat, 1am; not available Sun; in-house caterers; no dancing.

Great Fosters TW20

£M-E, (220,180,45,150)
Stroude Rd
T 01784 433822
F 01784 437383
W hardens.com/party/greatfosters
E conferences@greatfosters.co.uk
Near Windsor Forest, and reputedly once a royal hunting lodge, this Grade I listed building is now a hotel. It offers an impressive setting for a corporate gathering or a wedding. / midnight; in-house caterers; sound limit 97 decibels.

Green's SW1

£M, (60,36,–,–)
36 Duke St
T 020 7930 4566
F 020 7491 7463
W hardens.com/party/greens
E reservations@greens.org.uk
Situated in the heart of St. James's, this very traditional restaurant, in every sense, serves British dishes with emphasis on seasonal produce

and regional specialities. The private room can be divided into two rooms or can play host to a larger crowd.
/ midnight; available from noon; in-house caterers; no amplified music; Private Room (60,36,–,–).

Greenhouse W1
£B-M, (–,65,–,–)
27a Hay's Mews
T 020 7499 3331
F 020 7499 5368
W hardens.com/party/greenhouse
E reservations@greenhouserestaurant.co.uk
A restaurant quietly located in a Mayfair mews. Take the whole place, or the small private room.
/ 3am; available from noon; in-house caterers; no music; Private Room (–,10,–,–).

Greenwich Park Bar & Grill SE10
£B, (80,50,–,–)
King William Wk
T 020 8858 2437
F 020 8858 2507
W hardens.com/party/greenwichpkbg
E info@thegreenwichpark.com
A former pub, leafily located by an entrance to the park. It's ideal as a venue for a summer cocktail party and has also recently acquired a wedding license. / 11pm; in-house caterers; no amplified music.

Greenwich Playhouse SE10
£B-M, (150,–,–,84)
189 Greenwich High Rd
T 020 8858 9256
W hardens.com/party/greenwichplayhouse
E boxoffice@galleontheatre.co.uk
The auditorium of what claims to be London's newest purpose-built studio theatre offers flexible space, useful for presentations and rehearsals. Downstairs, the bar is well suited to social gatherings.
/ 1am, theatre 10.30pm - subject to constraints of current production; available subject to constraints of current production; in-house caterers.

Greenwich Theatre SE10
£B-M, (200,75,–,421)
Crooms Hill
T 020 8858 4447
F 020 8858 8042
W hardens.com/party/greenwichtheatre
E info@greenwichtheatre.org.uk
An auditorium suiting presentations and conferences. Alternatively, the bar would make quite a convivial rendezvous for a social gathering.
/ 11pm; available subject to constraints of current production; hirer's choice of caterer (in-house available); Bar (200,75,–,–).

Greenwich Yacht Club SE10
£M, (200,100,100,120)
Peartree Wharf
T 0844 736 5846
F 020 8858 7339
W hardens.com/party/greenwichyacht
E stephencatchpole@btinternet.com
Located halfway between the Millennium Dome and the Thames Barrier, this striking modern clubhouse offers a rather intriguing venue for an event. For best effect, make sure you arrive/leave by boat.
/ midnight; in-house caterers.

Greig's Restaurant W1
£B-M, (–,60,–,–)
28 Bruton Place
T 020 7629 5613
F 020 7495 0411
W www.greigs.com
E enquiries@greigs.com

Greig's Restaurant was established by Mr Alistair Greig, the highly acclaimed restaurateur from the last century. Located in Mayfair, off Berkeley Square, the restaurant continues Mr Greig's tradition of fine British food and guaranteeing the best steaks in London. There is no charge for the use of their private rooms. / noon-2.30pm, 6-11pm, Sun 10.30pm; in-house caterers; clients must eat in order to consume alcohol; The Wine Room (–,10,–,–); The Oak Room (–,18,–,–); The Main Room (–,45,–,–).

Grocers' Hall EC2
£M-E, (250,160,84,160)
Princes St
T 020 7606 3113
F 020 7600 6128
W hardens.com/party/grocers
E events@grocershall.co.uk

Rebuilt in 1970, the Grocers Company's accommodation, by the Bank of England, emerged relatively unscathed by the period's style-horrors. The Piper Room, named after the designer of its striking modern wall-hangings, may be used for a reception or dinner. The Livery Hall (with medieval gates) is an unusual modern re-creation of traditional style. / no public weddings; 11pm; not available Sat & Sun; in-house caterers; no rock music; no dancing; Piper Rm (100,126,–,100).

The Grosvenor House Hotel W1
£M-E, (2000,2000,1600,1770)
86-90 Park Ln
T 020 7499 6363
F 020 7629 8306
W hardens.com/party/thegrosvenorhousehotel
E grosvenor.house@marriotthotels.com

The Great Room is the largest hotel room in Europe (it is said) and hosts many major events. Its fame tends to overshadow the other facilities here, which include private dining rooms in a variety of styles and sizes. / age 18+ in Great Room; 2am; in-house, plus list of approved caterers; Great Rm (2000,2000,1600,1770); Ballroom (850,500,450,550); Court Suite (250,190,120,180).

Groucho Club W1
£M, (250,120,60,70)
45 Dean St
T 020 7432 6339
F 020 7479 7781
W hardens.com/party/groucho
E privatereceptions@thegrouchoclub.com

This well-known Soho media-world club has a variety of rooms, suitable for many types of function. Facilities can be hired by non-members. Coming soon – an outdoor space to accommodate smokers. / 2am; first floor available to non members Mon & Sat; in-house caterers; Soho Bar (150,–,–,–); Gennaro Rm (70,40,–,50); Dining Rm (100,60,–,70); Mary-Lou (60,40,–,50).

Guards Museum SW1
£M, (500,250,250,–)
Wellington Barracks
T 020 7414 3428
F 020 7414 3429
W hardens.com/party/guardsmuseum
E guardsmuseum@aol.com

Below the concrete of the Guards' parade ground, right by Buckingham Palace, these modern galleries of regimental dress, weapons and regalia make a colourful backdrop for a function. There is space for a free-standing marquee in the square, which increases capacity and permits dancing. / 11pm; hirer's choice of caterer (in-house available); no amplified music; no dancing, except in marquee; Museum (200,60,–,–); Marquee (500,250,250,–).

Guildhall EC2

£M-E, (1500,704,320,–)

Guildhall

- T 020 7332 1313
- W www.guildhall.cityoflondon.gov.uk
- E guildhall.events@cityoflondon.gov.uk

The City's imposing c14 HQ, used for many state and civic occasions. Organisations can also apply to use the cathedral-like Great Hall for very special events. Other rooms include the Crypts (which are not at all gloomy). / no weddings; 11pm; not available Sun; list of caterers; no cash bar; Great Hall (900,704,320,–); Crypt East (250,180,–,–); Art Gallery (330,–,–,–); Old Library (600,350,–,–); Basinghall Suite (100,80,–,–); Livery Hall (330,240,–,–); Crypt West (250,200,–,–).

Guinea Grill W1

£M, (–,74,–,–)

30 Bruton Pl

- T 020 7499 1210
- F 020 7491 1442
- W hardens.com/party/guineagrill
- E guinea@youngs.co.uk

Pleasantly old-fashioned Mayfair pub which is one of London's better steak houses. For a comfortable, traditional meal it has a first-floor, panelled boardroom. / midnight; in-house caterers; no amplified music; no dancing; Restaurant (–,46,–,–); Boardroom (–,28,–,–).

Gun E14

£B-M, (140,–,–,–)

27 Coldharbour

- T 020 7515 5222
- F 020 7407 2250
- W hardens.com/party/gundocklands
- E info@thegundocklands.com

An attractive Isle of Dogs gastropub, with a view across the river to the O2, and a heated terrace. It has a number of spaces available for private functions. / 2am; in-house caterers; no amplified music; Red Room (30,–,–,–).

Gunnersbury Park W3

£B-M, (60,35,–,–)

Gunnersbury Park

- T 0845 456 2796
- F 0845 4562773
- W hardens.com/party/gunnersbury
- E hounslow-info@laing.com

A huge park, just north of Kew Bridge, with three simple buildings, the largest of which in the Orangery, available for wedding receptions and similar events. Apply via the council (who were not particularly forthcoming with details when we last checked). / 1am; restricted availabilty in Aug; hirer's choice of caterer.

The Guoman Tower E1

£M, (500,500,450,550)

St Katharine's Wy

- T 020 7423 8853
- F 020 7702 0964
- W hardens.com/party/theguomantower

Some of the views (of the Tower and Tower Bridge) from the banqueting rooms of this hideous '70s hotel are most impressive, and it offers a good range of accommodation for smaller to medium-size events (including weddings). / 1am; in-house caterers; Mortimer Suite (25,20,–,30).

Guy's Hospital SE1

£B-M, (250,110,100,200)

St Thomas's St

- T 020 7188 7188
- F 020 7188 1134
- W hardens.com/party/guys
- E hospitalitybookings@gstt.nhs.uk

On the 29th floor of one of London's tallest blocks, the Robens Suite is one of the highest function venues in town. The view is, predictably, magnificent. The earth-bound Court Room, part of a much older building, is suitable for formal dinners. / 1am; in-house caterers; Robens Suite (180,110,100,110); Court Rm (40,25,30,38); Senior Staff Room (40,20,40,25); Governor's Hall (250,90,40,200).

Haberdashers' Hall EC1
£M-E, (350,132,100,200)
18 West Smithfield
T 020 7251 7171
F 020 7251 7170
W hardens.com/party/haberdashershall
E enquire@chesterboyd.co.uk
A modern livery hall, designed by Sir Michael Hopkins, which uses traditional materials and building skills to create a building in thoroughly contemporary style. / 11pm; usually not available Sun ; Chester Boyd; Court Rm (75,77,–,90).

The HAC EC1
£B-M, (750,450,250,450)
Armoury Hs
T 0844 824 6218
W www.hac.org.uk/events
E sales@hac.org.uk

THE HAC

The HAC is an exceptional and extremely versatile London venue, ideal for conferences, parties, lunches, dinners, sporting events and weddings. Located just a stone's throw from Moorgate and hidden away in a quiet location, the HAC, with its six acre garden, is an oasis of green in a City of glass and steel. / 2am; in-house caterers: religous & ethnic caterers permitted Sun; Prince Consort Rooms (750,450,250,450); Long Rm (250,172,120,150); Queen's Rm (60,40,40,50); Ante Room (60,40,–,50); LIbrary & Boardroom (20,14,–,–).

Hakkasan W1
£M-E, (300,220,–,–)
8 Hanway Pl
T 020 7907 1888
F 020 79071889
W hardens.com/party/hakkasan
E reservations@hakkasan.com
This much-acclaimed subterranean Chinese restaurant, has a very striking setting, and can be hired in its entirety (which is cheaper by day). In the second half of 2010, a new branch is to open in the heart of Mayfair. / Sun-Wed 11pm, Thu-Sat midnight ; in-house caterers.

The Halkin SW1
£M-E, (150,80,–,–)
5 Halkin St
T 020 7333 1234
F 020 7333 1100
W hardens.com/party/thehalkin
E events@halkin.como.bz
This discreet Belgravia hotel's options for functions all revolve around its Thai restaurant Nahm, run by celebrated Aussie chef David Thompson. There's a private room, or – for a stand-up – you can take over the whole restaurant, plus the hotel's cocktail bar. / 11.30pm; in-house caterers; no amplified music; no dancing; Private Dining Rm (50,45,–,–).

Ham House & Garden TW10
£M-E, (400,400,400,60)
Ham Richmond
T 020 8439 8230
F 020 8439 8241
W hardens.com/party/hamhouse
E hamhouse@nationaltrust.org.uk
A c17 National Trust house, whose Great Hall makes an impressive setting for a civil wedding. You might use the Orangery for drinks, moving to the Restaurant (same building) for dining. The adjacent terrace is available for al fresco events, and there is a marquee site in the Orangery Garden. / 11pm; Available Fri and Sat; list of caterers; Orangery (90,60,–,60); Gt Hall (–,–,–,60).

Ham Polo Club TW10
£M, (250,150,150,–)
Petersham Rd
T 020 8334 0001
F 020 8948 8443
W hardens.com/party/hampolo
E nick@hunt-kendall.com
London's only polo club, ten miles from the West End, has space for a marquee of virtually any size. Or you can take over the colonial-style clubhouse, with its floor-to-ceiling glass doors, which open onto vine-clad verandas on either side of the building. / midnight; not available Sun during polo season; in-house caterers.

Hamleys W1
£M, (1000,–,–,–)
188-196 Regent St
T 0870 333 2455
W hardens.com/party/hamleys
E party@hamleys.co.uk
With the run of the shop and seven floors to explore, the famous toyshop makes a perfect place for kids to party, and is equally suitable for clients or colleagues. The store hosts numerous corporate events, product launches and Christmas parties. / 11pm; available evenings and Sun mornings; Ingredients.

Hammersmith Town Hall W6
£B-M, (1000,400,350,900)
King St
T 0845 337 0314
F 020 8753 2353
W hardens.com/party/hammersmithth
E events@lbhf.gov.uk
The panelled Assembly Hall itself is a huge, atmospheric '30s room, suitable for a large ball. The other rooms, including the Marble Gallery, are also impressive. / no candles; 2am; hirer's choice of caterer; Marble Gallery (–,–,–,60).

Hampshire Hotel WC2
£M-E, (120,70,50,100)
Leicester Sq
T 020 7451 0228
F 020 7451 0191
W hardens.com/party/hamshirehotel
E hampcb@radisson.com
With its view towards Trafalgar Square, the Penthouse is the special feature of this Theatreland hotel, recently totally refurbished. / midnight ; in-house caterers; Penthouse (120,70,50,85); Digital Projection Suite (65,32,–,48).

Hampton Court Palace KT8
£E, (1200,280,–,–)
East Molesey
T 020 3166 6505
F 020 3166 6513
W www.hrp.org.uk
E hamptoncourtpalaceevents@hrp.org.uk
Wolsey's magnificent palace, subsequently adopted by Henry VIII, is occasionally used for major corporate and charity dinners. On a more intimate scale, the delightful Banqueting House in the grounds is used relatively frequently for medium-sized dinners. / midnight; available eves only (except Banqueting House); list of caterers; dancing restricted to certain rooms; red wine and port at table only; Great Hall (400,280,–,–); Cartoon Gallery (300,180,–,–); Queen's Public Dining Rm (150,50,–,–); William III's Banqueting House (80,50,–,–); Great Watching Chamber (125,100,–,–); Kings Guard Chamber (200,150,–,–); Marquee (1200,–,–,–).

Hard Rock Cafe W1
£M, (400,230,200,–)
150 Old Park Lane
T 020 1629 0382
F 020 7629 8702
W hardens.com/party/hardrockcafe
E london_sales@hardrock.com
Book the whole place and you won't need to queue for this legendary old rocker near Hyde Park Corner. Remember, though: "No drugs or nuclear weapons allowed inside". / 3am; in-house caterers; no music.

Harrods SW1
£M-E, (350,180,–,–)
87-135 Brompton Rd
T 020 7225 6736
F 020 7225 5903
W hardens.com/party/harrods
E eva.altingsiberg@harrods.com
The eminent Knightsbridge department store has long had its enormous Georgian restaurant available as a function venue. What's less well known is that it also offers a more general party service, so if you want to hold a a reception in the world-famous food halls, for example, it's worth enquiring. / 11.30pm; available Mon-Sat, Reception 7pm, Dinner, 8pm, closed Sunday; in-house caterers; no amplified music.

Harrow School HA1
£M, (1000,850,500,750)
5 High St
T 020 8872 8381
F 020 8864 7180
W hardens.com/party/harrow
E events@harrowschool.org.uk
When school's out you can hire various rooms around this well-known north London seat of

learning. / 11pm; available outside term time only; in-house caterers; Speech Room (–,–,–,500); Old Harrovian Rm (200,80,–,120); Ryan Theatre (–,389,–,–); Shepherd Churchill Hall (350,350,350,–).

Hatfield House AL9

£M-E, (300,200,100,300)
Hatfield Park
T 01707 262055
F 01707 260898
W hardens.com/party/hatfieldhouse
E hospitality@hatfield-house.co.uk

Originally built in the late c15, the seat of the Cecil family has been added to throughout the centuries. It provides a suitably grand setting for events of all sizes (including period banquets). / midnight, bar 11.30pm; Leith's; Riding School (180,120,–,200).

Hatton EC1

£M, (200,160,–,–)
51-53 Hatton Gdns
T 020 7242 4123
F 020 7242 1818
W hardens.com/party/hatton
E hatton@etcvenues.co.uk

In an Art Deco building near Holborn, 20 rooms suitable for training and conferences. Entertaining takes place in the restaurant. / 10.30pm; in-house caterers; no music; no dancing; Onyx Restaurant (100,70,–,–).

Haymarket Hotel SW1

£M-E, (220,40,160,35)
1 Suffolk Place
T 020 7470 4000
F 020 7470 4004
W hardens.com/party/haymarkethotel
E haymarket@firmdale.com

With the stylish decor that's the hallmark of Firmdale properties, this hotel in the heart of Theatreland offers a number of options for events: two smaller rooms for private entertaining, a larger function room (The Shooting Gallery), plus the swimming pool (which can be fully or partially covered). / in-house caterers; Private Room 1 (35,30,–,22); Private Room 2 (45,30,–,35); Shooting Gallery (120,40,70,–); Pool Area (220,30,160,–).

Haymarket Theatre SW1

£M, (80,–,–,895)
Haymarket
T 020 7930 8890
F 020 7389 9698
W hardens.com/party/theatreroyalhaymarket
E nigel@trh.co.uk

With its Nash façade, the Theatre Royal (as it is also known) is one of the most elegant playhouses in London. The auditorium offers a grand setting for a daytime presentation. / restricted availability; 5pm Mon-Fri; available subject to constraints of current production; hirer's choice of caterer (in-house available); no dancing; Stalls Bar (80,–,–,–); Oscar Wilde (30,–,–,–).

Hayward Gallery SE1

£M-E, (60,60,–,60)
Belvedere Rd
T 020 7921 0979
F 020 7921 0810
W hardens.com/party/hayward
E events@southbankcentre.co.uk

This brutalist gallery – part of the South Bank Centre – is not itself generally available for events, but the striking glass pavilion 'Waterloo Sunset' is. / 11pm; list of caterers.

Heights Bar & Restaurant W1

£M, (130,90,–,–)
Langham Pl
T 020 7580 0111
F 020 7291 6262
W hardens.com/party/heightsbar
E conferences@saintgeorgeshotel.com

The St George's Hotel is not the capital's most glamorous address (even if, being next door to Broadcasting House, it does draw in the BBC crowd). It does, though – unusually – have a 15th floor bar and restaurant with very impressive views over central London, which can be hired in its entirety. / 11pm; in-house caterers.

Hellenic Centre W1
£M, (250,180,140,190)
16-18 Paddington St
T 020 7487 5060
W hardens.com/party/hellenicentre
E bookings@helleniccentre.org
Not noticeably Greek in style, this is a pleasant medium-size venue, in Marylebone, well-suited to social events. / 11.30pm; hirer's choice of caterer; Great Hall (250,180,140,190); Boardroom (50,24,–,50).

The Hempel W2
£M-E, (600,300,300,80)
31-35 Craven Hill Gdns
T 020 7298 9000
F 020 7402 4666
W hardens.com/party/thehempel
E events@the-hempel.co.uk
Ultra-minimalist Hyde Park hotel, with a private garden square whose soundproof marquee can cater for up to 300 diners. / 1am; in-house caterers; music limited to 65 decibels in the Garden area; Zen Garden (350,300,300,–); No 17 (120,30,30,40); The Portland Room (24,16,–,–).

Henry J Beans SW3
£B-M, (400,–,–,–)
195 King's Rd
T 020 7352 9255
F 020 7376 5076
W hardens.com/party/hjbean
E admin@henryjbeansgroup.co.uk
This dark Chelsea burger parlour houses a great surprise – an attractively laid-out beer garden (to which the capacity given relates) available for exclusive hire. / 11pm, Fri & Sat, 1am; in-house caterers; no amplified music; no dancing.

Hever Castle TN8
£M-E, (100,64,100,50)
Nr Edenbridge
T 01732 865224
F 01732 867860
W hardens.com/party/hevercastle
E tudor@hevercastle.co.uk
Rich with Tudor historical associations, this intimate moated castle was substantially rebuilt by the Astors at the beginning of the c20 – it now benefits from an adjacent Tudor Village which makes it especially suitable for residential events. No dancing in the castle itself. / Midnight (restaurant)/ 1am; in-house caterers; no amplified music; no dancing in castle or Astor Wing; Tudor Suite (100,64,–,50); Castle Dining Hall (100,40,–,50); GuthriePavillion (250,200,100,120).

High Road House W4
£M-E, (130,60,–,130)
162 Chiswick High Road
T 020 8742 1717
F 020 8987 8762
W hardens.com/party/highroadhouse
E reservations@highroadhouse.co.uk
A trendy (for Chiswick) hang out comprising restaurant and private club. Upstairs, a private room seats up to 14 people, and is used for meetings, presentations or more intimate gatherings. Downstairs there are three spaces, for drinks parties, meetings, or meals. / 2am; in-house caterers; Downstairs (130,60,–,130); Upstairs (–,14,–,–).

Highgate School N6
£M, (400,300,300,160)
North Road
T 020 8340 1524
F 020 8340 7674
W hardens.com/party/highgateschool
E susy.prosserharries@highgateschool.org.uk
The Victorian buildings of this north London school can provide a pleasant setting for a social event, including weddings. / restricted availability, no fireworks; Sat 11.30pm, Sun 10.30pm; available during holidays only; hirer's choice of caterer; Dining Hall (400,300,–,–); Mills Centre (–,–,–,–); Senior School (–,–,–,–).

Hilton London Canary Wharf E14
£M-E, (–,240,200,400)
South Quay Marsh Wall
T 020 3002 2300
W hardens.com/party/hiltoncanarywhf
Very convenient for Canary Wharf, this modern hotel has a range of suites, all of quite modest capacity. / 1am; They offer in-house catering but if clients wish to bring in their own caterers, they must be approved by the hotel..

Hilton on Park Lane W1

£M-E, (1250,1250,1000,1200)
22 Park Ln
T 020 7493 8000
F 020 7208 4136
W hardens.com/party/hiltonparklane
E sales.parklane@hilton.com
This landmark hotel has one of the capital's largest ballrooms and also a full range of other accommodation for functions (especially dinner-dances). The fourth-floor Serpentine Room has one of the best views of any function room in London. / 4am; in-house caterers; Grand Ballroom (1250,1000,900,1200); Wellington Ballroom (550,200,150,200); Coronation Suite (200,140,100,140); Serpentine Suite (40,20,–,50); Argyll Suite (40,20,–,20).

RS Hispaniola WC2

£M, (150,150,150,130)
Victoria Embankment
T 020 7839 3011
F 020 7321 0547
W hardens.com/party/hispaniola
E info@hispaniola.co.uk
Moored by Hungerford Bridge for the last 30 years, this erstwhile Clyde steamer is quite a smart place to entertain. The Top Deck has outside areas, front and rear, while the Main Deck has an external area at the side. / midnight; in-house caterers; Main Deck (150,150,150,130); Upper Deck (100,90,90,90); Board Rm (50,–,–,50).

Holborn Bars EC1

£M-E, (160,90,–,200)
138-142 Holborn
T 0844 980 2327
F 020 7353 9291
W hardens.com/party/holbornbars
E holborn@deverevenues.co.uk
This huge Victorian Gothic building, complete with arched windows, stuccoed ceilings and period detailing, has a wide range of meeting rooms, and is an ideal, centrally located venue for conferences, training and other business events. / 10.30pm; in-house caterers; no music; Holborn Suite (–,–,–,200); Restaurant (–,90,–,–); Waterhouse (160,–,–,–).

Holiday Inn, Brentford Lock TW8

£M-E, (700,550,300,600)
Commerce Road
T 020 8232 2000
W hardens.com/party/holidayinnbrentford
E info@holidayinnbrentford.co.uk
For an event in outer West London, it's worth knowing about this newish branch of the well-known hotel chain, which has a very pleasant canal-side location, on the edge of Brentford near Syon House. 'The Waterfront' is the main space, and there are a couple of small meeting rooms. / weekdays midnight, weekends 1am; in-house caterers; sound limit 95 decibels; Waterfront Suite (700,550,–,600).

Holiday Inn, Camden Lock NW1

£M-E, (350,220,100,250)
Jamestown Road
T 020 7485 4343
W hardens.com/party/holidayinncamden
E info@holidayinncamden.co.uk
Just across the bridge from Camden Lock, this modern hotel enjoys a great position by Regent's Canal, and its 3-floor 'Glasshouse' has good views through floor-to-ceiling windows. / 1am-2am; in-house caterers; The Glasshouse (350,220,100,250); The Camden Suite (–,–,–,180); The Mezzanine Suite (–,–,–,40).

Home House W1

£E, (150,72,–,–)
20 Portman Square
T 020 7670 2000
F 020 7670 2020
W hardens.com/party/homehouse
E dany@homehouse.co.uk
Overlooking Portman Square, this stately Georgian townhouse (these days a members' club) has some extremely impressive rooms. Availability to non-members is very restricted. / members club; midnight, garden 10pm; in-house caterers; no amplified music; Front Parlour & Eating Room (150,72,–,–).

Hop Exchange SE1

£M, (400,250,200,–)
24 Southwark St
Ⓣ 020 8567 9090
Ⓕ 020 8566 3698
Ⓦ hardens.com/party/hopexchange
Ⓔ info@richmondcaterers.com

This lofty Victorian hall – with wrought iron galleries and a modern, translucent roof – is a large and atmospheric venue for those prepared to think a little about lighting and decoration. It's currently closed while Network Rail refurbish the viaducts leading to London Bridge – earliest likely re-opening: 2012. / midnight ; available from 7pm, weekends all day; in-house caterers.

Horniman Museum SE23

£M, (120,100,50,100)
100 London Rd
Ⓣ 020 8693 1476
Ⓕ 020 8693 5253
Ⓦ hardens.com/party/horniman
Ⓔ info@suzannejames.co.uk

An intriguing south London museum, set in 16 acres of impressive gardens. Function possibilities have shrunk in recent times, and only the Victorian conservatory is now generally made available. / 11pm; Fri & Sat only Apr-Oct; Suzanne James; musicians from accredited list only; With Marquee (120,120,120,120).

The Hospital Club WC2

£M-E, (290,150,150,180)
24 Endell Street
Ⓣ 020 7170 9148
Ⓕ 020 7170 9101
Ⓦ www.thehospitalclub.com
Ⓔ events@thehospitalclub.com

The Hospital Club is unique in that it is designed specifically for the creative industries. The Club boasts a range of stunning spaces and an award-winning events team who will take care of everything from planning to production, including HD TV studios accommodating web-streaming and video conferencing facilities. Whatever you're after, The Hospital Club will help you create an event never to be forgotten. / TV Studio (150,150,150,180); The Gallery (North & South together) (290,140,140,150); The Rocket Meeting Room (18,14,–,30); First Floor Bar & Restaurant (200,100,90,100); Bellini Bar & Lounge (65,–,–,–); Forest Room (Private Dining Room) (50,35,40,50); The Library & Terrace (25,12,–,40); Games Room (40,12,–,12).

Hotel Rafayel SW11

£M-E, (350,80,80,100)
Lombard Road
Ⓣ 020 7801 3600
Ⓦ hardens.com/party/hotelrafayel

This sizeable, 65-room five-star near Battersea Heliport claims to be 'one of the world's first environmentally-conscious luxury hotels'. Options for entertaining include a large 3rd floor event space with Thames views, a roof terrace with 360° views, and riverside cigar garden, complete with gazebo. / if residents at the hotel complain, the event will; 11pm; in-house caterers; no amplified music; Roof Terrace (350,–,–,–); 3rd Floor Event Space (150,129,80,40); Board Room (–,12,–,–); Penthouse (130,60,60,30); Havana Dreams (50,–,–,–).

Hotel Verta SW11

£M-E, (350,–,–,–)

Bridges Wharf

T 020 7801 3500

W hardens.com/party/hotelverta

E douglas.acton@hotelverta.co.uk

Arrive by Helicopter to make a big entrance at this new 70-room Von Essen property, next to Battersea Heliport – 'London's Vertical Gateway'. Highlights include the Rooftop event space on the 13th floor, and the Vertillon Bar. Conferencing is available for 10-200 delegates. / Vertillon (48,–,–,–).

The House NW1

£M-E, (50,12,–,10)

Albany Street

T 07887 516 516

F 0845 456 1557

W hardens.com/party/thehouse

E jennifer@jiantevents.co.uk

Overlooking Regent's Park, this eclectically converted five-floor property nowadays plays host to meetings, dinners, launches and cocktail parties. Accommodation includes a dining room with large Victorian-style fireplace, and two rooms with floor-to-ceiling sash windows looking towards the Park. / midnight; hirer's choice of caterer (in-house available).

House of St Barnabas W1

£M, (400,60,100,80)

No 1 Greek Street

T 020 7437 1894

F 020 7434 3080

W hardens.com/party/hosb

E venue@hosb.org.uk

Just off Soho Square, this Grade I listed Georgian building – complete with a chapel and secret courtyard garden – makes a very characterful venue for a range of events: meetings, launches, photo shoots, dinner parties and weddings. All income goes back into the charity running the place. / no music in gardens; Mon-Thu 11.30pm, Fri - Sat midnight; in-house caterers; acoustic only; Drawing Room (80,40,40,70); Silk Room (40,20,20,40); Bazelgette Room (40,25,25,40); Soho Room (–,40,–,–); Monro Room (50,–,–,40); Garden Room (50,25,–,30); Garden (75,–,–,–); Chapel (75,55,–,75).

Hoxton Hall N1

£B-M, (50,15,–,120)

130 Hoxton St

T 020 7684 0060

F 020 7729 3815

W hardens.com/party/hoxtonhall

E info@hoxtonhall.co.uk

The only Victorian saloon-type music hall left in London in its original form (1863). It is available for hire, subject to the constraints of the current performance. / no political or religious events; midnight (flexible); hirer's choice of caterer; Theatre (–,–,–,120); Dance Studio (50,–,–,–).

Hoxton Hotel EC2

£M, (100,26,18,30)

81-83 Great Eastern Street

T 020 7550 1000

W hardens.com/party/hoxtonhotel

'Luxury where it matters, budget where it counts' is the motto at this 205-room hotel in trendy Hoxton. There are a number of smaller rooms for daytime meetings and evening private dining, while for larger stand-ups options include the 'Lobby Bar' and their garden (the latter Mon-Thu only). / 2am; in-house, self-catering for Jewish food.; no excessive noise, as bedrooms are above private rooms; Room 1 (–,8,5,–); Room 2 (–,12,9,18); Room 3 (30,18,18,30); Lobby Bar (100,–,–,–); Garden (80,–,–,–); Larger Rooms (50,22,–,–).

Hurlingham Club SW6

£M-E, (1200,1000,1000,500)

Ranelagh Gdns

T 0844 824 3195

F 020 7736 7167

W hardens.com/party/hurlingham

E events@hurlinghamclub.org.uk

Set in 42 acres by the Thames, the large Georgian Clubhouse provides options for a wide range of events. A pier is a recent addition, so now you can arrive by boat. / members club; Mon-Thu 1am, Fri-Sat 2am, Sun midnight; available Mon-Fri all day, Sat-Sun evenings only; in-house caterers; Boomhouse Suite (450,370,280,500); Palm Court (1000,–,–,–); Murgrave Theatre (200,95,60,180); Quadrangle Suite (450,320,280,450); Terrace Room (100,60,–,65); Reading Room (25,14,–,–); Napier

Room (200,120,–,120); Rongelagh Room (200,120,–,120).

Hush - Private Dining W1

£M-E, (160,85,–,–)
2nd Floor
Ⓣ 020 7659 1500
Ⓕ 020 7659 1501
Ⓦ hardens.com/party/hush
Ⓔ info@hush.co.uk

The private dining floor of the fashionable Hush restaurant, in a mews just off Bond Street, has a brand identity separate from the main establishment. There are three rooms, decorated in African themes, which can be combined (though the cooking is a little more international in inspiration). / 12.30am; in-house caterers; no amplified music; no dancing; Zanzibar (80,60,–,–); Tangiers (–,16,–,–).

Institute of Contemporary Arts SW1

£M, (350,120,–,185)
The Mall
Ⓣ 020 7930 3647
Ⓕ 020 7873 0051
Ⓦ www.ica.org.uk
Ⓔ events@ica.org.uk

The ICA is one of the world's most influential centres for contemporary arts. Established in 1947 in a grade I listed Nash terrace overlooking St James's Park, Big Ben and the London Eye, it comprises galleries, cinemas, a theatre, education space, bookshop and café/bar. / 1am; in-house caterers; Nash & Brandon Rms (150,80,–,–); Cinema 1 (–,–,–,185); Cinema 2 (–,–,–,45); Theatre (350,120,–,–).

IET London: Savoy Place WC2

£M, (480,250,105,462)
2 Savoy Place
Ⓣ 020 7344 5479
Ⓕ 020 7344 5707
Ⓦ hardens.com/party/savoyplace
Ⓔ enquiries@savoyplace.co.uk

A large conference and banqueting venue – home to the Institution of Engineering & Technology – right by the Embankment, and with Thames views. There are 19 different rooms, that can accommodate 462 theatre style, 250 for a banquet or simply a meeting for 8. / 9.30pm (flexible); approved on-site caterers; Riverside Room (260,250,105,–); Thompson Room (100,60,40,80); Council Chamber (–,–,–,144); Faraday (100,60,40,80); Lecture Theatre (–,–,–,462); Common Room (100,40,–,50); Lancaster Room (100,–,–,–); Maxwell Suite (100,60,40,90); Haslett Room (20,12,–,–).

The Imagination Gallery WC1

£M-E, (350,110,110,200)
South Crescent
Ⓣ 020 7323 3300
Ⓕ 020 7323 5810
Ⓦ hardens.com/party/theimaginationgallery
Ⓔ gallery@imagination.com

You cross a metal bridge which spans the building's atrium to reach this light and airy fifth-floor gallery (which has a very good view of Bedford Square from its full-length balcony). The Atrium is also available for hire. / age 18+; 11pm; in-house caterers; no discos; no dancing; Atrium and Restaurant (350,70,–,–); Gallery (250,110,110,200).

Imbibe Bar SE1

£B, (200,–,–,–)
73 Blackfriars Road
Ⓣ 020 7928 3693
Ⓕ 020 7620 2092
Ⓦ hardens.com/party/imbibebar
Ⓔ info@imbibe-bar.co.uk

Two minutes from Southwark tube station, this lounge bar is well-suited to a private party, with the option in summer of a BBQ in the garden; minimum 80 guests for exclusive hire, or they'll find a section for you.

IMPERIAL WAR MUSEUM
IMPERIAL WAR MUSEUM LONDON
A dramatic and historic backdrop for any event
Tel 0844 873 3943 events@iwm.org.uk
www.iwm.org.uk/londonevents

Imperial City EC3
£M, (350,220,–,–)
Royal Exchange
Ⓣ 020 7626 3437
Ⓦ hardens.com/party/imperialcity
Ⓔ imperialcity@orientalrestaurantgroup.com
Impressively housed under the Royal Exchange, a good-quality oriental restaurant which offers good function-suitability. / in-house caterers; HalfVenue (120,90,–,–); Private Dining Rm (20,12,–,–).

Imperial College London SW7
£B-M, (600,500,440,750)
Exhibition Rd
Ⓣ 020 7594 9494
Ⓕ 020 7594 9504
Ⓦ hardens.com/party/imperialcollegelondon
Ⓔ conferenceandevents@imperial.ac.uk
This South Kensington college offers a wide range of function facilities, of which the most imposing (but most restrictive) is the Rector's residence, in Queensgate. The Council Room is much used, and the Music Room (or Solar) – with French windows to the garden – is also worth checking out. / evenings only during term time; in-house caterers; Main Dining Hall (600,500,440,–); Council Rm (100,64,–,67); Solar (50,–,–,40); Great Hall (–,–,–,750); Senior Common Rm (350,250,200,–).

Imperial War Museum London SE1
£M-E, (1000,400,350,220)
Lambeth Rd
Ⓣ 0844 873 3943
Ⓕ 020 7416 5457
Ⓦ www.iwm.org.uk/londonevents
Ⓔ events@iwm.org.uk

Close to Westminster and the City, this Grade II building with its large contemporary curved glass-roofed central gallery creates a light and spacious setting for events. Plus, four daytime spaces equipped with presentation facilities. The Museum's temporary exhibitions and award-winning permanent displays add fascinating elements for day and evening events. / no dry ice/smoke or naked flames; midnight, extensions available; available from 7pm (from 6.15pm for set-up); list of caterers; dance floor must be hired; Main Exhibits Gallery (1000,400,350,–); Upper Boardroom (70,50,50,50); Lower Boardroom (30,24,24,20); Conference Room (120,60,60,80); Cinema (220,120,120,200).

IndigO2 SE10

£M-E, (2400,504,–,1600)
The O2
T 020 8463 2730
W hardens.com/party/indigo
E bookings@theindigo2.com
Next to the O2 arena, this multi-purpose venue lends itself well to corporate events, comprising an adaptable open space at ground floor level, and conference configuration amphitheatre style seating on the first floor for a capacity of 777. Good AV! / list of caterers.

Inmarsat EC1

£M, (300,–,–,300)
99 City Rd
T 020 7728 1259
F 020 7728 1765
W hardens.com/party/inmarsat
E conference_services@inmarsat.com
A conference centre with over a dozen rooms, convenient for the City, accommodating between 10 and 300 people for business meetings and presentations. / 11.30pm; in-house caterers; no amplified music.

Inner Temple EC4

£M-E, (1200,250,250,300)
Temple
T 020 7797 8230
F 020 7797 8227
W hardens.com/party/innertemple
E catering@innertemple.org.uk
The traditionally elegant rooms at this Inn of Court all interconnect - have drinks in the Parliament Chamber or the Luncheon Room followed by dinner in the Hall. Their flexibility suits them to many types of events, including dinners, receptions and weddings. The Garden is perfect for marquee parties & barbeques. / midnight, Fri & Sat, 1am; evenings & weekends only; in-house, hirer's choice at weekends; no amplified music in garden; Hall (400,250,–,300); Parliament Chamber (200,90,90,150); Luncheon Rm (120,70,–,70); Garden (1200,–,–,–); Marquee (600,–,–,–); Smoking Room (80,–,–,–); Committee Rm (24,–,–,–).

Innholders' Hall EC4

£M-E, (200,87,90,120)
30 College St
T 020 7236 6703
F 020 7236 0059
W hardens.com/party/innholders
E mail@innholders.co.uk
Sombre but striking, this c17 hall, near Cannon Street, was substantially restored after the Blitz. It is accessed via a pretty hall and reception room. / 11pm; weekdays only; in-house caterers; no amplified music; no dancing; Dining Hall (200,87,90,120); Old Court Rm (–,27,–,–); New Court Room (–,–,–,30).

Institut Français SW7

£B-M, (100,50,–,–)
17 Queensberry Pl
T 020 7073 1365
F 020 7073 1350
W hardens.com/party/institutfrancais
E box.office@ambafrance.org.uk
The Salon de Réception of this South Kensington centre is a large, light, first-floor room that suits smartish receptions and dinners. The larger Art Deco Library is of some architectural note. / 11.30pm; hirer's choice of caterer; no amplified music; no dancing; no alcohol; Salon de Réception (100,50,–,–).

Institute of Directors SW1

£M-E, (400,250,200,300)
116 Pall Mall
T 020 7451 9178
F 020 7930 9060
W hardens.com/party/instituteofdirectors
E functions@iod.com
Very near Trafalgar Square, this huge, imposing club building offers a very wide range of rooms for events. / 11pm but they can extend their licence to 1am; in-house caterers; music limted to 80 decibels; Nash (350,250,200,250); Burton (160,80,60,120); Waterloo (150,60,40,100); Trafalgar II/St James II (80,50,–,50); Trafalgar I (30,30,–,30); St James's II (40,24,–,35); St James's I (80,50,–,50).

The Insurance Hall EC2
£M, (300,160,80,240)
20 Aldermanbury
T 020 7417 4417
F 0870 606 1812
W hardens.com/party/insurancehall
E natalie.follen@cii.co.uk
A flexible venue, behind the Guildhall, with a number of rooms of differing sizes. The hall has quite a capacity, but is much less imposing than some of its local competition – perhaps no bad thing – and the feel inside is of a cosy Edwardian town hall. / 11pm; Leith's; Court Room (120,40,–,80).

InterContinental London W1
£M-E, (1000,700,200,600)
1 Hamilton Pl
T 020 7409 3131
F 020 7409 7462
W hardens.com/party/intercontilondon
E londonevents@ihg.com
A de luxe modern hotel. It has extensive event facilities, and as prominent a location as you could want, at Hyde Park Corner. / 2am, Sun 12.30am; in-house caterers; Park Lane Events Suite (–,150,–,–).

International Coffee Organisation W1
£M, (200,240,–,168)
22 Berners St
T 020 7706 7700
F 020 7631 2055
W hardens.com/party/ico
E olga@mayfairconference.com
Purpose-built to meet the needs of a particular trade, this venue near Oxford Street offers very central facilities for meetings, lectures and conferences. / hirer's choice of caterer; no music; no dancing.

The Irish Centre W6
£B-M, (300,160,110,200)
3 Black's Rd
T 020 8563 8232
F 020 8563 8233
W hardens.com/party/irishcentre
E customercare@irishcentrehammersmith.co.uk
A simple Hammersmith space, with sprung dance-floor and cream walls – a relatively inexpensive venue for a dance, a dinner or a wedding reception. / 11.30pm - they can apply for an extension; in-house caterers.

Ironmongers' Hall EC2
£M, (250,150,–,–)
Shaftesbury Pl
T 020 7776 2300
F 020 7600 3519
W hardens.com/party/ironmongershall
E events@ironhall.co.uk
It may be surrounded by the Barbican, but – from the inside at least – this 1920s faux-medieval hall (complete with panelling, stone flags and stained glass) manages to feel surprisingly antique. The Drawing Room and Livery Hall are particularly impressive. / 11pm; in-house caterers; noise inhibitor; Court Rm (80,50,–,–).

Ivy WC2
£M-E, (120,60,–,–)
1 West Street
T 020 7379 6077
F 020 7497 3644
W hardens.com/party/ivy
This Theatreland legend has a sizeable private room just over the main dining room. It has also spawned a new A-list hang-out in the last couple of years: the neighbouring Ivy Club (and – though largely members-only – its top floor suite of rooms is occasionally made more widely available).

Jacksons Lane N6
£B, (120,–,–,163)
269a Archway Rd
T 020 8340 5226
F 020 8348 2424
W hardens.com/party/jacksonslane
E jenni.a@jacksonslane.org.uk
A converted Highgate church, with a number of rooms suitable for parties. / 11pm, Sat 12.30am; closed Mon; in-house caterers; Theatre (–,–,–,163); Studio 1 (120,–,–,–); Studio 2 (80,–,–,–)

Jerusalem W1
£M, (200,–,–,–)
33-34 Rathbone Pl
T 020 7255 1120
F 020 7436 2680
W hardens.com/party/jerusalem
Just north of Oxford Street, this

candlelit basement bar has a thoroughly ecclesiastical feel, complete with long tables and old church pews. Hired exclusively, it makes an atmospheric setting for a party. / Thu, 1am, Fri & Sat 2am; in-house caterers.

Jerwood Space SE1

£M-E, (300,100,–,–)

171 Union Street

T 020 7654 0171

F 020 7654 0172

W hardens.com/party/jerwoodspace

E space@jerwoodspace.co.uk

A light modern building recently created from an old Victorian school. It makes a good venue for a drinks party, and is a popular spot for media events. / 11pm; not available during gallery hours; in-house caterers; not suitable for loud discos or bands; Gallery & Glasshouse (300,100,–,–).

Jewel Piccadilly W1

£B-M, (650,–,–,–)

4-6 Glasshouse St

T 020 7439 4990

W hardens.com/party/jewelbar

E info.jewelpic@novausleisure.com

Right by Piccadilly Circus, this glitzy cocktail bar offers a number of decadently-themed spaces in varying styles, from cocktail-bar-chic to Eastern-calm. / 1am; in-house caterers; Jewel (300,–,–,–); Bar Blanca (200,–,–,–); The Ruby Room (100,–,–,–); Velvet 1 (80,–,–,–); Velvet 2 (60,–,–,–).

Jongleurs at Camden Lock NW1

£M, (800,340,–,450)

Middle Yard

T 0870 011 1890

F 0870 011 1970

W hardens.com/party/jongleurscamden

E anas.shaikh@jongleurs.com

The flagship Jongleurs comedy venue. With its interesting waterfront location, it's often used for music events and parties. / restricted availability, age 18+; 1am; available Sun-Thu; in-house caterers; Roof Terrace (75,60,–,–).

JuJu SW3

£B, (300,120,–,240)

316–318 Kings Road

T 020 7351 5998

W hardens.com/party/juju

Winner of 'The London Club and Bar Awards 2009' for best new bar – this Chelsea hang-out has a variety of options for private hire. / 1am; in-house caterers; no music; JuJu Lounge (80,50,–,40); Ground Floor (220,100,–,40); VIP (30,30,–,–); Booths (10,10,–,–).

Julie's Restaurant & Wine Bar W11

£M, (–,60,–,–)

1355-137 Portland Rd

T 020 7229 8331

F 020 7229 4050

W hardens.com/party/julies

E info@juliesrestaurant.com

This seductive, eclectically-decorated Holland Park labyrinth is one of London's longest-established party-restaurants. The best rooms are the panelled Banqueting Room (with its single oval table) and the Garden Room. / midnight, Fri & Sat, 1am; in-house caterers; no amplified music; no dancing; Garden Rm (–,34,–,–); Banqueting Rm (–,24,–,–); Moroccan Rm (–,12,–,–).

Jumeirah Carlton Tower SW1

£M-E, (700,400,250,400)

On Cadogan Place

T 020 7235 1234

F 020 7858 7164

W hardens.com/party/jumeirahct

E JCTevents@jumeirah.com

Voted 'Best UK Business Hotel' - Conde Nast Reader's Travel Awards 2008, Jumeirah Carlton Tower has 9 stunning private dining and meeting rooms designed for a wide range of functions from cocktails parties to dinners, conferences and weddings. / 1am; all day; in-house caterers, list of approved caterers; music max 95 decibels; Ballroom (700,400,250,400); Acacia, Birch, Cedar And Conservatory (350,180,–,–); Maple (–,14,–,–); The Boardroom (–,14,–,–).

Just St James SW1
£M-E, (800,470,–,–)
12 St James's St
T 020 7976 2222
F 020 7976 2020
W hardens.com/party/juststjames
E events@juststjames.com
A St James's bar and restaurant housed in a grandly marbled banking hall. The gallery makes an unusual venue for a cocktail party or for dinners from 30 up to 140 guests and there is no hire charge for this space. Alternatively you can hire the whole space for large events. / 11.30pm; in-house caterers; Just The Gallery (200,140,–,–).

Ken Lo's Memories of China SW1
£M, (–,120,–,–)
67-69 Ebury St
T 020 7730 7734
F 020 7730 2992
W hardens.com/party/kenlosw1
A quality restaurant of long standing, not far from Victoria, serving pricey oriental cuisine. It has two private rooms (which can be used together), or you can hire the whole place. / 11pm; not available Sun L; in-house caterers; no amplified music; no dancing; Private Rm 2 (–,11,–,–); Private Rm 1 (–,14,–,–).

Kensington Conference & Events Centre W8
£M, (600,500,400,800)
Hornton St
T 020 7361 2220
F 020 7361 3442
W www.rbkc.gov.uk/venues
E hall-let@rbkc.gov.uk
Discreetly located off Kensington High Street, this is one of the largest venues in central London, and is well equipped to cope with anything from an international conference to a dinner-dance, banquet, fair or exhibition. / no naked flames; 2am; list of caterers; Small Hall (250,100,70,190).

Kensington Palace W8
£M-E, (300,170,80,200)
Kensington Palace
T 020 3166 6115
F 020 3166 6110
W www.hrp.org.uk/KensingtonPalace/
E kensingtonpalaceevents@hrp.org.uk
A royal residence longer than Buckingham Palace, the palace is available for events where a suitable degree of formality is required. / 10.30pm; evenings only (except Apartment 1A and occasionally Orangery); list of caterers; no amplified music inside the palace; dancing in orangery only; State Apartments (200,–,–,170); Sunken Garden (80,–,–,–); Queens Gallery (150,76,–,–); Orangery (300,150,80,200); 1A (60,40,–,–).

Kent House Knightsbridge SW7
£M-E, (300,200,–,160)
Rutland Gardens
T 020 7591 3838
F 020 7581 8012
W hardens.com/party/kenthouseknightsbridge
E events@kenthouseknightsbridge.org
An impressive Knightsbridge house that makes a grand setting for receptions, dinners, fashion shows and conferences. It has an imposing staircase and four large and elegant rooms for entertaining. / 1am; not available Fri pm & Sat am; list of caterers; no live bands after 10.30pm; Sanctuary (300,200,–,160); The Rutland Room (120,50,–,60); The Library (50,40,–,40).

Kenwood House (The Orangery) NW3
£E, (120,–,–,–)
Hampstead Ln
T 020 8341 5384
F 020 8348 2643
W hardens.com/party/kenwoodhousetheorangery
E kenwoodevents@companyofcooks.com
This beautiful neo-classical house, at the top of Hampstead Heath, is not itself available for functions. For a tiny 'window' every afternoon, however, the Orangery may be hired. / very restricted availability; available only 3.30pm-5.30pm summer, 2.30pm-4.30pm winter; Company of Cooks; no amplified music; no dancing; only clear drinks.

Kenwood House (Old Kitchen) NW3

£M, (200,120,100,100)

Hampstead Ln

T 020 8341 5384

F 020 8348 2643

W hardens.com/party/kenwoodhouseoldkitchen

E kenwood@companyofcooks.com

If you're not in search of the 'full-on' grandeur of Kenwood House itself, you might like to consider the Old Kitchen and Brew House Restaurant – an airy and attractive stone-flagged room at the rear of the property, often used for wedding receptions. / 12.30pm; Company of Cooks; The Brew House (200,120,100,100); Old Kitchen (150,120,–,100).

Kenza EC2

£M, (300,200,–,–)

10 Devonshire Square

T 020 7929 5533

W hardens.com/party/kenza

E info@kenza-restaurant.com

Especially by the fairly straightlaced standards of City restaurants, this fun north African basement near Liverpool Street is a total wow. / Private Dining (70,50,–,–).

Kettners W1

£B, (500,200,–,–)

29 Romilly St

T 020 7734 6112

F 020 7287 6499

W hardens.com/party/kettners

E reservations@kettners.com

Recently relaunched, this intriguingly-housed old Soho restaurant is a warren of interesting rooms, all of which can be taken for private events. Or, for a large do, you could take the whole place. / midnight; in-house caterers; no amplified music; no dancing.

Kew Bridge Steam Museum TW8

£M, (150,120,–,45)

Green Dragon Ln

T 020 8568 4757

F 020 8569 9978

W www.kbsm.org

E functions@kbsm.org

A dramatic setting – complete with working steam engines – used for everything from wedding receptions to themed company events. / no college events or under-30 birthdays; 1am; hirer's choice of caterer; music limit 96 decibels; The Steam Hall (150,120,–,–); The Babcock Meeting Room (–,–,–,45); The Grand Junction Engine House (150,–,–,–); The Gallery (–,56,–,–).

Kew Gardens TW9

£M-E, (600,400,400,500)

Kew

T 0844 873 3963

F 020 8332 5632

W www.kew.org/venues

E venues@kew.org

PLANTS PEOPLE POSSIBILITIES

Kew Gardens is a UNESCO World Heritage Site and has a variety of stunning venues for any event. Our mission is to inspire and deliver science-based plant conservation worldwide, enhancing the quality of life. We are committed towards sustainability, have achieved ISO14001 status and are working towards BS8901 accreditation in Sustainable Event Management. / no candles; midnight upon request; availability on request; list of caterers; sound limiting divices in situ; Cambridge Cottage (150,80,–,100); The Orangery (400,200,200,–); Temperate House (400,200,200,–); Marquee Site (600,400,400,500); Orangery Conference Room (–,–,–,30).

Kew Palace TW9

£M-E, (60,30,–,–)

Kew

T 020 3166 6115

F 020 3166 6110

W www.hrp.org.uk/KewPalace

E kewpalaceevents@hrp.org.uk

Perfect summer venue for entertaining intimate parties. The beautifully tended Queen's Garden is a fragrant setting for guests to sip champagne before being treated to a guided tour of the palace. After discovering secrets about this once Royal residence, guests sit down to dinner in the elegant King's Dining Room. / 10.30pm; April - October, evenings only; list of caterers; no amplified music; no dancing.

King's College WC2

£B-M, (200,175,150,390)

138-142 Strand

T 020 7848 1700

F 020 7848 1717

W hardens.com/party/kingscollege

E conference@kcl.ac.uk

A very central site. The college's main hall is well maintained, quite grand and suitable for a wide range of functions. / 10pm; in-house caterers; music only in Great Hall; dancing only in Great Hall; Great Hall (200,175,150,200); Lecture Theatre (–,–,–,390).

King's College School SW19

£B-M, (250,180,180,–)

Southside

T 020 8255 5401

F 020 8255 5409

W hardens.com/party/kcs

E ents@kcs.org.uk

A Wimbledon school with a panelled Great Hall (used for weddings). The range of smaller facilities suited to social use also include the Boathouse club room, overlooking the river at Putney. / midnight; Great Hall available outside term time, Boathouse evening & w/e during term; hirer's choice of caterer; no live bands; Boathouse (100,40,–,–); Great Hall (300,180,180,–).

King's Head Theatre N1

£B, (300,130,–,130)

115 Upper St

T 020 7226 1916

F 020 7226 8507

W hardens.com/party/kingsheadtheatre

E info@kingsheadtheatre.org

If you're looking for somewhere with a lot of olde worlde atmosphere for a daytime presentation, you might consider this famous Islington theatre-pub. / 6pm; no food.

The Kingly Club W1

£M, (115,25,50,35)

4 Kingly Court

T 020 7287 9100

W www.kinglyclub.co.uk

E info@kinglyclub.co.uk

The Kingly Club is a contemporary, sleek and stylish space located in the fashionable part of Soho. We are known for our excellence, service, style and uplifting ambiance. We are also passionate about keeping the Kingly Club an exceptional, privileged and personal experience for all clients and their guests. / 9am - 12pm Sun, 3am Mon-Wed, 10pm Thu-Sat, accept hire during club hours on occasion; in-house caterers.

Kings Place N1
£B-M, (800,220,84,420)
Kings Place
T 020 7014 2838
F 020 7520 1488
W www.kingsplaceevents.co.uk
E events@kingsplaceevents.co.uk

With emphasis on technology, this amazing venue has seen the lights of some of London's most high profile events. Versatile for day time or evening events, the several different spaces set the tone to deliver great experiences. Water views onto Regent's Canal, two fantastic art galleries, concert halls, café, restaurant and bar complete this exciting building. / *midnight; 8.30am - Midnight; in-house caterers; Hall One (–,–,–,420); Hall Two (320,160,84,200); Battlebridge Room (330,220,100,200); St Pancras Room (120,90,48,100); Limehouse Room (37,30,18,37); Wenlock Room (32,20,12,32); Horsfall Room (20,–,–,24); Kings Place Art Gallery (450,–,–,–).*

Kingsway Hall Hotel WC2
£M-E, (300,60,150,250)
Great Queen Street
T 020 7309 0909
W hardens.com/party/kingswayhall
In the heart of Covent Garden, this large modern hotel has a large number of banqueting and conference suites (and is particularly popular with members of the nearby Masonic temple). / *1am; in-house caterers.*

Kingswood House SE21
£B-M, (250,160,80,–)
Kingswood Estate
T 020 7525 6441
F 020 7525 6439
W hardens.com/party/kingswoodhouse
E Kingswoodhouse@southwark.gov.uk
A c18 castle now run by Southwark Council as a library and community centre, but retaining much of the opulence of its original decorative style. It is available for weddings. / *midnight; hirer's choice of caterer; sound limit; Charles Suite (100,60,40,–).*

Knightsbridge 145 SW1
£B, (200,170,100,–)
145 Knightsbridge
T 020 7591 4664
W hardens.com/party/knightsbridge
E events@knightsbridge145.com
Knightsbridge 145 is a stylish – exposed brickwork, wooden floors, light and contemporary finish – new event space, for corporate and private events. / *12.30am; in-house caterers.*

KOKO NW1
£M, (1500,250,–,–)
1a Camden High St
T 0870 432 5527
F 020 7388 4388
W hardens.com/party/koko
E annette@koko.uk.com
Characterful, recently refurbished, converted theatre premises in Camden Town, now fully equipped to host many types of gathering, private or corporate. A smoking terrace is a recent addition. / *age 18+ only; 3am; list of caterers.*

LABAN SE8
£M-E, (130,100,400,400)
Creekside
T 020 8469 9453
F 020 8691 8400
W www.uniquevenuesoflondon.co.uk/laban/index.html
E events@laban.org
Housing one of Europe's leading institutions for contemporary dance artist training, this south-east London venue won the RIBA Stirling prize for its architects Herzog & de Meuron, which helps make it a

suitable backdrop for events of a fashionable or artistic nature. / midnight; restricted availability in term time; hirer's choice of caterer (in-house available); Max (130,100,294,400); Foyer (40,–,–,400); Outdoor Theatre (–,–,400,400); Studio Theatre (–,–,100,120); Meeting Room (–,20,35,50); Bonnie Bird Theatre (–,–,–,–); Conference Room (8,–,294,–); Conference Room (16,–,–,–).

Lainston House SO21
£M, (160,120,–,166)
Woodman Lane
Ⓣ 01962 776 088
Ⓕ 01926 776 672
Ⓦ hardens.com/party/lainstonhouse
Ⓔ enquiries@lainstonhouse.com
Surrounded by woodland, parkland and idyllic gardens, and only an hour away from London, Lainston House is the perfect venue for anything from private dining, wedding receptions and parties to conferences and corporate entertainment. / 24 hour licence; in-house caterers; Barn (160,120,–,166).

The Lamb Tavern EC3
£B, (300,65,–,–)
10-12 Leadenhall Mkt
Ⓣ 020 7626 2454
Ⓦ hardens.com/party/lambtavern
Ⓔ lambtavern@youngs.co.uk
One of the City's best pubs – in the centre of an atmospheric, covered market. Its basement bar and restaurant are available for private hire during the week, and at the weekend you can take over the whole pub. / 11pm; in-house caterers.

Lancaster House SW1
£E, (350,150,–,200)
Stable Yard
Ⓣ 020 7008 8169
Ⓕ 020 7008 8206
Ⓦ hardens.com/party/lancasterhouse
Ⓔ fcoevents@cvg.gov.uk
The St James's palace that has "entertained more heads of state than any other" is ornamented to a degree that can seem more French than English. It is – naturally – made available only for the most 'suitable' events. / very restricted availability; 11pm; list of caterers; State Dining Rm (120,52,–,72); The Music Rm (–,75,–,100); Long Gallery (350,150,–,200).

The Landau W1
£M-E, (30,100,–,–)
Portland Place
Ⓣ 020 7965 0165
Ⓕ 020 7973 7560
Ⓦ hardens.com/party/landau
Ⓔ info@thelandau.com
With a mix of stylish design by David Collins and high-quality cuisine, The Landau is consistently one of the London's better hotel dining rooms. / Mon-Sat 10.30pm, Sun 5pm; in-house caterers; light background music only; The Landau (–,100,–,–); Postillion (Private Dining Rm) (30,16,–,–).

Landmark NW1
£M-E, (1000,500,400,512)
222 Marylebone Rd
Ⓣ 020 7631 8000
Ⓦ hardens.com/party/landmark
Ⓔ sales@thelandmark.co.uk
An impressive hotel where skilful updating of a Victorian building (once the Great Central Hotel) has provided London with some of its grandest public rooms – particularly the marbled Ballroom and the oak-panelled Drawing Room. / 1am; in-house caterers; Grand Ballroom (1000,500,400,512); Drawing Rm (300,180,132,204); Tower Suite (60,36,–,–); Empire Rm (250,120,120,220).

The Lanesborough SW1
£M-E, (180,120,120,100)
Hyde Park Corner
Ⓣ 020 7259 5599
Ⓕ 020 7259 5606
Ⓦ hardens.com/party/thelanesborough
Ⓔ info@lanesborough.com
A neo-classical landmark, converted into a glossy hotel and furnished in a rather overblown Regency style. For functions, a variety of lofty, medium-sized rooms and a prettified wine cellar are available. Many rooms are licensed for weddings. / 1am; in-house caterers; Belgravia (180,120,120,100); Wellington Rm (80,60,40,60); Westminster Rm (60,40,–,45); Wine Cellar (–,12,–,–).

The Langley WD17
£M, (750,550,500,750)
Gade House
T 01923 218 553
F 01923 397 339
W www.langleybanqueting.co.uk
E angela@langleybanqueting.co.uk
Situated in the heart of Watford Town Centre with close links to M1 and M25, The Langley appreciates that clients require personal touches to their events. We provide the complete setting with multi-media functionality fully available for conducting complex presentations, conferences, seminars, marketing events, exhibitions and product launches. / 12.30am; 8am; in-house (hirer's choice avail); Ruby Suite (750,550,500,750); Sapphire Suite (750,550,500,750); Conference Room (150,–,–,150); Topaz Suite (750,550,500,750).

Lansdowne Club W1
£M, (250,150,150,170)
9 Fitzmaurice Pl
T 020 7318 6116
F 020 7318 6124
W hardens.com/party/lansdowneclub
E functions@lansdowneclub.com
A large Mayfair club with a very handy location. Its impressive Art Deco interiors provide a good range of function facilities. / midnight; in-house caterers; Ballroom (250,150,150,170); Sun Rm (20,12,–,–); Shelburne Rm (80,40,–,60); Findlay Rm (30,16,–,20).

Latium W1
£B-M, (–,50,–,–)
21 Berners St
T 020 7323 9123
F 020 7323 3205
W hardens.com/party/latium
E info@latiumrestaurant.com
Just north of Oxford Street, an Italian restaurant with an above-average reputation for its cooking. You can hire the whole restaurant or – for a small gathering – book the chef's table. / 11pm; available from noon; in-house caterers; no amplified music; Chef's Table (–,6,–,–).

Lauderdale House N6
£B-M, (160,100,–,–)
Waterlow Park
T 020 8348 8716
F 020 8442 9099
W hardens.com/party/lauderdalehouse
E kives@lauderdale.org.uk
Pretty c16 Highgate house, overlooking the park, that's much used for weddings, receptions and other social events. It is located in Waterlow Park. / no teenage parties; midnight; in-house caterers; Long Gallery (90,–,–,–); Lower Gallery (160,90,–,–).

Launceston Place W8
£M-E, (150,60,–,–)
1a Launceston Place
T 020 7937 6912
F 020 7938 2412
W hardens.com/party/launcestonplace
E lpr@egami.co.uk
A Kensington townhouse restaurant which would make a good function venue if hired in its entirety. There are also a couple of options for smaller events. / 1am; in-house caterers; no amplified music; no dancing; Chef's Office (–,10,–,–); Semi-Private Hire (–,20,–,–).

The Law Society WC2
£M-E, (280,180,128,280)
113 Chancery Ln
T 020 7320 9555
F 020 7320 5955
W hardens.com/party/thelawsociety
E angel.aculey@lawsociety.org.uk
This fine early c19 building, sensitively developed over the years and very well maintained, has a comfortable grandeur and surprising degrees of charm and flexibility. The Old Council Chamber stands out, but there is a good range of rooms – they claim 8 in total – for most occasions. / no gambling; 11pm; Reading Rm/Six Clerks Restaurant evening only; Charlton House; Old Council Chamber (130,55,–,65); The Common Room (280,180,160,280); The Reading Room (210,80,60,150); The Council Chamber (–,–,–,100); Strand/Fleet/Bell Suites (120,80,–,120); Six Clerks Room (35,30,–,35); The Old Bookshop (35,30,–,35); Six Clerks Restaurant/Bar (140,83,–,–).

Le Cafe Anglais W2

£B-M, (300,140,–,–)
8 Porchester Gardens
T 020 7221 1415
W hardens.com/party/cafeanglais
E info@lecafeanglais.co.uk
The private room of Le Cafe Anglais is a high ceilinged room with wonderful natural light, is fully air conditioned and is beautifully decorated. Our dedicated events co-ordinator will personally look after all your requirements. We offer an eclectic range of seasonal menus and an award winning wine list. / midnight; noon lunch and 6.30 evening; in-house caterers; no music; no dancing; Private Room (50,26,–,–).

The Ledbury W11

£M, (–,64,–,–)
127 Ledbury Rd
T 020 7792 9090
F 020 7792 9191
W hardens.com/party/theledbury
E info@theledbury.com
A sibling to the fabled Chez Bruce, this is one of the best restaurants in the environs of Notting Hill. Except for the terrace (in summer), the only private dining option is to take the whole place. / midnight; in-house caterers; no amplified music; no dancing; Terrace (–,34,–,–).

Legoland Windsor SL4

£M-E, (250,100,100,120)
Winkfield Rd
T 01753 626102
F 01753 626113
W hardens.com/party/legoland
E corporate.events@legoland.co.uk
With 150 acres of mature parkland and over 50 rides, shows and attractions, this popular theme park can accommodate a wide range of meetings, themed events and corporate fun days. / midnight; in-house caterers.

Leighton House Museum W14

£M-E, (150,60,–,–)
12 Holland Park Rd
T 020 7603 1123 or 020 77315282
F 020 7371 2467
W www.rbkc.gov.uk/museums
E enquiries@cooksandpartners.co.uk
Situated in leafy Kensington, Leighton House is the former home of Victorian artist Frederic, Lord Leighton (1830-1896). Opulent interiors combine with the intimacy of a private home to make this an exceptional venue for corporate and private entertaining. The peaceful private garden is accessible in the summer months. / 11pm; available eves, not Sun, garden available Apr-Sep; Cooks & Partners Ltd, list of caterers; no amplified music; no dancing; no red wine for standing events.

Lemonia NW1

£B-M, (–,180,–,–)
89 Regent's Park Rd
T 020 7586 7454
F 020 7483 2630
W hardens.com/party/lemonia
The private room of this ever-popular Primrose Hill Greek institution is a very handy size for many events, or – for a big gathering – hire the whole place. / 11.30pm; not available Sat L or Sun D; in-house caterers; no amplified music; no dancing; Private Room (–,20,–,–).

Les Ambassadeurs W1

£M-E, (150,100,–,–)
5 Hamilton Place
T 020 7495 5555
W hardens.com/party/ambassadeurs
E enquiries@lesaclub.com
This luxurious gaming club is one of the better-known casinos in town, and occupies an opulent mansion near Hyde Park Corner. Various rooms are available to hire, including the restaurant, and a major selling point is the venue's 6 am license. / 18+; 6am; in-house caterers.

Levant W1

£B-M, (200,120,120,–)
Jason's Court
T 020 7224 1111
F 020 74861216
W hardens.com/party/levant
E reservations@levant.co.uk
An exotic feel makes this stylish North African basement restaurant, just north of Oxford Street, a 'natural' party venue. There are lots of useful corners for informal parties, but if you want your 'own'

space the only option is to take the whole place. / *2am; in-house caterers; no amplified music.*

Level 7 Restaurant, Tate Modern SE1

£M-E, (300,150,–,–)

Bankside

T 020 7887 8689

F 020 7887 8702

W hardens.com/party/level7

E corporatehospitality@/tate.org.uk

You no longer need to hire out the whole of the Tate Modern to hold an event at its 7th floor café, which has the most stunning views over the Thames to St Paul's and the City. Only evening hires are available.

Leven is Strijd E14

£M, (50,22,–,–)

West India Quay

T 020 7987 4002

F 020 7987 4002

W hardens.com/party/leven

E info@theleven.co.uk

Permanently moored in Docklands, a barge catering for dinners for 12 or more people in comfortable and unusually private surroundings. / *12.30am; in-house caterers.*

Liberty W1

£E, (499,60,–,35)

Regent Street

T 020 7573 9443

W hardens.com/party/liberty

E corporate@liberty.co.uk

Liberty a name synonymous with Luxury since 1875 is available for events. From exclusive shopping to a champagne reception, private dinner or boardroom meeting – options range from 10 people in the Heritage Suite to 500 for a private shopping event on the 4th floor. / *10pm (late licence avail on req); Ford McDonald; no dancing; red wine restricted in most areas; Heritage Suite (40,20,–,35); Fashion Show (80,–,–,–); Cafe Liberty (100,60,–,–); Champagne & Oyster Bar (60,–,–,–).*

The Lincoln Centre WC2

£M, (150,50,–,160)

18 Lincoln's Inn Fields

T 020 7936 1300

F 020 7396 3535

W hardens.com/party/thelincolncentre

In an elegant building overlooking Lincoln's Inn Fields, a centre for conference and presentations. / *5am; in-house caterers; Central Boardroom (–,–,–,12); Break-out Area (150,50,–,–); Presentation 1 (–,–,–,160); Presentation 2 (–,–,–,45).*

Lincoln's Inn (Honourable Society of) WC2

£M-E, (600,300,–,300)

Treasury Office

T 020 7405 5969

W www.lincolnsinn.org.uk/banqueting

E liz.cox@lincolnsinn.org.uk

The historic buildings of Lincoln's Inn are set in spacious, beautifully maintained private gardens in the heart of London. The Halls and public rooms of Lincoln's Inn are steeped in tradition providing a sumptuous backdrop for all kinds or size of events. There are 3 venues available for hire. / *11.30pm; hirer's choice of caterer (in-house available); no amplified music outside; Great Hall (600,300,–,300); Old Hall (250,130,–,130); Old Court Room (100,40,–,50).*

Linden House W6

£B-M, (100,74,74,100)

Linden Hse

T 020 8748 1841

W hardens.com/party/lindenhouse

E manager@linden-house.org

An elegant Georgian house, complete with ballroom, by the river at Hammersmith. It makes a good venue for a private social event. / *11.30pm; in-house caterers; Ballroom (100,74,–,100); Captain's Rm (–,–,–,20); Commodore's Rm (–,30,–,30).*

The Little Ship Club EC4

£B-M, (250,120,120,130)

Bell Wharf Lane

T 020 7236 7729

F 020 7251 7170

W hardens.com/party/littleshipclub

E enquire@chesterboyd.co.uk

A comfortable and smart river-side yachtclub where guests may be welcomed at the river entrance. It enjoys wonderful views. / 1am; available weekday evenings and weekends; Chester Boyd; Library (70,50,–,60).

Lloyds Club EC3

£M-E, (80,24,–,–)
42 Crutched Friars
T 020 7863 6685
F 020 7481 4551
W hardens.com/party/lloydsclub

A City gym club with contemporary décor – its restaurant, available for hire in the evenings, makes a handy venue for a cocktail party. / 11pm (flexible); evenings only; in-house caterers.

Lloyd's of London EC3

£M, (600,330,200,–)
1 Lime St
T 020 7327 6321
F 020 7327 5014
W hardens.com/party/lloydsoflondon
E eventcatering@lloyds.co.uk

The large ground-floor Captain's Room of Lord Rogers's remarkable building is available at night for functions. For receptions, another possibility is the Old Library – a panelled hall from the market's old building transplanted into the frame of the new. / 11pm (flexible); available mainly evenings only Mon-Fri; Avenance Caterers; Captain's Rm (150,110,80,–); Banqueting Suite (600,330,200,–); Old Library (150,70,–,–); 1688 (400,220,180,–).

Local Government House SW1

£M-E, (200,60,–,140)
Smith Square
T 020 7664 3000
F 020 7664 3375
W hardens.com/party/localgovernmenthouse
E info@lga.gov.uk

Previously called 'Transport House', this '20s Westminster building is now the HQ and conference centre for the Local Government Association. / 10pm; no amplified music; Bevan Hall (200,–,–,140); Meeting Rooms (–,10,–,–); Conference Rooms 1&2 (–,–,–,50); Conference 3& 4 (–,–,–,–).

Loft SW4

£B, (260,60,–,–)
67 Clapham High St
T 020 7627 0792
F 020 7627 2210
W hardens.com/party/loft
E bar@theloft-clapham.co.uk

Situated on the first floor, with a bird's eye view of the hustle and bustle of Clapham High Street, a high-tech bar which would make a good space for taking over in its entirety. / 2.30am; hirer's choice of caterer (in-house available).

London Aquarium SE1

£M-E, (1000,180,180,–)
County Hall
T 020 7487 0224
F 020 7465 0884
W hardens.com/party/aquarium
E events@merlinvenues.com

One of Europe's largest collections of marine life. The ever-changing displays of shoaling fish, including sharks and stingrays, present a spectacular backdrop for your next event. / midnight; available from 7pm; list of caterers.

The London Art House N1

£M-E, (300,200,153,280)
2-18 Britannia Row
T 020 3227 3200
W hardens.com/party/londonarthouse
E info@londonarthouse.com

A versatile Islington venue for events. Each of the dozen rooms is decorated in accordance with a different artistic style. / midnight; Planet Organic/New Quebec; Manor Garden Hall (300,200,153,280); Baroque Hall (100,60,60,70); Egyptian Room (50,36,24,42); Orangery (50,36,24,42); Picasso Room (30,24,18,32); Bauhaus Room (25,16,12,20); Albert Moore Lounge (25,16,12,20).

London Canal Museum N1

£M, (200,120,120,150)
12-13 New Wharf Rd
T 020 7713 0836
W hardens.com/party/londoncanalmuseum

Arrive by long boat to stay in keeping with the theme at this intriguing museum near King's

Cross, which covers not only waterways, but also the history of ice and ice cream – these Victorian premises were once home to a famous ice cream maker! / 1am; noise control policy; no alcohol; 1st Floor (200,120,120,150); Meeting Rm (20,12,–,20).

London Capital Club EC4
£M-E, (150,60,–,80)
15 Abchurch Ln
T 020 7717 0088
F 020 7717 0099
W hardens.com/party/londoncapitalclub
E privaterooms@londoncapitalclub.com
A listed City building (1917), formerly known as the Gresham Club, with a number of rooms available for private events.
/ members club; weekdays only; in-house caterers; Boardroom (60,20,–,30); The Oriental Room (150,60,–,80).

London Corinthian Sailing Club W6
£M, (100,80,–,–)
Upper Mall
T 020 8748 1841
W hardens.com/party/londoncorinthiansailingclub
E manager@linden-house.org
Linden House is an 18th century, Grade II listed venue situated on the northern side of the River Thames. It is used for business meetings, seminars, team building, exhibitions, fund raising events, private parties and wedding receptions. It has also been used for filming. / 11pm; in-house caterers; Ballroom (100,80,–,–).

The London Dungeon SE1
£M-E, (220,–,–,–)
28-34 Tooley St
T 0844 824 6282
F 020 7465 0884
W www.merlinvenues.com
E events@merlinvenues.com
Deep in the heart of historic London, beneath the arches of London Bridge, lies the infamous London Dungeon, a unique combination of real history, horror and humour perfect for parties and networking events. / midnight; available from 6.45; list of caterers; Whole Attraction (220,–,–,–).

London Eye SE1
£M, (800,–,–,–)
Riverside Building
T 0870 220 2223
F 0870 990 8882
W www.londoneye.com
E corporate.event@londoneye.com
Experience the London Eye by enjoying anything from a standard flight to a Private Capsule with a range of hospitality, including Champagne and canapés, wine tasting and afternoon tea. Look out for their seasonal packages like Pimm's Flights in summer and Mulled Wine Flights in winter. Or even get married! / 8pm, Jun & Sep 9pm, Jul & Aug 9.30pm; Simply Gourmet; Per Capsule (25,–,–,–).

London Film Museum SE1
£M-E, (1200,120,–,220)
County Hall
T 020 7202 7040
W hardens.com/party/movieum
E info@londonfilmmuseum.com
In the imposing former County Hall, this new museum of cinema offers a very central venue suited to themed events. / 11pm; available from 5pm; list of caterers; alcohol restricted in debating chamber; Debating Chamber (–,–,–,220); Riverside Room 1 (220,120,–,–); Jubilee (75,–,–,35); Museum (1200,–,–,–).

The London Hippodrome WC2
£B-M, (1850,450,–,–)
Leicester Sq
T 020 7437 4311
F 020 7434 4225
W hardens.com/party/hippodrome
E info@thelondonhippodrome.com
A central venue that is well enough maintained to suit pretty much any event. It boasts an extremely impressive light system and is technically well equipped for major corporate functions, in which it does big business. It's currently undergoing a major refurbishment, and will open again in 2011. / age 18+ only; 2am; hirer's choice of caterer (in-house available).

London Marriott W1
£M, (1000,552,308,900)
Grosvenor Sq
T 020 7493 1232
F 020 7514 1528
W hardens.com/party/londonmarriott
E london.salesoffice@marriott.com
This Mayfair hotel generally seems to have rather a low profile, but it offers one of the largest pillar-free function spaces in central London. / 2am; list of caterers; music cannot exceed 92 decibels; Westminster Suite (1000,552,308,900); Whitehall Suite (540,164,–,–); Belgrave Rm (250,200,–,300).

London Marriott Hotel, County Hall SE1
£M-E, (200,150,120,80)
County Hall
T 020 7902 5556
F 020 7902 8026
W hardens.com/party/marriottcountyhall
E sales.countyhall@marriott.com
This River Thames-side hotel is situated in the grandest parts of the former GLC Building. Private functions are accommodated in eleven imposing Edwardian rooms, many with panelling, marble fireplaces and some function rooms with impressive views of Big Ben and the Houses of Parliament. / 1am; in-house caterers; King George V (90,60,–,80); Boardroom (–,12,–,–); Queen Mary (45,20,–,28); County Hall Suite (200,150,120,–).

London Metropole W2
£M, (1500,1000,800,1600)
Edgware Rd
T 020 7402 2400
F 020 7262 2921
W hardens.com/party/londonmetropole
E reservations.londonmet@hilton.com
Boasting over 1000 rooms, this businesslike Bayswater hotel claims to offer more event facilities than any other in town, including 37 meeting rooms of 44,000 square feet in total. / midnight; list of caterers; Palace Suite (600,600,500,800); Windsor Suite (200,250,140,250); Monarch Suite (1500,1000,800,1600); King's Suite (1500,1000,800,1600).

London Palladium W1
£M, (200,50,–,2270)
8 Argyll St
T 020 7379 4981
F 020 7379 4982
W hardens.com/party/palladium
E laura.acton@reallyuseful.co.uk
Atop the main staircase of this famous theatre, the large, light Cinderella bar attracts a fair number of daytime receptions. You can even get married here. / restricted availability; available subject to constraints of current production; in-house caterers; Cinderella Bar (120,50,–,–); Variety Bar (100,50,–,–); Hall Of Fame (–,20,–,–); Argyll Suite (–,15,–,–).

London Rowing Club SW15
£B, (150,100,55,100)
Embankment
T 020 8788 1400
F 020 8788 8643
W hardens.com/party/londonrowing
E manager@lrcvenue.org.uk
The first of the line of boathouses on the Putney 'hard', 'London' makes quite an economical venue for receptions and business meetings. / age 18+ only; midnight; in-house caterers; Long Rm (150,100,–,100); Fairbairn Rm (100,–,–,50); Members Rm (40,20,–,25); Balcony (60,30,–,–).

London School of Economics WC2
£B-M, (450,150,–,1000)
Houghton St
T 020 7955 7087
F 020 7955 6272
W hardens.com/party/lse
E event.services@lse.ac.uk
Handily located near Aldwych, the famous school offers reasonably-priced accommodation for meetings, conferences and events. / very restricted availability; 9.30pm; evenings and weekends only during term time; in-house caterers; no amplified music; no dancing.

London Scottish SW1
£B-M, (300,180,150,224)
95 Horseferry Rd
T 020 7384 4670
F 020 7414 3487
W hardens.com/party/londonscot
E info@alv.mod.uk

A very unusual Pimlico TA hall, reconstructed from pieces transported from the regiment's former building. With the messes also available, it can suit many different types of event. / *1am; not available Mon to Fri Evening; hirer's choice of caterer (in-house available); Dining Room (80,40,–,–).*

London Stock Exchange EC4
£M-E, (300,119,–,119)
10 Paternoster Square
T 020 779 72040
F 020 7920 4783
W hardens.com/party/londonstockexchange
E events@londonstockexchange.com

Having left its old site, the Exchange now occupies part of the new Paternoster Square development near St Paul's. It offers a (now rather larger) range of spaces for events of a corporate nature, especially where broadcast/media facilities are required. / *companies only; 10pm ; in-house caterers; no dancing; Theatre (–,–,–,119); Forum 1 (–,50,–,50); Forum 2 (–,40,–,40); Forum (whole) (300,100,–,110); Recess 1 (–,10,–,–).*

London Studios SE1
£M-E, (800,350,–,630)
Upper Ground
T 020 7737 8888
F 020 7928 8405
W www.londonstudios.co.uk
E sales@londonstudios.co.uk

These large TV studios on the South Bank are primarily used for production only. During gaps in their schedules, though, they can be used for events – generally presentations or something with a TV theme. / *2am; hirer's choice of caterer; Studio 1 (800,350,–,630); Studio 2 (600,200,–,430); Studio 3 (–,–,–,80).*

London Transport Museum WC2
£M, (500,180,–,120)
Covent Gdn
T 020 7379 6344
F 020 7565 7254
W www.ltmuseum.co.uk
E corphire@ltmuseum.co.uk

Reopened following a £24m refurbishment, this modern venue is situated in the heart of Covent Garden. The original Victorian flower market creates a spectacular backdrop for events, where you can mingle alongside iconic red London bus. The Cubic Theatre is ideal for presentations. / *midnight; available from 6pm (Cubic Theatre all day); list of caterers; sound limit 84 decibels; Cubic Theatre (–,–,–,120).*

The London Welsh Centre WC1
£B, (250,150,150,200)
157-163 Grays Inn Rd
T 020 7837 3722
W hardens.com/party/londonwelsh
E administrator@lwcentre.demon.co.uk

The light, gym-type Bloomsbury hall is largely used for rehearsals, but also for parties. The bar upstairs is suitable for informal get-togethers. / *11.30pm; in-house caterers; Bar (100,–,–,–).*

London Wetland Centre SW13
£M, (200,120,110,150)
Queen Elizabeth's Walk
T 020 8409 4400
F 020 8409 4401
W www.uniquevenuesoflondon.co.uk/london_wetland_centre/index.html
E functions.london@wwt.org.uk

There are over a hundred acres of lakes, pools and lagoons – and all within the range of a Zone 2 Travelcard! – at this eco-friendly Barnes project, whose visitors' centre incorporates quite extensive function facilities. / *no flashing lights; midnight; in-house caterers; Theatre (80,–,–,80); Waters Edge Rm (200,120,110,150); Observatory (180,–,–,–); Gallery (100,30,–,–); Bird Hide (Breakfast Only) (–,30,–,–); Tower (–,25,–,–).*

London Zoo NW1

£M-E, (300,240,240,250)
Regent's Park
Ⓣ 020 7449 6562
Ⓕ 020 7722 8617
Ⓦ www.zsl.org
Ⓔ functions@zsl.org
A unique setting for any corporate or private event – suites and meeting rooms overlooking exotic animals in 36 acres of gardens. Drink Receptions can range from Rainforest Lookouts to Animals Kingdoms, and some furry friends can even visit your event... / 12am, can be extended until 2am; catering in-house, with some exceptions; Prince Albert Suite (280,200,100,200); Mappin Pavilion (70,80,80,70); Raffles Suite (–,90,90,–); Council Room (–,20,–,–); Darwin Room (–,10,–,–); Bartlett Room (–,35,–,60); Huxley Theatre (–,–,–,200); Animal Houses (250,–,–,–).

Lonsdale W11

£M, (280,130,–,–)
48 Lonsdale Road
Ⓣ 020 7727 4080
Ⓕ 020 7727 6030
Ⓦ hardens.com/party/lonsdale
Ⓔ info@thelonsdale.co.uk
An atmospheric bar in a fashionable part of Notting Hill, with slickly retro décor. Its first floor (Genevieve), where you can dance, is a nice size for a private party. / midnight, Fri & Sat 1am; in-house caterers; dancing only upstairs; Genevieve (60,20,–,–).

Loose Cannon EC4

£B-M, (450,180,180,–)
Allhallows Ln
Ⓣ 020 7283 1505
Ⓕ 020 7283 9312
Ⓦ hardens.com/party/loosecannon
Ⓔ roy@loosecannonec4.co.uk
Lofty arches beneath Cannon Street railway bridge, well-suited to a party, reception or dinner. / 2am; in-house caterers.

Lord's Cricket Ground NW8

£M, (900,800,350,600)
Marylebone Cricket Club
Ⓣ 0844 824 6207
Ⓕ 020 7616 8750
Ⓦ www.lords.org/events
Ⓔ events@lords.org

You don't have to attend a match at Lord's to experience its year-round magic. From the old-world elegance of the Grade II listed Pavilion to the cutting-edge modernity of the Media Centre, Lord's is an exceptional venue for meetings, exhibitions, conferences and dinners. Outside space includes gardens and a roof terrace. / 11pm, midnight (Thomas Lord Suite); in-house caterers; amplified music in Thomas Lord Suite only; dancing only in Thomas Lord Suite; alcohol over 18s only; Thomas Lord Suite (500,350,350,250); Nursery Pavilion (900,800,–,600); Long Room (300,200,–,–); Media Centre (100,50,–,70); Writing Room (70,60,–,–); Pavilion Roof Terrace (May-Sep) (250,–,–,–); Harris Gardens (May-Sep) (200,–,–,–).*

Lost Society SW8

£M, (260,–,–,–)
697 Wandsworth Road
Ⓣ 020 7652 6526
Ⓦ hardens.com/party/lostsociety
Ⓔ info@lostsociety.co.uk
A 16th-century Clapham barn now equipped as a burlesque-style bar, with six distinct spaces (which can be hired individually if required). / Mon-Fri age 21+, Fri & Sat age 23+; 2am Sat & Sun, midnight weekdays; available from 5pm; in-house caterers.

Lotus Chinese Floating Restaurant E14
£B-M, (500,400,350,220)
38 Limeharbour
T 020 7515 6445
F 020 7515 6446
W hardens.com/party/lotus
E lotus@lotusfloating.co.uk
One of the more characterful venues on the Isle of Dogs – the name tells you pretty much everything about it. It is particularly well suited to larger events which do not have enormous budgets. / *midnight; in-house caterers; no amplified music; no dancing.*

Louise Blouin Foundation W11
£M, (500,360,–,–)
3 Olaf Street
T 020 7985 9600
F +44 20 7985 9671
W hardens.com/party/louiseblouin
E info@ltbfoundation.org
On the fringe of Holland Park near Latimer Road tube, this 35,000 sq ft old industrial building is nowadays a striking, white-walled arts space, complete with polished concrete floor, available for all kinds of events. / *midnight; hirer's choice of caterer (in-house available); Ground Gallery (500,360,–,–); Third Floor (300,250,–,–); Second Floor (250,140,–,–).*

Loungelover E1
£M, (170,–,–,–)
1 Whitby St
T 020 7012 1234
F 020 7012 1236
W hardens.com/party/loungelover
E info@loungelover.co.uk
Eccentric and eclectic, and filled with antiques and original pieces, this groovy bar has long had quite a name for its funky 'maximalist' style. If hired in its entirety, it makes a cool setting for a party. / *midnight, Fri & Sat 1am; in-house caterers; no dancing.*

Lowiczanka Restaurant W6
£B, (–,300,300,300)
238-246 King St
T 020 8741 1940
F 020 8563 9833
W hardens.com/party/lowiczanka
E manager@posk.org
As with many emigrés' clubs, it's the time-warp atmosphere which some may find a particular attraction of this basic '60s building in Hammersmith. On the social side, the club hosts a fair number of wedding receptions. / *11.30pm; in-house caterers.*

LSO St Luke's EC1
£M-E, (360,250,180,250)
161 Old St
T 020 7566 2871
F 020 7566 2881
W www.lso.co.uk/lsostlukes
E lsostlukes@lso.co.uk
Grade I conversion offering contemporary spaces for arts, corporate and private events. The Jerwood Hall is suited to conferences up to 250, banquets for up to 180 and standing receptions for as many as 360. / *equipment must be out by 11pm; midnight - they can apply for a late licence; list of caterers; Jerwood Hall (360,250,180,250); Crypt Café (150,80,–,–); Clore Rooms 1 & 2 (25,20,–,–); Clore Gamelan Room (50,40,–,–).*

Lucky Voice Private Karaoke N1
£B, (200,–,–,–)
173-174 Upper Street
T 020 7354 6280
W hardens.com/party/luckyvoice
E hello@luckyvoice.com
"Stress relief and mind-boosting" are the claimed benefits for Karaoke sessions at this fun venue, available privately for office parties, launches and so on (or hire one pod for 4-15 people). There's a smaller Soho branch (52 Poland Street W1F 7NQ - Tel 020 7439 3660). / *21+; Sun-Thu midnight, Friy & Sat 2am; 10 am; in-house caterers; Soho Branch (140,–,–,–); Individual Pod (15,–,–,–).*

SAATCHI GALLERY

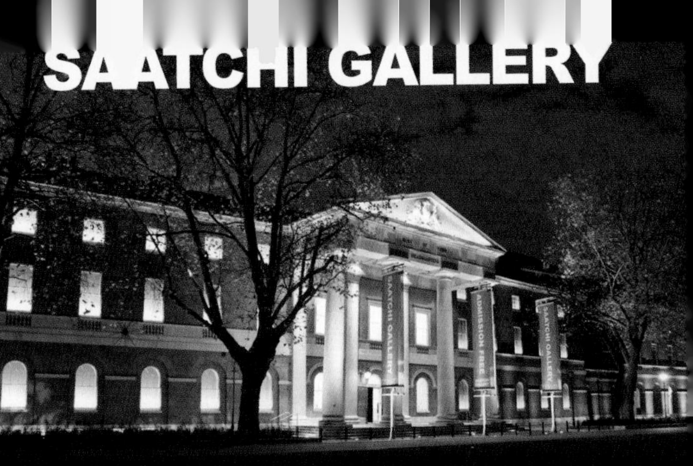

The Saatchi Gallery is an exclusive events venue spanning the entire 70,000 sq ft of the magnificent Duke of York's HQ in Chelsea, central London.

The Gallery is ideal for both large and more intimate events, with a capacity ranging from 10 to 1500 people. With all rooms available for hire during the day and evening, the Gallery is the ultimate blank canvas for any occasion including receptions, dinners, product launches, conferences and fashion shows.

Hiring the Gallery is a unique opportunity to host your event surrounded by one of the world's most exciting art collections, in London's most stunning events venue.

Please contact one of the GSP Venue Managers to discuss the details of your event or to book a site visit: call **+44 (0)20 8968 9331** or email: **venues@gsp-uk.com**

Saatchi Gallery
Duke of York's HQ | King's Road | Chelsea | London SW3 4SQ

Lyceum Theatre WC2

£M, (150,–,–,2100)

21 Wellington St

Ⓣ 020 7420 8100

Ⓦ hardens.com/party/lyceumtheatre

Ⓔ john.hindley@livenation.co.uk

Behind its grand façade, this Covent Garden theatre (home for the foreseeable future to 'The Lion King') was totally rebuilt as recently at 1996. During the day, it offers a large, central auditorium, available for hire. / restricted availability; 10.15pm; available Mon only; hirer's choice of caterer; no music; no dancing; Function Rm (150,–,–,–).

Madame Tussauds NW1

£M-E, (1000,380,350,250)

Marylebone Rd

Ⓣ 0844 824 6251

Ⓕ 020 7465 0884

Ⓦ www.merlinvenues.com

Ⓔ events@merlinvenues.com

Five immersive and interactive themed areas are fully adaptable for formal and informal events depending on your exact requirements with integrated lighting and audio-visual throughout. Available for exclusive hire Madame Tussauds can accommodate up to 1,000 for a cocktail party or 350 for a dinner dance or awards dinner / 2am; 7pm-2am; list of caterers; A-list Party (250,–,–,–); Tussauds - World Stage (500,380,300,–); Tussauds - whole attraction (1000,80,80,–); Tussauds Stardome 4D (300,–,–,250).

Madsen Restaurant SW7

£B-M, (75,40,–,30)

20 Old Brompton Road

Ⓣ 020 7225 2772

Ⓦ www.madsenrestaurant.com

Ⓔ reservations@madsenrestaurant.com

Nordic food is in vogue and this is your chance to treat your guests to a completely different experience. At Madsen we combine Nordic food with modern Scandinavian design. We source locally for our seasonal lunch, dinner and tasting menus. / 11pm; noon - midnight; in-house caterers; no dancing; Private Dining Room (20,10,–,10).

The Magic Circle Headquarters NW1

£M, (165,130,80,162)

12 Stephenson Way

Ⓣ 0845 006 2500

Ⓕ 0845 006 2501

Ⓦ hardens.com/party/themagiccircleheadquarters

Ⓔ mail@magiccirclevenue.co.uk

"Filled with mystery and magic and suitable for a wide variety of events!" Facilities of the HQ of the magicians' HQ include a fully-equipped theatre, club room and bar, as well as meeting, dining & function rooms (and a museum all featuring priceless magic memorabilia from the largest magic collection in Europe). / 3am; list of caterers.

Mahiki W1

£M, (300,–,–,–)

1 Dover Street

Ⓣ 020 7493 9529

Ⓦ hardens.com/party/mahiki

Ⓔ jane@mahiki.com

This 'Polynesian paradise', just off Piccadilly, is a fave rave for younger royals. There are bamboo walls, grass ceilings and wooden tiki figures here spread over two floors

– upstairs lounge, downstairs club. / *3.30am; available Mon-Fri 5.30pm, Sat 7.30pm; in-house caterers.*

Malabar Junction WC1

£B, (–,80,–,–)
107 Great Russell St
T 020 7580 5230
F 020 7436 9942
W hardens.com/party/malabarjunction
E malabarjunction@hotmail.com
A useful central venue that's not too pricey, this very comfortable Indian restaurant is hidden away not far from the British Museum. There is a private room, or you can take half the restaurant. / *11pm; available from noon; in-house caterers; Private Room (–,30,–,–).*

Mall Galleries SW1

£B-M, (500,200,–,350)
The Mall
T 020 7930 6844
F 020 7839 7830
W hardens.com/party/mallgalleries
E info@mallgalleries.com
A short step from Admiralty Arch, the Main Gallery at the Federation of British Artists offers an impressive and central function space. The East Gallery is smaller and rather more cosily proportioned. / *11pm; available from 5pm; hirer's choice of caterer (in-house available); no dancing; Main Gallery (500,200,–,350); East Gallery (100,60,–,60); North Gallery (80,30,–,–).*

Malmaison Hotel EC1

£M, (50,30,–,30)
18-21 Charterhouse Square
T 020 7012 3717
F 020 7012 3702
W hardens.com/party/malmaisonhotel
E danielm@malmaison.com
Smart boutique hotel with a cute Smithfield location. The attractive downstairs brasserie is not available for hire, though there is a private room leading off it, and boardrooms for hire elsewhere in the hotel. / *10pm; in-house caterers; no music; no dancing; Mal 1 (40,30,–,30); Mal 2 (–,–,–,14); Brasserie (–,14,–,–).*

Mandarin Oriental Hyde Park SW1

£M-E, (400,250,250,60)
66 Knightsbridge
T 020 7235 2000
F 020 7235 2001
W hardens.com/party/mandarinorientalhydepark
E molon-info@mohg.com
The interior of this externally overbearing redbrick Knightsbridge edifice boasts much charming late-Victorian detail, and offers one of the most impressive suites of inter-connecting entertaining rooms in London. Decorated in cream, blue and gold, they have splendid views of the park and are popular for grander weddings and receptions. / *midnight; in-house caterers; Ballroom (400,250,250,–); Carlyle Suite (250,200,70,60); Rosebery Rms (150,60,–,60); Balfour Rm (70,30,–,40).*

Mandeville Hotel W1

£M, (120,70,70,40)
Mandeville Place
T 020 7935 5599
F 020 7935 9588
W hardens.com/party/mandevillehotel
E sales@mandeville.co.uk
Marylebone hotel – the Red Room boasts natural daylight and contemporary style, and other options for entertaining include the DeVigne Bar and DeVille Restaurant. / *midnight; in-house caterers; no DJs; Red Room (50,20,–,40); Bar (70,55,–,–); deVille Restaurant (120,70,70,–).*

Marble Hill House TW1

£M-E, (50,–,–,50)
Richmond Rd
T 020 7973 3416
F 020 7973 3443
W hardens.com/party/marblehill
E hospitality@english-heritage.org.uk
Fine early c18 house, with grounds bordered by the Thames. The Great Room (based on the Cube Room at Wilton House) is decorated in white and gilt, and adorned with period paintings and furniture. / *8pm (but varies); list of caterers; no amplified music; no dancing; no red wine; Tetra Hall (50,–,–,–); Great Room (50,–,–,50).*

Marcus Wareing at the Berkeley SW1
£M-E, (–,50,–,–)
Berkeley Hotel
T 020 7235 1200
F 020 7235 1266
W hardens.com/party/marcuswareing
E privatedining@gordonramsay.com
Marcus Wareing is London's top chef, and his Gallic temple of gastronomy in Knightsbridge is also regularly voted London's best all-round restaurant. As well as a private dining room, you can also – if you want to experience the drama of the kitchen – book the chef's table. / 12.30am; no Sat L, closed Sun; in-house caterers; no music; no dancing; Chef's table (–,12,–,–).

The Mary Sumner House SW1
£B-M, (40,100,–,120)
24 Tufton St
T 020 7222 5533
F 020 7227 9731
W hardens.com/party/themarysumnerhouse
E conference@themothersunion.org
The facilities of this '20s building in Westminster, home of the Mothers' Union, are mainly used for conferences. For social events, however, they do offer bring-your-own-caterer space, very centrally. / 11pm; hirer's choice of caterer; no cash bar; Conference Hall (–,100,–,120); Mary Sumner Rm (40,24,–,40); Princess Helena (14,12,–,18); Princess Beatrice (–,16,–,30); Princess Mary (–,16,–,25); Princess Elizabeth (–,24,–,40); Princess Victoria (–,24,–,40); Princess Alexandra (–,16,–,30).

Mary Ward House WC1
£M-E, (500,220,180,350)
5/7 Tavistock Place
T 020 7387 9681
W hardens.com/party/maryward
Nowadays a conference and exhibition centre, this Grade I Victorian mansion in Bloomsbury offers 12 characterful spaces for all manner of events (a selection of which are listed) plus a large outdoor courtyard and garden. / midnight; in-house caterers; no live music; Mary Ward Hall (450,220,180,350); Brewer & Smith (300,160,130,200); Lethaby Room (150,80,70,110); Voysey Room (100,60,50,65); Boardroom (30,20,16,20).

Maya W1
£M-E, (300,50,–,–)
1a Dean St
T 020 7287 9608
F 020 7437 3500
W hardens.com/party/mayalondon
E enquiries@mayalondon.com
A Soho nightclub which can be hired in its entirely for suitable events. / age 18+; 3am; hirer's choice of caterer (in-house available).

The Mayfair W1
£M-E, (350,250,120,–)
Stratton St
T 020 7915 3898
F 020 7409 7016
W hardens.com/party/mayfairhotel
E events@themayfairhotel.co.uk
Of the banqueting facilities at this large and quite grand '20s Mayfair hotel, the rose-hued Crystal Room (capacities given) is of particular note. / 1am; in-house caterers.

Mayfair Conference Centre W2
£M, (140,80,–,140)
17 Connaught Place
T 020 7706 7700
F 020 7706 7711
W hardens.com/party/mayfairconferencecentre
E enquiries@mayfairconference.com
A smart and businesslike conference centre, near Marble Arch. / 5.30pm; in-house caterers; no music; no dancing.

McQueen EC2
£B-M, (330,60,–,–)
55-61 Tabernacle Street
T 0207 036 9229
W hardens.com/party/mcqueen
E anna@mcqueen-shoreditch.co.uk
This glamourous-looking, high-ceilinged Shoreditch lounge bar is expensively kitted out on a vaguely vintage Hollywood theme, with three spaces available for private hire. / Mon-Wed 1.30amThur-Sat 2.30amSun 1am; in-house caterers; Ground Floor (320,–,–,–); Restaurant (100,60,–,–); Basement (330,–,–,–).

Menier Chocolate Factory SE1
£M, (120,70,–,150)
53 Southwark St
T 020 7378 1712
F 020 7378 1713
W hardens.com/party/menier
E office@menierchocolatefactory.com
This brave venture – a characterful South Bank theatre-cum-dining room in a former factory – has been a big hit. It would make an interesting venue for more informal events (subject to the constraints of the current show). / 11pm; in-house caterers; Restaurant (120,70,–,–).

Mercers' Hall EC2
£M-E, (250,156,–,–)
Ironmonger Ln
T 020 7726 4991
F 020 7600 1158
W hardens.com/party/mercers
E mail@mercers.co.uk
What is probably the richest of the livery companies tells us that its hall is never available to outsiders (unless you are a member of another livery company, however, in which case your application may be graciously considered). / very restricted availability; Crown Society.

Merchant Taylors' Hall EC2
£M-E, (700,290,250,400)
30 Threadneedle St
T 020 7450 4445
F 020 7450 4455
W hardens.com/party/merchanttaylorshall
E lmorgan@mtaylorsevents.co.uk
In the heart of the City, a very grand, reconstructed (post-War) medieval hall. It comes complete with cloisters and paved garden, and is very popular for functions. / 2am; not available Sun; in-house caterers; Great Hall (700,290,192,400); Parlour (140,80,–,90); Cloisters & Garden (300,–,–,–); Library (50,30,–,25); Drawing Rm (140,80,–,90); Kings Gallery (60,–,–,30); Courtroom (70,50,–,60); Committee Rm (–,10,–,–).

Le Meridien Piccadilly W1
£M-E, (245,220,–,250)
21 Piccadilly
T 020 7851 3263
F 020 7851 3106
W hardens.com/party/lemeridienpiccadilly
E piccadillysales@lemeridien.com
Landmark hotel, near Piccadilly Circus, whose contemporary design is set against an Edwardian backdrop. It boasts a dedicated conference & banqueting floor made up of seven suites, most of which enjoy natural light. / 1am, Sun 11pm; in-house caterers; Georgian Suites (245,220,–,230); The Oak Room (200,150,–,180); Adams Suite (90,70,–,50); Edwardian Suite (200,160,–,250); Terrace Restaurant (200,150,–,–).

Mermaid Conference & Events Centre EC4
£B-M, (450,170,170,600)
Puddle Dock
T 020 7236 1919
F 020 7236 1819
W www.the-mermaid.co.uk
E sales@the-mermaid.co.uk

The Mermaid is a flexible venue in the City of London and the perfect setting for a wide range of corporate and social events. Whether you are planning a conference, drinks reception, party, or dinner our team is here to make sure the occasion will be a great success. The River Room and the Blackfriars Room have unparalleled

views of the river. / midnight; in-house caterers; Blackfriars Rm (300,170,170,–); River Rm (200,100,–,–); Studio (150,70,–,120); Miles Rm (100,70,–,100); Auditorium (400,–,–,600); Clifford Rm (300,–,–,120).

The Metropolitan W1

£M-E, (150,50,–,40)
Old Park Ln
T 020 7447 1040
F 020 7447 1042
W hardens.com/party/metropolitanhotel
E events.lon@metropolitan.como.bz

A minimalist Mayfair hotel, with five function rooms. The well-known Met Bar doesn't market itself as a venue, but it does do events during Fashion Week, and will consider others that measure up to its fashionista aspirations. / 3am; in-house caterers; no dancing; White Room (80,50,–,40); Met Bar (150,–,–,–); Met Space (50,30,–,40).

Mews of Mayfair W1

£M, (350,155,–,–)
10-11 Lancashire Court
T 020 7518 9388
W www. mewsofmayfair.com
E events@mewsofmayfair.com

Mews of Mayfair, offers all the privileges of a private institution but none of the pomp. More like a house than a club, whether you're looking for a VIP dinner for five or a private dinner for seventy, the four floors of these two converted Mews houses offer infinite possibilities. / 2am; all day; in-house caterers; Lounge (150,–,–,–); Cocktail Bar (100,–,–,–); Restaurant (80,65,–,–); Private Dining Room (40,28,–,–); Art Gallery (45,–,–,–); La Cave (25,16,–,–).

Meza W1

£M, (280,460,–,–)
100 Wardour Street
T 020 7314 4002
F 020 7314 4040
W www.danddlondon.com/restaurants/meza/about
E sohoreservations@danddlondon.com

Located in the heart of vibrant Soho, Meza Bar and Grill is the ideal venue for your event. On the site of the legendary Marquee Club, Meza continues to be one of Soho's leading venues offering delicious food, decadent cocktails and an amazing DJ line up. / 5.30pm - 2am Mon - Wed, 3am Thu - Sat; Private Dining Room (60,44,–,–); Atrium (80,60,–,–).

MIC Hotel & Conference Centre NW1

£M, (150,120,60,120)
81-103 Euston Street
T 020 7380 0001
F 020 7387 5300
W www.micentre.com
E james@micentre.com

Based in the Borough of Camden in central London and within 2 minutes walking distance of Euston station, MIC is an affordable, high quality and accessible choice of venue for your conference, event or accommodation requirements. Being a social enterprise means we have a strong commitment to environmental and ethical standards / 11pm; 7.30am; in-house caterers; music must be finished by 11pm; dancing must be finished by 11pm; licensed bar; Hilda Porter (150,60,60,120); Epworth (70,30,30,50); Alice (50,25,25,45); Wesley (30,15,15,25); Whitfield (25,12,12,20); Boadroom (–,14,–,–); Exeter (20,15,15,20); Norfolk (25,15,–,20); The Atrium (150,120,120,–); The Camden Room (–,18,–,–).

Michael Moore W1
£B, (22,16,–,–)
19 Blandford St
T 020 7224 1898
F 020 7224 0970
W hardens.com/party/mmoore
E info@michaelmoorerestaurant.com

It's not, to be honest, much to look at, but this Marylebone restaurant would make a good choice for an informal sort of event where the quality of the food was important. The eponymous chef is usually very much in evidence. There's a private room upstairs. / 1am; available from noon; in-house caterers; no amplified music; Private Rooms (22,16,–,–).

Middle Temple Hall EC4
£M-E, (500,300,225,350)
Middle Temple Lane
T 0844 858 0665
F 020 7427 4821
W www.middletemple.org.uk
E banqueting@middletemple.org.uk

Middle Temple Hall is one of the finest examples of an Elizabethan Hall in the country. This exclusive venue is the perfect place to host any kind of event. Our highly experienced team is on hand to look after your every need and help with anything that the occasion requires. / midnight; closed Aug; hirer's choice of caterer (in-house available); Prince's Room (100,–,–,–); Parliament Chamber (125,70,–,70); Queen's Rm (75,22,–,50); Hall (500,300,225,350).

Mile End Park Ecology Pavilion E3
£B-M, (220,–,–,–)
Mile End Park
T 020 7364 6573
F 020 7364 3286
W hardens.com/party/milenedparkecol

If you're looking for a large and empty East End hall for a presentation or event, this may be just the place. They're quite happy for you to provide food and drink, but note that there's little in the way of on-site facilities. (Note, the arts pavilion here is for exhibition-use only). / licences must be obtained by hirer; midnight; hirer's choice of caterer.

The Milestone Hotel & Apartments W8
£M-E, (50,40,–,–)
1 Kensington Court
T 020 7917 1000
F 020 7917 1133
W hardens.com/party/milestonehotel
E bookms@rchmail.com

This small hotel occupies a lavishly converted Victorian house near Kensington Gardens. Most rooms are in a panelled, traditional style, and there is quite a range of accommodation for smaller parties. For something a little different, you might consider a themed evening in the self-explanatory Safari Suite. / midnight; in-house caterers; no dancing; Windsor Suite (50,40,–,–); Cheneston's Restaurant (45,40,–,–); Conservatory (17,14,–,–); Oratory (12,8,–,–); Map Rm (15,8,–,–).

Milk & Honey W1
£M, (60,–,–,–)
Poland Street
T 07000 655 469
W hardens.com/party/mlkhny
E emma@mlkhny.com

One of Soho's most fashionable bars (co-owned by the founder of the New York original) operates as a members' club after 11pm. It can be hired privately, but, first you'll need to become a member – "just apply". / members club; 3am for members, 11pm for non-members; available Mon-Fri 11pm, Sat 6.30pm, not available Sun; in-house caterers; no dancing.

Millennium Gloucester Hotel SW7

£M-E, (450,300,600,500)
Harrington Gdns
T 020 7373 6030
F 020 7373 0409
W hardens.com/party/millenniumgloucesterhotel
E mcc.events@millenniumhotels.co.uk

A South Kensington hotel offering flexible banqueting facilities. These have been much extended with the Conservatory, an impressive open space with great scope for theming, and the Millennium Conference Centre. The latter offers two floors of column-free space, capable of a number of different configurations. / 1am; in-house caterers; Orchard Suite (640,450,400,500); Sentosa Suite (500,350,290,350); Conservatory (400,180,150,250).

Millennium London Mayfair W1

£M-E, (700,420,400,500)
Grosvenor Sq
T 020 7629 9400
F 020 7355 3129
W hardens.com/party/millenniumlondonmayfair
E eventssales.mayfair@millenniumhotels.co.uk

A discreetly-located hotel, which boasts quite a range of accommodation for functions. The ballroom (largest capacities shown) benefits from a private entrance. / 1am; list of caterers; Waterloo Rm (80,60,40,72); Ballroom (700,420,–,500); Manhattan Suite (75,60,–,75); Mayfair Suite (100,72,50,90); Kendal (25,12,–,–); Grosvenor Suite (–,18,–,–); Boardroom 2 & 3 (–,8,–,–).

Miller's House E3

£M-E, (100,–,–,40)
Three Mill Ln
T 020 8980 4626
F 020 8980 0725
W hardens.com/party/millershouse
E rltmt@bcos.demon.co.uk

On a small Lee Valley island, this is a Grade I-listed venue of character. Use is mainly corporate events (although film shoots also sometimes take place). / conferences, meetings & breakouts only; 6pm; in-house caterers; no music; no dancing.

The Ministry of Sound SE1

£B, (1500,200,150,250)
103 Gaunt St
T 020 7740 8728
F 020 7740 8654
W hardens.com/party/theministryofsound
E venuehire@ministryofsound.com

A famous Elephant & Castle club, which also does big business as a venue for corporate events. / 24 hrs; not available Fri & Sat; hirer's choice of caterer (in-house available).

Mint Leaf SW1

£M-E, (500,200,–,–)
1 Suffolk Pl
T 020 7930 9020
F 020 7930 6205
W hardens.com/party/mintleaf
E reservations@mintleafrestaurant.com

A large, darkly-decorated Indian bar/restaurant, just off the Haymarket – although it's just off Trafalgar Square, its hidden-away basement setting still gives it a slightly mysterious air. / in-house caterers; Private Rm (–,60,–,–).

Mint Leaf (City) EC2

£M-E, (200,60,–,–)
12 Angel Court
T 020 7600 0992
F 020 7600 6628
W hardens.com/party/mintleafcity
E reservations@mintleaflounge.com

Close to the old Stock Exchange, this extremely good-looking City Indian makes a very glam looking venue for a function. / Lounge (50,50,–,–); Mezzanine (60,60,–,–).

Momo W1

£M-E, (200,100,100,–)
25 Heddon Street
T 020 7434 4040
F 020 7287 0404
W hardens.com/party/momo

This lavish Moroccan restaurant is a key West End party place, especially for the fashion world. Exclusive hire possibilities are to hire the bar only, or to take the whole place (using

the bar for dancing). / 3am; in-house caterers; Kemia Bar (80,–,–,–).

Morgan M N7

£M, (–,57,–,–)
489 Liverpool Rd
T 020 7609 3560
W hardens.com/party/morganm

A north-Islington restaurant where the quality of the cooking by proprietor Morgan Meunier has quite a name. There is a private room, or you could book the whole place. / midnight; not available Sun D, Mon, Sat L; in-house caterers; no music; no dancing; Private Rm (–,14,–,–).

Mosimann's Academy SW11

£M-E, (80,50,–,45)
5 William Blake Hs
T 020 7326 8330
W hardens.com/party/mosimannsacademy
E academy@mosimann.com

Star chef Anton Mosimann's Batteresea HQ, which occupies a converted Victorian school building. It offers (well-catered) event possibilities, as well as cookery courses. / 11.30pm; closed Sun; in-house caterers; no music; no dancing.

Mosimann's Dining Club SW1

£M-E, (180,100,100,–)
11b West Halkin St
T 020 7235 9625
F 020 7245 6354
W hardens.com/party/mosimanndining
E sales.enquiries@mosimann.com

Impressively housed in a former chapel in Belgravia, a members' club with a series of rooms suited to events. The main dining room (available for private hire) is spectacular. / 1am; in-house caterers; no music in private dining rooms; no dancing in private dining rms; Mappin & Webb Rm (80,50,–,–); Parmigiani Fleurier Rm (60,24,–,–); Bentley Rm (–,14,–,–); Stapleford Rm (25,10,–,–); Davidoff Rm (–,4,–,–); Montblanc Rm (–,2,–,–).

Motcomb's Townhouse SW1

£M-E, (40,32,–,–)
26 Motcomb St
T 020 7235 3092
F 020 7245 6351
W hardens.com/party/motcombs
E nancy.motcombs@dial.pipex.com

A Belgravia townhouse for private dining, associated with the nearby restaurant of the same name. An attractive pine-panelled dining room suits parties of a dozen or more around a single table. / midnight; not available Sun; in-house caterers; no music; no dancing.

Mr Chow SW1

£B, (–,80,–,–)
151 Knightsbridge
T 020 7589 7347
F 020 7584 5780
W hardens.com/party/mrchow
E patricer@mrchow.com

A survivor of the swinging '60s, this Knightsbridge restaurant is known for its Chinese food, Italian waiters and high prices. For private events there are two private rooms to choose from. / midnight; available from noon; in-house caterers; no amplified music; Room 1 (–,80,–,–); Room 2 (–,60,–,–).

Museum of London EC2

£M, (550,350,–,400)
150 London Wall
T 020 7814 5613
F 020 7600 1058
W www.museumoflondon.org.uk
E venuehire@museumoflondon.org.uk

You're never short of a talking point at this large museum on the fringe of the Barbican, where exhibits range from the Lord Mayor's coach to Ms Dynamite's track suit. Recently treated to a £20m refit, there are a variety of venue options ranging from smaller screenings and meetings to really sizeable events. / Searcy's; Sackler Hall (550,350,–,400); City Gallery (150,100,–,–); Weston Theatre (–,–,–,220); Terrace Gallery (100,70,–,80); Terrace Boardroom (–,10,–,–); Garden Room (100,40,–,30).

Music Room W1

£B-M, (350,150,–,220)
26 South Molton Ln
T 020 7629 8199
F 020 7629 3279
W hardens.com/party/musicroom
E info@themusicroom.co.uk
This unusual first-floor venue is located in a Victorian building, not far from Oxford Street. It offers flexible and central space suited to most types of events. / 11pm; in-house caterers; no live bands; no cash bar.

Namco Station SE1

£M, (1200,–,–,40)
County Hall
T 020 7967 1067
F 020 7967 1060
W hardens.com/party/namcostation
E countyhall@namco.co.uk
"Fun and games on a massive scale" is the promise at this "pleasuredrome of interactive entertainment", by the London Eye. Ten pin bowling, an American pool hall and over 200 video games are among the attractions, not to mention "Europe's fastest bumper cars". / midnight; in-house, plus list of approved caterers; no alcohol in gallery area; Private Party Area (150,–,–,40).

National Army Museum SW3

£M, (300,140,90,300)
Royal Hospital Rd
T 020 7730 0717
F 020 7823 6573
W www.national-army-museum.ac.uk
E events@national-army-museum.ac.uk
A venue with martial associations and in a smart area (next to Chelsea's Royal Hospital), which comes complete with some fine military treasures and works of art. They can help you warm to the theme – gallery tours are a popular diversion, and you can book a Napoleonic-times soldier as your Master of Ceremonies. / no naked flames; some rstrictins on flowers; midnight; Crown Group; Art Gallery (300,140,90,275); Templer Centre (80,–,–,80); Lecture Theatre (120,–,–,120).

National Liberal Club SW1

£M-E, (120,200,30,140)
Whitehall Pl
T 020 7930 9871
F 020 7839 4768
W hardens.com/party/nationalliberal
E banqueting@nlc.org.uk
Especially at weekends (when access to the larger rooms is more easily obtained, albeit at additional cost), this august Victorian building, just off Whitehall, makes an interesting venue for events. It has the special advantage of a large terrace, overlooking the river. / midnight; in-house caterers; Lady Violet (70,30,30,50); David Lloyd George (120,200,–,140); Lawrence Robson Room (–,12,–,–).

National Maritime Museum SE10

£M-E, (750,500,450,450)
Romney Rd
T 020 8312 8517
F 020 8312 6572
W www.nmm.ac.uk/hospitality
E events@nmm.ac.uk
Located within the heart of the UNESCO World Heritage site of Greenwich, an impressively-located venue with a range of high-tech facilities. / no naked flames; 11pm; available from 5pm; list of caterers; no red wine at standing events; Neptune's Court (750,500,450,–); The Queen's House (150,120,–,–); Royal Observatory (150,60,–,–); Peter Harrison Planetarium (150,110,–,–).

National Portrait Gallery WC2

£E, (400,230,–,150)
2 St Martin's Pl
T 020 7306 0055
F 020 7306 0058
W hardens.com/party/nationalportraitgallery
E nmartin@npg.org.uk
Compared to many of London's major galleries, the NPG has a relatively intimate scale suited to entertaining, and offers a choice of interesting medium-sized spaces. The top-floor Portrait Restaurant has a wonderful panoramic view of the West End. / 11.30pm; available from 6.30pm Mon-Wed; list of caterers; no dancing; red wine in restaurant only; Tudor Gallery (80,–,–,–); Victorian Galleries (150,100,–,–); Contemporary Galleries (350,80,–,–); Ondaatje Wing

Theatre (–,–,–,150); c17 & c18 Galleries (400,100,–,–).

National Theatre SE1

£M, (120,90,–,1150)

South Bank

Ⓣ 020 7452 3264

Ⓕ 020 7452 3565

Ⓦ www.nationaltheatre.org.uk

Ⓔ functions@nationaltheatre.org.uk

Most entertaining at this South Bank landmark takes place around shows. At other times, however, the theatre's front-of-house spaces are available for events and a spectacular new roof-top event space, The Deck, with panoramic views and outdoor terraces, is exclusively available weekdays and weekends regardless of performances. / midnight (extensions available); some areas available subject to constraints of current production; in-house caterers; background music only in The Deck; no dancing in The Deck; Lyttelton Exhibition Level (350,–,–,–); Terrace Bar & Food (200,120,–,–); The Deck (120,90,–,100).

Natural History Museum SW7

£M-E, (1200,650,450,209)

Cromwell Rd

Ⓣ 0844 873 4972

Ⓕ 020 7942 5070

Ⓦ www.nhm.ac.uk/exclusive-events

Ⓔ exclusive-events@nhm.ac.uk

This famous museum offers a great range of possibilities for large events. It's most famous for dinners in its dramatic Central Hall, but the new Darwin Centre – with large atrium, vast concrete 'cocoon', and landscaped courtyard – can be used for a pre-dinner reception, or as a venue in its own right. / 1am (later available); evenings only in Central Hall & earth Galleries & Darwin Centre; list of caterers; Central Hall (1200,650,450,–); Earth Galleries (500,180,80,–); Darwin Centre (350,150,–,–); Flett Events Theatre (–,–,–,209).

The New Cavendish Club W1

£M, (100,80,–,80)

44 Great Cumberland Pl

Ⓣ 020 7723 0391

Ⓕ 020 7262 8411

Ⓦ hardens.com/party/newcavendishclub

Ⓔ events@newcavendishclub.co.uk

Near Marble Arch, a club building whose rooms may be used for company meetings and a range of social events. For summer drinks parties, you can use the roof garden. A member must be present at any private event. / midnight; in-house caterers; Library (20,12,–,20).

New End Theatre NW3

£B-M, (80,–,–,84)

27 New End

Ⓣ 020 7472 5800

Ⓕ 020 7794 4044

Ⓦ hardens.com/party/newendtheatre

Ⓔ info@newendtheatre.co.uk

Originally a mortuary for the New End Hospital, this Hampstead building was converted to a theatre in 1974. It offers an intimately-scaled venue, available subject to the constraints of performances. / restricted availability; 11pm; available Sun & Mon only, but conferences any daytime; hirer's choice of caterer (in-house available); Bar (80,–,–,–).

New Players Theatre WC2

£B-M, (–,125,–,275)

The Arches

Ⓣ 020 7930 5868

Ⓦ hardens.com/party/newplayerstheatre

Ⓔ info@newplayerstheatre.com

An intimate and charming theatre, under the arches at Charing Cross, refurbished in plush Victorian style. Dining facilities are quite extensive. / restricted availability; 3am; available subject to constraints of current production; in-house caterers; Players Bar And Restaurant (–,125,–,–).

Newbury Racecourse RG14
£M, (900,850,850,1000)
Newbury
T 01635 40015
F 01635 528354
W hardens.com/party/newburyracecourse
E events@newbury-racecourse.co.uk
Located on the M4 corridor, with its own railway station and free parking; the Berkshire Stand, Hampshire Stand and Grandstand all overlook the course, and can hold events from 10 to 1000 guests including dinners, weddings, conferences, outdoor, Christmas and summer events. / 12 extension available; in-house caterers; Grandstand Ground Floor (1000,600,800,1000); Grandstand First Floor (700,–,–,–); Grandstand Second Floor (700,500,600,700); Hennessy Suite (350,200,250,300); Royal Box (80,40,50,50); Berkshire Stand Concourse (300,200,250,300); Paddoc View (200,80,100,150); Long Room (200,130,150,–); Fred Winter (100,80,100,80); Private Boxes (16,10,–,12).

Newham City Farm E16
£B, (50,50,–,–)
King George Av
T 020 7474 4960
F 020 7474 4960
W hardens.com/party/newhamcityfarm
E julie.lummis@newham.gov.uk
The Visitors Centre of this city farm has a room particularly suited to children's parties (capacity shown). The whole venue, could, however, be made available for a suitable function. / 4pm; closed Mon; hirer's choice of caterer; no music; no dancing; no alcohol.

No 4 Hamilton Place W1
£M, (300,200,170,250)
4 Hamilton Pl
T 020 7670 4314
F 020 7670 4349
W hardens.com/party/nohamiltonplace
E aggi.bailey@4hp.org.uk
Much of the original grandeur of this impressive c19 townhouse, just off Hyde Park Corner, remains and it's most used for conferences, meetings and exhibitions. A terrace opens off the Argyll room, which can be used for a reception or even a barbecue. / midnight; in-house caterers; no music on terrace; Argyll Rm & Terrace (200,120,80,100); Council Rm & Foyer (100,60,–,60); Bill Boeing Rm (300,200,170,250); Sopwith Rm (70,40,–,40); Handley Page Rm (70,40,–,40).

No 5 W1
£M-E, (400,80,–,–)
5 Cavendish Sq
T 020 7079 5000
F 020 7079 5001
W hardens.com/party/no5
E events@no5ltd.com
'Townhouse' is really too small a word for this palace, just north of Oxford Street, which has been converted into a bar-club-restaurant-hotel in no-expense-spared style. / 3am; hirer's choice of caterer; Private Dining Rm (–,24,–,–); Rooftop Terrace (50,–,–,–).

No. 11 Cavendish Square W1
£M-E, (200,300,120,225)
11 Cavendish Square
T 020 7307 2474
F 020 7307 2815
W hardens.com/party/no11cavendishsq
E venue@11cavendishsq.com
A grade II listed townhouse on a square just off Regent Street that's nowadays used for events: from weddings to business seminars. As well as those rooms listed, the venue has 25 other spaces (including 2 theatres) for groups of 2-200. / The Burdett Theatre (150,300,120,225); The Conservatory & Courtyard Garden (200,100,–,–); Friends' Lounge (100,–,–,–); President's Room (24,24,–,–); Treasurer's Room (16,16,–,–).

Nobu Berkeley Street W1
£M-E, (400,200,–,–)
15 Berkeley St
T 020 7290 9222
F 020 7290 9223
W hardens.com/party/nobuberkeley
E nobuberkeley@noburestaurants.com
The newer (and more dramatically-styled) of the two Mayfair outposts of the fashionable international sushi-and-more chain. For a big-budget affair, you can hire the downstairs bar, the upstairs restaurant, or both. / 2am; not available

Sun; in-house caterers; no amplified music; no dancing.

Noel Coward Theatre WC2

£M, (25,–,–,886)
St Martin's Ln
T 020 7759 8010
F 020 7759 8087
W hardens.com/party/noelcowardtheatre
E hospitality@delmack.co.uk
A Victorian theatre (formerly known as the Albery), available for hire subject to the constraints of the current production. / restricted availability; 10.30pm; available daytime and Sun evenings; Mackintosh's; Royal Rm (10,–,–,–); Wyndham Rm (8,–,–,–); Sir Donald Albery Rm (25,–,–,–).

North Pole SE10

£B, (250,25,–,–)
131 Greenwich High Road
T 0872 148 5345
W hardens.com/party/northpole
A Greenwich bar/restaurant whose different areas offer very different styles for an event, from its basement DJ bar (the 'South Pole'), to its more loungey ground floor, to its traditionally decorated first floor dining room. / VIP (25,25,–,–).

Notting Hill Brasserie W11

£M-E, (–,80,–,–)
92 Kensington Park Rd
T 020 7229 4481
F 020 7221 1246
W hardens.com/party/nhb
E enquiries@nottinghillbrasserie.com
Rather grander than the name suggests, an imposing townhouse-restaurant of good quality, offering a flexible range of private dining opportunities. / 11pm; in-house caterers; no amplified music; no dancing; Semi-Private Areas By Bar (–,32,–,–).

Number Sixteen SW7

£M-E, (30,10,–,–)
16 Sumner Place
T 020 7589 5232
F 020 7584 8615
W hardens.com/party/16hotel
E events@firmdale.com
A small South Kensington hotel, whose conservatory is a popular venue for summer drinks parties. / 10pm; in-house caterers; no amplified music; no dancing.

Ochre EC4

£B, (200,90,–,–)
2-3 Creed Ln
T 020 7248 7799
W hardens.com/party/faucetinn
E ochre@faucetinn.com
A modern City bar/restaurant, with a basement private room. On Saturday night, you can hire the whole place. / 2am; in-house caterers; Function Rm (40,30,–,–).

The October Gallery WC1

£B, (150,80,–,–)
24 Old Gloucester St
T 020 7831 1618
F 020 7405 1851
W hardens.com/party/octobergallery
E rentals@octobergallery.co.uk
This former school, which has a small courtyard, is a good size to be taken over in its entirety, or the individual galleries could suit a wide range of smaller functions. Events with some kind of artistic tie-in are particularly encouraged. / no weddings; 10.30pm; available from 6.30pm; hirer's choice of caterer; no amplified music; no dancing.

Odeon Leicester Square WC2

£M, (50,1943,–,–)
24-26 Leicester Square
T 0871 7321 6237
W hardens.com/party/odeonleicestersq
From private film premieres to conferences – screening facilities don't come much better than at this famous cinema, at the heart of the West End. / in-house caterers; Meeting Room (50,25,–,–); Screen 1 (–,1943,–,–); Screens 2-6 (–,60,–,–).

Odette's NW1

£M, (–,30,–,–)
130 Regent's Park Rd
T 020 75868569
F 020 7722 5388
W hardens.com/party/odettes
E odettes@vpmg.com
One of north London's smartest and

more romantic restaurants, a Primrose Hill spot well-suited to private celebrations. / 10.30pm; not available Mon ; in-house caterers; no music; no dancing; Conservatory (–,30,–,–); Private Rm (–,8,–,–).

Ognisko SW7

£B-M, (300,150,–,–)
55 Exhibition Rd
T 020 7589 4635
F 020 7581 7926
W hardens.com/party/ognisko
E info@ognisko.com

For old-fashioned charm, this South Kensington emigrés' club (formerly known as the Polish Club) scores very highly. Parts have been refurbished in recent years, but it remains a characterful, quite grand, mid-priced venue for most kinds of events. The restaurant has a terrace, and is popular for summer cocktails. / 1am; in-house caterers; Dining Rm (200,150,–,–); Ballroom (–,150,–,–).

Old Billingsgate EC3

£M-E, (2000,1700,1200,1000)
1 Old Billingsgate Walk
T 020 7283 2800
F 020 7626 1095
W hardens.com/party/oldbillingsgate
E info@oldbillingsgate.co.uk

On the site of the ancient fishmarket, a very large and flexible space, not too distant from Tower Bridge, and with some impressive river views. / 3am; list of caterers; Grand Hall, Mezzanine And Terrace (2000,1700,1200,1000); Gallery (300,150,–,200); Vault (900,600,–,–).

Old Finsbury Town Hall EC1

£B-M, (300,200,200,220)
Rosebery Avenue
T 020 7713 7710 ext 2234
F 020 72786727
W hardens.com/party/finsburyth
E events@theurdangacademy.com

By day used as a school for performing arts, this self-explanatory venue, recently renovated, offers a number of rooms for smaller to medium-size events (including weddings). / restricted availability; midnight, Fri- Sat 2am; Great Hall (300,200,200,220); Council Chamber (100,60,60,100); Wedding Room (30,–,–,20); Yellow Room (80,40,–,40).

Old Operating Theatre, Museum & Herb Garret SE1

£B-M, (60,–,–,–)
9a St Thomas's St
T 020 7188 2679
F 020 7378 8383
W hardens.com/party/garret
E curator@thegarret.org.uk

Bizarre and fascinating, a c19 operating theatre, up tortuous spiral stairs in the belfry of a church near London Bridge. It now houses a collection of surgical instruments and pickled internal organs – tough to beat for a drinks party with a touch of the macabre. / available from 5pm; hirer's choice of caterer; no amplified music; no dancing; alcohol only in the garrett.

Old Royal Naval College SE10

£M-E, (480,480,250,–)
Greenwich
T 020 8269 2131
F 020 8269 4757
W www.greenwichfoundation.org.uk
E leiths.greenwich@compass-group.co.uk

This Baroque set piece offers a setting as magnificent as any in London. The Painted Hall is modestly described as "probably the finest dining hall in the Western world", and it's certainly impressive. The King William Restaurant (in an undercroft) offers plainer, but still elegant, accommodation. / 11pm; Leith's; King William Restaurant (150,120,120,–); Queen Mary Ante Rm (480,200,250,–); Admiral's House (50,50,–,–).

The Old Sessions House EC1

£M, (200,120,70,180)
22 Clerkenwell Grn
T 020 7250 1212
F 020 7253 2302
W hardens.com/party/sessionshouse
E conference@sessionshouse.com

An imposing listed building overlooking Clerkenwell Green, this former courthouse offers a range of function accommodation, in quite a traditional style. / 11pm; in-house caterers; Westminster (200,120,–,180); London Rm (100,40,40,70); Jailers Rm (80,60,–,60); Recorder Rm (40,30,–,40).

The Old Thameside Inn SE1

£B, (300,–,–,–)
Clink St
T 020 7403 4243
F 020 7407 2063
W hardens.com/party/oldthamessideinn

A South Bank riverside pub, with a large, stone-floored cellar bar available for private parties (and where you can also have a disco). A section of the terrace overlooking the river can be roped off for 80 or so people. / 11pm; in-house caterers; Ground Floor (300,–,–,–); Cellar Bar (150,–,–,–); Terrace (80,–,–,–).

Old Truman Brewery E1

£B-M, (1000,800,800,700)
91 Brick Ln
T 020 7770 6100
F 020 7770 6005
W hardens.com/party/oldtrumanbrewery
E events@trumanbrewery.com

On the City's eastern fringe, a self-descriptive venue, with 17 different spaces for hire, used for a wide variety of events. / 1am; hirer's choice of caterer; Boiler House (500,–,–,–); Bridge (220,80,–,150).

One Aldwych WC2

£M-E, (100,50,100,60)
1 Aldwych
T 020 7300 0700
F 020 7300 1084
W hardens.com/party/onealdwych
E privatedining@onealdwych.com

A very central location is just one of the distinguishing features of this comfortably understated Covent Garden design-hotel, which offers a selection of smaller accommodation. / midnight; in-house caterers; no music in some rooms.; Private Rms 1&2 (100,50,–,60); Private Rm 3 (50,30,–,30); Screen Room (–,–,–,30).

One Birdcage Walk SW1

£M, (200,150,–,210)
1 Birdcage Walk
T 020 7973 1248
F 020 7304 6914
W hardens.com/party/onebirdcagewalk
E onebirdcagewalk@imeche.org

Although the common parts and entrance of this prettily-located St James's institute (of Mechanical Engineers) are rather, well, institutional, the panelled Council room, the Hinton room (park views) and the odd but striking Marble Hall are all well suited to quite grand entertaining – the last being the best place for receptions. / 10pm; weekdays only; Charlton House; Marble Hall/gallery (200,70,–,–); Hinton Rm (60,40,–,60); Council (80,48,–,70); Courses Rm (–,22,–,40); Lecture Theatre (–,–,–,210); Library (200,150,–,–); Napier (60,50,–,50).

One Great George Street SW1

£M, (400,260,220,400)
Westminster
T 020 7665 2323
F 020 7976 0697
W hardens.com/party/onegreatgeorgestreet
E info@onegreatgeorgestreet.com

The high-ceilinged lobby, staircase, and, in particular, the huge marbled Great Hall of this impressive building, just off Parliament Square, all possess much neo-classical ('30s) grandeur. It suits a whole range of events, from grand dinners to weddings, and the whole would make a good setting for a ball. Extensive meeting facilities also available. / 11pm; in-house caterers; Great Hall (400,260,220,300); Smeaton Rm (150,100,60,150); Brunel Rm or Council Rm (100,80,–,100); Stephenson Rm (30,24,–,30); Telford Theatre (–,–,–,240).

The 108 SE10

£M-E, (900,500,–,–)
Peninsula Square
T 020 8305 3091
F 020 8858 2507
W hardens.com/party/108
E info@the108.co.uk

Within the O2, what's long been planned as a highly flexible, purpose-built event space, available 24/7. As of mid 2010, it's still under construction with no definitive launch date. / *24 hour license available; in-house caterers; list of approved musicians.*

1 Lombard Street EC3

£M-E, (450,200,150,–)

1 Lombard St

T 020 7929 6611

F 020 7929 6622

W hardens.com/party/1lombardstreet

E el@jessen.co.uk

A well known restaurant in the heart of the City. Located in an impressive former banking hall, it is well geared-up for larger-scale events. / *1am; in-house caterers; no restrictions, play background music; Private Room (60,40,–,–).*

One Marylebone Road NW1

£M, (350,200,200,–)

1 Marylebone Road

T 020 7380 1663

F 020 7380 1662

W hardens.com/party/onemaryleboneroad

E events@onemaryleboneroad.com

A conversion of Sir John Soane's former Holy Trinity Church, this impressive deconsecrated building in Marylebone has been an events venue since 2007 and each of its spaces provides a 'blank canvas' for theming. A sizeable garden adds to the possibilities. / *midnight; list of caterers; Soane Hall (200,200,200,–); Baccarat Room (120,60,120,–).*

One Mayfair W1

£M-E, (650,300,300,400)

North Audley Street

T 020 7380 1663

F 020 7380 1662

W hardens.com/party/onemayfair

A new sister venue to One Marylebone, also inhabiting a church – this time St Mark's – a Grade I listed building deconsecrated in the '70s. It's a big space, well-suited to private celebrations or themed occasions. / *Grand Hall (650,300,300,400); Mezzanine (400,200,200,150).*

One Moorgate Place EC2

£M, (600,250,200,325)

Moorgate Pl

T 020 7920 8613

F 020 7920 8629

W hardens.com/party/charteredaccountantshall

E events@onemoorgateplace.com

An elegant, attractive and extremely well-maintained City complex, which includes two interesting, traditional-style rooms (Members' and Main Reception) and a tasteful modern hall. The restaurant is also available in the evenings for private hire. / *11pm (can extend); in-house caterers; Great Hall (600,250,–,325); Main Reception Rm (100,50,40,70); Members' Rm (70,28,–,40); Small Reception Rm (35,18,–,–).*

One Whitehall Place SW1

£M-E, (600,250,180,250)

One Whitehall Pl

T 020 7451 9301

F 020 7839 3366

W hardens.com/party/onewhitehallplace

E onewhitehallplace@guoman.co.uk

Sumptuous Grade I listed Victorian building, now exclusively used for functions (including weddings). The balconies of the River Room and the Reading and Writing Rooms have views of Whitehall Gardens and the Thames, and there is a fine library, with minstrels' gallery. / *1am; in-house caterers; Gladstone Library (350,250,150,250); Whitehall Suite (250,250,150,250); Reading And Writing Rms (Sold In Conjunction With Gladstone Library) (250,150,80,140); Meston Suite (80,70,50,70); River Rm (80,70,50,70).*

One Wimpole Street W1

£M-E, (200,110,90,300)

1 Wimpole Street

T 020 7290 2951

F 020 7290 2959

W hardens.com/party/onewimpolestreet

E conference@rsm.ac.uk

The home of the Royal Society of Medicine, just north of Oxford Street. It offers a wide range of spaces for events and meetings of a, business and social nature. / *11pm; in-house caterers; no amplified music; Lecture Theatre (–,–,–,300); Max Rayne Auditorium (–,–,–,150); The Wimpole*

Rm (100,50,–,60); Cavendish Boardroom (–,14,–,14); Max Rayne Foyer (80,40,–,–); Garden Rm (50,50,90,50); Lower Atrium Theatre (–,–,–,50); Marcus Beck Library (–,–,–,30).

Orangery (Holland Park) W8

£M, (150,80,–,100)

Holland Park

T 020 7603 1123 or 020 77315282
F 020 7371 2467
W www.rbkc.gov.uk/museums
E enquiries@cooksandpartners.co.uk

Situated within the grounds of Holland Park lies the Orangery Gallery – a tranquil and elegant room flooded with natural light. Formerly the summer ballroom of the fourth Lord Holland, this prestigious venue is available to hire for corporate and private events including weddings. A marquee may be added to the lawn to extend numbers. / 11.30pm; Cooks & Partners Ltd, list of caterers; no amplified music; no dancing.

Orangery (Kensington Palace) W8

£M-E, (300,150,120,–)

Kensington Palace

T 020 3166 6115
F 020 3166 6110
W hardens.com/party/orangerykp
E kensingtonpalace@hrp.org.uk

Beautifully situated, at the back of the Palace, this long, white-painted, Queen Anne summer house is a lovely venue, nowadays made more generally available than once it was. / no naked flames; 10.30pm; available evenings only; list of caterers.

Osteria dell'Arancio SW10

£M, (100,85,–,–)

383 King's Rd

T 020 7349 8111
W hardens.com/party/osteriadellarancio

This Chelsea Italian has a particular name for the quality of its wine list. Above the informal downstairs, there's an agreeable dining room for a special dinner, perhaps accompanied by a wine tasting, or you can hire the whole restaurant. / Upstairs (–,30,–,–).

Osterley Park & House TW7

£M-E, (–,300,–,–)

Jersey Rd

T 020 8232 5050
F 020 8232 5080
W hardens.com/party/osterley
E osterley@nationaltrust.org.uk

Set in 350 acres of landscaped park and farmland with ornamental lakes and woodland, this house, which was re-built in 1761, is one of London's best-kept secrets. Put up a marquee, and you can have a dinner dance for up to 250. / 11.30pm; in-house, plus list of approved caterers.

The Oval SE11

£M, (600,510,380,500)

Kennington

T 020 7820 5737
F 020 7735 7769
W hardens.com/party/oval
E enquiries@ovalevents.com

The banqueting suites – many overlooking the pitch – inside the OCS stand provide the largest event spaces at this famous ground, and the roof terrace is a good summer option. Some of the smaller more characterful and historic spaces are to be found inside the Brit Insurance Oval Pavilion. / 11pm; Facilities Management Catering.

Oxford & Cambridge Club SW1

£M, (80,70,60,–)

71 Pall Mall

T 020 7930 5151
W hardens.com/party/oxbridge
E club@oxfordandcambridgeclub.co.uk

Those who spent their salad days at the Varsity (or who have friends who did) should bear this imposing St James's institution in mind for an event. A member must be present at any function. / members club; midnight; in-house caterers; no amplified music; Edward VII (25,18,–,–).

Oxford House E2
£B-M, (200,100,–,120)
Derbyshire St
T 020 7739 9001
F 020 7729 0435
W hardens.com/party/oxfordhouse
E room.bookings@oxfordhouse.org.uk
Not far from Bethnal Green tube, this is a pleasant, modern arts centre offering a good range of possibilities for medium-size events. / 10pm, Sat 10am- 2pm, closed Sun; in-house caterers; no cash bar, no alcohol outside; Theatre (–,–,–,–); Scott Rm (–,35,–,45); Classroom (–,–,–,20); Basement Gallery (80,–,–,–).

Oxo Tower SE1
£M-E, (250,150,–,–)
Barge House St
T 020 7803 3888
F 020 7803 3838
W hardens.com/party/oxotower
The views from this famous South Bank restaurant (with terraces overlooking the river) really are without equal. From the private hire point of view, the most obvious option here is a large private drinks party. / in-house caterers; Restaurant (350,150,–,–); Brasserie (350,150,–,–).

Pacha SW1
£M, (1000,180,150,230)
205 Victoria St
T 020 7284 0513
W hardens.com/party/pachalondon
E info@blondeproductions.co.uk
"The most glamorous nightclub in the world" – well, that's what they say – now occupies the former dance-hall site which older groovers may remember as the SW1 Club. Now substantially upgraded, it can cater for a large variety of events at this very central site, adjacent to Victoria Station. / 3am; Last Supper Catering; Main Rm (700,180,–,230); Funky Rm (200,–,–,40); Terrace (150,–,–,–).

Pacific Oriental EC2
£M-E, (450,300,200,–)
52 Threadneedle Street
T 0871 704 4060
F 0871 704 4061
W hardens.com/party/pacificoriental
E pacificoriental@orientalrestaurantgroup.com
Oriental restaurant in the heart of the City. Its spacious premises – a former banking hall – would well suit events. / 11pm; in-house caterers; Mezzanine Floor (150,120,–,–); Ground Floor (300,180,–,–).

Painters' Hall EC4
£M, (250,156,130,200)
9 Little Trinity Ln
T 020 7236 6258
F 020 726 0500
W hardens.com/party/paintershall
E beadle@painters-hall.co.uk
A relatively modest – and quite flexible – livery hall. The décor of the hall itself (re-opened in the '60s) is quite sparse, but the small Painted Chamber is particularly charming. / 11pm; no Aug bookings; Life's Kitchen; no alcohol outside; Painted Chamber (20,14,–,14); The Court Rm (150,60,–,80).

Palace Theatre W1
£M, (100,50,–,1400)
Shaftesbury Ave
T 020 7379 4981
F 020 7379 4982
W hardens.com/party/palacetheatre
E laura.acton@reallyuseful.co.uk
Sunday evening concerts and post-film launch parties are among the private events accommodated at this impressive theatre – opened in 1891 as the Royal English Opera House – on the fringe of Soho. / restricted availability; 12am; available subject to constraints of current production; in-house caterers; D'Oyly Carte Bar (100,50,–,–); VIP Suite (–,10,–,–).

Pantechnicon Rooms SW1

£M, (–,14,–,–)

10 Motcomb Street

T 020 7730 6074

W hardens.com/party/pantechnicon

E reservations@thepantechnicon.com

This Belgravia pub is decked out in a cosy, comfy, luxurious style akin to a St James's club. Though prices are not bargain basement, an event in one of the upstairs rooms here offers a fair degree of affordable luxury.

Paradise by Way of Kensal Green W10

£B, (400,100,–,–)

19 Kilburn Lane

T 020 8969 0098

F 020 8960 9968

W hardens.com/party/paradise

E shelley@thecolumbogroup.com

This vast, trendy gastropub can cater for small and large events alike. There are numerous spaces to hire, including private rooms, rooms with dance floors, karaoke rooms and hidden rooftop terraces. / Mon-Fri, midnight, Thu 1am, Sat-Sun 2am; in-house caterers.

Paramount WC1

£M, (450,150,90,175)

Centre Point

T 020 7420 2904

F 020 7420 2919

W www.paramount.uk.net

E level31@paramount.uk.net

Paramount's Level 31 at the top of Centre Point is a self-contained 4,550 sq ft space created by award winning British designer Tom Dixon, exclusively for private hire. Offering spectacular views across London throughout the day and night, Level 31 can accommodate between 50-500 guests for a wide variety of events from weddings to corporate receptions. / Mon-Wed 1am, Thu-Sat 2am, Sun 12am, 24-hour license available; 24 hours; in-house caterers; Level 31 (450,150,90,175); Red Room (–,24,–,–); Viewing Gallery (70,–,–,–).

Park Crescent Conference Centre W1

£M, (600,280,120,280)

229 Great Portland Street

T 020 7631 8306

F 020 7631 8307

W hardens.com/party/parkcrescentconferencecentre

E conference@ish.org.uk

Very near one of the gates to Regent's Park, an elegantly-housed seven-room conference centre, with modern facilities. / 1am; list of caterers; no dancing after 1 am; The Gulbekian Room (150,60,–,100); The Theatre (450,220,120,280); The Club Room (100,40,–,50).

Park Inn London Russell Square WC1

£M, (220,150,150,200)

92 Southampton Row

T 020 7400 3808

F 020 7400 3817

W hardens.com/party/parkinnrussellsq

E meeting.russellsquare@rezidorparkinn.com

Formerly known as the Bonnington.

One of the nicer Bloomsbury hotels, which, with its 14 function rooms, can accommodate a wide variety of events. (Refurbishment of their meeting rooms will be complete in November 2010.) / 1am; in-house caterers.

The Park Lane Hotel W1
£M-E, (1200,700,390,500)
112 Piccadilly
T 020 7290 7294
F 020 7290 7566
W hardens.com/party/theparklanehotel
E events.centrallondon@sheraton.com
Not far from Hyde Park corner, a large and comfortably old-fashioned hotel whose star feature is the beautiful Art Deco Ballroom. / 2am; in-house caterers; Ballroom (1200,700,390,500); Balcony Suite (60,60,–,50); Tudor Rose Rm (250,200,150,160); Oak Rm (120,90,50,90); Smart Rms (–,22,–,22); Orchard Suite (60,42,–,60); Mirror Rm (50,40,–,30); Drawing Rm (30,24,–,18).

Park Plaza County Hall SE1
£M-E, (120,80,64,100)
1 Addington Street
T 020 7021 1800
F 020 7021 1801
W hardens.com/party/parkplazacountyhall
E ppchres@pphe.com
Next to County Hall, this modern south bank 400-bedroom hotel offers a good location, and a variety of meeting and conference rooms (largest listed) for conferences and private dining. / in-house caterers.

Park Plaza Westminster SE1
£M-E, (1400,1000,800,1400)
200 Westminster Bridge Road
T 0844 415 6790
F 0844 415 6791
W hardens.com/party/parkplazawestminster
E ppwlres@pphe.com
Opened in 2010, this new hotel has great views of Westminster Bridge from its public spaces. Ironically, its stand-out attraction from a banqueting point of view is subterranean, in the form of its huge ballroom. It also has myriads of conference options, with 20 suites and 11 boardrooms. / 1am; in-house caterers; Ballroom (1400,1000,800,1400).

Parkstead House SW15
£M-E, (1500,1000,1000,300)
Holybourne Avenue
T 020 8392 3505
F 020 8392 3746
W hardens.com/party/parksteadhouse
E info@parksteadhouse.co.uk
The flexibility of Parkstead House enables party and conference organisers to tailor their events to suit the client's needs, with a wide range of rooms in Grade I listed buildings, a stunning Georgian Villa, and vast grounds and lecture theatres. / no red wine in corridor; 1am; list of caterers; dancing in ground floor rooms and bar only; Parkstead Lawns (1500,1000,1000,–); Richmond Room (100,50,–,–); Loyola Room (100,80,60,80); Manresa Hall (200,150,150,80); Ponsonby Room (40,60,–,60); Cluttons Corridor (50,–,–,–); Central Courtyard (500,300,–,–); Ruskin Room (40,30,–,–); Bessborough Room (40,60,–,60).

Parliament Square (RICS) SW1
£M, (135,80,–,130)
12 Gt George St
T 020 7334 3875
F 020 7334 3871
W hardens.com/party/parliamentsquarerics
E venues@rics.org
Just off Parliament Square, the home of the Royal Institution of Chartered Surveyors offers traditional Victorian rooms with an easy-going atmosphere. The dark-panelled Lecture Hall is the best room and is popular for receptions. / midnight; Compass; Lecture Hall (120,40,–,100); Brussels Room (40,25,–,40); New York/Hong Kong Rooms (–,12,–,–); Council Chamber (120,30,–,100); Dubai (–,10,–,–); President's Suite and its Terrace (–,–,–,–).

Pasha N1
£M, (150,78,–,–)
301 Upper St
T 020 7226 1454
F 020 7226 1617
W hardens.com/party/pasha
E thepasha@yahoo.co.uk
A friendly Turkish restaurant in Islington, handily-sized for taking

over in its entirety. / *in-house caterers; no amplified music; no dancing.*

Patio W12

£B, (–,50,–,–)
5 Goldhawk Rd
T 020 8743 5194
F 020 8743 5194
W hardens.com/party/patiorestaurant

Fun Shepherd's Bush institution – a Polish party restaurant – whose cheap prices for hearty nosh and vodka, plus charming service have earned it a deserved festive reputation. For exclusive hires, you can take over the basement or the whole place. / *12.30am; not available Sat & Sun L; in-house caterers; no music; no dancing; Basement (–,40,–,–).*

Pattersons's W1

£M, (90,80,–,–)
4 Mill St
T 020 7499 1308
F 020 7491 2122
W hardens.com/party/pattersons
E enquiries@pattersonsrestaurant.com

A Mayfair restaurant, in contemporary style. Being family-run, it's a touch more personal in its approach than many of the venues which have such central locations. The private function room downstairs is suitable for quiet dinners and discos alike. / *1am; in-house caterers; no amplified music; no dancing; Function Rm (40,22,–,–).*

The Penthouse WC2

£M-E, (850,–,–,–)
1 Leicester Sq
T 020 7734 0900
W hardens.com/party/penthouselondon
E jason@thepenthouselondon.com

Recently expanded, a prominently located West End nightclub with great views from the 6th, 7th and 8th floors of 1 Leicester Square. You can hire the venue floor by floor or in its entirety. / *3am; hirer's choice of caterer (in-house available).*

Pestana Chelsea Bridge SW8

£M-E, (500,350,210,420)
354 Queenstown Road
T 020 7062 8000
F 020 7978 2430
W hardens.com/party/pestanachelseabridge
E res.uk@pestana.com

On the Thames near Battersea Park, this modern 4-star property is the flagship of a Portuguese hotel chain. It has 6 meeting and banqueting rooms, all with natural light, accommodating events for from 10 to 500 people. / *1am; in-house caterers.*

The Petersham TW10

£M-E, (70,26,–,35)
Nightingale Ln
T 020 8940 7471
F 020 8939 1002
W hardens.com/party/petershamhotel
E enq@petershamhotel.co.uk

An intriguing Victorian building, prettily located, and with a number of pleasantly furnished rooms for functions, some with charming views. The Claret Room is appropriately housed, in the cellars. / *11.30pm; in-house caterers; no amplified music; no dancing; River Rm (70,–,–,35); Terrace Suite (70,26,–,35); Cellars (35,16,–,–); Meeting Rm (–,–,–,30).*

Pewterers' Hall EC2

£M, (150,100,72,110)
Oat Ln
T 020 7397 8198
W hardens.com/party/pewterershall
E beadle@pewterers.org.uk

A mid-sized '60s livery hall, with panelling from an earlier hall. It is available for dinners and receptions. / *11pm; Richmond Caterers; no amplified music; no dancing; Court Room (–,–,–,–); Livery Room (–,–,–,–).*

Philbeach Hall SW5

£B, (300,220,–,–)
51 Philbeach Gdns
T 020 7373 4631
F 020 7341 9889
W hardens.com/party/philbeachhall
E dropin@stcuthbertscentre.org.uk

Especially in the 'fashionable SWs', it's no easy task to find do-your-

own-catering venues with fully-equipped kitchens. All the more worth knowing about this elegant church hall, in a listed building just a minute's walk from Earl's Court tube. / midnight; evenings and weekends only; hirer's choice of caterer.

Photographers' Gallery W1

£B-M, (300,50,–,80)
16 - 18 Ramillies Street
T 0845 262 1618
F 020 7734 2884
W hardens.com/party/photogallery
E info@photonet.org.uk

This modern space, near Oxford Circus, is the largest gallery in London devoted to photography, and is most obviously suited to receptions. An autumn 2010 refurbishment is planned, after which more spaces will be available for private hire. / 9.30pm; available Mon-Wed, Sat & Sun after 6.30pm, after 8pm on Thu & Fri; hirer's choice of caterer (in-house available).

Phyllis Court RG9

£M-E, (300,250,40,250)
Marlow Road
T 01491 570511
F 01491 570528
W hardens.com/party/phylliscourt

Next to the Thames overlooking the famous Henley Royal Regatta course, this very civilised club has large banqueting facilities, well suited either to social events or somewhat less formal business occasions. / Ballroom (300,250,–,250); Grandstand Pavilion (130,100,40,80); Finlay (100,70,–,60); Thames Room (60,50,–,60); Kennet Room (–,–,–,16).

Piccolino W1

£M, (150,100,–,–)
21 Heddon Street
T 020 7287 4029
F 020 7734 8066
W www.piccolinorestaurants.co.uk
E heddonst.events@ircplc.co.uk

Located a stone's throw from the hustle and bustle of Regent Street the Private Dining Room in this modern Italian brasserie is ideal for guests who want to enjoy authentic Italian food in their own privacy. Seating up to 40, standing up to 60 it is the perfect setting for corporate/private functions. / 11pm, late license available; all day; in-house caterers; Private Room (60,40,–,–).

Piccolino - Exchange Square EC2

£M, (40,110,–,225)
11 Exchange Square
T 020 7375 2568
F 020 7375 1975
W www.piccolinorestaurants.co.uk
E piccolinoexchangesq.events@ircplc.co.uk

Located near to the arches of Liverpool Street Station this vibrant Italian Restaurant & Bar offers Private Dining on the mezzanine up to 22 seated, 40 standing. At the weekend guests can hire the entire restaurant, up to 200 people making it the ideal venue for a large corporate event/celebratory party-Italian style! / 11pm, late license available; all day; in-house caterers; no dancing; Private Room (40,22,–,–).

Pied à Terre W1

£B-M, (60,40,–,–)
34 Charlotte St
T 020 7636 1178
F 020 7916 1171
W hardens.com/party/piedaterre
E info@pied-a-terre.co.uk

A Fitzrovia restaurant whose cuisine is amongst the best in town. There's a swish private room on one of the upper floors, or you can hire the whole place. / 1am; available from noon; in-house caterers; Private Room (20,12,–,–).

Pig's Ear SW3

£B-M, (45,35,–,–)
35 Old Church St
T 020 7352 2908
F 020 7352 9321
W hardens.com/party/pigsear
E info@thepigsear.co.uk

A popular Chelsea side street pub, once known as the Front Page, which has been impressively kitted out in Art Nouveau style by its new owners. The upstairs dining room is a very congenial venue for a private party. / midnight; in-house caterers; no amplified music; no dancing.

Pinewood Studios SL0
£M, (300,280,90,200)
Pinewood Rd
T 01753 651126
W hardens.com/party/pinewood
E pinewood@trulydifferent.com
The country house at the centre of this famous studio complex offers good facilities for medium-size events, such as weddings. / 1am; Couture Hospitality; Ballroom (300,280,–,200); Pools Theatre (150,100,–,150); Hitchcock (100,100,–,100); Pine (50,12,–,30).

The Pirate Castle NW1
£B-M, (150,70,–,–)
Gilbey's Wharf
T 020 7267 6605
F 020 7267 6563
W www.thepiratecastle.org
E info@thepiratecastle.org
Voted Number 1 Castle in London by Time Out magazine. Located only 100 yards from the famous Camden Lock. We have a large recently refurbished Hall for Hire, with lots of natural light, a balcony and a panoramic view of the Regent's Canal. Catering kitchen and roof terrace also available. / midnight; hirer's choice of caterer; Main Hall (150,70,–,–); Meeting/activity Room (–,12,–,–); Club Room (50,25,–,–).

Pissarro's on the River W4
£M, (200,120,–,–)
Corney Reach Way
T 020 8994 3111
F 020 8994 3222
W hardens.com/party/pissarro
E info@pissarro.co.uk
A beautiful riverside location and a conservatory set an away-from-it-all tone at this usual restaurant (available for private hire), in deepest Chiswick. For a touch of style, arrive by boat at the nearby pier. / midnight; in-house caterers.

Pitzhanger Manor W5
£M, (120,80,–,100)
Walpole Park
T 020 8567 1227
F 020 8567 0595
W hardens.com/party/pitzhangermanor
E pmgallery&house@ealing.gov.uk
By the venerated architect Sir John Soane, this Georgian villa in the heart of Ealing offers an elegant setting in beautiful parkland, particularly suited to civil wedding ceremonies. There is also a large gallery space attached to the house, offering modern art exhibitions as a backdrop for functions. / midnight; generally not available Tue-Fri 1pm-5pm & Sat 11am-5pm; hirer's choice of caterer; no amplified music; no dancing; Gallery (200,–,–,–).

Pizza East E1
£M, (–,–,–,–)
Tea Building
T 020 7729 1888
W hardens.com/party/pizzaeast
E reception@pizzaeast.com
If you have very deep pockets, you might consider taking over this very groovy pizzeria on the trendy fringes of the City, which can be combined with the space below it – 'Concrete' (see also). Events, though, mostly happen at the latter

PJ's Bar & Grill SW3
£M, (70,40,–,–)
52 Fulham Rd
T 020 7581 0025
F 020 7584 0820
W hardens.com/party/pjsbarandgrill
E info@pjsbarandgrill.co.uk
Unlike most venues we list, the mezzanine of this buzzy Chelsea American restaurant is only semi-private, but it makes a fun venue for an informal party. / midnight; in-house caterers; no amplified music; no dancing.

The Place WC1
£M, (150,80,–,70)
17 Dukes Rd
T 020 7121 1000
F 020 7121 1142
W hardens.com/party/theplace
E info@theplace.org.uk

The home of London's Contemporary Dance School, near Euston, offers a variety of spaces for studio hire, as well as a bar and theatre for more traditional corporate events. / 10pm; restricted availability; in-house caterers; Theatre Bar (70,–,–,30).

Plaisterers' Hall EC2
£M-E, (600,370,280,480)
One London Wall
- T 0870 423 3560
- F 020 7796 9444
- W www.plaisterershall.com
- E events@plaisterershall.com

From conferences, roadshows and presentations to weddings and parties, Plaisterers' is the pre-eminent City venue. With its contemporary exterior and neo-classical halls it offers a wonderfully intimate, attractive and flexible space for every style of event. The building has a modern technical infrastructure including state-of-the-art lighting, audio-visual and communications equipment. / midnight; Create Food and Party Design; Great Hall (600,370,280,480); Livery Hall (250,80,–,110); Humber Room (50,–,–,24); Mott Room (–,–,–,–).

Planit Finsbury Square EC2
£M-E, (2300,1200,1200,1200)
Finsbury Square
- T 020 8682 4900
- F 020 8682 0602
- W hardens.com/party/planit
- E enquiries@planitevents.co.uk

Every December for the last few years, this events company has erected a huge marquee in Victoria Embankment Gardens pre-Christmas, offering corporate events for a minimum of 500 people. / midnight; in-house caterers.

Plateau E14
£M, (500,200,–,–)
4th Floor Canada Pl
- T 020 7715 7100
- F 020 7715 7110
- W hardens.com/party/plateau
- E plateaureservations@conran-restaurants.co.uk

If you're looking for a Canary Wharf venue with views that seem more like Manhattan than London, you won't do much better than this fourth-floor D&D (fka Conran) group restaurant, which is well geared up for small to medium-size events. / in-house caterers; no amplified music; no dancing; Private Dining Rm (40,24,–,–).

The Player W1
£M, (120,–,–,–)
8-12 Broadwick St
- T 020 7494 9125
- F 020 7494 9126
- W hardens.com/party/player

A nothingy-looking doorway adds to the thrill of discovering this superior Soho cocktail bar. It can – at certain times – be hired privately. / 1am.

Poetry Society WC2
£B-M, (40,–,–,–)
22 Betterton St
- T 020 7420 9887
- F 020 7240 4818
- W hardens.com/party/poetrysociety
- E info@poetrysociety.org.uk

A Covent Garden society whose HQ is, as one might expect, most used for book launches and readings. The café, however, is also used for more social occasions. / members club; 11pm; not available Sun; in-house caterers; no amplified music.

Poissonnerie de l'Avenue SW3
£M-E, (–,70,–,–)
82 Sloane Av
- T 020 7589 2457
- W hardens.com/party/poissonnerie

A grand and rather old-fashioned Chelsea fish and seafood parlour, with an upstairs private room. / in-house caterers; Private Room (–,20,–,–).

Polka Theatre for Children SW19

£B-M, (150,–,–,300)
240 The Broadway
T 020 8545 8328
F 020 8545 8365
W hardens.com/party/polkatheatre
E kim@polkatheatre.com

London's original theatre for children with its own permanent base comes complete with a small but attractive playground. It's used for a wide range of (adult) readings and receptions. The studio theatre is popular for children's events. / 11pm; not available Sun; hirer's choice of caterer (in-house available); Studio Theatre (–,–,–,80).

Pont de la Tour SE1

£M-E, (400,160,–,–)
36d Shad Thames
T 020 7403 8403
F 020 7940 1835
W hardens.com/party/pontdelatour
E lepontres@danddlondon.com

This D&D group riverside is famed for its Tower Bridge views, and can be hired in its entirety. It also has a couple of private areas – one a wine cave – particularly suited to City entertaining. / Private Dining (35,20,–,–); Semi-Private Wine Cellar (24,35,–,–).

Porchester Centre W2

£B-M, (630,450,–,–)
Queensway
T 020 7792 2823
F 020 7641 4493
W hardens.com/party/porchesterhall
E porchester.hall@nuffieldhealth.com

An ornate, panelled Art Deco ballroom, hidden away in a municipal-looking Bayswater building. The famous marbled Turkish baths in the same building are available only for product launches (and photo shoots). / midnight-12.30am; hirer's choice of caterer.

Portal EC1

£M, (350,120,–,–)
88 St John St
T 020 7253 6950
F 020 7490 5836
W hardens.com/party/portal
E antonio@portalrestaurant.com

An attractive Portuguese restaurant of high ambition, with a strong list of native wines and, of course, Ports. It's an attractive space, complete with conservatory, off which there's also a small private room. / 11.30pm; not available Sun, Sat L; in-house caterers; no music; no dancing; Adega Rm (–,14,–,–); Glasshouse (–,50,–,–).

Porte des Indes W1

£M-E, (500,300,200,–)
32 Bryanston St
T 020 7224 0055
F 020 7224 1144
W hardens.com/party/portedesindes
E london.reservations@laportedesindes.com

This vast Indian restaurant near Marble Arch is extremely flexible as a function venue, and offers obvious theming potential. One or other of the restaurant's two floors can be used to accommodate parties of anywhere between 100 and 200, and there are some smaller private rooms. / 11.30pm, Sun 10.30pm; no Sat L; in-house caterers; no amplified music; no dancing.

Portland Place Conference Centre W1

£M-E, (60,40,–,40)
17 Portland Place
T 020 7323 9084
F 020 7580 6945
W hardens.com/party/portlandplaceconference
E portland@deverevenues.co.uk

An Adam-style building near Oxford Circus, which offers a range of meeting rooms which have natural light, as well as a full range of audio-visual equipment and technical support. / in-house caterers; no music; no dancing; Tavistock/Grosvenor (40,–,–,40); Chiswick (24,–,–,24); Regent (35,–,–,35); Saville Suite (16,16,–,–).

Portman Hotel W1
£M-E, (700,550,–,600)
22 Portman Sq
Ⓣ 020 7208 6000
Ⓕ 020 7208 6001
Ⓦ hardens.com/party/portmanhotel
Ⓔ londonevents@radissonsas.com
The banqueting facilities of this modern hotel reflect a certain conference-orientation (though it does have a wedding licence). There's a good variety of rooms, though, most with floor-to-ceiling windows. / 1am; in-house caterers; Portman Ballroom (700,550,–,600); Montagu Suite (90,80,–,90); Berkley. Gloucester & Bryanston Suite (–,130,–,150); Library (–,24,–,–).

Poule au Pot SW1
£M, (–,16,–,–)
231 Ebury St
Ⓣ 020 7730 7763
Ⓦ hardens.com/party/pouleaupot
Famously London's most romantic restaurant, this bricks-and-candles Pimlico stalwart has a cosy basement area, especially suited to family gatherings. / in-house caterers.

Prenelle Gallery E14
£M, (150,60,60,70)
West India Quay
Ⓣ 020 7093 0628
Ⓦ hardens.com/party/prenelle
Ⓔ aprenelle@googlemail.com
A 130ft Dutch barge, moored in the East End, which claims to be London's only floating contemporary art gallery. It is used for a wide variety of shows, launches and parties. / midnight; hirer's choice of caterer (in-house available); no music outside; Main Gallery (150,60,60,70); Library (30,–,–,–); Outer Deck (150,–,–,–).

HMS President EC4
£B-M, (350,210,210,–)
Victoria Embankment
Ⓣ 020 7583 1918
Ⓕ 020 7583 4577
Ⓦ hardens.com/party/hmspresident
Ⓔ enquiries@hmspresident.com
A WWI, Q-class boat, moored just above Blackfriars Bridge, which offers good value, and the sense of occasion that being afloat brings. / 2am; in-house caterers; Ball Rm (350,210,210,–); President Suite (210,90,–,–); Wardroom (120,80,–,–); Boardroom II (–,20,–,–); Boardroom I (–,8,–,–).

Prism EC3
£M-E, (350,120,120,–)
147 Leadenhall St
Ⓣ 020 7256 3875
Ⓕ 0870 2386 345
Ⓦ hardens.com/party/prism
Ⓔ emma.morrison@harveynichols.com
A converted banking hall now provides the impressive setting for this Harvey Nichols group restaurant in the heart of the City. It has a number of rooms for private hire, or the whole venue is well suited to holding a function. / 2am; weekdays only; in-house caterers; Library (40,20,–,–); Bar (80,–,–,–).

The Private Rooms at Buckingham Gate SW1
£M, (300,140,140,180)
51 Buckingham Gate
Ⓣ 020 7963 8377
Ⓕ 020 7828 7826
Ⓦ hardens.com/party/theprivateroomsatbuckinghamgate
Ⓔ events@theprivaterooms.co.uk
Ornately furnished rooms with turn-of-the century panelling, chandeliers and custom-made woven carpets, which provide a good backdrop for a more formal type of occasion. / 1am; in-house caterers; music must end at midnight; Edwardian I (300,140,140,180); Edwardian II (50,40,–,50); Taj (45,27,–,40); Buckingham (45,40,–,25); Windsor (8,6,–,–); Clarence (10,10,–,–).

Proud Cabaret EC3
£B-M, (350,280,240,200)
1 Mark Lane
T 020 7283 1940
W www.proud.co.uk
E hire@proudcabaret.com

Proud Cabaret is the place in the City to entertain and be entertained while you dine. Known for showcasing high calibre cabaret and burlesque acts, the sumptuous 1920s speakeasy-inspired venue captures all the excitement of a bygone era. With a great British menu and mind-blowing cocktails you have the recipe for a successful party! / no under 18's after 5pm; 5am license; All day depending on availability; in-house caterers.

Proud Camden NW1
£B-M, (700,300,150,300)
The Horse Hosptial
T 020 7482 3867
W www.proudcamden.com
E info@proud.co.uk

Renowned gallery, bar and live music venue in the Grade II listed old Horse Hospital is a unique setting for any event; including giant skylights, exposed brick, high-beamed ceilings and seven individual stables. The main gig room is decked out in iconic rock'n'roll photography, a stage and state of the art sound system. / no under 18's after 5pm; Mon-Wed 1.30am, Thu-Sat 2.30am, Sun 12.30am; all day; Hirer's choice of caterer (in-house available from Oct); live music midnight curfew; Main Room Alone (600,300,–,–); South Gallery Alone (180,100,–,–); Stables (each) (40,25,–,–); Covered Outdoor Café (–,50,–,–).

Proud Chelsea SW3
£B-M, (140,–,–,–)
161 King's Road
T 020 7349 0822
W www.proud.co.uk
E info@proudgalleries.co.uk

Situated in the heart of Chelsea's arts hub, Proud Chelsea is the perfect space in which to hold your event. Set over two sleek and versatile floors, the gallery lends itself to a range of events with ease. The space can accommodate receptions up to 140 people beginning at £500. / all day; hirer's choice of caterer; Single Floor (70,–,–,–).

The Pump House Gallery SW11
£B, (250,150,–,–)
Battersea Park
T 020 7350 0523
F 020 7228 9062
W hardens.com/party/pumphousegallery
E cdavies@wandsworth.gov.uk

Prettily located on the lakeside in Battersea Park, this square tower (with four floors) makes an attractive and rather unusual place for a wedding or cocktail party. For a sit-down, you can boost the ground floor area with a marquee. / 11pm; available Mon-Tue all day, Wed-Thu & Sun from 5pm, Fri-Sat from 4pm; hirer's choice of caterer; no dancing; Marquee (250,150,–,–).

Punk W1

£B, (264,–,–,–)

14 Soho Street

Ⓣ 020 7734 4004
Ⓦ hardens.com/party/punk
Ⓔ love@punksoho.co.uk

Open plan Soho bar, with a large stage area, plenty of space for dancing and a 10m bar stretching most of the length of the main room. The comfy VIP room can be used as an add-on, or for smaller events. / 3am; in-house caterers; VIP Room (60,–,–,–).

Quaglino's SW1

£M-E, (440,300,180,200)

16 Bury St

Ⓣ 020 74842002
Ⓕ 7839 2866
Ⓦ www.quaglinos.co.uk
Ⓔ GeorginaS@DandDLondon.com

This fashionably glamorous restaurant has, over the decades, welcomed royalty and rock stars, high society and paparazzi. Quaglino's lends a "wow factor" to private parties for fashion shows, weddings and Bar mitzvahs; two stunning private rooms seat up to 60 guests. / approx 7.30 am - 1 am; in-house caterers; music restricted; Private Room 1 (60,44,27,35); Private Room 2 (20,16,14,24).

Queen Elizabeth II Conference Centre SW1

£M-E, (800,930,–,1400)

Broad Sanctuary

Ⓣ 020 7222 5000
Ⓕ 020 7798 4200
Ⓦ hardens.com/party/queenelizabethiiconferencecentre
Ⓔ info@qeiicc.co.uk

The appeal of this purpose-built centre by Westminster Abbey is perhaps more obvious for conferences than for social events. However, the place can be geared up for the latter upon request. / midnight; Leith's; Benjamin Britten (800,450,–,–); Whittle & Fleming Rooms (–,930,–,1400).

Queen Mary College E1

£B, (500,180,150,800)

Mile End Rd

Ⓣ 020 7882 8174
Ⓕ 020 7882 7055
Ⓦ hardens.com/party/qmc
Ⓔ conference@qmul.ac.uk

This London University college has several venues – all at different East End sites, and in different styles ancient and modern – which are available for hire. The Octagon is the plushest. / restricted availability; midnight; available from 6pm weekdays & all day Sat & Sun, Octagon 7 days; in-house caterers; The Octagon (500,180,150,–); Great Hall (–,–,–,800).

Queen Mary Students' Union E1

£B, (650,350,250,–)

University Of London

Ⓣ 020 7882 8455
Ⓕ 020 8981 0802
Ⓦ hardens.com/party/qmsu
Ⓔ entertainments@qmsu.org

The Drapers Bar at this East End campus offers a suitable venue for a large and relatively inexpensive party. / 2am; available weekends and out of term; hirer's choice of caterer (in-house available).

The Queen's Club W14

£M-E, (180,120,120,120)

Palliser Rd

Ⓣ 020 7386 3432
Ⓕ 020 7386 8295
Ⓦ hardens.com/party/thequeensclub
Ⓔ catering@queensclub.co.uk

A multipurpose sports complex located near Hammersmith. There are 40 tennis courts, two rackets courts, two squash courts and a gym as well as a restaurant, cafe, museum and the Presidents Room which are available to hire. / functions restricted to private rooms only; 1am; available from 8am; in-house caterers; The Presidents Room (180,120,120,120); Club Restaurant (80,45,–,–); Real Tennis Museum (20,12,–,12); Board Room (30,20,–,30); Committee Room (100,50,–,50).

Queen's Eyot SL6

£M, (200,150,150,60)
Monkey Island Ln
Ⓣ 01753 832 756
Ⓦ hardens.com/party/queenseyot
Ⓔ info@queenseyot.co.uk
Eton College's island retreat has an impressive modern clubhouse reached by ferry. Uses of the eyot range from corporate sports days to wedding receptions. Larger capacities indicated require the erection of a marquee. / 11.30pm; in-house caterers; Clubhouse (80,60,–,60); Marquee (200,150,150,–).

Queen's House SE10

£M-E, (200,120,–,–)
National Maritime Mus
Ⓣ 020 8312 8517
Ⓕ 020 8312 6572
Ⓦ hardens.com/party/queenshouse
Ⓔ events@nmm.ac.uk
Sited picturesquely between the former Royal Naval College and Greenwich Park, a highly unusual house (by Inigo Jones et al), comprehensively restored. The lofty Great Hall and pretty Orangery are the areas most used, and are ideal for wedding receptions. / no naked flames; 11pm; available from 5pm, weddings 2.30pm; list of caterers; no dancing in great hall; no red wine for standing receptions; Orangery Suite (120,50,–,–); Great Hall (200,120,–,–).

Quo Vadis Club W1

£M-E, (80,24,–,–)
26-29 Dean St
Ⓣ 020 7437 9585
Ⓕ 020 7734 7593
Ⓦ hardens.com/party/quovadisclub
Ⓔ info@quovadissoho.co.uk
Above the Hart Brothers well-known Soho restaurant, this comfortable and stylish private member's club is fashioned out of the upstairs rooms of a series of interlocking townhouses. It's a cosy, elegant space ideal for social entertaining.

Radisson Edwardian Berkshire Hotel W1

£M, (50,20,–,35)
350 Oxford St
Ⓣ 020 7845 8680
Ⓕ 020 8750 9262
Ⓦ hardens.com/party/berkshire
Ⓔ londonmeetings@radisson.com
The pretty, panelled top-floor Sonning Suite – suitable for dinners and smaller receptions – is the main function facility at this modern, wedge-shaped hotel, not far from Selfridges. / midnight; in-house caterers; Sonning Suite (50,20,–,35); Sandhurst Suite (–,12,–,–).

The Rag Factory E1

£B-M, (300,–,–,200)
16-18 Heneage Street
Ⓣ 020 7650 8749
Ⓕ 020 7092 9099
Ⓦ hardens.com/party/ragfactory
Ⓔ hello@ragfactory.org.uk
Entered through a small courtyard near trendy Brick Lane, this ex-industrial Victorian building recently opened as an arts space. If you're not seeking a look for your event that's glossy and corporate, it has much to offer as a characterful, flexible venue. / midnight; hirer's choice of caterer (in-house available); need licence to sell alcohol.

Red W1

£B-M, (200,–,–,–)
5 Kingly St
Ⓣ 020 7434 3417
Ⓕ 020 7434 3418
Ⓦ hardens.com/party/redsoho
Ⓔ info@redsoho.com
A popular two-floor West Soho lounge bar, which makes a very central venue for a stand-up event. / 1am; in-house caterers; Downstairs (100,–,–,–).

Red Monkey SW11

£B-M, (150,30,–,–)
50-52 Battersea Rise
Ⓣ 0207 924 6288
Ⓦ hardens.com/party/redmonkey
Ⓔ info@redmonkeylounge.co.uk
This cool new Japanese lounge bar – serving small Japanese 'Izakaya'

dishes – makes a funky venue for an informal party. Either hire the whole place, or – for parties of 2–60 – have a sing-along in their downstairs Karaoke pods. / 2am; in-house caterers; Karaoke Pod (25,–,–,–).

The Red Room W1

£M, (150,150,–,–)

6 Hamilton Place

T 0207 317 6180

W hardens.com/party/redroom

E info@theredroomclub.co.uk

Adjacent to Les Ambassadeurs casino, this lounge and cigar bar (there's a small garden) has long been a feature of the area near Hyde Park Corner, and its louche and loungy style well suits both private and corporate events. Late license till 6am. / 4am; in-house caterers.

The Red Rooms WC2

£B-M, (200,–,–,–)

4 Great Queen St

T 020 7831 0802

W hardens.com/party/cougarpinks

E soraya@theredrooms.co.uk

Previously Browns and then Cougar Pinks, this large, nightclub on the fringe of Covent Garden is nowadays more 'gentleman's club' with a scarlet theme, and dancing pole. For a sexily themed evening, though, it would suit a private hire, or you can just use the VIP room. / 3am; available Mon-Thu; hirer's choice of caterer (in-house available); VIP Room (100,–,–,–).

The Regalia EC4

£M, (400,250,250,–)

Swan Pier

T 020 7623 1805

F 020 7283 4002

W hardens.com/party/regalia

E info@thamesleisure.co.uk

A lunchtime watering-hole for younger City types, this permanently-moored barge is an ideal place for a large, casual get-together. In summer 2010, it's up for sale, so change may be afoot. / 2am; in-house caterers.

Regent's College NW1

£M, (500,200,150,100)

Inner Circle

T 020 7487 7540

F 020 7487 7657

W hardens.com/party/regentscollege

E conferences@regents.ac.uk

A great position, in the heart of the Park, makes this a very attractive venue. The rooms available are light and airy, in good decorative order. The Tuke Common Room has a particularly leafy prospect. / 11pm; in-house caterers; no amplified music outside; Gardens (500,200,150,–); Herringham Hall (180,70,70,100); Tuke Common Rm (100,50,50,80); Knapp Gallery (100,40,40,40).

Relax BBC W12

£M, (75,–,–,–)

2-3 The Media Centre

T 020 8811 8844

F 020 7494 3399

W hardens.com/party/relaxbbc

E relaxbbc@relax.org.uk

A spa venue for corporate events – offering a wide range of full body, chair massage and natural beauty treatments. / 7pm; in-house caterers.

Renaissance London Chancery Court Hotel WC1

£M-E, (500,360,224,262)

252 High Holborn

T 020 8897 6363

F 020 7012 7194

W hardens.com/party/renaissancelondonchancerycourthotel

E sales.chancerycourt@renaissancehotels.com

Built in 1914 as the impressive headquarters of the Pearl Assurance Company, this grand hotel is a handy resource in the 'Midtown' area between the City and the West End. It offers a large variety of function and conference rooms, many of which interconnect. The capacity shown is for the ballroom. / 2am; in-house caterers.

The Research House W1
£B-M, (–,18,–,25)
124 Wigmore Street
T 020 7935 4979
F 020 7224 2494
W hardens.com/party/meetinghouse
E enquiries@meeting-house.co.uk
In Marylebone, an elegant townhouse suited to smaller meetings, usually of a business nature. / *5pm; in-house caterers; no music; no dancing; Studio 1 (–,18,–,25); Studio 2 (–,18,–,25); Studio 3 (–,16,–,18).*

Rex Whistler (Tate Britain) SW1
£M-E, (120,80,–,–)
Millbank
T 020 7887 8825
F 020 7887 8902
W hardens.com/party/whistler
E britain.restaurant@tate.org.uk
You no longer need to hire the whole of Tate Britain to use this charming dining room, famed for its wines list and beautiful Whistler murals, which is now available independently for evening events.

Rich Mix E1
£B-M, (350,200,200,180)
35-47 Bethnal Green Road
T 020 7613 7663
F 020 7613 7499
W hardens.com/party/richmix
E kate.wilson@richmix.org.uk
In addition to a modern digital cinema, this Shoreditch arts venue has a number of different workspaces, screening rooms and studios available for hire. / *restricted availability; midnight, weekends 1am; in-house caterers.*

The Ritz W1
£M-E, (180,100,–,–)
150 Piccadilly
T 020 7493 8181
F 020 7300 2235
W hardens.com/party/ritz
E enquire@theritzlondon.com
Other than the Marie Antoinette suite, the function facilities of this famous Louis XVI-style hotel are situated in the relatively recently acquired William Kent House, next door. / *no product launches or exhibitions; 12am; in-house caterers; no amplified music; Music Room (100,60,–,–); William Kent Room (–,24,–,–); Marie Antoinette Suite (100,–,–,–).*

River & Rowing Museum RG9
£M-E, (300,120,100,110)
Mill Meadows
T 01491 415610
F 01491 415601
W hardens.com/party/rrm
E events@rrm.co.uk
This architectural-award-winning Henley museum offers a very pleasant space for functions, benefiting from river views. / *midnight; in-house caterers; Thames Room (–,100,–,–); Rowing Gallery (200,120,–,–); Henley Room (–,10,–,–).*

River Lounge E1
£M, (120,70,–,70)
St Katharine's Way
T 020 7702 4588
W hardens.com/party/riverlounge
E info@theriverlounge.co.uk
Formerly a yacht club, this brilliantly positioned venue by the side of St Katherine's dock has great views over the marina both inside its main room and from its first-floor balcony. / *11pm, although a late licence is available; in-house caterers; no alcohol on the balcony.*

Riverbank Park Plaza SE1
£M, (660,540,490,650)
18 Albert Embankment
T 020 7769 2577
F 020 7769 2402
W hardens.com/party/parkplazariverbank
E pprlconf@pphe.com
Just over Lambeth Bridge, this new South Bank hotel comes equipped with a wide range of flexible, state-of-the-art conference and event facilities, and can deal with events on quite a scale. Of most interest is the Thames Room, which offers the view the name suggests. / *2am; hirer's choice of caterer (in-house available).*

Riverside Studios W6

£B-M, (200,120,–,444)
Crisp Rd
T 020 8237 1000
F 020 8237 1001
W hardens.com/party/riversidestudios
E heatherruck@riversidestudios.co.uk

TV studio and arts centre, offering flexible space. The studios are without windows, but the café-bar and gallery are quite light and bright, and the terrace has views towards Hammersmith Bridge. / 11.30pm, Sun 10.30pm; in-house caterers; no amplified music outside; Studio 2 (–,–,–,400); Studio 4 (–,–,–,156).

Rivington Place EC2

£M, (180,100,–,60)
Rivington Place
T 020 7749 1240
W hardens.com/party/rivingtonplace
E bookings@rivingtonplace.org

An arty new arts centre/venue on the fringe of the City (designed, remarkably, by the same man who did the Hayward Gallery back in 1968, but in a totally different style). An interesting setting for an event, but somewhat constrained by the building's other requirements. / 11.30pm; hirer's choice of caterer (in-house available); PS1 (180,100,–,–); PS2 (–,60,–,60); Meeting Room (30,20,–,20).

Rock & Rose TW9

£M, (–,90,–,–)
106-108 Kew Raod
T 020 8948 8008
W hardens.com/party/rockrose
E talk@rockandroserestaurant.co.uk

Richmond-fringe restaurant whose romantic decor suits it to private events. / Private Room (–,15,–,–); Garden Room (–,25,–,–).

Roehampton Club SW15

£M-E, (200,140,140,200)
Roehampton Ln
T 020 8480 4225
F 020 8480 4265
W hardens.com/party/roehamptonclub
E nicola.moorhouse@roehamptonclub.co.uk

It's not necessary to be a member to book function facilities at this impressive club. Sports facilities include an 18-hole golf course, 28 tennis and five squash courts, three croquet lawns, pools indoor and outdoor, and a gymnasium. The larger rooms benefit from huge windows overlooking the garden. / midnight; in-house caterers; Garden Rm (100,60,–,60).

Ronnie Scotts W1

£M, (220,220,200,250)
47 Frith St
T 020 7439 0747
F 020 7437 5081
W hardens.com/party/ronniescotts
E events@ronniescotts.co.uk

This famous Soho jazz night club, recently revamped, is available for private hire in the daytime only. It is most commonly used for product launches and record company showcases. / 3am; daytime only, Tue-Fri; in-house caterers; no dancing.

The Roof Gardens W8

£M-E, (500,180,70,–)
99 High St Kensington (entrance off Derry St)
T 020 7368 3993
F 020 7938 2774
W hardens.com/party/theroofgardens
E events@roofgardens.virgin.com

A nightclub set in two acres of beautiful gardens would be a popular venue anywhere. Six floors above Kensington it seems all the more remarkable, and the place is constantly in demand for all types of events. / 1am; not available Fri or Sat evenings; list of caterers; no amplified music outside.

Roundhouse NW1

£M-E, (1800,1000,850,1200)
Chalk Farm Rd
T 020 7424 6771
F 020 7424 9992
W www.roundhouse.org.uk/hire
E hire@roundhouse.org.uk

A legendary venue and a Grade II listed building, the Roundhouse reopened in June 2006 following a £30million restoration. This world class venue for Arts and Music performances is available for exclusive hire for a limited time each year. The flexible spaces can host receptions, dinners and meetings for 100 - 1800. / *restricted availability; available subject to constraints of current production; list of caterers; Circle Bar (200,20,–,–); Torquils Bar (200,20,–,–); Dr. Martens Free DM Studio (180,–,–,90).*

Roux at Parliament Square SW1

£M-E, (200,120,80,100)
Parliament Square
T 020 7334 3737
W hardens.com/party/rouxatparliamentsquare
E roux@rics.org

Next to the main entrance to the 'Parliament Square' building – home to the RICS – this new Roux venture (in association with caterers Restaurant Associates) is a bright dining room providing classic Gallic fare, and can be hired for a sit-down meal. / *11pm but they can extend their licence to 4am; in-house caterers.*

The Royal Academy of Arts W1

£E, (800,250,–,–)
Burlington Hs
T 020 7300 5987
F 020 7300 8001
W www.royalacademy.org.uk
E entertaining@royalacademy.org.uk

The sumptuous Fine Rooms at the Royal Academy make an amazing backdrop for entertaining. Events can combine a private exhibition view with parties being held in the Main Galleries amongst the art works during the Summer Exhibition. Two free event hires are included when you join the Corporate Membership scheme. / *corporate members only; 11pm; available from 6.45pm, not available weekends; list of caterers; no dancing in Fine Rooms; Fine Rms (350,100,–,–).*

Royal Academy of Engineering SW1

£M-E, (85,40,–,85)
3 Carlton House Terrace
T 020 7766 0600
F 020 7930 1549
W hardens.com/party/raengingeering
E events@raeng.org.uk

A smart and very central for a businesslike gathering or conference, in a grand stucco building near Pall Mall. / *10pm; weekdays only; in-house caterers; no dancing; F4 (–,–,–,85); G1 (–,28,–,–); F2 (85,40,–,–); F1 (–,20,–,–).*

Royal Air Force Club W1

£M, (250,140,120,140)
128 Piccadilly
T 020 7399 1000
F 020 7629 1316
W hardens.com/party/rafclub
E confbanq@rafclub.org.uk

A member must sponsor (and attend) events but, once you're in, this club is more flexible than many, and has a ballroom and also a bar/disco area. In the basement, the Running Horse (the 'pub within the club') and Millennium Suite suit discos, dances and wedding receptions. / *members club; 11pm; in-house caterers; no amplified music; Ballroom (250,140,–,140); Running Horse/Millennium Suite (120,–,120,–).*

Royal Air Force Museum NW9

£M-E, (800,444,444,250)
Grahame Park Way
T 0844 824 6293
F 020 8358 4981
W www.rafmuseum.org.uk/london/corporate-events/
E events@rafmuseum.com

ROYAL AIR FORCE museum LONDON

Whether you are looking for a business meeting for 50 people or a dinner for 400, Royal Air Force Museum, London can ensure that your event takes off with great success! If you are looking for an exclusive venue to really impress your guests, you can't get more unique than our selection of three Hangars available for evening receptions, dinners and dinner dances.
/ *no naked flames, no balloons; aircraft halls after 6pm; approved list of caterers; no dancing in some aircraft halls; Milestones Of Flight (250,168,–,–); Battle Of Britain Hall (400,280,180,–); Historic Hangars (800,444,444,–); Cosford Rm (Dermot Boyle Wing) (312,120,–,250); Locking Rm (Dermot Boyle Wing) (300,100,–,170); Halton Gallery (250,100,–,100); Lecture Theatre (–,–,–,224); Art Gallery (150,80,–,–).*

ROYAL AIR FORCE museum LONDON

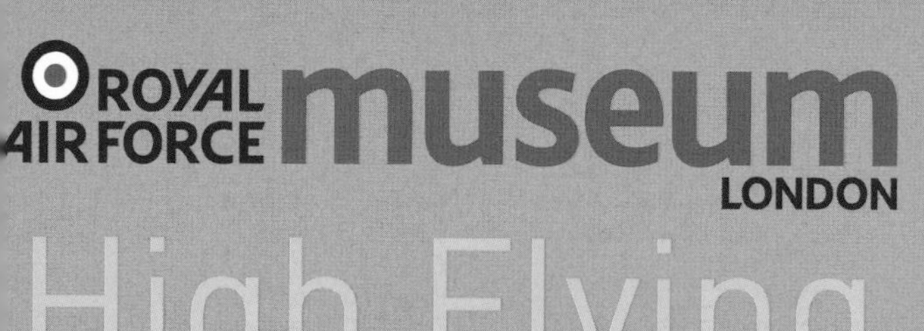

High Flying Events

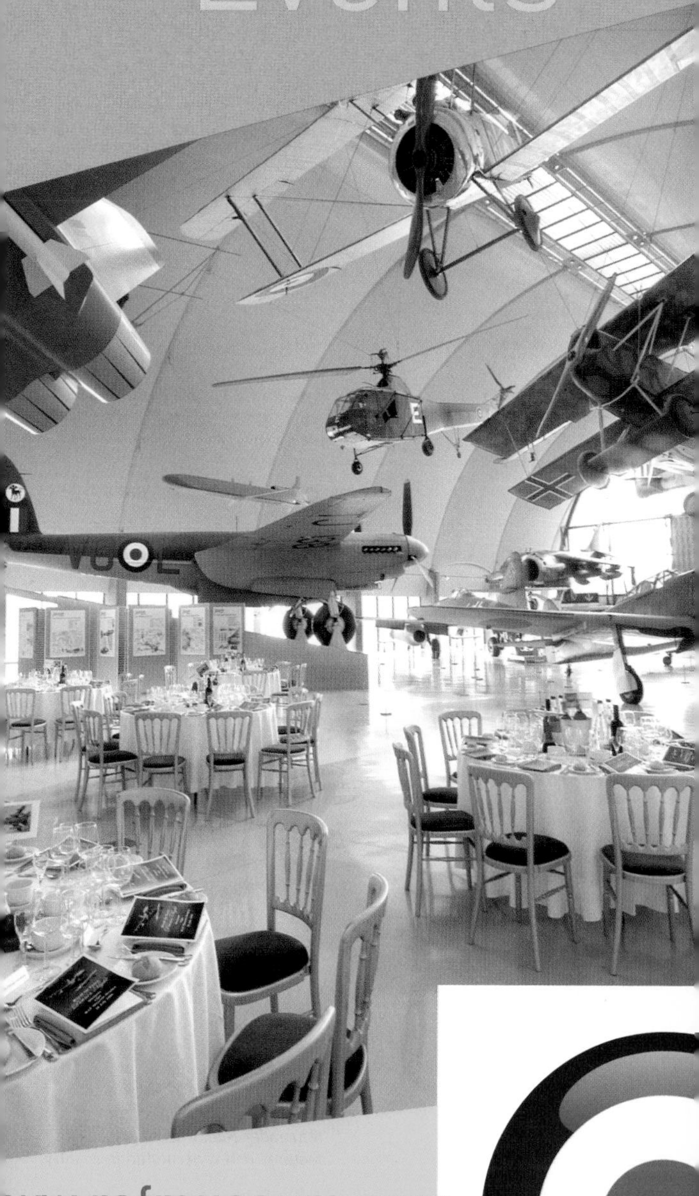

www.rafmuseum.com

Royal Albert Hall SW7

£M-E, (150,1900,–,5200)

Kensington Gore

Ⓣ 020 7589 3203

Ⓕ 020 7823 7725

Ⓦ www.royalalberthall.com

Ⓔ entertain@royalalberthall.com

You can entertain huge numbers in this great Victorian hall (although full loading requires use of the stalls and boxes). Smaller events may be arranged in private rooms. The Elgar Room is a relatively recent addition to the range of private hire possibilities. / 1am; Leith's; Gallery (500,300,–,–); Henry Cole (20,32,–,–); Elgar Room (350,–,–,–); Arena Foyers (180,100,–,–); Prince Of Wales (40,30,–,–); Royal Retiring (30,20,–,–).

Royal Astronomical Society W1

£M-E, (–,20,–,100)

Burlington House Piccadilly

Ⓣ 020 7734 4582

Ⓕ 020 7494 0166

Ⓦ hardens.com/party/ras.uk

Ⓔ cf@ras.org.uk

Next to the Royal Academy, a venue that's worth knowing about if you want a small, central conference followed by lunch. / 5.30pm; weekdays only; list of caterers; no amplified music; no dancing; wine only.

Royal College of Art SW7

£B-M, (1100,350,300,136)

Kensington Gore

Ⓣ 020 7590 4118

Ⓕ 020 7590 4500

Ⓦ hardens.com/party/rca

Ⓔ galleries@rca.ac.uk

These large, white-walled galleries look on to Kensington Gardens, and offer large, open spaces for modest-budget gatherings – from a private view to a party – or are an ideal blank canvas within which to stage more lavish themed events. / midnight; hirer's choice of caterer (in-house available); no red wine; Entrance Gallery (100,–,–,–); Henry Moore Gallery (600,350,300,–); Gulbenkian Galleries (250,150,100,–); Seminar Rm 1 (100,50,–,–); Lecture Theatre 1 (–,–,–,136); Senior Common Room (150,80,–,–).

Royal College of Music SW7

£M, (300,400,–,400)

Prince Consort Rd

Ⓣ 020 7589 3643

Ⓦ hardens.com/party/rcm

Ⓔ mcosgrave@rcm.ac.uk

The main Concert Hall, and also the Britten Theatre, of this grand institution by the Albert Hall are sometimes available for private hire (particularly out of term). / restricted availability, no weddings; 11pm ; list of caterers; Britten Theatre (–,–,–,350); Concert Hall (–,–,–,400).

Royal College of Pathologists SW1

£M-E, (150,80,–,100)

2 Carlton House Terr

Ⓣ 020 7451 6740

Ⓕ 020 7451 6702

Ⓦ hardens.com/party/rcpathologists

Ⓔ meetings@rcpath.org

A Nash terrace house, elegantly refurbished in understated modern style. It offers a prestigious central venue, whose terrace has an exceptional view. / midnight; in-house caterers.

Royal College of Physicians NW1

£M-E, (450,220,–,300)

11 St Andrew's Place

Ⓣ 020 7034 4900

Ⓕ 020 7224 0900

Ⓦ www.rcplondon.ac.uk/venue

Ⓔ events@rcplondon.ac.uk

A striking modern edifice, beside Regent's Park, that's of such note that it's Grade I listed. It also has a garden, plus a theatre which was recently refurbished. / 11pm; in-house caterers; Platt Rm (140,–,–,–).

Royal College of Radiologists W1

£M-E, (–,20,–,60)

38 Portland Pl

Ⓣ 020 7636 4432

Ⓕ 020 7323 3110

Ⓦ hardens.com/party/reradiologists

Ⓔ enquiries@rcr.ac.uk

The basement of this Adam townhouse (circa 1776) has been modernised, but most of the remainder retains its original features and is decorated in country house style. Only the Council Chamber is really suitable for entertaining. / *6pm; not available Sat & Sun; in-house caterers; no music; no dancing; Robens Room (–,14,–,–); Lecture Theatre (–,–,–,60); Council Room (–,20,–,–).*

Royal Court Theatre SW1
£M, (230,90,–,380)
Sloane Sq
Ⓣ 020 7565 5050
Ⓕ 020 7565 5001
Ⓦ hardens.com/party/royalcourt
Ⓔ info@royalcourttheatre.com
A famous Victorian theatre, extensively revamped in recent times, and offering good facilities for a presentation in a smart location. / *restricted availability; Mon-Thu midnight, Fri-Sat 1am; available subject to constraints of current production; in-house caterers; Balcony Bar (80,21,–,–); Jerwood Theatre Downstairs (–,–,–,380); Jerwood Theatre Upstairs (–,–,–,80); Cafe Bar (230,90,–,–).*

Royal Courts of Justice WC2
£M, (800,600,550,700)
Strand
Ⓣ 020 7947 7726
Ⓕ 020 7242 9121
Ⓦ www.royalcourtsofjustice-events.co.uk
Ⓔ enquiries@seasonedevents.co.uk
Home to the Court of Appeal and High Court, this Grade I Victorian Gothic landmark can be used by night for corporate events. / *Midnight (1am extension available); Mon-Fri only available for evening events; in-house caterers.*

Royal Exchange EC3
£M-E, (1000,350,30,30)
The Courtyard
Ⓣ 020 7628 3500
Ⓦ www.royalexchangegrandcafeandbar.com
Ⓔ rexevents@danddlondon.com
The Royal Exchange is a Grade I listed historical gem in the heart of the city adding a touch of luxury to every event that takes place. Available for breakfast, lunch or dinner for events of 8 to 1000, the event team make sure the event meets your specific needs / *11pm; 8am - 2pm; hirer's choice of caterer (in-house available); restrictions apply to music; corkage fees apply for own alcohol; PDR (50,26,30,30); Mezzanine Bar (200,100,–,–); Courtyard (350,–,–,–); Exclusive Use (1000,350,–,–).*

Royal Garden Hotel W8
£M-E, (500,400,168,550)
2-24 Kensington High St
Ⓣ 020 7361 0605
Ⓕ 020 7361 1921
Ⓦ www.royalgardenhotel.co.uk/Meetings-Events
Ⓔ banqueting@royalgardenhotel.co.uk

ROYAL GARDEN HOTEL

LONDON

Impeccable service, a choice of 10 private meeting rooms and award-winning food and drink make the Royal Garden Hotel one of the best conference and event venues in London. From intricate business meetings to extravagant 550 delegate events, the unbeatable service and flexibility is unsurpassed. / *2am; in-house caterers; Palace Suite (500,400,168,550); Kensington Suite (100,108,42,120); Bertie's Bar (50,–,–,–); York Suite (100,84,48,120).*

Royal Geographical Society SW7
£B-M, (400,120,60,750)
1 Kensington Gore
Ⓣ 020 7591 3090
Ⓦ www.rgs.org/roomhire
Ⓔ house@rgs.org
A characterful building with a great South Kensington address, and quite reasonably priced too. It offers a range of modern facilities. / *midnight; Lodge Catering; no outdoor amp music; The Hall (150,–,60,–); Theatre (–,–,–,750).*

Royal Holloway College TW20
£B-M, (200,200,–,400)
Egham
Ⓣ 01784 443045
Ⓕ 01784 443797
Ⓦ hardens.com/party/royalholloway
Ⓔ sales-office@rhul.ac.uk
The impressive Picture Gallery of this extraordinary Victorian confection (which claims to house the country's top collection of art of the era) makes a striking venue for

a dinner. You can also use the Dining Hall, which is larger (and, when dressed, almost as impressive). / 12.30am; conferences - university vacation only; in-house caterers; some restrictions on music; no dancing in Picture Gallery; Picture Gallery (200,120,–,200); Windsor Auditorium (–,–,–,400); Large Boardroom (–,26,–,24); Small Boardroom (–,10,–,16); Founder's Dining Hall (200,200,–,200).

Royal Horseguards SW1
£M-E, (50,48,–,35)
2 Whitehall Court
T 0871 376 9033
F 0871 376 9133
W hardens.com/party/royalhorseguards

Most venue enquiries at this huge Victorian hotel are accommodated at its adjacent conference centre, One Whitehall Place. The hotel does have a few smaller rooms of its own, however, including 'The Terrace', which has exclusive use of an outside terrace next to Victoria Embankment Gardens. / 1am; hirer's choice of caterer (in-house available); The Thames Suite (50,48,–,35); The Terrace (50,30,–,20); The Chelsea Suite (–,–,–,35); The Waterloo (–,–,–,20); The London (–,12,–,–).

DONT FORGET THE INDEXES!

see the back of this guide for venues listed by price, capacity, area, wedding license, outside area and hirer's choice of caterer

The Royal Horticultural Halls SW1
£B-M, (1800,900,750,1000)
80 Vincent Sq
T 0845 370 4606
F 020 7834 2072
W www.rhhonline.co.uk
E horthalls@rhs.org.uk

Available for events for up to 1000 guests, The RHH provides a flexible space for a wide variety of events including award ceremonies, banquets, fashion shows and product launches. Whether you're looking for a dramatic Art Deco setting, a stylish Edwardian backdrop or an elegant blank canvas, The RHH offers the perfect location. / midnight; Leith's; max 85 decibels in Lawrence; Lawrence Hall (1800,900,750,1000); Lindley Hall (650,420,350,450).

Royal Hospital Chelsea SW3
£M-E, (300,275,150,150)
Royal Hospital Rd
T 020 7881 5298
F 020 7881 5319
W hardens.com/party/royalhospital
E eventsao@chelsea-pensioners.org.uk

Charles II founded this impressive hospital, designed by Wren, as a home for old soldiers. That primary role – as the home of the Chelsea Pensioner – continues to this day. Its impressive buildings sit in 66 acres of grounds. A number of event facilities are available. / CoE services

only- special circumstances; midnight; list of caterers; no amplified music; no dancing; Great Hall (350,272,–,–); State Apartments (200,96,150,150).

Royal Institute of British Architects W1

£M, (400,250,70,300)

66 Portland Pl

T 020 7307 3888
F 020 7307 3763
W hardens.com/party/riba
E venues@inst.riba.org

This is an elegant '30s building, and its central (Florence) hall makes an impressive venue for receptions and dinners. A large terrace and an impressive café space are among other accommodation also available. / outside area unavailable after 9pm; 11.30pm (flexible); Charlton House; Lutyens Rm (70,30,–,70); Florence Hall (400,250,70,–); Jarvis Auditorium (–,–,–,280); Wren (120,40,–,100); Council Chamber (–,20,–,60); Aston Webb (–,25,–,40).

Royal Institution of Great Britain W1

£B-M, (300,440,–,440)

21 Albemarle St

T 020 7670 2905
F 020 7670 2920
W hardens.com/party/rigb
E venuehire@ri.ac.uk

The renowned Mayfair science institution, where Faraday discovered electricity, has recently undergone a major redevelopment. The Grade I listed spaces, including the libraries and famous 440 seat theatre, have been fully refurbished while new additions to the building include a glass atrium, bar, restaurant and exhibition spaces. / 11pm; available Sat & Sun; Digby Trout in-house; Library (100,70,–,60); Ante Rm (70,–,–,–); Georgian Rm (100,30,–,–).

Royal Lancaster W2

£M-E, (2000,1050,700,1000)

Lancaster Terr

T 020 7262 6737
F 020 77068174
W hardens.com/party/royallancaster
E events@royallancaster.com

An (over-) prominent feature of the Kensington Gardens landscape, offers one of the largest ballrooms in town. / 2am; in-house caterers.

Royal Observatory SE10

£E, (150,60,–,–)

The Avenue

T 020 8312 8517
F 020 8312 6572
W hardens.com/party/royalobs
E events@nmm.ac.uk

Survey London from this lofty 0° vantage-point in Greenwich Park. The charming top-floor Octagon room is one of the few surviving Wren interiors, and its long, narrow windows have one of the best views of the metropolis. Guests can enjoy telescope viewings, with the Observatory's team of astronomers. / no naked flames; 11pm; available evenings only; list of caterers; no dancing; no red wine.

Royal Opera House WC2

£M-E, (1000,450,400,450)

Bow St

T 020 7212 9150
F 020 7212 9172
W www.royalopera.org
E commercialevents@roh.org.uk

The ROH offers a wealth of event spaces for daytime hire and is an ideal venue for conferences, launches and lunches. Evening evening availability is very limited, please contact the venue for available dates. / all functions must involve food; 11pm; limited evening availability; Searcy's; Paul Hamlyn Hall (1000,450,400,450); Crush Room (220,100,60,160); Conservatory (60,30,–,40); Amphitheatre Bar (480,200,150,–); Amphi Restaurant (200,130,80,70); Linbury Theatre (400,300,250,394); Trust Rooms (60,40,–,40); Lambert Studio (60,40,–,50); Macmillan (110,100,–,80); Ashton Studio (300,250,200,200).

Royal Over-Seas League SW1

£B-M, (250,180,140,250)

Park Pl

T 020 7629 0406
F 020 7629 9586
W hardens.com/party/rosl
E rosl@convexleisure.co.uk

A reasonable degree of grandeur, relatively affordably, is the attraction of this clubby establishment near the Ritz. The smaller rooms of the older buildings, overlooking Green Park, are better suited to entertaining than the larger ones in the '30s annexe. / 11pm; Convex Leisure; Mountbatten (45,32,–,–).

Royal Society of Arts WC2

£M, (250,120,120,202)
8 John Adam St
T 020 7930 5115
F 020 7321 0271
W hardens.com/party/royalsocietyofarts
E conference@rsa.org.uk
Five converted c18 houses, just off the Strand, whose vaults offer most flexibility for functions (even if the space is rather broken up). The other accommodation includes small dining rooms, with original Adam ceilings. / 11pm ; in-house caterers; dancing only in the Vaults; Great Rm (–,–,–,202); Benjamin Franklin Rm (150,110,–,100); Vaults (220,120,120,–); Tavern Rm (50,30,–,50); Folkestone Rm (30,14,–,–); Adelphi (50,28,–,50); Romney (40,20,–,30).

Royal Statistical Society EC1

£M, (150,100,–,200)
12 Errol St
T 020 7614 3904
F 020 7614 3905
W hardens.com/party/rss
E rooms@rss.org.uk
Following conversion of a former Victorian school, the Barbican headquarters of the Royal Statistical Society now provides a light and airy working environment for meetings and small conferences. / 5.30pm; list of caterers; Lecture Theatre (150,100,–,200); Council Chamber (80,40,–,60); New Meeting Rm (25,16,–,20); Old Meeting Rm (–,14,–,–); Basement (150,50,–,–).

Rubens SW1

£M, (130,160,120,90)
39 Buckingham Palace Rd
T 020 7963 0703
F 020 7233 6037
W hardens.com/party/rubenshotel
E ksnyman@rchmail.com
Facing the Royal Mews, this Victoria hotel has agreeable banqueting facilities, fairly traditional in style. / 11pm; in-house caterers; Old Masters Restaurant (–,160,120,–); Rembrandt Rm (80,44,–,–); Rubens Suite (60,22,–,–).

Ruby Blue WC2

£M, (550,200,200,70)
1 Leicester Place
T 020 7287 8050
F 020 7287 0100
W hardens.com/party/rubybluebar
E info@rubybluebar.co.uk
A clubby bar/restaurant, just off Leicester Square. It would make a very central location for a large party. / 3am; in-house caterers; Conference (50,36,–,36); Balcony Bar (–,60,–,70); Main Bar (450,150,–,–); Restaurant (150,120,–,–).

Saatchi Gallery SW3

£M-E, (1500,1100,–,1500)
Duke of York's HQ
T 020 8968 9331
W www.saatchigallery.com/events
E venues@gsp-uk.com

In the heart of Chelsea, set within the striking Duke of York's HQ, the acclaimed Saatchi Gallery offers 70,000 sq ft over three floors of stunning event space, comprising twelve interlinking galleries, suitable as a blank canvas for memorable bespoke events for up to 1500 guests. / 10pm - extension to midnight avaliable; always available; approved list of caterers; Gallery 1, 5, 7, 8, 12 (300,200,–,320); Gallery 2, 4, 6, 9, 11 (280,180,–,280); Gallery 3 (320,200,–,300); Gallery 10 (260,160,–,260).

Saddlers' Hall EC2

£M-E, (250,139,–,150)
40 Gutter Ln
T 020 7726 8661
F 020 7600 0386
W hardens.com/party/saddlershall
E hallmanager@saddlersco.co.uk
This traditional livery hall, erected in the '50s, can accommodate a wide range of functions such as business meetings, presentations, receptions,

informal dinner parties and banquets. / 11pm; weekdays only; list of caterers; no amplified music; no dancing; The Great Hall (250,139,–,150); The Court Room (60,28,–,–); The Livery Room (80,–,–,43); The Warden's Room (–,8,–,–).

Sadler's Wells Theatre EC1

£M-E, (1500,300,80,1500)
Rosebery Av
T 020 7863 8065
F 020 7863 8061
W hardens.com/party/sadlerswells
E events@sadlerswells.com

This famous theatre occupies a striking modern building on the fringe of Islington, with a good range of rooms for presentations, dinners and receptions. / auditorium limited; 11pm; in-house caterers; Lillian Bayliss Theatre (350,150,60,200); Fonteyn Rm (50,30,22,30); Sackler (–,16,–,–); Cripplegate (–,16,–,–); Kahn Theatre (50,50,–,75); Cable & Wireless (190,70,40,100); Mezzanine Wood (180,150,40,–).

Salters' Hall EC2

£M-E, (250,150,80,180)
4 Fore St
T 020 7826 4059
F 020 7638 3679
W hardens.com/party/saltershall
E beadle@salters.co.uk

Intriguingly designed '70s hall in the heart of the City. It provides a calming backdrop for events both social (including weddings) and corporate. / midnight; Create; Mail Hall (200,125,–,180); Court Rm (100,50,–,60); Dining Rm (–,22,–,–); Garden (250,–,–,–).

The Sanctuary WC2

£M-E, (100,–,–,–)
12 Floral St
T 0870 770 3350
F 01442 43001
W hardens.com/party/sanctuary
E info@thesanctuary.co.uk

This Covent Garden health spa is among the most exotic settings central London affords. You can twist by the pool (complete with palms and tropical fish). Private parties are the only times men are allowed on the premises. / 10.30pm; available Tue after 6:30pm; Restaurant Associates; no amplified music; no dancing; only wines and champagnes.

Sartoria W1

£M-E, (80,150,140,–)
20 Savile Row
T 020 7534 7000
F 020 7534 7070
W www.sartoriabar.com
E sartoriareservations@danddlondon.com

Sartoria brings excellent Italian cooking to the home of English tailoring, Savile Row. The restaurant is elegant and airy and inspired in design by the Italian Rationalist period. The menu features robust, uncomplicated Italian food using organic and seasonal produce along with an extensive and varied wine list offering over 200 wines. / in-house caterers; Private Rm 1 (40,24,–,–); Private Rm 2 (40,24,–,–); Combined Rooms (80,48,–,–).

Sauterelle EC3

£M-E, (–,60,–,–)
The Royal Exchange
T 020 7628 3500
W www.restaurantsauterelle.co.uk
E rexevents@danddlondon.com

Situated on the mezzanine level of the Royal Exchange, Sauterelle is sophisticated dining at its best. This fine dining restaurant offers contemporary French cooking, expertly prepared, with flavours that are fresh and light. Sauterelle is available for groups of up to 20 or for exclusive use for up to 50 guests. / special requests to be mentioned at point of booking; 11pm; noon-4 am, 6pm-11pm; in-house caterers; restrictions on music; restrictions on dancing; restrictions on alcohol.

Savile Club W1

£M, (300,200,200,200)
69 Brook St
T 020 7629 5462
F 020 7499 7087
W hardens.com/party/savileclub
E admin@savileclub.co.uk

A Georgian Mayfair house, remodelled in opulent Gallic style at the end of the 19th century, and offering a characterful setting for private events. / 11pm, 1am extension available for weekend bookings; in-house caterers; classical music is fine during the week.

Savoy WC2

£M-E, (800,500,375,–)
Strand
T 020 7836 4343
W hardens.com/party/savoy
E savoy@fairmont.com

This world-famous riverside hotel is set to re-open after years of major refurbishment in October 2010. The main event spaces – the riverside ballroom, and large suite of small rooms for private dinners – have been refurbished, but not undergone the massive changes some parts of the building have. / 1am; in-house caterers; Lancaster Rm (800,500,375,–); Abraham Lincoln & Manhattan Rms (400,200,150,–); River Rm (350,120,120,–); Beaufort Rm (–,120,80,–); Pinafore (–,80,50,–); Gondoliers (–,50,30,–); Mikado (–,35,18,–).

Schochu Lounge W1

£M, (80,55,–,–)
37 Charlotte Street
T 0871 223 7951
F 020 7580 0220
W hardens.com/party/shochulounge
E info@roka.com

Named after the Japanese vodka-style spirit that is its speciality (bottles of which adorn the shelves), this richly decorated den is in stark contrast to the bright restaurant (Roka), above. It makes a luxurious venue for a loungey event. / very restricted availability; midnight; in-house caterers; no dancing.

School of Pharmacy WC1

£B-M, (300,150,–,196)
29-39 Brunswick Sq
T 020 7753 5816
F 020 7753 5941
W hardens.com/party/pharmacy
E jean.goodyear@pharmacy.ac.uk

A large hall – with big windows facing on to Bayswater's Brunswick Square – with potential for many kinds of functions. / midnight; available evenings & weekends; in-house caterers; John Hanbury Lecture Theatre (–,–,–,196); Maplethorpe Theatre (–,–,–,184); Refectory (200,80,–,–).

Science Museum SW7

£M-E, (2000,500,430,416)
Exhibition Rd
T 020 7942 4340
F 020 7942 4345
W www.sciencemuseum.org.uk/functions
E science.eventsoffice@nmsi.ac.uk

You aren't short of talking points at this renowned museum, which offers a diverse range of daytime and evening corporate hire facilities. The galleries have the added bonus of being pre-themed. / 11.30pm; galleries from 6pm; list of caterers; Flight Gallery (500,500,350,–); Imax Cinema (–,–,–,416); Energy Hall (600,–,–,–); Exploring Space (250,150,–,–); Making The Modern World (750,430,400,–); Welcome Wing (Ground) (600,350,–,–); Level 1 (400,400,–,400); Director's Suite (150,80,–,100); Dana Centre (–,50,–,110).

The Scotch Malt Whisky Society EC1

£M, (20,12,–,12)
19 Greville St
T 020 7831 4447
F 020 7242 8494
W hardens.com/party/maltlondon
E events@smws.co.uk

You don't have to finish with a whisky tasting if you entertain in these elegant Clerkenwell rooms. Rude not to, though! / 11pm; Bleeding Heart; no amplified music; no dancing.

Scott's W1
£B-M, (50,40,–,–)
20 Mount St
Ⓣ 020 7495 7309
Ⓕ 020 7647 6236
Ⓦ hardens.com/party/scotts
Ⓔ reception@scotts-restaurant.com

Perhaps the grandest all-purpose restaurant in town nowadays, Richard Caring's revamped Mayfair seafood specialist has an Art-Deco styled private dining room available for lunch and dinner parties, receptions and presentations. */ midnight; available from noon; in-house caterers; Private Room (50,40,–,–).*

Serpentine Bar & Kitchen W2
£B-M, (300,150,–,–)
Serpentine Rd
Ⓣ 020 7706 8114
Ⓦ hardens.com/party/serpentinebarkitchen
Ⓔ events@benugo.com

Located within the picturesque surroundings of Hyde Park overlooking the lake, this public space that opened in mid-2009 is only available to hire privately half a dozen times during the summer months. There are no restrictions on hiring during the rest of the year. */ midnight; in-house caterers.*

Serpentine Gallery W2
£M-E, (150,70,–,70)
Kensington Gdns
Ⓣ 020 7298 1522
Ⓕ 020 7402 4103
Ⓦ hardens.com/party/serpentinegallery
Ⓔ judithc@serpentinegallery.org

With its idyllic location for a summer function, the gallery is well suited to entertaining. It has four chambers fanning out from the domed central gallery, and, from Jun-Sep, capacity is extended by the addition of a temporary 'structure', by a world-renowned architect. */ companies only; 11pm; available from 6 pm; list of caterers.*

7 Rifles Battalion W1
£B-M, (300,250,200,–)
56 Davies St
Ⓣ 020 7629 3674
Ⓕ 020 7414 3488
Ⓦ hardens.com/party/7rifles
Ⓔ 7rifles-focy-psao@mod.uk

This Mayfair TA outpost, just off Oxford Street, offers a large hall, suited to events such as dinner dances and wedding receptions. The Club Bar is worth considering for stag nights, discos and so on. */ restricted availability; 1am; not Tue; hirer's choice of caterer (in-house available); Club Bar (100,–,–,–).*

76 Portland Place W1
£M, (–,170,120,170)
76 Portland Place
Ⓣ 020 7470 4884
Ⓕ 020 7470 4931
Ⓦ hardens.com/party/portlandplace
Ⓔ enquiries@76portlandplace.com

The conference and banqueting facility of the Institute of Physics is marketed as an independent venture. The Rutherford Suite is a flexible conference or presentation space. It is complemented by a separate catering suite, which can also be used independently. */ 10pm; in-house caterers; Rutherford Suite (–,–,120,170); Eddington Room (–,24,–,–); Franklin Theatre (–,–,–,90); Herschel Room (–,60,30,40); Phillips Room (–,33,–,45); Ada Lovelace Room (–,20,–,40); Gutherie Room (–,24,–,–); Faraday Room (–,20,–,–); Garnder Meeting (–,11,–,–); Hooke Room (–,40,–,80).*

Shadow Lounge W1
£M, (300,120,150,–)
5 Brewer St
Ⓣ 020 7317 9270
Ⓕ 020 7287 8389
Ⓦ hardens.com/party/shadowlounge
Ⓔ info@theshadowlounge.co.uk

This Soho venue claims to be the capital's No.1 gay venue. Popularity is such that private hire is generally only available on Sunday. */ 3am; in-house caterers.*

Shaftesbury Theatre WC2

£M, (150,1278,–,1301)

210 Shaftesbury Av

T 020 7379 3345
F 020 7836 8181
W hardens.com/party/shaftesburytheatre
E swatson@toc.dltentertainment.co.uk

Large Edwardian theatre, not a million miles from the British Museum, available for hire subject to the constraints of performances (which is usually on Sundays). / restricted availability; available subject to constraints of current production; hirer's choice of caterer (in-house available); no dancing; Bars (150,20,–,–).

Shaka Zulu NW1

£M, (850,470,–,–)

Stables Market

T 020 7428 8990
W www.shaka-zulu.com
E samantha@shaka-zulu.com

Shaka-Zulu is an authentic South African restaurant & lounge bar. 27,000 sq ft over 2 floors. 1000 standing 600 seated. Available for part or exclusive hire. Breakfast meetings, intimate dinners, product launches, canapé parties, show cases, fashion shows, full exclusive takeovers, Christmas packages available on request. / *Seated Downstairs (–,350,–,–); Seated Upstairs (–,120,–,–).*

Shampers W1

£B, (130,90,–,–)

4 Kingly St

T 020 7439 9910
F 020 7287 1097
W hardens.com/party/shampers.net

You can organise private dinners and receptions in the basement of this comfortably worn-in Soho wine bar and restaurant. At weekends, the whole place is available. / *midnight; in-house caterers; Restaurant (Ground Floor & Basement) (90,90,–,–); Bar (40,–,–,–); Downstairs Lounge (60,45,–,–).*

Shanghai Blues WC1

£M, (400,200,–,–)

193-197 High Holborn

T 020 7404 1668
F 020 7404 1448
W hardens.com/party/shanghaiblues
E info@shanghaiblues.co.uk

In north Covent Garden – an area with few competing attractions – this elegantly kitted-out Chinese restaurant offers a variety of lofty spaces for private (or semi-private) events. The private dining room is particularly impressive. / *midnight; in-house caterers; Private Dining Rm (40,30,–,–).*

Shepherd's SW1

£M, (–,32,–,–)

Marsham Court

T 020 7834 9552
F 020 7233 6047
W hardens.com/party/shepherds
E admin@langansrestaurants.co.uk

Bright, art-filled and clubby, this English restaurant in Westminster is of note for its large, comfortable and rather grand private dining room. / *12.30am; in-house caterers; no amplified music; no dancing.*

Sheraton Park Tower SW1

£M-E, (150,120,–,80)

101 Knightsbridge

T 020 7290 7294
F 020 7290 7566
W hardens.com/party/sheratonparktower
E events.centrallondon@sheraton.com

Central London's most prominent cylindrical hotel has a number of rooms for events. Perhaps of most interest is the Trianon, on the terrace of which you can have a barbecue. / *1am; in-house caterers; Trianon Rm (150,120,–,80); Venture Rm (60,30,–,40); Inspiration Rm (40,22,–,25); Discovery Rm (40,16,–,20).*

Ship & Shovell WC2

£B, (30,–,–,–)
1-3 Craven Pas
T 020 7839 1311
F 020 7839 1313
W hardens.com/party/shipshovell

Locations don't come much more central than this boozer by – or rather under – Charing Cross station. The place is divided into two entirely distinct halves, which has the advantage that you can take one side for a private event without upsetting the regulars too much. / 11pm; in-house caterers; no music.

Shoreditch House E1

£M-E, (200,160,–,–)
Ebor Street
T 020 7739 5040
W hardens.com/party/shoreditchhouse

You have to be signed up as a member to organise a party around the rooftop pool of this über-chic new club (from the Soho House Group), or for at the private dining room or 'Snug'. The 'Biscuit Tin' space, and adjacent 'Biscuit Pin' bowling alleys are open to all. / Biscuit Tin (120,80,–,–); Biscuit Pin (50,–,–,–); Snug (Members Only) (–,18,–,–); Private Dining Room (Members Only) (–,14,–,–); Roof Top Bar (Members Only) (200,160,–,–).

Shoreditch Town Hall EC1

£B-M, (700,500,400,–)
380 Old Street
T 020 7739 6176
F 020 7729 8909
W hardens.com/party/shoreditchtownhall
E frontdoor@shoreditch.org.uk

An impressive and very characterful Victorian building, now run by a charitable trust, offering a couple of rooms suited to larger gatherings. / midnight; hirer's choice of caterer; Council Room (200,150,100,–).

Signor Sassi SW1

£B-M, (50,30,–,–)
14 Knightsbridge Green
T 020 7584 2277
F 020 7225 3953
W hardens.com/party/signorsassi
E signorsassi@sancarlos.com

Perennially popular with the Knightsbridge crowd, a jolly Italian restaurant well suited to private parties. The first-floor private room is decorated in Venetian style. / 11.30pm; available from noon; in-house caterers; Private Room (50,30,–,–).

Simon Drake's House of Magic SE1

£M, (150,85,150,–)
PO Box 20457
T 020 7735 4777
W hardens.com/party/houseofmagic
E info@houseofmagic.co.uk

One of London's more original venues – a permanently themed Victorian haunted house. (It's owned by the star of Channel 4's 'The Secret Cabaret' – illusionist, Simon Drake.) Includes Haunted Cellar Tours, Fortune-Telling on The Whispering Chair and Simon Drake's Mind-Blowing Magical Extravaganza. / 1am (flexible); list of caterers; no live bands.

Simpsons-in-the-Strand WC2

£M, (500,270,200,–)
100 Strand
T 020 7836 9112
F 020 7836 1381
W hardens.com/party/simpsonsstrand
E svy.simpsons@fairmont.com

A famous solidly Edwardian English restaurant. The Bishops' Room downstairs is one of the oldest in London, and perfect for a mid-sized dinner. The upper floors could accommodate quite grand events. / 10.30pm; in-house caterers; no amplified music; no dancing; Bishops' Rm (150,50,–,–).

Siobhan Davies Studios SE1

£M-E, (250,150,100,150)
85 St George's Road
T 020 7091 9650
F 020 7091 9669
W hardens.com/party/siobhandavies
E info@siobhandavies.com

South Bank dance studios whose light and airy design received a prestigious RIBA award in 2006. With two studios and several ancillary spaces, events can occupy one room or the entire building. The Roof Studio holds a wedding licence.

Suitable for conferences, seminars and smaller meetings too. / midnight; hirer's choice of caterer.

Sir John Soane's Museum WC2

£E, (80,30,–,–)
13 Lincoln's Inn Fields
Ⓣ 020 7405 2107
Ⓕ 020 7831 3957
Ⓦ www.soane.org.uk
Ⓔ jbrock@soane.org.uk

One of the most original Regency house-museums in the world and designed by one of Britain's greatest architects, Sir John Soane. A pre-dinner tour of Soane's collections of architectural fragments, marbles, paintings and sculpture can be arranged, and dinner is served in the candlelit, mirrored Library-Dining Room. / no stilettos; 11.30pm; generally 5pm-11.30pm Mon-Sat; Mustard, By Word of Mouth, Zaperona, Rhubarb, Blue Strawberry (lisr; no amplified music; no dancing; no red wine at receptions.

606 Club SW10

£B-M, (165,135,–,–)
90 Lots Rd
Ⓣ 020 7352 5953
Ⓕ 020 7349 0655
Ⓦ hardens.com/party/606club
Ⓔ jazz@606club.co.uk

Cellar jazz club/restaurant, intriguingly located down an anonymous staircase, opposite Chelsea's former Lots Road power station. For private hires there is no fee – just a minimum catering-spend. / 2am; not available Fri & Sat; in-house caterers.

06 St Chad's Place WC1

£B-M, (120,–,–,–)
6 St Chad's Pl
Ⓣ 020 7278 3355
Ⓕ 020 7278 6336
Ⓦ hardens.com/party/6stchadsplace
Ⓔ info@6stchadsplace.com

In the back streets near King's Cross, right by a tube line, this contemporary conversion of former industrial premises comes as a real surprise, and makes an intriguing setting for an event. / 11pm; not Thurs or Fri (except Christmas); in-house caterers.

Sixteen Park Crescent W1

£M, (80,40,40,60)
16 Park Crescent
Ⓣ 020 7612 7070
Ⓦ hardens.com/party/16parkcrescent

Run by the Institute of Chartered Secretaries and Administrators (who also use the building), this Nash house near Regent's Park, and with agreeable views of the neighbouring gardens, makes a pleasant venue, primarily for seminars and daytime meetings (though evening events are possible). / 5pm (out of hours charges apply if clients wish to stay on until 9pm); in-house caterers.

SixtyOne Whitehall SW1

£M, (200,100,80,180)
Whitehall
Ⓣ 020 7747 2622
Ⓦ hardens.com/party/rusi

The airy D-shaped Lecture Theatre at these Whitehall premises (formerly known by the name of its owners – the RUSI) is particularly suited to receptions (and has held discos). The clubby Library (with books, for once) is a cosy and interesting place for a formal dinner. / 1am; hirer's choice of caterer; Duke of Wellington Rm (200,100,80,180); Reading Rm (80,40,–,–); Library (100,60,–,–).

Sketch W1

£M-E, (650,150,120,150)
9 Conduit Street
Ⓣ 0870 777 4488
Ⓕ 0870 777 4400
Ⓦ hardens.com/party/sketch
Ⓔ emilyg@sketch.uk.com

A no-expense-spared conversion of a grand Mayfair townhouse, famous as a haunt of the media and fashion worlds. If you have really deep pockets you can have a meal in the stratospherically expensive Lecture Room (either privately or in the semi-private Library section)… or just take over the whole building. / 2am; not available Sun; in-house caterers; Gallery (250,140,120,150); Lecture Rm (–,45,–,–); Glade (80,50,–,–).

Skinners' Hall EC4
£M-E, (300,170,170,150)
8 1/2 Dowgate Hill
T 020 7213 0553
F 020 7213 0568
W hardens.com/party/skinners
E sales@skinnershall.co.uk
Imposing but charming, the Skinners' Company's accommodation near Cannon Street, entered via a courtyard, offers a number of possibilities. The restored c17 Hall is rich and red. Other rooms are grand, in a relaxed country house style, and there is a modern roof garden, with fountain, for fair-weather receptions. / midnight; *not August; in-house caterers; Banqueting Hall (300,170,80,160); Old Court Rm (120,60,–,80); Roof Garden (200,–,–,–); Outer Hall (100,–,–,–); Parlour (–,12,–,–); Commitee Room (–,16,–,–).*

Skylon SE1
£M-E, (500,200,–,–)
Southbank Centre
T 020 7654 7800
F 020 7654 7801
W hardens.com/party/skylon
E skylonreservations@danddlondon.com
Once known as 'The People's Palace' – this '50s-tastic chamber in the Royal Festival Hall is a wonderful, if cavernous space, with splendid views over the Thames. There are three sections – bar, grill and restaurant, each of which may be hired individually. / in-house caterers; *Restaurant (–,74,–,–); Grill (–,112,–,–); Bar (60,30,–,–).*

Smith's of Smithfield EC1
£M-E, (900,130,130,–)
67-77 Charterhouse St
T 020 7236 7666
F 020 7236 0488
W hardens.com/party/sos
E natasha@smithsofsmithfield.com
This four-floor Smithfield warehouse-conversion bar/restaurant offers a variety of settings for events. Most spectacular is the top floor, with its open-air terrace. / midnight, *Sun 10.30pm; in-house caterers; Top Floor (250,130,80,–); Wine Room (150,70,–,–); Private Rm 1 (–,24,–,–); Private Rm 2 (–,12,–,–).*

Sofitel London St James SW1
£M, (200,130,90,180)
6 Waterloo Place
T 020 7747 2237
F 020 7747 2210
W www.sofitelstjames.com
E H3144-SB@sofitel.com

The hotel offers 12 function rooms with some of the latest technology. The facilities are ideal for meetings for 2-180 delegates, banquets and wedding receptions for up to 150 guests. In addition, the hotel offers a boardroom for up to 12 guests including a reception area and private dining room. / midnight but can *be extended; in-house caterers; Westminister (200,130,90,180); Mayfair A&B (170,100,60,160); Piccadilly/Bloomsbury (80,50,40,70); Kensington (45,20,16,40); Boardroom & Private Dining Room (–,12,–,–).*

Soho Hotel W1
£M-E, (180,50,–,100)
4 Richmond Mews
T 020 7559 3000
F 020 7287 5551
W hardens.com/party/sohohotel
E events@firmdale.com
Soho is surprisingly short of sophisticated spaces for events. This Firmdale Group boutique hotel fits the bill well, and its basement has an attractive suite of function/meeting rooms, incorporating a bar, and next to two private screening rooms. The ground floor bar/restaurant, also has a small private dining room. / midnight; *in-house caterers.*

Soho House W1
£M, (200,42,–,40)
40 Greek St
Ⓣ 020 7734 5188
Ⓕ 020 7292 0170
Ⓦ hardens.com/party/sohohouse

This fashionable media club in Soho has a number of rooms for events which can be hired by non-members. / no disabled access; 3am; in-house caterers; Roof Deck (70,42,–,40); Cinema (–,–,–,27).

Somerset House WC2
£M-E, (1500,550,450,100)
Strand
Ⓣ 0844 858 0601
Ⓕ 020 7836 7613
Ⓦ www.somersethouse.org.uk
Ⓔ events@somersethouse.org.uk

With nine venues available to host your meeting, dinner, reception or wedding, Somerset House is the ideal central London, riverside destination for any occasion. With diverse and flexible spaces, including alfresco, Somerset House can offer a host of opportunities for corporate and private events from 8 to 1,500 guests. / 11pm; only Navy Board Rm and Portico Rm available for daytime hire; list of caterers; Edmond J. Safra Fountain Court (with marquee) (1500,550,450,–); The Courtauld Gallery (220,50,–,–); Seamen's Hall (200,120,80,–); River Terrace (550,250,200,–); Portico Rooms (200,80,–,100); Navy Board Rooms (100,60,–,60); Terrace Rooms (100,50,50,–); Screening Room (–,–,–,60); Embankment East (350,120,80,100).

Souk WC2
£B-M, (–,130,–,–)
27 Litchfield St
Ⓣ 020 7240 1796
Ⓕ 020 7240 3382
Ⓦ hardens.com/party/souk
Ⓔ info@soukrestaurant.co.uk

For a budget party meal in the heart of the West End, this younger-scene Moroccan, a few doors down from the Ivy, is well worth knowing about. It has lots of nooks and crannies for different sized tables, or – so long as you are approaching capacity – you could book the whole place. / midnight; in-house caterers; no amplified music; no dancing.

Sound London WC2
£M, (1000,180,180,–)
1 Leicester Square
Ⓣ 0870 863 1010
Ⓕ 0870 862 1111
Ⓦ hardens.com/party/soundlondon
Ⓔ events@soundlondon.com

Incorporating the third, fourth and fifth floors of no 1 Leicester Sq, this versatile venue is available to hire for a range of events including corporate events, product launches, and conferences. / 3am; in-house caterers.

South London Gallery SE5
£M, (300,200,150,–)
65 Peckham Rd
Ⓣ 020 7703 6120
Ⓕ 020 7252 4730
Ⓦ hardens.com/party/southlondongallery
Ⓔ soh@southlondongallery.org

A purpose-built Victorian gallery, naturally top-lit, associated with some of the BritArt 'greats'. Following a major expansion programme in 2009, there are now three different areas for hire in the venue. / 11pm; selected times - upon request; in-house caterers; Clore Studio (60,60,–,–); Double Height (–,20,–,–).

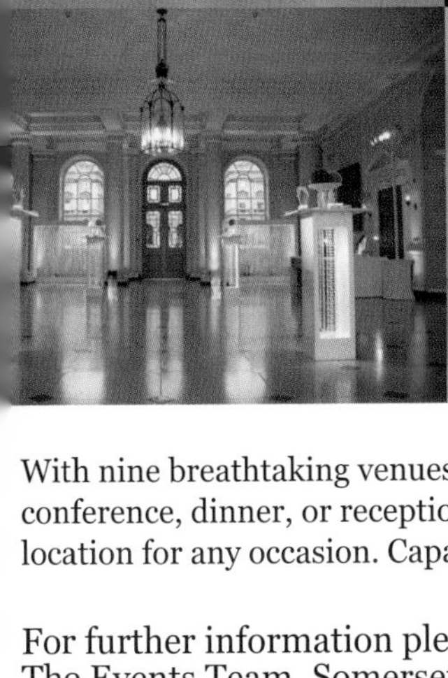

Southbank Centre SE1

£M-E, (900,400,300,2500)
Belvedere Road
Ⓣ 020 7921 0702
Ⓕ 020 7921 0810
Ⓦ www.southbankcentre.co.uk
Ⓔ events@southbankcentre.co.uk

From the grandeur of the Royal Festival Hall auditorium, to the intimate surroundings of the Sunley Pavilion, the Southbank Centre has a venue to meet your needs. As well as the three auditoria we have a wide variety of meeting and reception rooms to accommodate everything from award ceremonies to weddings. / no branding outside or in public foyer areas; 11pm; 8am - 11pm; list of caterers; Royal Festival Hall Auditorium (–,–,–,2500); Queen Elizabeth Hall Auditorium (–,–,–,900); Purcell Room (–,–,–,365); Level 5 Function Room (250,160,120,160); St Paul's Roof Pavilion (150,70,60,80); Weston Roof Pavilion (150,80,60,80); Sunley Pavilion (60,40,–,40); Level 3 Function Room (60,40,–,40); Clore Ballroom (900,400,300,400); Queen Elizabeth Hall foyer (900,200,150,200).

Southwark Cathedral SE1

£M, (400,150,–,80)
London Bridge
Ⓣ 020 7367 6722
Ⓕ 020 7367 6725
Ⓦ www.southwarkcathedral.org.uk
Ⓔ conferences@southwark.anglican.org

Next to London Bridge, and near the City and the Thames, this large cathedral offers a number of spaces for conferences and private dining. It also has a large courtyard, available for parties and marquee receptions. / 10pm; list of caterers; acapella or acoustic only; Garry Weston Library (120,50,–,80); Chapter Room (60,24,–,30); The New Room (60,24,–,30); The ECB Room (–,8,–,–); The Tutu Room (–,10,–,–); The JTW Room (60,20,–,40); The Courtyard (400,150,–,–).

SPACE E8

£M, (500,–,–,–)
129-131 Mare Street
Ⓣ 020 8525 4330
Ⓕ 020 8525 4342
Ⓦ hardens.com/party/spacestudios
Ⓔ hires@spacestudios.org.uk

If you're looking for a blank-canvas style venue you can dress to suit your needs, consider the gallery spaces run by this educational arts charity at The Triangle, which includes Hackney's largest gallery space. Also a converted riverside warehouse in Barking. / consciencous levels of noise; midnight; hirer's choice of caterer; no alcohol sales; Gallery 1 (200,–,–,–); Gallery 2 (100,–,–,–).

Space E14

£B-M, (120,90,90,–)
269 Westferry Road
Ⓣ 020 7515 7799
Ⓦ hardens.com/party/spacee14
Ⓔ info@space.org.uk

A multi-arts centre in Docklands, available for private hire. A converted church, it makes an atmospheric venue. / midnight; hirer's choice of caterer (in-house available).

Spencer House W1

£E, (450,126,–,–)
27 St James's Pl
Ⓣ 020 7514 1964
Ⓕ 020 7409 2952
Ⓦ www.spencerhouse.co.uk
Ⓔ events@spencerhouse.co.uk

One of London's more impressive palazzos, restored to its former 18th Century splendour and decorated with fine paintings and furniture – available for private and corporate events, receptions, civil weddings, recitals and presentations. / no stilettos; 11.30pm; available Mon-Sat lunch & dinner (not Jan, not Aug); in-house caterers; dancing on the Terrace only; Great Rm (180,90,–,–); Dining Room (180,–,–,–).

Spitalfields Market E1

£B-M, (1500,360,–,–)
105a Commercial Streeet
Ⓣ 020 7247 8556
Ⓕ 01952 245863
Ⓦ hardens.com/party/spitalfields
Ⓔ info@tcmarkets.co.uk

With 1000 square metres of covered space to play with, this atmospheric covered market to the east of the City may be just the place if you're trying to organise a really large happening that's not subject to the vagaries of the weather. / Areas 1-3 (500,120,–,–).

Spread Eagle SE10

£M, (–,30,–,–)
1-2 Stockwell St
T 020 8853 2333
W hardens.com/party/spreadeagle

An elegantly refurbished restaurant (in a former coaching inn), quietly located in Greenwich. There is a ground-floor private room, or you could hire the restaurant upstairs. / in-house caterers; Private Rm (–,14,–,–).

Spring Grove House TW7

£M, (120,80,–,–)
West Thames College
T 020 8569 7173
F 020 8847 2421
W hardens.com/party/springgrove
E ianb@west-thames.ac.uk

The Georgian house of Sir Joseph Banks (creator of Kew Gardens), remodelled in Victorian times, and now part of West Thames College. The largest room, the Winter Garden Room, features palms, a domed glass ceiling and mosaic floor. Starting in 2010, a three-year rebuilding project will limit its availability for hire. / no cooking on site; midnight; closed Sun; hirer's choice of caterer; Music Rm (50,50,–,–).

Square W1

£M, (–,75,–,–)
6-10 Bruton St
T 020 7495 7100
F 020 7495 7150
W hardens.com/party/square
E info@squarerestaurant.com

One of the 'safest' and most accomplished grand restaurants in town, this Mayfair stalwart boasts a private room situated next to the bar, ideal for small parties. / 1am; available from noon; in-house caterers; no amplified music; Private Room (–,18,–,–).

SS Robin E14

£M-E, (100,50,–,50)
West India Quay
T 020 7538 0652
F 0870 131 6566
W hardens.com/party/ssrobin
E info@ssrobin.org

The world's oldest complete steamship is currently undergoing a major programme of works, and is set to re-open for service – hopefully at a mooring at Bankside – in 2012. / midnight; list of caterers.

St Andrew Holborn EC4

£M, (200,130,–,300)
5 St Andrew St
T 020 7583 3498
F 020 7583 3488
W hardens.com/party/standrewholborn
E events@standrewholborn.org.uk

This 1870 courthouse, located just off Holborn Circus, incorporates an ornate and colourful Jacobean fireplace in the Court Room. The Crypt and Church are now available for hire. / no stag nights; midnight; hirer's choice of caterer (in-house available); no amplified music; no dancing; Crypt (100,–,–,40); Church (200,130,–,200); Courtroom (130,70,–,80).

St Bartholomew's Hospital EC1

£M, (300,190,–,–)
West Smithfield
T 020 7601 7871
F 020 7601 7080
W hardens.com/party/barts

Ascend the Hogarth staircase to find one of the most atmospheric halls in London (c18), all cream, gold and dark wood. / 11.30pm; not available on Sun; in-house caterers; Treasurer's Rm (40,18,–,–).

St Botolph's Hall EC2

£B-M, (150,80,50,100)
Bishopsgate
T 020 7588 1053
F 020 7638 1256
W hardens.com/party/stbotolphshall
E hallandcourt@botolph.org.uk

An oak-panelled Victorian church hall, next to Liverpool Street Station,

used for receptions, dinners and Christmas parties by City firms. The lower hall could be used for a disco or for children's entertainment.
/ 10pm; hirer's choice of caterer; Lower Hall (45,–,–,–).

St Bride Foundation EC4
£B, (200,80,90,150)
Bride Ln Fleet Street
Ⓣ 020 7353 3331
Ⓕ 020 7353 1547
Ⓦ hardens.com/party/stbridefoundation
Ⓔ info@stbridefoundation.org
A bright Victorian building, offering rooms of character to suit a wide range of occasions – from board meetings to receptions and banquets. It is attractively situated near the 'wedding cake' church of the same name, just off Fleet Street.
/ limited disabled access to certain rooms; 10pm; hirer's choice of caterer (in-house available); Bridewell Hall (200,80,90,150); Farringdon Rm (80,30,–,60); Salisbury Rm (45,20,–,50); Layton (40,25,–,40); Caxton (–,8,–,–); Parssmore Edwards Rm (50,30,–,30).

St James's Club & Hotel SW1
£M-E, (80,40,–,45)
7-8 Park Pl
Ⓣ 020 7629 7688
Ⓕ 020 7491 0987
Ⓦ hardens.com/party/stjclub
Ⓔ info@stjameshotelandclub.com
A discreet venue, in the heart of St James's. "London's only 5-star residential club hotel", it offers a number of venues suited to smaller events. / 11pm; in-house caterers; Mayfair Suite (60,40,–,45); Wellington Board Room (–,10,–,–); Library (20,16,–,25); Granville (–,8,–,–).

St John EC1
£M, (–,110,–,–)
26 St John St
Ⓣ 020 7251 0848
Ⓦ hardens.com/party/stjohnrestaurant
A Clerkenwell restaurant whose 'nose-to-tail' culinary style is a legend among foodies. There is a private room – where a 'feast' is the preferred catering style – at the front of the restaurant. / in-house caterers; Private Room (–,18,–,–).

St John's Gate EC1
£M, (260,100,–,–)
St John's Lane
Ⓣ 020 7324 4083
Ⓕ 020 7490 8835
Ⓦ hardens.com/party/stjohnsgate
Ⓔ alan.beggs@nhq.sja.org.uk
North of Smithfield market, this romantic medieval gatehouse – home to the Order of St John – is a local landmark. The stately Chapter Hall is a lofty, panelled room used for dinners and receptions. (It is opening again after quite a major redevelopment in September 2010).
/ 11pm; not available Sun; hirer's choice of caterer; no dancing; Chapter Hall (200,100,–,–).

St Martin In The Fields WC2
£B-M, (350,200,160,120)
Duncannon St
Ⓣ 020 7766 1100
Ⓕ 020 7839 5163
Ⓦ hardens.com/party/smitf
Ⓔ cafe@smitf.org
This atmospheric café in the crypt of Trafalgar Square's impressive church, recently refurbished, makes an interesting venue for a central party. / 2am; available evenings only; in-house caterers; no spirits; The Gallery (150,60,–,–); St Martins Hall (120,110,–,120).

St Martin's Lane Hotel WC2
£M-E, (180,96,–,130)
45 St Martin's Lane
Ⓣ 020 7300 5542
Ⓕ 020 7300 5529
Ⓦ hardens.com/party/stmlanehotel
Ⓔ fiona.helder@morganshotelgroup.com
This Covent Garden-fringe design hotel offers a fair range of accommodation suited to smaller events. / midnight; in-house caterers; music restrictions apply; The Studio (180,96,–,–); The Backroom (70,48,–,50); Board Rm (–,14,–,–).

St Mary's Church W1

£M, (600,300,300,600)
Wyndham Place
T 020 7258 5040
W hardens.com/party/stmary
E contact@stmaryslondon.com
Near Bryanston Square, a deconsecrated church, suited to event hire. / 10.30pm; not available Sun; hirer's choice of caterer (in-house available).

St Moritz W1

£B, (120,70,–,–)
159 Wardour St
T 020 7734 3324
F 020 7734 8995
W hardens.com/party/stmoritz
Despite its fame as a rock music venue, this Soho basement of Swiss grottoes – dance-floor, bar, and seating areas – lends itself well to other types of parties. / 3am; not available Thu-Sat; hirer's choice of caterer, alcohol in-house.

St Paul's Cathedral EC4

£M-E, (350,250,–,70)
The Chapter House
T 020 7246 8346
F 020 7248 3104
W www.stpaulscathedral.org.uk/corporateevents
E corporateevents@stpaulscathedral.org.uk

St Paul's Cathedral offers a unique venue for corporate events in one of the capital's great landmarks. Daytime meetings for up to 70 people can be accommodated, and also evening events for up to 350 guests. Temple Bar (next to Paternoster Square) can also be hired for events. / 10pm; list of caterers; no amplified music; no dancing; Wren Suite (100,60,70,70); Crypt (350,250,250,–); Temple Bar (20,12,–,–).

St Paul's Church W1

£B-M, (300,230,–,390)
Robert Adam St
T 020 7580 3522
F 020 7935 7486
W hardens.com/party/stpaulschurch
E bookings@allsouls.org
If you're organising a daytime gathering (of a suitably uplifting nature), it may be particularly worth considering the Blue Lounge room of this modern church, behind Selfridges. / very restricted availability; 10pm; not available Sun, restricted weekday evenings; hirer's choice of caterer; Blue Lounge (100,70,–,90); Church Area (200,160,–,300).

St Peter's Hall W11

£B-M, (100,80,–,–)
59a Portobello Rd
T 020 7792 8227
F 020 7727 4003
W hardens.com/party/stpeterw11
E admin@stpetershall.org.uk
This Victorian school building in Notting Hill, built around a small central courtyard, makes an atmospheric place for a party. / restricted availability; 10pm; available subject to constraints of nursery; hirer's choice of caterer; no amplified music; no hard liquors.

St Stephen's Club SW1

£M, (200,100,100,90)
34 Queen Anne's Gate
T 020 7222 1382
F 020 7222 8740
W hardens.com/party/ststephensclub
E info@ststephensclub.co.uk
A pleasant building overlooking St James's Park. It is a nice size to be taken over in its entirety, say for a wedding reception, and imparts a sense of occasion without stuffiness. / 11pm; in-house caterers; Queensborough Room (200,100,100,90); Garden Room (90,36,–,–).

St Thomas' Hospital SE1

£M, (250,200,90,200)
Westminster Bridge Road
T 020 7188 6522
F 020 7188 1154
W hardens.com/party/tommies
E hospitalitybookings@gstt.nhs.uk
Situated opposite the Houses of

Parliament in St Thomas' Hospital, the Governors Hall and Grand Committee Room are made available for a wide variety of events. / *1am; in-house caterers; Grand Committee Rm (50,24,–,–); Governor's Hall (250,125,90,200).*

The Stafford SW1

£M-E, (75,44,–,–)

16 St James's Pl

T 020 7493 0111

F 020 7493 7121

W hardens.com/party/staffordhotel

E info@thestaffordhotel.co.uk

It also has a good range of traditionally-furnished function rooms, but it is the wonderful wine-cellars – heading for four centuries old, but still very much in use – which are the special attraction of this cosy St James's hotel. / *12.30am; in-house caterers; no amplified music; Panel Rm & Sutherland Rm (50,40,–,–); The Cellar (75,44,–,–); Sutherland Rm (40,24,–,–); Pink & Argyll Rm (30,16,–,–).*

Stationers' Hall EC4

£M-E, (400,205,88,200)

Ave Maria Lane

T 020 7246 0999

F 020 7489 1975

W hardens.com/party/stationers

E marketing@stationers.org

Stationers' Hall is located next to St Paul's Cathedral and is within easy walking distance of most of the City. Its historic atmosphere provides the ideal venue for all types of events. In addition to three function rooms it also features a delightfully secluded garden – complete with 100-capacity Gazebo – also available. / *midnight; closed August; list of caterers; Livery Hall (400,205,88,200); Court Rm (160,90,–,120); Stock Rm (100,60,–,60); Ante Rm (–,22,–,–); Garden (250,–,–,–).*

Stoke Place SL2

£E, (500,200,80,200)

Stoke Green

T 01753 534790

F 01753 512743

W hardens.com/party/stokeplace

E enquiries@stokeplace.co.uk

An impressive William & Mary house, sympathetically restored as a luxurious boutique-style hotel. In 25 acres of parkland, it's just half an hour from the metropolis. / *1am; in-house caterers; Ballroom (400,180,200,200); Howard Vyse Rm (100,60,60,70); Lakeside (200,50,50,80); Thomas Gray (50,30,–,30).*

The Strand Gallery WC2

£B-M, (220,–,–,–)

5 Buckingham St

T 020 7839 4942

F 020 7839 4947

W www.proud.co.uk

E info@proudgalleries.co.uk

A stone's throw from Trafalgar Square, The Strand Gallery is a superb and competitively priced venue for holding events. The gallery occupies two floors and includes a catering room, storage facilities and a state of the art LINN sound system. The gallery can be hired without time restrictions beginning at £500. / *all day; hirer's choice of caterer; Gallery (140,–,–,–); Single Floor (70,–,–,–); Gallery With Marquee (220,–,–,–).*

Streatham Ice Arena SW16

£B-M, (1500,100,–,500)

386 Streatham High Rd

T 020 8769 7771

F 020 8769 9979

W hardens.com/party/streathamice

E starburstltd@lineone.net

For a skating party, numbers here are limited to 900, but if you board over the ice, you can accommodate 1500. There is a function room complete with kitchen, suitable for smaller parties. / *4pm; in-house caterers; no alcohol.*

Studio Valbonne W1
£M, (500,200,200,350)
62 Kingly St
T 020 7434 0888
F 020 7434 0999
W hardens.com/party/studiovalbonne
E allison@studiovalbonne.co.uk
An opulently decorated basement club, with a handy Soho location. / 6am; hirer's choice of caterer (in-house available).

Sugar Cane SW11
£B, (130,–,–,–)
247-249 Lavender Hill
T 020 7223 8866
W hardens.com/party/sugarcane
E info@thesugarcane.co.uk
If you want to achieve an 'Aloha vibe', this Tiki-style bar in Clapham might be just the thing for your party or event. Smaller gatherings can book out Tiki Huts or the 'Sunset Area', or for larger gatherings hire the whole place. / 12.30am.

Sugar Quay EC3
£M-E, (500,250,220,300)
Lower Thames Street
T 020 7518 2480
W hardens.com/party/sugarquay
On a Quay near the Tower of London – a luxury marquee with views of Tower Bridge and HMS Belfast, available for all kinds of receptions, dinners and product launches. / midnight (flexible); in-house caterers.

Summerhouse W9
£M, (120,60,–,–)
60 Blomfield Rd
T 020 7286 6752
W hardens.com/party/summerhouse
A lovely location, right by the canal in Little Venice, is the highlight at this summer restaurant (open April to October) run by the nearby Waterway bar, and available for exclusive hire.

Sumosan W1
£M, (200,100,–,–)
26 Albemarle St
T 020 7495 5999
F 020 7355 1247
W hardens.com/party/sumosan
E info@sumosan.com
This fashionably minimalist Japanese Mayfair restaurant is available for hire in its entirety. Alternatively take one of the private rooms. / 3am; available from noon; in-house caterers; no amplified music; Private Room (60,32,–,–).

Le Suquet SW3
£M, (–,25,–,–)
104 Draycott Av
T 020 7581 1785
W hardens.com/party/suquet
An old-fashioned Chelsea French fish restaurant, with a couple of nicely-proportioned private rooms upstairs. / in-house caterers; Private Rm (–,25,–,–); Private Rm (–,16,–,–).

Sutton House E9
£M, (–,–,–,100)
2-4 Homerton High St
T 020 8525 9055
W hardens.com/party/suttonhouse
E suttonhouse@nationaltrust.org.uk
The oldest house in Hackney (1535), this National Trust property has interiors ranging from dark oak panelling to lighter Georgian additions, and an enclosed courtyard. It offers an interesting setting for a civil wedding – availability is limited, though, and the reception must be held elsewhere. / wedding ceremonies only; noon; not available Mon-Thu; no food; no amplified music; no red wine; Wenlock Barn (including Café-Bar/Linenfold Parlour) (–,–,–,100); Marriage Suite (Great and Little Chambers) (–,–,–,50); Linenfold Parlour (–,–,–,16).

Swan at the Globe at Shakespeare's Globe SE1
£M, (450,300,250,300)
21 New Globe Walk
T 020 7902 1451
F 020 7902 1460
W www.swanattheglobe.co.uk
E swan@shakespearesglobe.com
Swan at the Globe Brasserie & Bar is a bar/restaurant, alongside

Shakespeare's Globe, where an ex-Ramsay chef has pepped up the food. Other private dining and event spaces include The Balcony Room with beautiful views to St Pauls and the UnderGlobe for up to 450 guests. / *no Elizabethan, Tudor or Stuart costumes; 1am; in-house caterers; no music on the balcony after 9pm; Balcony Rm (120,70,–,70).*

Sway WC2
£B, (400,150,–,250)
61-65 Great Queen St
T 020 7404 6114
F 020 7404 6003
W hardens.com/party/swaybar
E info@swaybar.co.uk
A large bar, restaurant and nightclub, with a handy Covent Garden location. It offers a number of different spaces suited to private events. / *21+; 3am; in-house caterers; Crystal Lounge (300,200,–,150).*

Sweetings EC4
£M, (90,30,–,–)
39 Queen Victoria St
T 020 7248 3062
W hardens.com/party/sweetings
This quirky Victorian fish parlour is a famous City lunching spot. It is less well-known that it will do private evening parties, at which optional extras include live jazz, and cod 'n' chips wrapped in the newspaper of your choice. / *midnight; in-house caterers; no amplified music; no dancing.*

Swissôtel The Howard, London WC2
£M-E, (200,120,70,120)
Temple Pl
T 020 7836 3555
F 020 7379 4547
W hardens.com/party/howardhotel
E conference.london@swissotel.com
This small, luxurious, modern hotel by the Temple offers a couple of straight-laced suites for events and conferences. It also has a charming garden, which is available for hire, and in autumn 2010 and spring 2011 is adding the quirky charm for entertaining of a 'pop up' Swiss Chalet. / *midnight; in-house caterers; Fitzalan Suite (200,120,70,120); Arundel Suite (100,80,50,100); Swiss Chalet (250,–,–,–); Temple Garden (150,80,–,–).*

Syon Park TW8
£M, (2000,600,150,150)
Brentford
T 020 8758 1888
F 020 8568 0936
W www.syonpark.co.uk
E beccy@syonpark.co.uk
Vast and imposing 1820s glasshouse, suitable for a range of events and very popular (especially for wedding receptions). Hire includes access to the Capability Brown garden (but note that use of marquees is generally limited to corporate events and weddings). / *1am; Great Conservatory available Apr-mid Oct, from 6pm; list of caterers; music limited to band of 6 players; Great Conservatory (200,150,150,120); Private Dining Rm (–,50,–,–); Lime Ave. Marquee (2000,600,–,–); South Lawn Marquee (1000,600,–,–); Syon Park House (120,120,80,–).*

Tab Centre E2
£B-M, (150,110,–,150)
18-20 Hackney Rd
T 020 7739 3076
W hardens.com/party/tabcentre
E hello@thetabcentre.co.uk
An elegant venue, in a nicely-modernised Victorian building near Shoreditch High Street. It's something of a 'blank canvas', but comes complete with proper onsite kitchen, for use by the caterer of your choice. / *midnight; not available Sundays; Easy Gourmet; no spirits; Main Hall (150,110,–,150); Richard Pearson Hall (40,35,–,–); Balcony Space (65,–,–,–).*

Tallow Chandlers' Hall EC4
£M, (120,100,–,–)
4 Dowgate Hill
T 020 7248 4726
F 020 7236 0844
W hardens.com/party/tallowchandlershall
E clerk@tallowchandlers.org
Charming c17 livery hall, set back in its own courtyard. It's quite grand, but has a very relaxed atmosphere. / *no weddings; 11pm; not available Sat & Sun; Crowns Society; no amplified music; no dancing; Livery Hall (120,100,–,–); Parlour (60,30,–,–).*

Taman Gang W1

£M-E, (220,100,–,–)
141 Park Ln
T 020 7518 3160
F 020 7518 3161
W hardens.com/party/tamangang
E info@tamangang.com
A Thai restaurant on the fringe of Mayfair, with the sort of expensively exotic décor that makes it a natural for a lavish function. You can reserve a number of tables, or book the whole place. / 1am; in-house caterers.

Tamarai WC2

£B-M, (300,100,250,50)
167 Drury Lane
T 020 7831 9399
F 020 7831 5710
W hardens.com/party/tamarai
E info@tamarai.co.uk
A stylish pan Asian restaurant, bar and club in Covent Garden. State-of-the-art audio visual equipment and a screening room makes Tamarai ideal for day-time hire, screenings, training and product launches / Mon-Thu 2am, Fri & Sat 3am, Sun 12.30am; closed Sun, lunchtime; in-house caterers; Lotus Lounge (40,15,–,–); Gallery (50,20,–,–); Dining Room (40,15,–,–); Screening Room (45,20,–,45).

Tate Britain SW1

£E, (300,200,–,190)
Millbank
T 020 7887 8689
F 020 7887 8702
W www.tate.org.uk
E corporatehospitality@tate.org.uk
Home to the greatest collection of British art in the world, Tate Britain is available for corporate entertaining. This original of the Tate Galleries boasts six entertaining spaces to suit a variety of events: from dinner for 40 to receptions for 600. / corporate entertainment only; 11pm; Tate Entertaining; no dancing; Sackler Octagon (300,120,–,–); Gallery 9 (300,200,–,100); Manton Foyer (300,–,–,–); Rex Whistler Restauran (120,80,–,–); Clore Auditorium (–,–,–,190); Duffield Room (50,40,–,40).

Tate Modern SE1

£M-E, (350,200,100,240)
Bankside
T 020 7887 8689
F 020 7887 8702
W www.tate.org.uk
E corporatehospitality@tate.org.uk
Home to the renowned national collection of international modern art, Tate Modern is one of London's most recognisable and best loved buildings. This once disused power station boasts five sleek and contemporary spaces available for corporate hospitality. / corporate entertainment only; 11pm; Tate Entertaining; East Room (150,100,–,100); Tate Modern Restaurant (300,150,–,–); Members Room (120,–,–,–); Cafe 2 (350,200,100,–); Starr Auditorium (–,–,–,240); Starr Foyer (150,–,–,–).

Temple Island RG9

£M-E, (60,40,120,–)
c/o Henley Royal Regatta HQ
T 01491 572153
F 01491 575509
W hardens.com/party/hrr
E temple@hrr.co.uk
A fantasy location, this restored Georgian island folly, picturesquely sited at the start of the Henley Regatta course, can be reached only by boat. It's difficult to beat for summer entertaining. The dinner dance capacity shown requires the erection of a marquee. / midnight; available April-October; list of caterers.

Theatre 503 at the Latchmere Pub SW11
£B-M, (–,63,–,65)
503 Battersea Park Rd
T 020 7978 7040
W hardens.com/party/theatre503
E info@theatre503.com
If you're looking for a presentation space around Battersea, this recently modernised Victorian pub-theatre is well worth considering. (The social elements of events are hosted in the pub downstairs rather than in the theatre.) / restricted availability; 11pm; available subject to constraints of current production; in-house caterers; no dancing.

Theatre Royal, Drury Lane WC2
£M, (750,120,100,2196)
Catherine St
T 020 7379 4981
F 020 7379 4982
W hardens.com/party/theatreroyaldrurylane
E laura.acton@reallyuseful.co.uk
A crimson-and-gilt Covent Garden theatre, whose building, dating from 1812, is on a monumental scale. The impressive Grand Saloon is regularly used for events during the daytime and on Sundays. / restricted availability; 12am; available subject to constraints of current production; in-house caterers; Royal Room (–,20,–,–); Boardroom (40,20,–,–); Grand Saloon (400,120,–,–); Novello Suite (–,20,–,–); Prince Of Wales Room (–,10,–,–); Ballet Room (100,50,–,–).

30 Pavilion Road SW1
£M-E, (240,120,120,–)
30 Pavilion Rd
T 020 7823 9212
F 020 7823 8694
W hardens.com/party/pavilionroad
E 30pr@searcys.co.uk
Traditionally-styled in a way that manages to be both grand and intimate, this Knightsbridge venue has always had a particular name for wedding receptions. There are some bedrooms too, so the home team can even stay the night. / heavy equipment 8am- 10pm delivery; midnight-1am; Searcy's; Stone Hall (120,120,–,–); Ballroom (120,120,–,–); Library (80,28,–,–).

30 St Mary Axe EC3
£M-E, (260,100,90,–)
30 St Mary Axe
T 020 7071 5009
F 020 7071 5003
W hardens.com/party/stmaryaxe
E entertaining@searcys.co.uk
Affectionately known as "The Gherkin", this iconic building is one of London's most unique and prestigious landmarks. The top floors house an elegant event space offering 360 degree views across the city, and two exclusive private dining rooms. Bookings are subject to landlord approval. / all bookings subject to landlord approval; 11pm; in-house caterers; music from approved suppliers only; 39th & 40th Floor (260,70,90,–); Private Dining Rooms 1 & 5 (–,8,–,–); Private Dining Rooms 2 & 4 (–,12,–,–); Private Dining Room 3 (–,16,–,–).

33 Portland Place W1
£M-E, (450,200,–,–)
33 Portland Place
T 020 7636 0900
W hardens.com/party/33portlandplace
E info@33portlandplace.com
Built in 1775 and still retaining many original features, this historic house offers a number of rooms available for private hire, including one with London's only hydraulic wall. / 4am; list of caterers.

Thistle Charing Cross Hotel WC2
£M-E, (200,150,150,150)
The Strand
T 0871 376 9012
W hardens.com/party/charingxhotel
E charingcross@guoman.co.uk
Right by Trafalgar Square, a hotel with a range of grand accommodation for functions of up to 150 people. / 1am; in-house caterers; Regency Rm (100,100,70,112); Canterbury Rm (70,50,40,50); Betjeman (200,150,150,150).

Thomas Cubitt SW1
£M, (120,50,–,–)
44 Elizabeth St
T 020 7730 6060
F 020 7730 6055
W hardens.com/party/cubitt
E reservations@thethomascubitt.com

In the heart of Belgravia, this elegant pub – a recent conversion of a sad old boozer – has been a great success. The upstairs room provides a gracious space for an event. / midnight; in-house caterers; no live music; no dancing.

Thomas Goode W1

£M-E, (150,70,–,–)
19 South Audley St
T 020 7499 2823
F 020 7629 4230
W hardens.com/party/thomasgoode
E info@thomasgoode.co.uk
If you're looking for an imposing Mayfair venue for a cocktail party (in particular), London's grandest china shop is sometimes made available. / restricted availability; hirer's choice of caterer; no music; no dancing; Chairman's Rm (–,24,–,–).

Thorpe Park KT16

£M, (7000,400,370,300)
Staines Rd
T 0870 141 3334
F 020 7465 0884
W hardens.com/party/thorpepark
E events@merlinvenues.com
A hundred rides await you at this adventure park, located just off the M25. For a mega-event you could take over the whole place, or alternatively hire one of the individual facilities and give your guests the run of the place. Some attractions only function in the summer. / midnight; whole park available 7pm-11pm only; list of caterers; Lake View Events Zone (600,400,370,300).

Three Kings of Clerkenwell EC1

£B, (200,–,–,–)
7 Clerkenwell Close
T 020 7253 0483
W hardens.com/party/3kings
Funky 3-D signage advertises the presence of this freehouse, nearly three centuries old – a characterful place, offering a good range of ales and lagers. Hired exclusively, it makes a characterful venue for a party. / in-house caterers.

Tiger Tiger SW1

£M, (1770,240,120,170)
29 Haymarket
T 020 7930 1885
F 020 7930 3060
W hardens.com/party/tigertiger
E info@tigertiger-london.co.uk
This large West End nitespot is available in its entirety during the day for corporate functions and drinks parties. In the evening, it has a number of spaces available for private hire. / 3am; in-house caterers.

Tom Aikens SW3

£M-E, (90,52,–,–)
43 Elystan Street
T 020 7584 2003/7349 0161
W www.tomaikens.co.uk
E info@tomaikens.co.uk
Michelin starred, Tom Aikens restaurant is among the top restaurants in the UK. A modern take on classical French food, the menus offer imaginative dishes complemented by an extensive wine list. Private dining is available for lunch and dinner. Tailor the menus and wine pairings for a totally unique experience. / 12.30pm; 9am; in-house caterers; Private Dining Room (–,10,–,–).

Tom's Kitchen SW3

£M, (200,70,–,–)
27 Cale Street
T 020 7349 0202/ 7349 0161
W www.tomskitchen.co.uk
E info@tomskitchen.co.uk
Spanning three floors, Tom's Kitchen offers affordable British brasserie-style food. With a separate lounge, the second floor private dining room is available for private events. Emphasising mostly British ingredients, the menu offers real comfort value. The first floor bar offers the full Brasserie menu, WiFi and an extensive drinks list. / 12.30pm; 8am; in-house caterers; Private Dining Room (–,22,–,–); First Floor Bar (65,40,–,–); Brasserie (100,70,–,–).

Tottenham Hotspur N17

£M, (400,250,200,160)
Bill Nicholson Way
T 0844 873 3997
F 020 8365 5154
W hardens.com/party/spurs
E events@

tottenhamhotspur.com
White Hart Lane boasts a wide variety of different function spaces for social and business-related events. / 1am; catering by an approved caterer; Pat Jennings Lounge (400,250,200,160); Box Holders' North (100,40,40,50); Bill Nicholson Suite (220,160,140,160); Steve Perryman Lounge (150,120,100,150); Box Holders' West (300,120,90,100); The Goalmouth (220,–,–,60); Gary Mabbutt Lounge (150,120,100,100); Danny Blanchflower Suite (130,100,–,70); Centenary Lounge (180,130,100,60); Highlights (80,64,40,–).

Tower Bridge SE1

£M-E, (250,120,100,36)
Tower Bridge
T 020 7407 9222
F 020 7403 4477
W www.towerbridge.org.uk
E enquiries@towerbridge.org.uk
This symbol of the capital is available for social and corporate events. Its accommodation tends to be used mainly for daytime events, especially meetings. / no naked flames; April-September 11.30pm, October-March 11pm; walkways & engine rooms available from 6.30pm-7.30pm; in-house caterers; Walkways (250,120,100,–); Engine Rms (80,40,40,–); Bridge Master's Dining Rm (20,12,–,36); North Tower Lounge (daytime Only) (45,20,–,–).

HM Tower of London EC3

£M-E, (300,240,–,150)
London
T 020 3166 6226
F 020 3166 6211
W hardens.com/party/hmtower
E toweroflondonevents@hrp.org.uk
For a very grand party, hirers can use part of this World Heritage Site. Areas available include the Norman White Tower, with its display of arms, and armour. There is also the possibility of a private visit to the Crown Jewels. / no fire, Medieval Palace available May-Sept only; 10.30pm; list of caterers; no amplified music; no dancing; White Tower (250,80,–,–); St Thomas's Tower (–,20,–,–); Royal Fusiliers Association Rm (100,70,–,–); Jewel House (80,–,–,–); New Armouries (300,240,–,150); Upper Wakefield Tower (80,40,–,–).

Tower Paintball SE1

£B-M, (70,–,–,–)
68, Tooley Street
T 0845 643 9568
W hardens.com/party/towerpaintball
Two minutes walk from London Bridge Station, three varied game zones, spanning 50,000 square feet of space. In each zone, you need 25 during the week (30 at weekends) to play privately, up to a maximum of 70 participants. / 10pm; 10-1.30 pm, 2pm-5.30 pm, 6 pm-10 pm; no music; no alcohol.

The Trafalgar SW1

£M-E, (250,60,–,40)
2 Spring Gdns
T 020 7870 2900
F 020 7870 2911
W hardens.com/party/thetrafalgar
E sales.trafalgar@hilton.com
Locations don't come much more central than this Hilton group design-hotel (whose rooftop bar is particularly intriguing). Occupying most of the ground floor is a stylish lounge bar with London's largest selection of bourbons. (The boardroom is in more traditional style than the rest of the building). / 1am; in-house caterers; Rockwell (250,60,–,–); Boardroom (50,28,–,35); Strategy (40,20,–,30); Roof Garden (70,–,–,–).

Trafalgar Events WC2

£B-M, (80,25,–,60)
8-9 Northumberland St
T 020 7766 6660
W hardens.com/party/trafalgarevents
E info@trafalgarevents.co.uk
Right by Trafalgar Square, a modern conference centre behind the Georgian facade of an old townhouse that can also cater for evening drinks receptions and events. / 1am; in-house caterers; Purple Room (80,25,–,60); Red Room (80,25,–,60); Orange Room (80,25,–,60); Blue Room (40,15,–,40).

Trafalgar Tavern SE10
£B-M, (300,200,180,–)
Park Row
T 020 8858 2909
F 020 8858 2507
W hardens.com/party/trafalgartavern
E Johanne.Hardwick@greenwich-inc.com
This historic Thames-side Greenwich pub has spectacular views. Its function rooms feel much more like those of a county town hotel than of a boozer, making it an attractive wedding (or reception) venue.
/ midnight; in-house caterers; Nelson Rm (300,200,180,–); Trafalgar Club (100,40,–,–).

Trailer Happiness W11
£M, (85,15,–,–)
177 Portobello Road
T 020 7727 2700
W hardens.com/party/trailerhappiness
E bookings@trailerh.com
In a Notting Hill basement, a "retro-sexual haven of cosmopolitan kitsch and faded trailer park glamour" – ideal to take over for a drinks party!
/ 11.30pm; available Sun–Thu; hirer's choice of caterer (in-house available).

Trailfinders Sports Club W13
£B-M, (2000,170,150,–)
Vallis Way
T 0845 050 5939
F 020 8998 8006
W hardens.com/party/trailfinders
E dave@tfsc.co.uk
Extensive and versatile facilities available for private or corporate functions including weddings, conferences, parties and fun days. Set within 18 acres of grounds, there are two pavilions, one of which is a new £6.5 million clubhouse. Events from 100 to 2000 catered for with extensive car parking. */ midnight; in-house caterers; Olympic Pavilion (250,170,150,–); Centenary Club (200,150,–,–).*

Tricycle Theatre NW6
£B-M, (–,–,–,300)
269 Kilburn High Rd
T 020 7372 6611
F 020 7328 0795
W hardens.com/party/tricycle
E admin@tricycle.co.uk
Although there is a theatre, built in the 1980s, it is the plush adjacent cinema (with stage) which is this Kilburn establishment's main attraction for those organising presentations and private views.
/ restricted availability; midnight; available subject to constraints of current production; hirer's choice of caterer (in-house available); no music; no dancing; Theatre (–,–,–,239); Cinema (–,–,–,300).

Trinity House EC3
£M, (120,120,120,120)
Trinity Sq
T 020 7481 6927
F 020 7481 6959
W www.trinityhouse.co.uk
E edgar.king@thls.org
Trinity House, the elegant HQ of the General Lighthouse Authority, was designed by Samuel Wyatt and built in 1796. It has five rooms overlooking Trinity Square and The Tower of London, suitable for lunches, dinners, conferences and receptions. */ 1am; list of caterers; no red wine in Courtroom for standing receptions; Court Rm (120,60,–,80); Library (120,120,–,120); Reading Rm (20,15,–,–); Luncheon Rm (40,20,–,–).*

Les Trois Garçons EC2
£M, (–,80,–,–)
1 Club Row
T 020 7613 1924
F 020 76133067
W hardens.com/party/3garcons
E info@lestroisgarcons.com
Stuffed animals wearing tiaras may seem an odd decorative theme, but it's won fame for this impressively converted former East End boozer. There's a small private room downstairs, but hiring the whole place is probably a more attractive choice. */ midnight; not available Sun; in-house caterers; no amplified music; no dancing; Private Rm (–,10,–,–).*

Troubadour SW5

£B-M, (120,60,–,–)

263-7 Old Brompton Road

Ⓣ 020 7370 1434

Ⓦ hardens.com/party/troubadour

Ⓔ info@troubadour.co.uk

This Bohemian café has long been a fixture of Earl's Court. It's been expanded and become more professionally run in recent years, and nowadays offers a number of options for entertaining, including use of its event space.
/ Club (120,60,–,–); Gallery (70,32,–,–); Shackleton Room (–,16,–,–).

Trouvaille W1

£B-M, (90,45,–,–)

12a Newburgh

Ⓣ 020 7287 8488

Ⓕ 020 7434 4170

Ⓦ hardens.com/party/trouvaille

Ⓔ contact@latrouvaille.co.uk

Hidden-away just off Carnaby Street, this rather charming restaurant is one of the best French establishments in the heart of the West End. For a private event you can choose from either the wine bar or the first floor dining rooms.
/ midnight; available from noon; in-house caterers; no amplified music; Bar (60,–,–,–); Private Room (–,15,–,–).

Troxy E1

£B, (2600,1016,850,2000)

490 Commercial Rd

Ⓣ 020 7790 9000

Ⓕ 020 7790 4446

Ⓦ www.troxy.co.uk

Ⓔ info@troxy.co.uk

Troxy, London's most versatile venue, is conveniently located equidistant between Canary Wharf and the City. Originally opened in the 1930s as a cinema, this 2,600 capacity venue has been fully restored to meet the needs of today's event organisers, whilst retaining its historical Grade II listed art deco features. / 2am; licensed hours: 10 am - 2 am; hirer's choice of caterer, list avaliable; Grand Hall (2600,1050,630,2000); White Room (120,60,36,100).

Tudor Barn Eltham SE9

£B-M, (200,150,120,200)

Well Hall Road

Ⓣ 0845 4592351

Ⓕ 020 8850 6383

Ⓦ www.tudorbarneltham.co.uk

Ⓔ info@tudorbarneltham.co.uk

Tudor Barn Eltham is a fully restored Grade 2 16th century building and the only remaining Tudor Barn in London. Set in 13 acres of award winning gardens including a medieval moat and scented gardens, this stunning building is steeped in history and is the perfect location for any event.*
/ midnight; 8 am - 1 am; in-house caterers;

acredited suppliers of music; Heritage Centre (100,70,–,50).

Tussaud's Showdome NW1

£M-E, (1000,300,–,–)
Allsop Pl
T 020 7487 0224
W hardens.com/party/showdome
E events@madame-tussauds.com

An auditorium which can genuinely claim to be unique, at least in the capital, and which comes complete with the latest multimedia facilities. / 2am; available from 7pm; list of caterers.

Tuttons WC2

£B-M, (70,50,–,–)
11-12 Russell St
T 0871 3327459
F 020 7379 9979
W hardens.com/party/tuttons
E office@tuttons.com

Below a large English brasserie overlooking Covent Garden, there are some impressive, white-painted vaults which provide an atmospheric setting for a party. / 11.30pm, midnight Fri & Sat; in-house caterers; no amplified music; no dancing; Larger Vault (–,30,–,–); Smaller Vault (–,20,–,–).

20th Century Theatre W11

£B-M, (240,120,100,200)
291 Westbourne Grove
T 020 7229 4179
F 020 7243 1526
W www.20thcenturytheatre.com
E gus@20thcenturytheatre.com

Located in the heart of Notting Hill, this stunning Victorian theatre is a unique setting for memorable celebrations of every kind. With its white walls, wooden floor and high atrium ceiling, the 20th Century Theatre is a blank canvas to be transformed into the perfect setting for your event. / 11pm; hirer's choice of caterer.

28 Portland Place W1

£M-E, (110,104,72,90)
28 Portland Place
T 020 7251 7171
F 020 7251 7170
W hardens.com/party/28portland
E enquire@chesterboyd.co.uk

The headquarters of the Royal Institute of Public Health. The buildings – dating from 1775 and designed by the Adam Brothers – are claimed as among the finest examples of townhouses of the period. / 11pm (or late access charges); Chester Boyd; Adam's Rm (70,40,20,40); Sainsbury's Rm (100,56,30,90); Harben Rm (70,40,–,40); Heggie Rm (110,64,–,100); Harben Suite (100,104,–,90); Adam Suite (100,96,–,90).

Twickenham Experience TW1

£M, (1150,800,800,625)
Rugby Rd
T 0871 22 22 120
W hardens.com/party/twickenhamexperience
E conferencesandevents@therfu.com

The home of England Rugby has extensive event facilities, including those of the purpose-built banqueting suite. Hire can include tours of the grounds and visits to the Museum, and – no doubt every bride's dream – one can get married here. / 1am; in-house caterers; Spirit Of Rugby (300,300,280,200); Council Rm (80,48,–,40); Cellar (–,14,–,–).

2 Amici SW1

£B, (100,90,–,–)
48a Rochester Rw
T 020 7976 5660
W hardens.com/party/2amici
E ristorante@hotmail.co.uk

A traditional Italian restaurant, located near Victoria station. The restaurant is available in its entirety or you can hire the private room. / 1am; available from noon; in-house caterers; no music; Private Room (45,35,–,–).

229 The Venue W1
£B, (760,300,380,300)
229 Great Portland St
Ⓣ 020 7631 8379
Ⓕ 020 7631 8307
Ⓦ www.229thevenue.co.uk
Ⓔ info@229thevenue.co.uk

One of the West End's leading live music/entertainments venues. With the recent installation of state of the art sound and lighting, 229's two venue multi-faceted layout enables us to host a wide variety of events including: live gigs, corporate events, gala dinners, awards ceremonies, club nights, Christmas parties and more. / Sun-Wed midnight, Thu 1am, Fri & Sat 3am; in-house caterers; Venue 1 (620,220,300,300); Venue 2 (140,80,80,–).

Two Temple Place WC2
£E, (350,120,60,165)
2 Temple Pl
Ⓣ 020 7836 3715
Ⓕ 020 7836 5416
Ⓦ hardens.com/party/twotempleplace
Ⓔ enquiries@twotempleplace.co.uk
Built to elaborate specification by the first Viscount Astor in 1895, this extraordinary house by Temple underground station offers comfortable, neo-Gothic grandeur in an unusually convenient location. Now owned by a charitable trust, it is available for events both private and corporate. / midnight; list of caterers; Lower Gallery (180,–,–,150); The Great Hall (200,120,120,165).

229 W1
£B, (760,250,200,300)
229 Great Portland Street
Ⓣ 020 7631 8388
Ⓕ 020 7631 8307
Ⓦ hardens.com/party/229thevenue
Ⓔ info@229thevenue.co.uk
The multi-faceted layout and extensive technical facilities of this West End venue means it's capable of handling a wide range of events including......live music gigs, club nights, corporate events, live comedy nights, parties, fashion shows, filming & photo shoots, gala dinners & more. / Sun-Wed 12am, Thu 1am, Fri & Sat 3am; in-house caterers; Venue 1 (620,250,200,300); Venue 2 (150,80,80,–); Gulbenkian Room (100,80,50,–).

Umu W1
£M-E, (–,12,–,–)
14-16 Bruton Pl
Ⓣ 020 7499 8881
Ⓦ hardens.com/party/umu
One of London's most expensive restaurants, this modernistic Mayfair Japanese has no totally private area. For parties of up to a dozen, though, a discreetly-located tasting table is available. / in-house caterers.

The Union Club W1
£M-E, (180,60,–,–)
50 Greek Street
Ⓣ 0207 734 4113
Ⓕ 0207 439 0329
Ⓦ hardens.com/party/unionclub
Ⓔ info@unionclub.co.uk
Despite its Soho media-land location, this panelled club in a listed Georgian townhouse – with its real fires and chandeliers – is wittingly styled on cosy, traditional lines and well-suited to private social occasions, including wedding receptions. / 12am - 1am; in-house caterers.

University of London Union WC1
£B-M, (828,220,–,300)
Malet St
Ⓣ 020 7664 2020/2021
Ⓕ 020 637 5928
Ⓦ hardens.com/party/ulu
Ⓔ conference@ulu.lon.ac.uk
The main hall (now called Room 101 in homage to Orwell, who used to write in the neighbouring Senate House) is sound-proofed (how appropriate) and air-conditioned, and has a disco lighting system. The bar is popular for receptions and discos. / 10pm, Fri & Sat 2am; in-house caterers; Bar 101 (150,–,–,–).

University of Westminster NW1

£B-M, (200,120,–,300)

35 Marylebone Rd

T 020 7911 5181

F 020 7911 5141

W hardens.com/party/univwestminster

E uniletconferences@westminster.ac.uk

The University has a number of meeting and party spaces, mainly around its Regent Street site. Numerous small rooms are available for conferences and seminars. / 5pm Sat & Sun, 9pm weekdays; restricted availability in term time; in-house caterers; AV approval required; Old Cinema (200,–,–,196); Deep End (200,120,–,–); Hogg Lecture Theatre (–,–,–,300).

University Women's Club W1

£M, (100,70,–,70)

2 Audley Sq

T 020 7499 2268

F 020 7499 7046

W hardens.com/party/universitywomensclub

E lorraine@uwc-london.com

With a member's sponsorship, many kinds of events are possible at this Mayfair club, which is ideal for smaller wedding receptions. Attractions include a pretty garden. / members club; midnight; in-house caterers; Drawing Room (100,70,–,70); Library (100,70,–,70); Dining Room (100,70,–,70).

V&A Museum of Childhood E2

£M, (400,250,80,150)

Cambridge Heath Road

T 020 8983 5200

F 020 8983 5225

W hardens.com/party/childhood

E moc@vam.ac.uk

This sizeable Victorian museum in Bethnal Green is marketing itself more strongly as an events venue nowadays. The principle space is the main hall, but other rooms (The Summerly Room and two class rooms) are available for dancing and meetings, and there's also a new-build gallery space for smaller stand-up events (under 100). / 12.30am; list of caterers.

Vanderbilt Hotel SW7

£M, (150,90,55,110)

68-86 Cromwell Rd

T 020 7761 9013

F 020 7761 9045

W hardens.com/party/vanderbilthotel

E vandcb@radisson.com

The listed Vanderbilt Suite of this South Kensington hotel is decorated in extraordinary French château style. The other accommodation is all much more businessy. / 11pm, although a late license is available; in-house caterers; Vanderbilt (–,12,–,–); Victoria & Albert (90,90,–,100); Edwardian (50,50,–,40); Harrington (20,16,–,25).

Vanilla W1

£M, (150,75,–,–)

131 Great Titchfield Street

T 020 3008 7763

F 020 3008 6652

W hardens.com/party/vanilla

E info@vanillalondon.com

With its über-cool, bright, white decor and floaty drapes, this slightly ethereal looking bar/restaurant is ideal for style-conscious events and as well as being used for private hire boasts a long list of corporate customers.

Vasco & Piero's Pavilion W1

£B-M, (–,60,55,–)

15 Poland St

T 020 7437 8774

F 020 7437 0467

W hardens.com/party/vasco

E eat@vascosfood.com

Quite a fixture of 'old Soho', this friendly Italian restaurant has an elegant private room downstairs, which can be used for business and social functions. / midnight; available from noon; in-house caterers; no amplified music; Main Room (–,60,55,–); Private Room (–,36,–,–).

Vats WC1

£B, (130,75,–,–)

51 Lamb's Conduit St

T 020 7242 8963

F 020 7831 7299

W hardens.com/party/vats

E vatswineco@tiscali.co.uk

Convivial, street-level Bloomsbury

wine bar. It has been owned by the same couple for over 30 years, and its back room has long been a popular spot for get-togethers. / 1am; in-house caterers; no amplified music; no dancing; no beer; Private Dining Room (–,12,–,–).

Veeraswamy W1

£M, (–,114,–,–)
Victory House
T 020 7734 1401
F 020 7439 8434
W hardens.com/party/veeraswamy
E veeraswamy@realindianfood.com

For over 80 years, Britain's oldest Indian restaurant has remained a high quality destination. It underwent a sophisticated contemporary makeover a few years ago, and is available for meetings, cocktail receptions, lunches, and dinners. / midnight; in-house caterers; Palmer Room (–,24,–,–).

Vertigo EC2

£M-E, (100,–,–,–)
Old Broad St
T 020 7877 7842
F 020 7877 7788
W hardens.com/party/vertigo
E privateevents@vertigo42.co.uk

If you really want to push the boat out for a drinks party, you could hire the highest cocktail bar in London, on the 42nd floor of this city landmark. / 11pm; not available Sat, Sun and bank hols; in-house caterers.

Il Vicolo SW1

£M, (50,45,–,–)
3-4 Crown Passage
T 020 7839 3960
W hardens.com/party/vicolo

One of the few privately-owned mid-price restaurants in St James's, this old-style Italian – hidden-away in a pedestrian lane – provides a handy venue for a party. / in-house caterers.

Victoria and Albert Museum SW7

£E, (700,400,250,–)
Cromwell Rd
T 020 7942 2646/2647/2628
F 020 7942 2645
W www.vam.ac.uk
E corporateevents@vam.ac.uk

The V&A, the largest and most outstanding museum of decorative arts in the world, has a range of impressive galleries for all types of entertainment. Drinks and dinners may be combined with viewing of major exhibitions. The John Madejski Garden, particularly dramatic at night, is available for receptions. / 12am; not available during daytime or on Fri; list of caterers; Dome (700,250,250,–); Raphael Gallery (400,400,–,–); Silver Galleries (250,–,–,–); Cast Court (100,–,–,–); Paintings Gallery (150,70,–,–); John Madejski Garden (700,–,–,–).

Victory Services Club W2

£B-M, (300,240,240,300)
63-79 Seymour St
T 020 7616 8305
F 020 7724 1134
W hardens.com/party/vsc
E events@vsc.co.uk

The Club (for current and former members of the armed services) has a fair number of rooms for hire – all available to non-members – at its Marble Arch premises. Facilities are available in styles both traditional and modern. / 11pm (hourly charge for an extension til 1am); in-house caterers; some restrictions on music; Allenby Rm (30,24,–,35); Chetwode Rm (20,14,–,16); Grill Rm (70,70,–,50); Trafalgar Rm (70,70,–,70); El Alamein Rm (150,90,–,150); Carisbrooke Hall (300,240,240,300); Committee Rm (20,20,–,24).

The Village W1

£B, (400,–,–,–)
81 Wardour St
T 020 7478 0530
F 020 7434 0344
W hardens.com/party/villagesoho
E events@village-soho.co.uk

A quarter of a century old, this veteran bar claims 'founder member' status on the Soho gay scene. Its interior is thoroughly contemporary, though, and the various floors offer private event possibilities in a handy variety of capacities. / *Mon-Sat 1am, Sun 11.30pm ; in-house caterers; Boudoir (50,–,–,–); Main Floor (250,–,–,–); V Underground (100,–,–,–).*

The Village Underground EC2

£B-M, (700,350,–,150)

54 Holywell Lane

Ⓣ 020 7422 7505

Ⓦ hardens.com/party/villageunderground

Ⓔ tam@villageunderground.co.uk

A large Shoreditch arts space in a vast Victorian warehouse – a main atrium and two vaulted brick arches, with natural light coming through the numerous skylights in the roof. An ideal blank canvas for a large themed event. / *no entertainment after 2 am; no alcohol after 2 am.*

Vincent Rooms SW1

£B, (50,30,–,–)

Westminster Kingsway College

Ⓣ 020 7802 8391

Ⓦ hardens.com/party/vincentrooms

Ⓔ restaurant@westking.ac.uk

The elegant Art Deco dining room of a catering college – Jamie was here! – just five minutes walk from St James's Park tube. The private room is available for smaller parties, and you can hire the brasserie for large parties and presentations, or the bar for drinks parties and informal functions. / *11.30pm; available from noon; in-house caterers; no amplified music; Private Room (50,30,–,–).*

Vinopolis: The Venue SE1

£M, (1250,550,450,400)

1 Bank End

Ⓣ 020 7940 8322

Ⓕ 020 7940 8302

Ⓦ www.vinopolis.co.uk

Ⓔ events@vinopolis.co.uk

With a choice of seven distinct yet equally stunning event spaces, Vinopolis merges Victorian splendour with 21st Century facilities, offering state of the art lighting and AV solutions / *midnight; in-house caterers; Great Halls (800,550,450,250); The Mezzanine (450,350,300,400); The Gallery (200,200,140,150); Academia (200,100,70,100); The Vineyard (50,–,–,50); The New World Odyssey (200,50,30,50); The European Odyssey (350,80,50,80).*

The Vinyl Factory W1

£M, (450,250,–,250)

The Vinyl Factory @ Phonica Records

Ⓣ 020 7025 1385

Ⓦ hardens.com/party/thevinylfactory

Ⓔ antony.hill@thevinylfactory.com

In the heart of Soho, a warehouse-style event space that derives greater grooviness from its association with the music publishing business. / *11pm; hirer's choice of caterer; Gallery (250,–,–,–); Studio (200,–,–,–).*

Volt Lounge SW1

£M-E, (220,110,–,–)

17 Hobart Place

Ⓣ 020 7235 9696

Ⓕ 020 7235 9599

Ⓦ hardens.com/party/voltlounge

Ⓔ info@voltlounge.com

A smart bar/restaurant, on the fringe of Belgravia (and handily near the transport links from Victoria). A clubby sort of space, divided into different zones, it's well suited to party use. / *available from noon; in-house caterers; Restaurant (150,80,–,–); Cognac Room (25,15,–,–); Diamond Room (20,10,–,–); Crystal Room (50,30,–,–).*

Waddesdon Manor, The Dairy HP18

£M-E, (200,110,80,110)

Near Aylesbury

Ⓣ 01296 653 243

Ⓕ 01296 653237

Ⓦ hardens.com/party/waddesdon

Ⓔ events.waddesdon@nationaltrust.org.uk

The Dairy at Waddesdon Manor, set in tranquil parkland just over an hour from London and close to Oxford, is a perfect retreat for company away-days, meetings and corporate entertaining. Tutored tastings of delicious Rothschild wines or private tours of the remarkable 18th century Rothschild Collection can be arranged. / *dairy licensed for weddings, marquee by arrangement; midnight; in-house or approved caterers by special arrangement; West Hall (150,110,80,110); Winter Garden (110,60,–,–); Terrace (200,–,–,40);*

Manor Restaurant (60,60,80,40); Dieppe (–,14,–,12).

Waldorf Hotel WC2

£M, (700,380,350,300)
Aldwych
Ⓣ 020 7836 2400
Ⓕ 020 7836 7244
Ⓦ hardens.com/party/waldorfhotel
Ⓔ events.waldorf@hilton.com

For receptions and dinner-dances – or perhaps for a fashion show or product launch – this recently refurbished fringe-of-Covent Garden hotel will close its rightly famous Palm Court. Smaller rooms are also available. / 1am; list of caterers; no amplified music in Palm Court; Adelphi Suite (–,380,350,–); Aldwych Suite (50,–,–,30).

Wallace Collection W1

£M-E, (400,160,140,–)
Hertford House
Ⓣ 020 7563 9546
Ⓕ 020 7563 9581
Ⓦ www.wallacecollection.org/entertain
Ⓔ events@wallacecollection.org

The sumptuous rooms of this enormous townhouse – home to 6,000 works of fine and decorative art – are available for receptions and dinners. The glazed-roofed courtyard is available for events all year. / 11pm; available from 6.30pm; list of caterers; dancing only permitted in Courtyard; no red wine in galleries; Main Galleries (400,120,–,–); Courtyard (300,160,140,–); Great Gallery (250,120,–,–); Dining Rm (–,40,–,–); State Rm (–,30,–,–).

Wandsworth Civic Suite SW18

£B, (800,520,460,748)
Wandsworth High St
Ⓣ 020 8871 6394
Ⓕ 020 8871 6391
Ⓦ hardens.com/party/wandsworthcivic
Ⓔ publichalls@wandsworth.gov.uk

Remodelled '30s suite of rooms, comfortably decorated in municipal style, and ideal for a dinner-dance. / midnight, Fri- Sat 2am; hirer's choice of caterer.

Wapping Food E1

£M, (300,150,–,–)
Wapping Hydraulic Power Station
Ⓣ 020 7680 2080
Ⓦ hardens.com/party/wappingproject
Ⓔ jules@thewappingproject.com

This East End arts site occupies a very impressive post-industrial site (an old hydraulic power station), and its restaurant has made quite a name in its own right. Use for functions is subject to the constraints of the current installation. / midnight; in-house caterers; no dancing.

Warwick Castle CV34

£M-E, (300,130,100,70)
Warwick
Ⓣ 0870 999 0122
Ⓦ hardens.com/party/warwickcastle
Ⓔ events@warwick-castle.com

"Britain's ultimate castle", they claim, and it certainly has the full fairytale look. Now licensed for weddings. / 12.30am; in-house caterers; Great Hall (–,130,100,–); Restaurant (–,120,–,–); Central Courtyard (300,–,–,–); Coach House (–,–,–,70).

Washington W1

£M, (500,130,120,110)
5 Curzon St
Ⓣ 020 7499 7000
Ⓕ 020 7495 6172
Ⓦ hardens.com/party/washingtonhotel
Ⓔ conference@washington-mayfair.co.uk

The style of this Mayfair hotel is perhaps more obviously suited to corporate than social events. It is possible to use the restaurant for a small dinner-dance. / 1am; in-house caterers; Richmond Suite (120,70,62,110); Fairfax (45,15,–,40); Winchester (60,30,–,50).

Water House N1

£M, (90,72,–,–)
10 Orsman Road
Ⓣ 020 7033 0123
Ⓦ hardens.com/party/waterhouse
Ⓔ eat@waterhouserestaurant.co.uk

Perhaps the capital's most eco-friendly restaurant, in a hidden-away canalside location, in Shoreditch.

Taken over in its entirety, it would make a good space for an event. / 11.30pm; in-house caterers; no music; no dancing.

Watermen's Hall EC3
£M, (100,73,–,70)
16 St Mary-at-Hill
T 020 7283 2373
F 020 7283 0477
W hardens.com/party/watermen
E events@watermenshall.org
An appealing mix of charm, a flexible attitude and a fair degree of stateliness makes this – the only Georgian livery hall in the square mile – ideal for a wide variety of business and social events. / 11.30pm; list of caterers; no amplified music; Freemen's Rm (100,73,–,70); Court Rm (70,37,–,40); The Parlour (20,10,–,–); The Silver Rm (20,16,–,20).

Waterstone's W1
£M, (150,100,–,60)
203-206 Piccadilly
T 020 7851 2468
W hardens.com/party/waterstones
E waterstones@digbytrout.co.uk
The surprise star attraction at the largest bookshop in Europe is a top (5th-floor) bar, with impressive Westminster views. A lecture room is also available. / 10pm, Sun 5pm; in-house caterers; no dancing.

Wax Chandlers' Hall EC2
£M-E, (100,68,–,80)
6 Gresham St
T 020 7606 3591
W hardens.com/party/6gresham
The Wax Chandlers' sixth hall (on a site they have occupied for over 500 years) is a postwar building that's undergone major refurbishment in recent years. / 11pm; Inn or Out Catering; no amplified music; no dancing; Great Rm (100,68,–,80); Courtroom (68,32,–,30); Parlour (–,6,–,–).

HQS Wellington WC2
£M-E, (220,120,80,180)
Victoria Embankment
T 020 7251 7171
F 020 7251 7170
W hardens.com/party/hqswellington
E enquire@chesterboyd.co.uk
The Master Mariners' hall, a WWII naval sloop, boasts a fine location (opposite the National Theatre). Its hall, in the bowels of the ship, gives little clue that you are afloat, but other rooms are more nautical in flavour (with superb models of ships). The decks suit summer parties. / 11pm; Chester Boyd; Court Rm (180,120,80,180); Committee Rm (50,–,–,25); Model Rm (120,30,–,40).

Wellington Arch W1
£M-E, (80,36,–,–)
Hyde Park Corner
T 020 7973 3292
F 020 7973 3443
W www.english-heritage.org.uk
E Vanessa.adlard@english-heritage.org.uk
This prominent monument (erected in 1826, and now bearing the largest bronze sculpture in the UK) makes an intriguing place for a party. / no political events; 11pm; list of caterers; no amplified music.

West Wycombe Caves HP14
£M, (120,50,40,–)
Park Ln
T 01494 524411
F 01494 471617
W hardens.com/party/wwcaves
E info@westwycombe.co.uk
The caves – legacy of a c18 job-creation scheme – were the meeting place for the Hell-Fire Club. They are used for a variety of functions. / in-house caterers.

Westminster Abbey SW1
£M-E, (500,230,–,–)
20 Dean's Yard
T 020 7222 5152
F 020 7233 2072
W www.westminster-abbey.org/venue-bookings
E bookings@westminster-abbey.org
Entertaining options at the 'parish church of the House of Commons' have expanded in recent years. It's still primarily a place for summer entertaining, with the the College Garden – an acre where medicinal herbs once grew – and St Catherine's Garden overlooking the Palace of Westminster. The Abbey also now has two all-year-round venues: Cheyneygates and the

undercroft museum, available for both evening events as well as daytime meetings. / 9.30pm; available Mon-Thu; in-house caterers; no amplified music; no dancing; Museum (150,–,–,–); St Catherine's Chapel Garden (120,–,–,–); Cheney Gates (100,–,–,–); Abbey Cloisters (400,–,–,–).

Westminster Boating Base SW1

£B-M, (350,150,150,–)
136 Grosvenor Rd
T 020 7821 7389
F 020 7821 7389
W hardens.com/party/westminsterboatingbase
E enquiries@westminsterboatingbase.co.uk

Located on the river at Pimlico, the base offers an unusually central location which can be turned to most types of function. Prices are reasonable and there are good facilities, including a modern pavilion, sited on the piers. For major events, marquees may be erected in the adjoining park. / midnight; hirer's choice of caterer (in-house available).

Westminster Cathedral Hall SW1

£B, (300,200,–,400)
Ambrosden Ave
T 020 7798 9064
F 020 7798 9090
W hardens.com/party/westminstercathedral
E westminstercatherdral@rcdow.org.uk

An attractive and colourful Edwardian hall, behind the (Roman Catholic) cathedral. It has an arched roof, natural wood floor and period chandeliers. / 11pm; not available Sun mornings or Mon & Fri evening; hirer's choice of caterer; amplified music not encouarged.

Whipsnade Wild Animal Park LU6

£M, (565,400,380,565)
Dunstable
T 01582 873831
F 01582 873748
W hardens.com/party/whipsnade
E zoofunctions@zsl.org

The park, home to 2500 creatures, makes an interesting location for a variety of events. Packages can include tours in an open top double-decker bus or on a narrow-gauge railway. / no fireworks; midnight; in-house caterers.

Whisky Mist at Zeta W1

£M, (240,240,–,–)
35 Hertford Street
T 020 7208 4067
W hardens.com/party/whiskymist
E events@whiskymist.com

This Park Lane bar is one of the more glam Mayfair watering holes. It's particularly popular as an after-party type place, after one of the awards ceremonies which seem to occur nightly somewhere on Park Lane. / 22.30; Lux Room (80,80,–,–).

The White House SW4

£B-M, (250,50,–,–)
65 Clapham Park Rd
T 020 7498 3388
F 020 7498 5588
W hardens.com/party/whitehouse
E info@thewhitehouselondon.co.uk

Rooms for private parties are a fundamental part of the set-up of this three-floor bar/club/restaurant, complete with roof terrace, which aims to keep the flame of "West End sophistication" alive in deepest Clapham. Some facilities are available on weekdays only. / 2am; in-house caterers; no dancing; Banquet Room (–,26,–,–); Rockstar Room (–,8,–,–).

Whitechapel Art Gallery E1

£B-M, (1500,400,450,400)
80-82 Whitechapel High St
T 020 7522 7888
F 020 7377 1635
W hardens.com/party/whitechapelgallery
E emilydaw@whitechapelgallery.org

A spacious Art Nouveau gallery on the eastern fringe of the City, which emerged from a major refurbishment a couple of years ago. / 11pm; Vacherin; no red wine in galleries.

Wiltons SW1
£M-E, (–,80,–,–)
55 Jermyn St
T 020 7629 9955
F 020 7495 6233
W hardens.com/party/wiltons
E wiltons@wiltons.co.uk
Famously clubby St James's restaurant of long standing, known as one of the last bastions of traditional British dining. / 10.30pm; weekends only; in-house caterers; no music; no dancing; Private Room (–,20,–,–).

Winchester House SW15
£M, (300,200,180,140)
10 Lower Richmond Rd
T 020 8789 4447
W www.winchesterhouse.co.uk
E info@ampmcatering.co.uk

Occupying an unrivalled position within its own walled grounds overlooking the Thames, Winchester House is an attractive venue for conferences, Christmas parties, dinners, dances, civil ceremonies and weddings. / no; 11pm-1am; usually in-house caterers, but worth enquiring; bands by arrangement; no dancing; no alcohol restrictions, within the law; River Rm (180,124,120,140); Library (40,24,–,30); River Lawn (300,200,–,–); Front Lawn (150,100,–,–).

Wine Gallery SW10
£B-M, (–,45,–,–)
49 Hollywood Rd
T 020 7352 7572
F 020 7376 5083
W hardens.com/party/winegallery
E winegallery@brinkleys.com
A cosily unchanging bistro on the fringe of Chelsea has nooks and crannies to accommodate smaller parties, as well as private rooms. You can also hire the garden. / 12.30am; in-house caterers; no live bands; no dancing; Private Rm 1 (–,18,–,–); Private Rm 2 (–,22,–,–); Private Rm 3 (–,40,–,–); Garden (–,20,–,–).

Winston Churchill's Britain at War SE1
£M, (100,–,–,–)
64-66 Tooley St
T 020 7403 3171
F 020 7403 5104
W hardens.com/party/britainatwar
E info@britainatwar.org.uk
Life in Britain during WWII is the theme of this museum near London Bridge. Events take place among the exhibits, which include a dramatic re-creation of the Blitz. / available Mon-Sat from 6pm ; hirer's choice of caterer.

Women's Library E1
£M, (200,60,–,55)
London Metropolitan University
T 020 7320 1191
F 020 7320 2333
W hardens.com/party/womenslibrary
E hires@thewomenslibrary.ac.uk
An elegant (RIBA award-winning) contemporary building, near Aldgate East, which is well geared up for business and local government events and receptions. / 8.30pm; not available Sun; in-house caterers; Clore Seminar Rm (–,–,–,55); Activties Rm (–,–,–,20); Exhibition Hall (200,–,–,–); Clore Mezzanine (100,46,–,–); Wash House (100,60,–,–).

Worx SW6
£B-M, (350,150,100,200)
10 Heathmans Rd
T 020 7371 9777
F 020 7371 9888
W hardens.com/party/worx
E enquiries@theworx.co.uk
Though primarily designed as photographic studios, these Parson's Green facilities (which range from 400-2,500 sq ft) are, with theming, suitable for receptions and corporate events. There is a soundproofed area suitable for dancing. / 2am, weekdays 1am; in-house caterer daytime, hirer's choice at evening; Studio 1 (300,100,–,200); Studio 2 (350,150,–,200); Studio 3 (30,10,–,20); Studio 4 (100,30,–,50).

Wyndham Grand London SW10

£M, (900,500,500,800)
Chelsea Harbour
T 020 7823 3000
F 020 7351 6525
W hardens.com/party/wyndhamgrand
E alexandra.dauth@wyndham.com
This modern waterside hotel (formerly called the Conrad) has the benefit – or disadvantage – of feeling much further from the centre of town than it actually is. There is a wide range of facilities for functions which, though rather corporate in feel, are fitted to a high standard. / 2am; in-house caterers; The Grand Room (900,500,500,800); Albert Suite (40,30,–,40); Battersea (40,30,–,40); The Ballroom (–,18,–,–).

Yard W1

£B-M, (250,60,–,–)
57 Rupert St
T 020 7437 2652
F 020 7287 3602
W hardens.com/party/yardbar
The unusual galleried setting (converted from former stables), around a small open yard, would make this hidden-away Soho (gay) bar rather an intriguing setting for a large drinks party. / in-house caterers.

Zafferano SW1

£M, (–,20,–,–)
15 Lowndes St
T 020 7235 5800
F 020 7235 1971
W hardens.com/party/zafferano
E info@zafferanorestaurant.com
This restaurant is devoid of the glitz you sometimes find in this part of town. There is a private room downstairs in the wine cellar which can accommodate small parties. / midnight; available from noon; in-house caterers; no amplified music; Private Room (–,20,–,–).

Zebrano (at the establishment) W1

£B, (250,60,–,–)
18 Greek Street
T 020 7287 2051
W hardens.com/party/zebrano
E info@zebrano-bar.com
Old timers remember this atmospheric Soho bar as 'Boardwalk'. It's a two-level space which can accommodate smaller parties, or for a larger (often media-related) bash, you can hire the whole place.

The Zetter Hotel EC1

£M, (80,50,40,50)
86-88 Clerkenwell Road
T 020 7324 4444
F 020 7324 4445
W hardens.com/party/zetterhotel
E events@thezetter.com
A design hotel in ever-trendier Clerkenwell. The restaurant (nowadays with Bruno Loubet at the stoves) is a sizeable part of the operation, and there are two private dining rooms, catering for between 10 and 50 guests. / midnight; in-house caterers; River Fleet Room (20,10,–,–); New River Room (80,–,–,–); Zetter Restaurant (–,50,–,–).

Zuma SW7

£M, (14,–,–,–)
5 Raphael St
T 020 7584 1010
F 020 7584 5005
W hardens.com/party/zuma
E info@zumarestaurant.com
Perennially 'in' with the Euro-crowd, this Knightsbridge Japanese restaurant has two rooms for private dining. The whole establishment, however, is not generally available. / midnight; available from noon, Sat & Sun 12.30pm; in-house caterers; no music; Private Rm (14,–,–,–); Private Rm (12,–,–,–).

Private Venues
Major Destinations

Bath

Assembly Rooms BA1

£M-E, (400,310,220,500)
Bennett Street
T 01225 477782
F 01225 477476
W hardens.com/party/bathassembly
E bath_venues@bathnes.gov.uk

The Ball Room is the largest Georgian interior in the city. Décor of the neighbouring Great Octagon includes paintings by Gainsborough. / 1am; not available before 4.30pm in August; Searcy's; Tea Room (300,170,100,250); Octagon (250,120,80,120).

Guildhall BA1

£M-E, (250,200,120,360)
High Street
T 01225 477782
F 01225 477476
W hardens.com/party/bathguildhall
E bath_venues@bathnes.gov.uk

Situated in the heart of the city, an impressive venue suited to dinners, weddings, meetings and smaller conferences. / 1am; hirer's choice of caterer; Banqueting Room (250,200,120,360); Brunswick Room (130,–,48,120); Kaposvar Room (60,25,–,50).

Pump Room and Roman Baths BA1

£M-E, (300,180,160,300)
Stall Street
T 01225 477782
F 01225 477476
W hardens.com/party/bathpump
E bath_venues@bathnes.gov.uk

Built in 1795 as the focal point of Georgian society, the Pump Room is still the "social heart of the city", they claim. Spa water flows from the pretty fountain, which overlooks the natural hot spring. / 1am; evenings only; 8.30 am for wedding ceremonies; Searcy's; Pump Room (300,160,–,300); Roman Baths (320,–,–,–); Terrace (120,80,–,–); Kingston Room (50,40,–,40).

Victoria Art Gallery BA2

£M-E, (150,80,–,50)
Bridge Street
T 01225 477782
F 01225 477476
W hardens.com/party/bathvictoria
E bath_venues@bathnes.gov.uk

Three separate spaces provide a variety of accommodation for smaller events in this attractive c19 art gallery. / 1am; hirer's choice of caterer; no red wine in the upper gallery; Upper Gallery (100,40,–,25).

Birmingham

Aston Villa Hospitality and Events B6

£M, (800,552,516,800)
Villa Park
T 0800 612 0960
F 0800 612 0966
W hardens.com/party/avilla
E enquiries@avhe.co.uk

With an extensive range of banqueting suites, plus packages for weddings and birthdays, Villa Park is a flexible venue suiting many types of special function or business event. / 2am, application for extension; in-house, plus list of approved caterers; Holte Suite (800,552,516,800); Trinity and 82 Lounge (600,500,150,250); McGregors Suite (290,70,140,140); The Park Suite (120,40,50,60); 1874 (450,250,250,250); The Champions Lounge (40,25,–,35); Directors (200,110,70,110); Sky Lounge (120,60,50,60); The Players Lounge (80,60,–,60); The Corner Flag (200,120,–,60).

The International Convention Centre B1

£B-M, (3000,2060,1379,3000)
Broad Street
T 0121 200 2000
F 0121 643 0388
W hardens.com/party/iccbirmingham
E info@theicc.co.uk

Eleven halls for business events, just a few minutes' walk from Broad Street station. / 5pm; in-house caterers; Symphony Hall (–,–,–,2000); Hall 3 (3000,2060,1379,3000); Hall 4 (–,630,413,825); Hall 8 (300,270,175,300); Hall 11 (–,320,210,345).

The Pavilion B6
£B-M, (450,180,120,200)
Moor Lane
T 0121 331 6515
F 0121 331 6516
W hardens.com/party/pavilionbirmingham
E pavilion.enquiries@bcu.ac.uk
In Perry Bar, a flexible modern venue suited to corporate, social and sporting events. / 1am; Britain Catering; Pearson Suite (300,180,120,200); Bar Area (200,–,–,–).

Brighton

Brighton Pier BN2
£M, (600,–,–,–)
Madeira Drive
T 01273 609361
F 01273 684289
W hardens.com/party/brightonpier
E info@brightonpier.co.uk
Above the briney, a world–famous location for your event. / midnight; available Mon-Fri, Sep-May only; in-house caterers; Restaurant (250,–,–,–); Horatio's Bar (250,–,–,–); Victoria Bar (100,–,–,–); Glitter Ball Bar (100,–,–,–).

The Old Courtroom BN1
£M, (152,–,–,152)
118 Church Street
T 01273 292813
F 01273 292871
W hardens.com/party/oldcourtroom
E pavilionfunctions@brighton-hove.gov.uk
A light, bright and lofty Victorian chamber – set up lecture room style – handily situated if you're looking for a central venue for an event. / 11pm; list of caterers, cold food only.

Preston Manor BN1
£M, (200,50,–,–)
Preston Drove
T 01273 292813
W hardens.com/party/prestonmanor
E pavilionfunctions@brighton-hove.gov.uk
An Edwardian house, in a park, that makes an impressive setting for an event. The lawns may be used for garden parties (for up to 200). / 11pm; list of caterers; no dancing; Lawns (200,–,–,–).

The Royal Pavilion BN1
£M-E, (200,90,–,180)
Brighton
T 01273 292813
F 01273 292871
W hardens.com/party/royalpavilion
E trish.baker@brighton-hove.gov.uk
George IV's splendid seaside palace offers the ideal setting for a Regency banquet, or for a range of other functions, including weddings. / companies only in the evening; 11pm; list of caterers; no amplified music; no dancing; Great Kitchen (90,40,–,–); Banqueting Room (200,90,–,–); Music Room (–,–,–,180).

Bristol

SS Great Britain BS1
£M, (140,140,140,100)
Great Western Dock
T 0117 9225737
F 0117 9255788
W hardens.com/party/ssgb
E events@ssgreatbritain.org
No longer ruling the waves, the world's first iron-hulled, screw propeller-driven, steam-powered passenger liner offers an unusual venue for your party (or in which to get married). / no fire; midnight; dining saloon evenings only; in-house caterers; Hayward Saloon (60,40,–,–); Dining Saloon (140,140,140,–); Lecture Theatre (100,–,–,100).

Cardiff

Cardiff City Hall CF10
£M-E, (1000,500,450,600)
Cathays Park
T 029 2087 1736
F 029 2087 1734
W hardens.com/party/cardiffcityhall
E cityhall@cardiff.gov.uk
"The centrepiece of one of the world's finest civic centres", they say, and it's certainly true that the city hall is an impressive venue, suiting a wide range of events. / 1am; in house, unless for religious events; Assembly Room (600,500,400,600); Marble Hall (200,150,110,200); Council Chamber (–,–,–,94); Ferrier Hall (200,100,100,200).

National Museum of Wales CF10

£M-E, (400,300,–,340)
Cathays Park
T 029 2057 3387
F 029 2057 3326
W hardens.com/party/museumwales
E neil.harrison@museumwales.ac.uk
Not far from the City Hall, another impressive building, offering a wide range of function capability. / *midnight; in-house caterers; no red wine in galleries; Grand Hall (–,300,–,–); Art Galleries (250,–,–,–); Reardon Smith Theatre (–,–,–,340); Court Room (–,30,–,50); Oriel Suite (–,40,–,90).*

Edinburgh

Hopetoun House EH30

£M-E, (650,300,250,350)
South Queensferry
T 0131 331 2451
F 0131 319 1885
W hardens.com/party/hopetoun
E events@hopetoun.co.uk
If you're looking for grandeur, you won't do much better than "Scotland's finest stately home" (part of which is still occupied by the Marquess of Linlithgow), on the outskirts of the city. As you might expect, it offers a range of impressive venues for entertaining. / *midnight; in-house caterers; clear drinks only in historic rooms, if not seated; Ballroom (400,300,250,350); Tapestry Room (150,60,–,100); Adam Stables (250,140,100,200).*

Edinburgh International Conference Centre EH3

£M-E, (1200,850,–,1200)
The Exchange
T 0131 300 3000
F 0131 300 3030
W hardens.com/party/eicc
E pamelaw@eicc.co.uk
A self-evidently suitable venue for larger gatherings, with an impressive setting not far from the Castle. / *in-house caterers; no dancing; Pentland Suite (–,–,–,1200); Strathblane Hall (850,500,–,–); Cromdale Hall (1200,850,–,500); Soutra Room (–,14,–,–).*

The Merchants Hall EH2

£M-E, (250,120,80,150)
22 Hanover Street
T 0131 220 9283
F 0131 220 4842
W hardens.com/party/glasgowmerchants
E susan.walsh@mcoe.org.uk
A livery hall (at least in London parlance), this impressive New Town building provides an august setting for an event. / *midnight; list of caterers; The Hall (250,120,80,150); The Court Room & Crush Hall (80,50,–,40).*

Museum of Flight EH39

£M-E, (650,650,650,400)
East Fortune Airfield
T 0131 247 4113
F 0131 247 4307
W hardens.com/party/flightmuseum
E hospitality@nms.ac.uk
An aircraft which once flew faster than sound provides the evocative centrepiece for this museum display (the "Concorde Experience") which makes an intriguing location for a larger-scale event. / *midnight (flexible); evenings only; list of caterers; Concorde Experience (650,650,650,400).*

National Gallery of Scotland EH2

£M-E, (1000,150,–,200)
The Mound
T 0131 624 6216
F 0131 623 7046
W hardens.com/party/natgalscot
E events@nationalgalleries.org
As august a venue as you're going to find for an event, and a central landmark too. The complex offers a number of galleries, each of which has a different character. / *11pm; available after opening hours (5 pm+); list of caterers; no dancing; no red wine; National Gallery (400,150,–,200); Weston Link (300,140,–,200); Royal Scottish Academy (400,100,–,200).*

RY Britannia EH6

£M-E, (380,176,–,–)
Ocean Terminal
T 0131 555 8800
W hardens.com/party/rybritannia
E events@tryb.co.uk
HM The Queen's former yacht, now permanently moored at Leith, and providing a grand and interesting

setting for an event. / midnight; evenings only ; in-house caterers; no dancing; no red wine in drawing room; State Apartments (250,–,–,–); The Royal Deck (130,80,–,–); State Dining Room (–,96,–,–).

The Scotch Malt Whisky Society EH2

£M-E, (65,48,–,50)
28 Queen Street
Ⓣ 0131 555 2266
Ⓕ 0131 553 1003
Ⓦ hardens.com/party/edinburghmalt
Ⓔ events@smws.com

An elegant New Town house, recently acquired by the Society, offering a range of accommodation for smaller events. / 11pm; in-house caterers; no dancing; Hunter Room (18,18,–,–); Oval Room (20,14,–,12); Library (8,8,–,–); North View (65,48,–,50).

Surgeon's Hall Complex EH8

£M-E, (300,230,150,230)
Nicolson Street
Ⓣ 0131 527 3434
Ⓕ 0131 527 1688
Ⓦ hardens.com/party/surgeons
Ⓔ events@surgeonshall.com

An impressive series of facilities, recently refurbished and expanded, centred on an imposing neo-classical hall, near the Castle. / midnight; Heritage; Playfair Hall (200,175,–,200); Fellows Library (100,55,–,–); Quincentenary Main Hall (300,230,150,230); Auditorium (–,–,–,158); Reception Room (120,90,–,–).

Glasgow

Burrell Collection G43

£M-E, (200,150,–,180)
Pollok Country Park
Ⓣ 0141 276 9565
Ⓕ 0141 276 9587
Ⓦ hardens.com/party/burrell
Ⓔ ellen.dunlop@cordiae.co.uk

The home of a major one-man art collection, this low-lying modern building benefits in particular from a charming parkland location, and offers space well-suited to smaller to medium size events. / midnight; available after 7pm (5pm for set up); Encore Catering; no amplified music; no dancing; Lecture Theatre (–,–,–,180).

Gallery of Modern Art G1

£M-E, (150,–,–,–)
Royal Exchange Square
Ⓣ 0141 276 9565
Ⓕ 0141 276 9587
Ⓦ hardens.com/party/glasgowmodernart
Ⓔ ellen.dunlop@cortia.co.uk

In the heart of the city, an imposing neo-classical building (which houses the UK's second most-visited modern art gallery outside London). There are four spaces, each with roughly the same capacity, but they are not suitable for combining. / midnight; available from 7pm except Sat and Thurs; Encore Catering; no dancing; Gallery 1 (150,–,–,–).

Museum of Transport G3

£M, (1000,150,150,30)
1 Bunhouse Road
Ⓣ 0141 276 9565
Ⓕ 0141 276 9587
Ⓦ hardens.com/party/glasgowtransport
Ⓔ ellen.dunlop@tecs.glasgow.gov.uk

A major museum (attracting 0.5m visitors annually), and offering space particularly suited to larger receptions. / midnight; available from 7pm; Encore Catering; Cinema (–,–,–,30).

Scotland Street School Museum G5

£M, (150,70,–,–)
225 Scotland Street
Ⓣ 0141 276 9565
Ⓕ 0141 276 9587
Ⓦ hardens.com/party/scotstreetschool
Ⓔ ellen.dunlop@tecs.glasgow.gov.uk

A self-explanatory and slightly 'different' venue for a reception, where drinks receptions can be held in the former gym. / midnight; available from 7pm; willow cafe.

St. Mungo Museum of Religious Life and Art G4

£M-E, (120,80,80,100)
2 Castle Street
Ⓣ 0141 276 9565
Ⓕ 0141 276 9587
Ⓦ hardens.com/party/stmungo

E ellen.dunlop@tecs.glasgow.gov.uk
A rare and rather intriguing museum of religious life and art. Housed in an attractive traditional-style building, it has an intimate scale well suiting smaller events.
/ midnight; Encore Catering.

Leeds

Royal Armouries LS10

£M-E, (1000,800,700,250)
Armouries Drive
T 0113 220 1990
F 0113 220 1997
W hardens.com/party/royalarmouries
E enquiries@rai-events.co.uk
An interesting modern building that's not just a museum, but also a venue unusually well geared up for functions of all types. / 1.30am; in-house caterers; Royal Armouries Hall (1000,800,700,–); Bury Theatre (–,–,–,250); Wellington Suite (200,168,144,200); Tower Gallery (100,60,–,60); Nelson Bistro (200,–,150,–).

Liverpool

Everton FC L4

£M-E, (300,300,–,300)
Goodison Road
T 0151 330 2499
F 0151 286 9120
W hardens.com/party/evertonfc
E events@evertonfc.com
The home of the Blues offers a large range of venues suited to events on a variety of scales.
/ 12.30am; not available matchdays; Sodexo Prestige; no live music in the marquee; Dixie Dean Suite (–,70,–,70); The Marquee (–,300,–,300); The People's Club (250,180,–,200).

FACT L1

£M-E, (250,60,–,254)
88 Wood St
T 0151 707 4406
W hardens.com/party/fact
E kerry.moore@fact.co.uk
In the city-centre, the Foundation for Art and Creative Technology is a contemporary building, with facilities including three cinemas – ideal if you're looking to put on something with a bit of a techno-bent.
/ 10.30pm; in-house caterers; no dancing; Screen 1 (–,–,–,254); The Box (80,60,–,50); The Cafe (100,50,–,–); Screen 2 (–,–,–,136); Screen 3 (–,–,–,104); Bar (150,–,–,–).

Liverpool FC L4

£M-E, (500,350,–,350)
Anfield Road
T 0151 263 7744
F 0151 260 1434
W hardens.com/party/liverpoolfc
E events@liverpoolfc.tv
Anfield – home of LFC, and also of a fairly good range of spaces suited to medium-size events. / 1am; not available matchdays; in-house caterers; Reds Combined (500,–,–,200); Champions Lounge (350,350,–,350); European Lounge (200,250,–,250); Directors Lounge (60,40,–,48).

Philharmonic Hall L1

£M-E, (150,90,90,1650)
Hope Street
T 0151 210 2896
F 0151 210 2902
W hardens.com/party/liverpoolphil
E hall@liverpoolphil.com
Home of the 'Phil', a fine Art Deco building with a number of options for medium-size events. / midnight; hirer's choice of caterer; no alcohol in auditorium; Auditorium (–,–,–,1650); Grand Foyer Bar (150,–,90,120); Rodewald Suite (150,–,90,120); Green Room (40,25,25,25).

St George's Hall L1

£M-E, (1000,500,500,900)
William Brown Street
T 0151 225 6911
F 0151 709 5204
W hardens.com/party/liverpoolstg
E carol.hickey@liverpool.gov.uk
Sometimes claimed to be "the finest neo-classical building in the world", this hugely imposing city-centre hall contains a series of halls within, a number of which are suited to events. / 1am; in-house caterers; The Great Hall (1000,500,500,900); Small Concert Room (–,–,–,400); Cockerel Room (–,50,–,70).

 CAPACITIES: (Standing, Seated, Dinner Dance, Theatre-Style)

Liverpool Town Hall L2

£M-E, (270,210,180,270)
Liverpool
T 0151 225 5530
F 0151 225 5544
W hardens.com/party/liverpoolth
E town.hall@liverpool.gov.uk

Liverpool claims to have more Georgian buildings of note than Bath, and the Town Hall, in the heart of the contemporary business district, is one of the more charming ones. / 1am; in-house caterers; Large Ballroom (270,210,160,270); Council Chamber (–,166,–,230); Reception Rooms (60,–,40,60); Small Ballroom (130,80,80,130).

Manchester

Bridgewater Hall M2

£M-E, (500,240,136,1800)
Lower Mosley Street
T 0161 950 0000
F 0161 950 0001
W hardens.com/party/bridgewater
E conferences@bridgewater-hall.co.uk

The home of the Hallé (the UK's oldest full time symphony orchestra). The Barbirolli Room is a modern chamber, well suited to large get-togethers. / 6pm for daytime hire and midnight for evening hire; in-house caterers; no alcohol in auditorium; Barbirolli (–,170,136,240); Charles Halle (50,40,–,50); Circle Foyer (500,240,–,–); Green Room (40,30,24,40).

Imperial War Museum North M17

£M-E, (700,330,200,300)
The Quays
T 0161 836 4032
F 0161 836 4091
W hardens.com/party/iwmnorth
E conferencesnorth@iwm.org.uk

By the waterside, two miles from the city-centre, a striking contemporary building (Daniel Libeskind), with spaces suited to a range of events. / 2am; main exhibition space not available during museum opening hours; in-house caterers; The Niveskind (80,80,–,100); Watershard Cafe (200,200,–,140).

The Lowry M50

£M-E, (350,280,250,1730)
Pier 8
T 0161 876 2040
W hardens.com/party/lowry
E andersons@thelowry.com

An impressive waterside modern arts centre, not far from Manchester city centre, with a range of spaces suitable for events. / 1.30am; in-house caterers; The Studio (350,280,250,350); Quays Bar (250,–,–,–); Terrace Rest. (–,120,–,–); South Room (40,24,–,–).

Manchester Central M2

£M-E, (–,4800,–,9000)
Petersfield
T 0161 834 2700
F 0161 832 3621
W hardens.com/party/mancentral
E events@manchestercentral.co.uk

Manchester Central is the new name for the former GMEX (the elegant former Central Station building) plus the Manchester International Convention Centre. / in-house caterers; Central 1 (–,1200,–,1600); Central 2 (–,3000,–,8000); Exhange Auditorium (–,–,–,804).

Manchester Town Hall M60

£M-E, (500,300,280,500)
Albert Sq
T 0161 234 4343
F 0161 234 3242
W hardens.com/party/manchesterth
E conferenceoffice@manchester.gov.uk

The clocktower of the Town Hall is to Manchester what the tower housing Big Ben is to London. If you're looking for an impressive and central venue for an event, you won't do much better than this lavishly constructed, neo-Gothic Victorian pile. / 1am; in-house caterers; Banqueting Hall (200,150,–,200); Conference Hall (120,80,–,100); Great Hall (500,300,280,500).

Museum of Science and Industry M3

£M-E, (350,140,–,130)
Liverpool Rd
Ⓣ 0161 606 0174
Ⓕ 0161 606 0212
Ⓦ hardens.com/party/mosimanchester
Ⓔ conference@mosi.org.uk

In trendy Castlefield, a mile or so from the city-centre, a collection of 19th century buildings which have been impressively renovated in recent times, and with a number of spaces suited to events. From November 2010, it will also be able to offer conference facilities. / 1am; available from 5pm for dinner, all day for conferences (from Sept 2010); Milburns; no music in Air & Space Hall; no dancing in Air & Space Hall; Power Hall (250,120,–,–); Air & Space Hall (350,170,–,–); Manchester Science (100,–,–,–).

Old Trafford (Manchester United) M16

£M-E, (1100,950,650,1104)
Sir Matt Busby Way
Ⓣ 0161 868 8000
Ⓕ 0161 868 8809
Ⓦ hardens.com/party/manutd
Ⓔ conference@manutd.co.uk

A venue which needs no introduction. It can house events – whether football-related or not – on quite a scale. / 1am; limited availability on match days; in-house caterers; Manchester Suite (1100,1000,800,1200); International Suite (600,500,450,450); Trafford Suite (300,240,180,220); Lounge Bars (350,–,–,50).

Royal Northern College of Music M13

£M-E, (100,–,–,616)
124 Oxford Rd
Ⓣ 0161 907 5289
Ⓦ hardens.com/party/rncm
Ⓔ clare.preston-pollit@rncm.ac.uk

A self-explanatory institution, in modern buildings not far from the city-centre, offering a range of spaces for events and conferences. / 11pm; in-house caterers; Theatre (–,–,–,616); Concert Hall (–,–,–,466); Lecture Theatre (–,–,–,107); Lord Rhodes Room (100,–,–,–); Studio Theatre (–,–,–,120).

Nottingham

Newstead Abbey NG15

£M-E, (250,80,60,100)
Newstead Abbey Park
Ⓣ 0115 915 3940
Ⓦ hardens.com/party/newsteadabbey
Ⓔ privatehire@ncmg.org.uk

The ancestral home of Lord Byron, originally a priory established in the 12th century. It provides an attractive setting for an event. / 11pm; in-house caterers; dancing only in Suite; no dark drinks in Great Hall; The Great Hall (100,80,–,100); The Orangery (100,50,–,–); The Cloisters (150,–,–,–); The West Front Suite (120,80,60,70).

Nottingham Castle NG1

£M-E, (250,120,–,250)
Friar Lane
Ⓣ 0115 915 3940
Ⓕ 0115 915 3949
Ⓦ hardens.com/party/nottinghamcastle
Ⓔ privatehire@ncmg.org.uk

A c17 ducal mansion built on the site of the city's original medieval castle. It enjoys spectacular views across the city, and its grounds can house a marquee for up to 500 people. / 11pm; list of caterers; some restrictions on music; Long Gallery (250,120,–,250); Cafe (150,100,–,100).

Wollaton Hall NG8

£M-E, (150,100,100,150)
Nottingham
Ⓣ 0115 915 3940
Ⓦ hardens.com/party/wollatonhall
Ⓔ sharonp@ncmg.org.uk

A spectacular Elizabethan house (recently revamped at a cost of nearly £40m) which can provide quite a backdrop for a marquee event (as well as a number of entertaining spaces within). / no balloons, nothing attached to walls; 11pm; evenings only; hirer's choice of caterer (in-house available); Great Hall (150,100,100,150); Willoby Room (100,70,–,100); Cafe (150,–,–,–).

Boat Charter

City Cruises SE16
£M, (240,490,200,495)
Cherry Garden Pier
T 020 7740 0400
F 020 7740 0495
W hardens.com/party/citycruises
E info@citycruises.com
A Thames riverboat operator offers extensive sightseeing, entertainment and charter services. / 2am; in-house caterers; Sightseeing on Riverliner (–,490,–,495); Millennium of London (–,350,–,–); Mayflower Garden (240,–,200,–); Eltham (200,64,–,–); Westminster (80,50,–,–); Princess Rose (100,–,–,–).

Floating Boater W2
£M, (80,45,–,–)
The Waterside
T 020 7266 1066
F 020 7266 4665
W hardens.com/party/floatingboater
E enquiries@floatingboater.co.uk

Edwardian style boats operating exclusive charter cruises, all year around, from Little Venice, Paddington along the quiet waters of Regents Park, through London Zoo to Camden Lock. Formal dining, receptions and buffets, 12 to 80 guests, excellent catering, full bar and extensive wine list. Jazz Bands, Disco, Casino Tables etc. / in-house caterers; Prince Regent (80,45,–,–); Lapwing (30,16,–,–).

Sailing Barge Will E1
£M, (50,40,–,40)
St Katharine's Dock
T 020 7022 2201
F 01273 776 104
W hardens.com/party/sailingbargewill
E enquiries@topsailevents.co.uk
An impressive mahogany-panelled boat (1926), now available for boardroom meetings, private dining and wedding receptions. It is normally quietly moored in St Katharine's Dock, or you can go for a cruise upriver (max capacity 50). / midnight; hirer's choice of caterer (in-house available).

Thames Luxury Charters SW15
£M, (1000,420,400,300)
5 The Mews
T 020 8780 1562
F 020 8788 0072
W hardens.com/party/thamesluxurycharters
E sales@thamesluxurycharters.co.uk
London's largest boats, the "Dixie Queen" and the "Elizabethan" offer a high level of facilities and are well-suited to dining and dancing. (The smaller "Golden Salamander" and "Edwardian" are useful for smaller events and transfers). / 6am; hirer's choice of caterer (in-house available); music cannot exceed 96 decibels; Elizabethan (235,140,140,100); Dixie Queen (static) (1000,400,400,300); Dixie Queen (cruising) (520,400,400,300); Golden Salamander (150,70,70,30); Edwardian (100,60,60,64); Erasmus (320,150,150,–).

Services

1.00 Organisers

1.01 Party planners & event managers

Absolute Taste

14 Edgel St, London SW18 1SR
T 020 8870 5151
F 020 8870 9191
W www.absolutetaste.com
E info@absolutetaste.com

ABSOLUTE
taste

Passionate about creating the perfect event, we guarantee to look after every aspect: from delicious food, chic and fun canapés to table design, venue styling and entertainment through to lighting and full production for your party, launch or wedding. Our professional team is dedicated to making every event a success.

Added Dimension Events

12 Spice Crt, Plantation Wharf, Battersea, London SW11 3UE
T 020 7978 7400
F 020 7978 7447
W www.addeddimension.co.uk
E events@addeddimension.co.uk

Added Dimension offers high quality event management services. We bring individual ideas to life through conferences, launches and parties. We're fresh and innovative in our approach: from the initial creative concept to the very last detail, our friendly team are committed to super-serving every client.

Lucy Attwood Events

26 Berens Road,
London NW10 5DT
T 020 8964 2657
F 0870 751 5079
W www.lucyattwoodevents.com
E parties@lucyattwoodevents.com

LUCY ATTWOOD EVENT

Lucy Attwood has over 10 years experience in the food and event design industry. She organises weddings, private and corporate events of all sizes and budgets. 'Lucy works miracles! She is totally discreet, full of really imaginative ideas, enthusiastic, unflappable, understanding and unbelievably efficient. I cannot recommend her higher!'

Collective Minds

Soho, London W1
T 0207 856 2092
F 0845 370 4666
W www.collective-minds.com
E fascinate@collective-minds.com

"Collective Minds says it all – it's about bringing your thoughts and our creative expertise together to give you an event that takes you beyond your greatest expectations". "We want our clients to know that whatever they need to create the perfect event, no matter how much or how little, we are here to provide it."

Event Source
PO Box 697,
Richmond TW10 6YH
T 020 8605 3636
F 0870 130 6022
W www.event-source.co.uk
E info@event-source.co.uk
Event Source provides fresh ideas and solutions for Corporate Events and wide expertise in organising Summer & Christmas Parties. Unrivalled knowledge of all types of venues is coupled with access to top suppliers and a professional event management service to give you inspiration and peace of mind for your next event.

EventOracle
Unit 20b, 7-11 Minerva Road,
London NW10 6EU
T 020 7828 5332
Mob: 07590 414 656
W www.EventOracle.com
E info@eventoracle.com
EventOracle is a new company bringing a bright and fresh outlook to the world of catering and events. The concept is simple; no task too extraordinary and no job too small – A Food and Events Concierge.

Fait Accompli
212 The Plaza, 535 Kings Rd,
London SW10 0SZ
T 020 7352 2777
F 020 7352 8118
W www.faitaccompli.co.uk
E info@faitaccompli.co.uk

FAITACCOMPLI
LEGENDARY PARTIES WORLDWIDE EVENTS

"One of the leading party organisers – worldwide". Their reputation is based on discretion, excellence and meticulous attention to detail. "Flair and innovation coupled with their reputation for sticking to the budget has proved a winning formula for countless private and corporate clients."

Impulse Events
159 Brent Street,
London NW4 4DH
T 0870 383 4595
F 020 8203 7475
W www.impulseevents.co.uk
E info@impulseevents.co.uk

impulse events

Impulse Events are an independent, passionate and innovative event management company, who hold an enviable position within the events industry. We use our exceptional knowledge of the very best venues and suppliers to deliver phenomenal events ensuring out clients total peace of mind.

Lillingston
One Folly Mews, 223A
Portobello Road,
London W11 1LU
T 020 7221 5820
F 020 7221 5830
W www.lillingston.co.uk
E info@lillingston.co.uk
Over 17 years experience in organising spectacular events for high profile corporate & private clients including dinners in palaces, weekends in private stately homes, weddings on romantic Italian clifftops and parties on the Montanan plains! "Renowned for their discretion, personal service, attention to detail and above all, their creative flair!"

MacEvents
Hurlingham Studios, Ranelagh Gardens, Fulham,
London SW6 3PA
T 020 7736 6606
F 020 7736 6616
W www.macevents.co.uk
E cm@macevents.co.uk

MacEvents
Event Management
QUALITY WITHOUT COMPROMISE

Colin MacGregor believes in the art of looking and listening with appreciative eyes and ears for what makes the perfect corporate or private party. Creative design, impeccable taste and a personal attention to detail are brought to the party planning process in either London or Edinburgh.

Starlight Design
Unit 12, Gateway Trading Est,
Hythe Rd, London NW10 6RJ
T 020 8960 6078
F 020 8960 7991
W www.starlightdesign.co.uk
E info@starlightdesign.co.uk
Starlight are the ones the "others" go to. Why? Because their unique design team and expertise in lighting, sound, fireworks and production can be relied on to deliver world class parties, whatever the budget, whatever the location.

Theme Traders
The Stadium, Oaklands Rd,
London NW2 6DL
T 020 8452 8518
F 020 8450 7322
W www.themetraders.com
E mailroom@themetraders.com
Be a guest at your own party. Established for 15 years Theme Traders offers a one-stop in-house service for all aspects of events including full installation and back-up support for UK and Europe. Event management, style and project management or any individual elements of party planning.

William Bartholomew
33 Park Mansions, Battersea,
London SW11 4HQ
T 020 7731 8328
F 020 7384 1807
W www.wbpo.com
E mail@wbpo.com

WILLIAM BARTHOLOMEW
PARTY ORGANISING

We have been at the forefront of organising events and parties for more than 20 years. Imagination, co-ordination, attention to detail, and not least, inspiration, are second nature to us. Our depth of experience and organisational expertise will ensure that your event runs smoothly and is both a memorable and successful occasion.

Zest Events
2 Swan Mews, Parsons Green
Lane, London SW6 4QT
T 020 7384 9336
F 020 7384 9337
W www.zestevents.com
E parties@zestevents.com
"One of the more creative party planners, known for its chic, originality and fun!" Headed by Wonkie Hills, the company gives a personalised service, with attention to detail that's second to none – for events both private and corporate, in the UK and Europe.

DONT FORGET THE INDEXES!

see the back of this guide for venues listed by price, capacity, area, wedding license, outside area and hirer's choice of caterer

1.02 Event management

Theme Traders

The Stadium, Oaklands Rd,
London NW2 6DL
T 020 8452 8518
F 020 8450 7322
W www.themetraders.com
E mailroom@themetraders.com

Be a guest at your own party. Established for 15 years Theme Traders offers a one-stop in-house service for all aspects of events including full installation and back-up support for UK and Europe. Event management, style and project management or any individual elements of party planning.

2.00 Food & Beverage

2.01 Caterers

Absolute Taste

14 Edgel St, London SW18 1SR
T 020 8870 5151
F 020 8870 9191
W www.absolutetaste.com
E info@absolutetaste.com

Passionate about creating the perfect event, we guarantee to look after every aspect: from delicious food, chic and fun canapés to table design, venue styling and entertainment through to lighting and full production for your party, launch or wedding. Our professional team is dedicated to making every event a success.

Alex Risdale Catering

177 Ferndale Road, Stockwell,
London SW9 8BA
T 020 7501 9933
Mob: 07711 718 717
F 020 7501 9933
W www.bluestrawberry.co.uk
E info@alexrisdalecatering.co.uk

Alex Risdale Catering is an innovative catering company bringing you the best in seasonal produce. Whether its canapes for 500, an intimate dinner party or a corporate lunch we deliver fresh, delicious and interesting food with a friendly and professional service.

Blue Strawberry

OPB House, 26-28 Sidney Road,
London SW9 0TS
T 020 7733 3151
F 020 7733 3154
W www.bluestrawberry.co.uk
E info@bluestrawberry.co.uk

Blue Strawberry is a privately owned catering company with more than 20 years of experience in hosting the most memorable parties and weddings in London and further afield. Our menus follow the culinary trends in style, taste and presentation. A Blue Strawberry experience will always leave you wanting more.

Clare's Kitchen

Ⓣ 020 7722 6554
Mob: 07930 321 889
Ⓦ www.clareskitchen.co.uk
Ⓔ clare@clareskitchen.co.uk

Clare Latimer has provided catering for all types of events for 30 years with the same small team of cooks. Most work comes from word of mouth and they are well known to be very reliable, friendly and exceptionally caring. Apart from getting the food right they set the tone for a slick and smoothly run party.

Cooks & Partners Ltd.

Studio 21, The Talina Centre,
Bagley's Ln, London SW6 2BW
Ⓣ 020 7731 5282
Ⓕ 020 7731 7957
Ⓦ www.cooksandpartners.co.uk
Ⓔ enquiries@cooksandpartners.co.uk

Cooks & Partners specialise in delicious food, exceptional service, creative styling and amazing venues for corporate events, launches, weddings and private parties. Privately owned and with over 20 years experience in London and the S. East, our expertise, professionalism and friendly service will help create a bespoke, slick and memorable event, whatever the occasion.

Create Food & Party Design

24 Endeavour Way,
London SW19 8UH
Ⓣ 020 8944 4900
Ⓕ 020 8944 4901
Ⓦ www.createfood.co.uk
Ⓔ info@createfood.co.uk

Design, detail, delicious, destination and delivery - the mantra that underlines commitment to quality, innovation and detail that has made Create one of London's pre-eminent caterers and party designers. Create have an unrivalled depth of experience to deliver the finest quality event, whether with our venue partners or in clients' locations.

deWintons

4 Sleaford Street,
London SW8 5AB
Ⓣ 020 7627 5550
Ⓦ www.dewintons.co.uk
Ⓔ info@dewintons.co.uk

Using deWintons for a party creates a buzz which always ensures the impact for your event will be a 'wow'. deWintons catering is some of the most flavourful in London, reflected in their inspirational menus. deWintons use of ingredients is undeniably tantalising with their creative use of fragrance, herbs & spices to leave you reeling in a taste sensation.

Eat to the Beat

Studio 4-5, Garnett Cl,
Watford WD24 7GN
Ⓣ 01923 211702
Ⓕ 01923 211704
Ⓦ www.globalinfusiongroup.com
Ⓔ catering@eattothebeat.com

A leading worldwide production, location and tour catering company based in the UK, US, China and Dubai. The unique combination of highly experienced staff; flight-cased equipment; mobile kitchens and unlimited enthusiasm, enables us to be creative and supportive; whenever and wherever you event is.

EventOracle
Unit 20b, 7-11 Minerva Road,
London NW10 6EU
Ⓣ 020 7828 5332
Mob: 07590 414 656
Ⓦ www.EventOracle.com
Ⓔ info@eventoracle.com
See listing under Party Planners p209

Food Show
100a Hackford Rd,
London SW9 0QU
Ⓣ 020 7793 1877
Mob: 07710 277 852
Ⓕ 020 7793 1878
Ⓦ www.foodshowltd.com
Ⓔ info@foodshowltd.com

Corporate and Private Event Caterers

THE PROOF OF THE PUDDING IS IN THE EATING... "Food Show were recommended to us and I can see why. A continuous focus on what we wanted, excellent service that went that extra mile, outstanding quality of food and flexibility. All our guests were impressed - I highly recommend them to anyone."

Gorgeous Foods
Gresham Way, Wimbledon,
London SW19 8ED
Ⓣ 020 8944 7771
Ⓕ 020 8946 1639
Ⓦ www.gorgeous-foods.co.uk
Ⓔ food@
gorgeousgourmets.co.uk

GORGEOUS FOODS is passionate about providing beautifully presented foods, made with the freshest of ingredients by a team of high performance, inspirational and talented chefs, complimented with exemplary service creating value for both corporate and private clients. Our breadth of experience ensures parties are delivered with flair and imagination.

Last Supper
Unit 6, Newington Court
Business Centre, Newington
Causeway, London SE1 6DD
Ⓣ 020 7378 0101
Ⓕ 020 7407 3902
Ⓦ www.lastsupperltd.co.uk
Ⓔ info@lastsupperltd.co.uk

last Supper

'Classic cocktail parties to vodka revolutions' – whether your event be 'Mild or Wild' Last Supper offer a witty & creative approach to party catering.

Lodge Catering

Unit 13, Mitre Bridge Industrial Est, Mitre Way, London W10 6AU
T 020 8960 5794
F 020 8964 8363
W www.lodge-catering.co.uk
E lodge-catering@lodge-catering.co.uk

"The food was of an extremely high standard throughout the event, as was the service". Lodge are a well established firm who provide a wide ranging service. They bring a blend of innovative, honest food along with a much complimented personal service to some of London's top venues.

Mackintosh's

Unit B05 Acton Business Centre, School Road, London NW10 6TD
T 020 84531020
W www.mackintoshs.co.uk
E info@mackintoshs.co.uk

mackintosh's
fabulous food & exceptional events

White Chocolate Wedding, Lemon Meringue Launch, Crab Salad Conference, Profiterole Premiere, Goulash Gig, Cupcake Christening or Bangers & Mash Ball. Whatever the celebration, Mackintosh's talented team will plan and deliver imaginative food, fabulous cocktails, styling and entertainment. Contact London Caterer Mackintosh's about your next event.

Madsen Catering

20 Old Brompton Road , London SW7 3DL
T 020 7225 2772
W reservations@madsenrestaurant.com
E www.madsenrestaurant.com

MADSEN

Nordic food is in vogue and this is your chance to treat your guests to a completely different experience. At Madsen we combine traditional Nordic cuisine with modern influences. We source locally for our canapes, open sandwiches and buffets. Delivery in London and proximity.

Mange

Unit 19, City North, Fonthill Rd, London N4 3HF
T 020 7263 5000
F 020 7263 2233
W www.mange.co.uk
E info@mange.co.uk

Mange has been providing stylish, innovative food and imaginative event design for over 15 years. Having catered for thousands of events, from cocktail parties to gala dinners, press days to conferences, intimate private soirees to elaborate weddings, Mange has forged a reputation for personal, professional and exceptional service.

Mange Tout

38 Melgund Rd, London N5 1PT
T 020 7609 0640
F 020 7503 5421
W www.mangetoutlondon.com
E audreyknight.mangetout@blueyonder.co.uk

Mange Tout have been providing delicious high quality food for 25 years. Extensive menus include food from around the world and an excellent choice of vegetarian dishes. Lists of alternative dishes are available for customers to make up their own menus. Whatever the occasion Audrey Knight is happy to advise.

Melissa Webb

Green Trees, Hawks Hill, Bourne End, Bucks SL8 5JQ
T 01628 524634
Mob: 07966 440 798
W www.melissawebb.com
E mel@melissawebb.com

A privately owned company with over 18 years experience we provide delicious bespoke food for any event, anywhere: London, New York, Paris! With smiles on our faces we add a little love to our food and warmth to our parties.

Mustard Catering Ltd

38 Weir Road,
London SW19 8UG
T 020 8971 7800
F 020 8971 7829
W www.mustardcatering.com
E sales@mustardcatering.com

Mustard's food professionalism is unequalled, reflecting their integrity and ability to deliver events as agreed. Contemporary or traditional, informal or classical, they have been leading the field since day one. Listed and welcomed at more London venues than anyone else, for canapes, tapas, dinners and buffets, Simply Add Mustard.

Party Ingredients

Unit 1a Tideway Industrial Est, Kirtling St, London SW8 5BP
T 020 7627 3800
F 020 7720 6249
W www.partyingredients.co.uk
E sales@partyingredients.co.uk

Party Ingredients are experts in events, passionate about cooking and dedicated to personal service. With an impeccable record of delivering successful events, Party Ingredients is a food led caterer with a hands-on management team. Whatever your event we will use our expertise and enthusiasm to make your wishes a reality.

Rare Food

2 Carlton Tavern, 73 Grafton Road, London NW5 4BB
T 7428 0313
W www.rarefood.com
E info@rarefood.com

Divine, decadent, hip or wholesome, each event we create is original, unique and all about you. We take a detailed brief to capture precisely what you want for you and your guests and respond with inspired solutions geared to your needs. Our constants are quality, style, attention to detail, value for money and above all, exceptional delivery.

Rhubarb

5-25 Burr Rd,
London SW18 4SQ
T 8812 3200
F 8812 3201
W www.rhubarb.net
E paulscannell@rhubarb.net

"rhubarb" food design is an experienced, innovative and highly professional company that delivers fabulous food, unrivalled attention to detail and reassuring reliability. We are a caterer with vision. We plan with precision and execute beyond expectation. We tailor specifically to a person's needs and those of their guests. We are committed to creating delicious food with style and flair.

Richmond Creative Event Catering
17 Studley Grange Rd,
London W7 2LU
T 020 8567 9090
F 020 8566 3698
W www.richmondcaterers.com
E info@richmondcaterers.com

richmond
creative event catering

As one of London's leading independent catering companies, we draw on 30 years experience in corporate and private entertaining to provide mouth watering food, innovative drinks and exceptional service. Working in some of the most prestigious venues in London we offer a bespoke venue finding, event management and catering service.

Rocket Food Ltd
Unit 5 Southside Ind Estate,
Havelock Terrace,
London SW8 4AH
T 020 7622 2320
F 020 7622 3826
W www.rocketfood.net
E parties@rocketfood.net

Friendly and charming catering company WLTM like-minded clients for receptions, dinners, weddings and parties. Hobbies include enjoying excellent food and drink, organizing great events and thinking up fresh ideas. Looking to form lasting relationship - GSOH helpful, but not essential.

Sherlock Parties
Hazeldene Manor, North Oakley,
Hampshire RG26 5TT
T 01256 780544
F 01256 782921
W www.sherlockparties.com
E info@sherlockparties.com

A well-established caterer and party planner, based in Hampshire but with clients throughout London and the UK. They offer modern menus in contemporary style, and believe their team of event managers, chefs and waiting staff maintain 'an exceptional' eye for detail.

Stones Events
PO Box 8283, Kibworth,
Leicester LE8 0WU
T 0845 370 4777
F 0845 370 4666
W www.stonesevents.co.uk
E events@stonesevents.co.uk

Table Talk
OPB House, 26-28 Sidney Road,
London SW9 0TS
T 020 7401 3200
F 020 7401 9500
W www.tabletalk.co.uk
E info@tabletalk.co.uk

Table Talk is a leading London-based party design and catering company with core values of: Sensational food, Impeccable service, Exceptional design. They put the finest ingredients in the hands of the very best chefs and are proud to cater in London's most prestigious venues for an impressive client base.

Tray Gourmet

240 Fulham Rd,
London SW10 9NA
T 020 7352 7676
W info@traygourmet.co.uk
E www.traygourmet.co.uk

Tray Gourmet, a French delicatessen and catering company in London, was created in the early 90's to provide private and corporate catering with a hint of Frenchness. Tray Gourmet introduced the "Assiettes Repas" concept for company boardroom an exclusive way of eating while working. They are also creating mouthwatering canapés. They import weekly: cheese, charcuterie, fruit, vegetables and French delicacies.

Upbeat Event Design

Studio 4-5, Garnett Cl,
Watford WD24 7GN
T 01923 211702
F 01923 211704
W www.globalinfusiongroup.com
E bonnie@upbeateventdesign.com

Upbeat Event Design, (sister company to Eat To The Beat), is part of the international Global Infusion Group. We take pride in offering a personal approach to your special event; assisting you with beautiful design, venue finding, catering, and event management. You can trust Upbeat for your total event solution.

2.02 Staff

At Your Service

12 The Talina Centre, Bagleys Lane, London SW6 2BW
T 020 7352 7676
F 020 7610 8611
W www.ays.co.uk
E info@ays.co.uk

The leading event staffing and management specialist. Supplying staff to many of the top caterers and party planners in the world. With offices in Bristol, Birmingham, Edinburgh, Guildford, Leeds, London, Manchester, Oxford, Dublin and New York.

The Esprit Group

The Esprit Group, 4 Hurlingham Business Park, Sulivan Rd, London SW6 3DU
T 020 7384 4100
F 020 7384 4101
W www.esprit-group.com
E account.manager@esprit-group.com

The Esprit Group is renowned throughout the events and hospitality industry as a leader in providing fully trained managed teams to their clients. Esprit has been recognised for its high-level training and development programmes and for its committment to providing the highest standards to every event.

Front Promotions

Basement Floor, 8 Marylebone Passage, London W1W 8EX
T 7436 8484
F 7436 8434
W www.frontuk.co.uk
E info@frontuk.co.uk

Front is a leading national recruitment agency. We specialise in the supply of professional and charismatic promotional staff working at any private or corporate event. We also supply entertainment and source and produce main stream artists. Our database boasts thousands of artists from musicians to street dancers, magicians to burlesque.

High Society

50 Northcote Road, Battersea, London SW11 1PA
T 020 7228 0333
F 020 7228 0373
W www.high-society.co.uk
E info@high-society.co.uk

HIGH
SOCIETY
QUALITY STAFF FOR
EVENTS AND PARTIES

High Society has been providing London's finest waiting staff for over ten years. They have an excellent reputation in the staffing business. Without exception all staff are well presented, articulate, punctual, charming and proactive.

SHERPA

12 The Talina Centre, Bagleys Ln, London SW6 2BW
T 020 7610 8626
F 020 7610 8611
W www.eventsherpa.co.uk
E info@eventsherpa.co.uk

The leading specialist supplier of intelligent, articulate and professional event crew and back of house staff to the UK event industry.

DONT FORGET THE INDEXES!

see the back of this guide for venues listed by price, capacity, area, wedding license, outside area and hirer's choice of caterer

2.03 Bars

BAMBOO LONDON
12 The Talina Centre, Bagleys Ln,
London SW6 2BW
T 020 7610 8606
F 020 7610 8611
W www.bamboolondon.com
E info@bamboolondon.com

New York and London based drink strategy agency that creates and manages incredible bar experiences. From experiential consumer events to festivals and weddings, BAMBOO provide a full bar service.

3.00 Theme & equipment

3.01 Equipment

Theme Traders
The Stadium, Oaklands Rd,
London NW2 6DL
T 020 8452 8518
F 020 8450 7322
W www.themetraders.com
E mailroom@themetraders.com

Everything from furniture and popcorn warmers to chill-out tables and cushions, this is a company with a big name for its full range of specialist event services including prop hire, backdrops, scenery, lighting, costumes and greenery, and a full party planning service. Visit the website for information and image database.

3.02 Production services

inGenius Productions
Unit16 , Wimbledon Stadium Business Centre, Riverside Rd,
London SW17 0BA
T 020 8971 7888
F 020 8947 2616
W www.ingeniusuk.com
E mail@ingeniusuk.com

At the forefront of interior design for the event industry, we design and build sensory experiences through a multi-disciplined team of designers and producers. Our clients come to us for the very best in design, creativity and seamless organisation providing unique and and breathtaking party solutions.

3.03 Marquees

Toby's Tents
52 Hoddesdon Road, Stanstead Abbots, Hertfordshire SG12 8EQ
T 01920 411548
Mob: 07500 907620
W www.tobystents.com
E toby@tobystents.com

toby's tents

FRIENDLY PRICES AND FRIENDLY SERVICE, to suit all budgets. With over 25 years of wonderful marquee experience, we provide marquees of all shapes and sizes. Clearspan, Traditional and Chinese Hats; together with a wide range of linings & carpets, dancefloors & stages, lighting & heating, dining & lounge furniture. Covering your every need...

3.04 Sound equipment

Starlight Design
Unit 12, Gateway Trading Est, Hythe Rd, London NW10 6RJ
T 020 8960 6078
F 020 8960 7991
W www.starlightdesign.co.uk
E info@starlightdesign.co.uk
See listing under Party Planners p202

3.05 Lighting

inGenius Productions
Unit16 ,Wimbledon Stadium Business Centre, Riverside Rd, London SW17 0BA
T 020 8971 7888
F 020 8947 2616
W www.ingeniusuk.com
E mail@ingeniusuk.com
See listing under Production Services p211

Starlight Design
Unit 12, Gateway Trading Est, Hythe Rd, London NW10 6RJ
T 020 8960 6078
F 020 8960 7991
W www.starlightdesign.co.uk
E info@starlightdesign.co.uk
See listing under Party Planners p202

3.06 Themes & props

Theme Traders
The Stadium, Oaklands Rd, London NW2 6DL
T 020 8452 8518
F 020 8450 7322
W www.themetraders.com
E mailroom@themetraders.com
Transform your house, marquee or venue into the theme of your dreams. With 1 1/2 acres of props, lighting, scenery and furniture, you can either have a full installation and production...or just hire the kit for the budget conscious - D.I.Y.

3.07 Specialist furniture

inGenius Productions
Unit16 ,Wimbledon Stadium Business Centre, Riverside Rd, London SW17 0BA
T 020 8971 7888
F 020 8947 2616
W www.ingeniusuk.com
E mail@ingeniusuk.com
See listing under Production Services p211

3.08 Ice sculptures

The Ice Box
A35-36, New Covent Garden Market, London SW8 5EE
T 020 7498 0800
F 020 7498 0900
W www.theicebox.com
E info@theicebox.com
The Ice Box are the UK's leading Ice sculpture and Ice specialists. Amazing creations in Ice for Parties, PR stunts and Brand Communications. The market leader, we will provide amazing solutions in ice, guaranteed to impress your guests. From Luges to Logos and Ice Bars, Ice Box will always deliver!

3.09 Event badges & registration

OutStand
PO Box 195, Canterbury CT13 3AJ
T 07946 622787
W www.outstand.co.uk
E info@outstand.co.uk
OutStand offers a range of stylish name badges for use at conferences, meetings and events. Specialising in the provision of onsite registration desk services with the facility for onsite badge printing, OutStand is the perfect partner to ensure effective and efficient guest registration at your event.

4.00 Entertainment

Musicians Inc
No 4, Solar Court, 22 Chambers Street, London SE16 4XL
T 0845 450 1962
24 HOURS 07872 936 297
W www.musiciansinc.co.uk
E enquiries@musiciansinc.co.uk
Bespoke music and entertainment specialists. Run by a team of award winning industry professionals. Musicians Inc. tailors musicians, dancers, casinos and actors to suit your individual requirements. Providing you with affordable bespoke entertainment unique and personal to you. Clients include the BBC, Heart 106.2 fm, Asda PR.

The Three Waiters
Level 4, 116 New Oxford St, London WC1A 1HH
T 020 7436 4484
F 020 7436 6977
W www.thethreewaiters.co.uk
E uk@thethreewaiters.co.uk

THE THREE WAITERS

Arguably the World's most successful corporate act, three operatic performers secretly masquerade as real catering staff before culminating to perform a dynamic "Three Tenors" style rendition of the famous opera classics. The original and most successful act of its kind. They perform brilliantly at all types of event, tailoring their performance to suit.

4.01 Casinos

Viva Vegas
144a Old South Lambeth Rd,
London SW8 1XX
Ⓣ 020 7820 0999
Ⓕ 020 7820 0998
Ⓦ www.viva-vegas.co.uk
Ⓔ enquiries@vivavegas.co.uk
The UK's no. 1 Casino, poker and games company with over 80 full-size Casino and poker tables, including roulette, blackjack, Texas hold'em poker and craps. Corporate games with 8 lane scalextric tracks, football tables, giant board games and the latest games and simulators.

4.02 Fireworks

Starlight Design
Unit 12, Gateway Trading Est,
Hythe Rd, London NW10 6RJ
Ⓣ 020 8960 6078
Ⓕ 020 8960 7991
Ⓦ www.starlightdesign.co.uk
Ⓔ info@starlightdesign.co.uk
Starlight are the ones the "others" go to. Why? Because their unique design team and expertise in lighting, sound, fireworks and production can be relied on to deliver world class parties, whatever the budget, whatever the location.

5.00 Extras

5.01 Photographers

PR Photography
Studio 12, 7 Wenlock Road,
London N1 7SL
Ⓣ..0207 183 1625
Ⓦ..www.pr-photography.org
Ⓔ..info@pr-photography.org

PR PHOTOGRAPHY
LONDON - ENGLAND

PR Photography is London's premier production studio, creating inspired cinematic film and photography coverage for clients across the UK and the world. Our approach is underpinned by a passion for innovative story telling, utilising the latest in technology and equipment to constantly push the boundaries of excellence and creativity.

5.02 Transport

Timebus Travel
Boleyn Drive, St. Albans,
Hertfordshire AL1 2BP
T 01727 866 248
W www.timebus.co.uk
E book@timebus.co.uk

We have exclusively operated classic London buses for 20 years. We provide bright red Routemasters, open toppers, or older double and single deck vehicles; beautifully restored. Suitable for stylish guest travel, sightseeing, conferences and dinners. We hold details of access to over 2500 venues visited around London and the Home Counties

Indexes
Private Venues

VENUES BY TYPE AND AREA

Halls

Central
Banqueting House *(SW1)*
Central Hall Westminster *(SW1)*
Conway Hall *(WC1)*
Freemason's Hall *(WC2)*
Gray's Inn *(WC1)*
Lincoln's Inn (Honourable Society of) *(WC2)*
London Scottish *(SW1)*
The London Welsh Centre *(WC1)*
Queen Elizabeth II Conference Centre *(SW1)*
The Royal Horticultural Halls *(SW1)*
7 Rifles Battalion *(W1)*
Westminster Cathedral Hall *(SW1)*

West
Amadeus Centre *(W9)*
Brompton Oratory *(SW7)*
Bush Hall *(W12)*
Chelsea Old Town Hall *(SW3)*
Ealing Town Hall *(W5)*
Fulham Town Hall *(SW6)*
Hammersmith Town Hall *(W6)*
Philbeach Hall *(SW5)*
Porchester Centre *(W2)*
St Peter's Hall *(W11)*

North
Alexandra Palace & Park *(N22)*
The Business Design Centre *(N1)*
Cecil Sharp House *(NW1)*

South
BAC *(SW11)*
Blackheath Concert Halls *(SE3)*
Chatham Hall *(SW11)*
Hop Exchange *(SE1)*
St Thomas' Hospital *(SE1)*
Tudor Barn Eltham *(SE9)*
Wandsworth Civic Suite *(SW18)*

East
Balls Brothers Minster Pavement *(EC3)*
Barnard's Inn Hall *(EC1)*
Bishopsgate Institute *(EC2)*
Gibson Hall *(EC2)*
Inner Temple *(EC4)*
Middle Temple Hall *(EC4)*
Mile End Park Ecology Pavilion *(E3)*
Old Finsbury Town Hall *(EC1)*
Old Truman Brewery *(E1)*
Shoreditch Town Hall *(EC1)*
SPACE *(E8)*
Space *(E14)*
St Bartholomew's Hospital *(EC1)*
St Botolph's Hall *(EC2)*
St Bride Foundation *(EC4)*
St John's Gate *(EC1)*
Tab Centre *(E2)*

Outside London
Assembly Rooms *(Bath)*
Bridgewater Hall *(Manchester)*
Cardiff City Hall *(Cardiff)*
Forty Hall *(Middx)*
Guildhall *(Bath)*
Manchester Town Hall *(Manchester)*
Philharmonic Hall *(Liverpool)*
Pump Room and Roman Baths *(Bath)*
Royal Holloway College *(TW20)*
St George's Hall *(Liverpool)*
Surgeon's Hall Complex *(Edinburgh)*
Liverpool Town Hall *(Liverpool)*

Banqueting Halls

Central
Dartmouth House *(W1)*
Grand Connaught Rooms *(WC2)*
One Whitehall Place *(SW1)*
Parliament Square (RICS) *(SW1)*

West
Royal Hospital Chelsea *(SW3)*

South
Le Gothique *(SW18)*
Guy's Hospital *(SE1)*
The Oval *(SE11)*

East
The Brewery *(EC1)*

Outside London
Addington Palace *(Surrey)*
The Langley *(Herts)*

Livery halls

South
Glaziers' Hall *(SE1)*

East

Apothecaries' Hall *(EC4)*
Armourers' & Braisers' Hall *(EC2)*
Bakers' Hall *(EC3)*
Barber-Surgeons' Hall *(EC2)*
Brewers' Hall *(EC2)*
Butchers' Hall *(EC1)*
Carpenters' Hall *(EC2)*
Clothworkers' Hall *(EC3)*
Coopers' Hall *(EC2)*
Drapers' Hall *(EC2)*
Farmers' & Fletchers' Hall *(EC1)*
Fishmongers' Hall *(EC4)*
Founders' Hall *(EC1)*
Goldsmiths' Hall *(EC2)*
Grocers' Hall *(EC2)*
Guildhall *(EC2)*
Haberdashers' Hall *(EC1)*
Innholders' Hall *(EC4)*
The Insurance Hall *(EC2)*
Ironmongers' Hall *(EC2)*
Mercers' Hall *(EC2)*
Merchant Taylors' Hall *(EC2)*
One Moorgate Place *(EC2)*
Painters' Hall *(EC4)*
Pewterers' Hall *(EC2)*
Plaisterers' Hall *(EC2)*
Saddlers' Hall *(EC2)*
Salters' Hall *(EC2)*
Skinners' Hall *(EC4)*
Stationers' Hall *(EC4)*
Tallow Chandlers' Hall *(EC4)*
Watermen's Hall *(EC3)*
Wax Chandlers' Hall *(EC2)*

Outside London

The Merchants Hall *(Edinburgh)*

Houses

Central

Arndale House *(WC2)*
Artworkers Guild, The *(WC1)*
Benjamin Franklin House *(WC2)*
BMA House *(WC1)*
Il Bottaccio *(SW1)*
British Acadamy *(SW1)*
Canning House *(SW1)*
Fitzroy Square *(W1)*
Forbes House *(SW1)*
Home House *(W1)*
House of St Barnabas *(W1)*
Lancaster House *(SW1)*
Local Government House *(SW1)*
Motcomb's Townhouse *(SW1)*
Somerset House *(WC2)*
Spencer House *(W1)*
30 Pavilion Road *(SW1)*
33 Portland Place *(W1)*
28 Portland Place *(W1)*
Two Temple Place *(WC2)*

West

Chiswick House *(W4)*
Fulham House *(SW6)*
Fulham Palace *(SW6)*
Kensington Palace *(W8)*
Kent House Knightsbridge *(SW7)*
Pitzhanger Manor *(W5)*

North

Avenue House *(N3)*
Canonbury Academy *(N1)*
The House *(NW1)*
Kenwood House (The Orangery) *(NW3)*
Kenwood House (Old Kitchen) *(NW3)*
Lauderdale House *(N6)*

South

Devonport House *(SE10)*
Eltham Palace *(SE9)*
Parkstead House *(SW15)*
Queen's House *(SE10)*

East

Dr Johnsons' House *(EC4)*
The HAC *(EC1)*
Miller's House *(E3)*
Oxford House *(E2)*
Sutton House *(E9)*

Outside London

Blakemore House Conference and Wedding Venue *(Stevenage)*
Blenheim Palace *(Oxon)*
Brocket Hall *(Herts)*
East Hampstead Park Conference Centre *(Berks)*
Great Fosters *(Surrey)*
Ham House & Garden *(Surrey)*
Hampton Court Palace *(Surrey)*
Hatfield House *(Herts)*
Hever Castle *(Kent)*
Hopetoun House *(Edinburgh)*
Kew Palace *(Surrey)*
Lainston House *(Winchester)*
Marble Hill House *(Surrey)*
Newstead Abbey *(Nottingham)*
Nottingham Castle *(Nottingham)*
Osterley Park & House *(Middx)*
Preston Manor *(Brighton)*

Syon Park *(Middx)*
Waddesdon Manor, The Dairy *(Bucks)*
Wollaton Hall *(Nottingham)*

Museums

Central
British Museum *(WC1)*
The Charles Dickens Museum *(WC1)*
Churchill Museum and Cabinet War Rooms *(SW1)*
The Foundling Museum *(WC1)*
Guards Museum *(SW1)*
London Transport Museum *(WC2)*
Sir John Soane's Museum *(WC2)*

West
Leighton House Museum *(W14)*
National Army Museum *(SW3)*
Natural History Museum *(SW7)*
Science Museum *(SW7)*
Victoria and Albert Museum *(SW7)*

North
Estorick Collection *(N1)*
Freud Museum *(NW3)*
London Canal Museum *(N1)*
Royal Air Force Museum *(NW9)*

South
Design Museum *(SE1)*
Fan Museum *(SE10)*
The Fashion and Textile Museum *(SE1)*
Firepower - The Royal Artillery Museum *(SE18)*
The Garden Museum *(SE1)*
Horniman Museum *(SE23)*
Imperial War Museum London *(SE1)*
London Film Museum *(SE1)*
National Maritime Museum *(SE10)*
Old Operating Theatre, Museum & Herb Garret *(SE1)*
Royal Observatory *(SE10)*

East
Geffrye Museum *(E2)*
Museum of London *(EC2)*
V&A Museum of Childhood *(E2)*

Outside London
Imperial War Museum North *(Manchester)*
Kew Bridge Steam Museum *(Middx)*
Museum of Flight *(Edinburgh)*
Museum of Science and Industry *(Manchester)*
Museum of Transport *(Glasgow)*
National Museum of Wales *(Cardiff)*
River & Rowing Museum *(Oxon)*
Royal Armouries *(Leeds)*
St. Mungo Museum of Religious Life and Art *(Glasgow)*

Galleries

Central
Courtauld Gallery *(WC2)*
Gallery Soho *(WC2)*
ICA *(SW1)*
The Imagination Gallery *(WC1)*
Mall Galleries *(SW1)*
Music Room *(W1)*
National Portrait Gallery *(WC2)*
The October Gallery *(WC1)*
Photographers' Gallery *(W1)*
The Royal Academy of Arts *(W1)*
The Strand Gallery *(WC2)*
Tate Britain *(SW1)*
Wallace Collection *(W1)*

West
Louise Blouin Foundation *(W11)*
Orangery (Holland Park) *(W8)*
Proud Chelsea *(SW3)*
Royal College of Art *(SW7)*
Saatchi Gallery *(SW3)*
Serpentine Gallery *(W2)*

North
Proud Camden *(NW1)*

South
Bankside Gallery *(SE1)*
Dali Universe *(SE1)*
Delfina Galleries *(SE1)*
Dulwich Picture Gallery *(SE21)*
Hayward Gallery *(SE1)*
Jerwood Space *(SE1)*
The Pump House Gallery *(SW11)*
South London Gallery *(SE5)*
Tate Modern *(SE1)*

East
AOP Gallery (The Association of Photographers) *(EC2)*
Barbican Art Gallery *(EC2)*
Candid Arts Trust, The *(EC1)*
Prenelle Gallery *(E14)*
Proud Cabaret *(EC3)*

The Village Underground *(EC2)*
Whitechapel Art Gallery *(E1)*

Outside London
Burrell Collection *(Glasgow)*
FACT *(Liverpool)*
Gallery of Modern Art *(Glasgow)*
National Gallery of Scotland *(Edinburgh)*
Victoria Art Gallery *(Bath)*

Tourist attractions

North
Madame Tussauds *(NW1)*
Tussaud's Showdome *(NW1)*

South
The Clink *(SE1)*
Cutty Sark *(SE10)*
London Aquarium *(SE1)*
The London Dungeon *(SE1)*
London Eye *(SE1)*
London Wetland Centre *(SW13)*
Winston Churchill's Britain at War *(SE1)*

East
HM Tower of London *(EC3)*

Outside London
Chessington World of Adventures *(Surrey)*
Eton College (Dorney Lake) *(Berks)*
Kew Gardens *(Surrey)*
Legoland Windsor *(Berks)*
Thorpe Park *(Surrey)*
Warwick Castle *(Warwickshire)*
West Wycombe Caves *(Bucks)*
Whipsnade Wild Animal Park *(Beds)*

Colleges & Universities

Central
45 Millbank *(SW1)*
Goodenough College *(WC1)*
King's College *(WC2)*
London School of Economics *(WC2)*
Royal College of Pathologists *(SW1)*
Royal College of Radiologists *(W1)*
University of London Union *(WC1)*

West
Imperial College London *(SW7)*
Royal College of Music *(SW7)*

North
Highgate School *(N6)*
Regent's College *(NW1)*
Royal College of Physicians *(NW1)*
University of Westminster *(NW1)*

South
Dulwich College *(SE21)*
Froebel College *(SW15)*
Goldsmiths College *(SE14)*
King's College School *(SW19)*

East
Queen Mary College *(E1)*
Queen Mary Students' Union *(E1)*
Women's Library *(E1)*

Outside London
Harrow School *(Middx)*
Royal Northen College of Music *(Manchester)*
Spring Grove House *(Middx)*

Institutions

Central
BAFTA, 195 Piccadilly *(W1)*
Chandos House *(W1)*
Chartered Institute of Public Finance & Accountancy *(WC2)*
52-53 Russell Square *(WC1)*
The Geological Society of London *(W1)*
Hospital *(WC2)*
Institute of Directors *(SW1)*
The Law Society *(WC2)*
No 4 Hamilton Place *(W1)*
One Birdcage Walk *(SW1)*
One Great George Street *(SW1)*
One Wimpole Street *(W1)*
Royal Academy of Engineering *(SW1)*
Royal Institute of British Architects *(W1)*
Royal Institution of Great Britain *(W1)*
Royal Society of Arts *(WC2)*
School of Pharmacy *(WC1)*
SixtyOne Whitehall *(SW1)*

West
Institut Français *(SW7)*
Royal Geographical Society *(SW7)*

East
Baltic Exchange *(EC3)*
Lloyd's of London *(EC3)*
The Scotch Malt Whisky Society *(EC1)*
Trinity House *(EC3)*

Moored boats

Central
RS Hispaniola *(WC2)*
HQS Wellington *(WC2)*

South
HMS Belfast *(SE1)*
The Golden Hinde *(SE1)*

East
Leven is Strijd *(E14)*
HMS President *(EC4)*
The Regalia *(EC4)*
SS Robin *(E14)*

Outside London
SS Great Britain *(Bristol)*
RY Britannia *(Edinburgh)*

Theatres

Central
Aldwych Theatre *(WC2)*
Ambassadors Theatre *(WC2)*
Bloomsbury Theatre *(WC1)*
Cochrane Theatre *(WC1)*
The Coliseum *(WC2)*
The Comedy Store *(SW1)*
Comedy Theatre *(SW1)*
Dominion Theatre *(W1)*
Duchess Theatre *(WC2)*
Fortune Theatre *(WC2)*
Haymarket Theatre *(SW1)*
London Palladium *(W1)*
Lyceum Theatre *(WC2)*
New Players Theatre *(WC2)*
Noel Coward Theatre *(WC2)*
Palace Theatre *(W1)*
Royal Court Theatre *(SW1)*
Royal Opera House *(WC2)*
Shaftesbury Theatre *(WC2)*
Theatre Royal, Drury Lane *(WC2)*

West
Canal Café Theatre *(W2)*
Royal Albert Hall *(SW7)*
20th Century Theatre *(W11)*

North
Hoxton Hall *(N1)*
Jongleurs at Camden Lock *(NW1)*
King's Head Theatre *(N1)*
New End Theatre *(NW3)*
Roundhouse *(NW1)*
Tricycle Theatre *(NW6)*

South
BFI IMAX *(SE1)*
Greenwich Playhouse *(SE10)*
Greenwich Theatre *(SE10)*
National Theatre *(SE1)*
Polka Theatre for Children *(SW19)*
Swan at the Globe at Shakespeare's Globe *(SE1)*
Theatre 503 at the Latchmere Pub *(SW11)*

East
Sadler's Wells Theatre *(EC1)*

Miscellaneous

Central
Berry Bros. & Rudd *(SW1)*
The Casino at the Empire *(WC2)*
Christie's *(SW1)*
The Commonwealth Club *(WC2)*
Congress Centre *(WC1)*
Coram's Fields *(WC1)*
Covent Garden Market *(WC2)*
Dolphin House *(SW1)*
Fortnum & Mason *(W1)*
Hamleys *(W1)*
Harrods *(SW1)*
Hellenic Centre *(W1)*
International Coffee Organisation *(W1)*
Knightsbridge 145 *(SW1)*
Liberty *(W1)*
Odeon Leicester Square *(WC2)*
One Mayfair *(W1)*
The Place *(WC1)*
Royal Astronomical Society *(W1)*
Royal Courts of Justice *(WC2)*
The Sanctuary *(WC2)*
Savile Club *(W1)*
St Martin In The Fields *(WC2)*
St Mary's Church *(W1)*
Thomas Goode *(W1)*
The Vinyl Factory *(W1)*
Waterstone's *(W1)*
Wellington Arch *(W1)*
Westminster Abbey Garden *(SW1)*
Westminster Boating Base *(SW1)*

West

Apartment 195 *(SW3)*
The Chelsea Gardener *(SW3)*
Chelsea Physic Garden *(SW3)*
Conservatory at Chelsea *(SW3)*
First Bowl Queensway *(W2)*
Gunnersbury Park *(W3)*
The Irish Centre *(W6)*
Jasmine Studios *(W6)*
Linden House *(W6)*
Lowiczanka Restaurant *(W6)*
Orangery (Kensington Palace) *(W8)*
The Queen's Club *(W14)*
Riverside Studios *(W6)*
Trailfinders Sports Club *(W13)*
Worx *(SW6)*

North

Alexandra Palace Ice Rink *(N22)*
The British Library *(NW1)*
Burgh House *(NW3)*
Circus Space *(N1)*
The Decorium *(N22)*
ecurie25 *(EC1)*
Jacksons Lane *(N6)*
The London Art House *(N1)*
Lord's Cricket Ground *(NW8)*
The Magic Circle Headquarters *(NW1)*
One Marylebone Road *(NW1)*
Phyllis Court *(Oxfordshire)*
The Pirate Castle *(NW1)*

South

Battersea Evolution *(SW11)*
Battersea Park *(SW11)*
BFI Southbank *(SE1)*
City Hall - London's Living Room *(SE1)*
Coin Street Neighbourhood Centre *(SE1)*
Common Ground Cafe & Bar *(SW18)*
The Coronet *(SE1)*
Debut London *(SE1)*
Earls Court & Olympia *(SW5)*
Earlsfield Library *(SW18)*
Greenwich Yacht Club *(SE10)*
Kingswood House *(SE21)*
LABAN *(SE8)*
London Studios *(SE1)*
Menier Chocolate Factory *(SE1)*
Mosimann's Academy *(SW11)*
Namco Station *(SE1)*
Old Royal Naval College *(SE10)*
The 108 *(SE10)*
Simon Drake's House of Magic *(SE1)*
Siobhan Davies Studios *(SE1)*
Southbank Centre *(SE1)*
Streatham Ice Arena *(SW16)*
Tower Bridge *(SE1)*
Tower Paintball *(SE1)*
Vinopolis: The Venue *(SE1)*
Winchester House *(SW15)*

East

Barbican Centre *(EC2)*
Broadgate Estates *(EC2)*
Cannon Bridge Roof Garden *(EC4)*
Christ Church Spitalfields *(E1)*
Concrete *(Street London)*
Crypt *(EC1)*
Docklands Sailing & Watersports Centre *(E14)*
Dyers' Hall *(EC4)*
The E Rejuvenation Centre *(E1)*
East Wintergarden *(E14)*
ExCeL London *(E16)*
Forman's Fish Island *(E3)*
London Capital Club *(EC4)*
London Stock Exchange *(EC4)*
LSO St Luke's *(EC1)*
Newham City Farm *(E16)*
Old Billingsgate *(EC3)*
Planit Finsbury Square *(EC2)*
The Rag Factory *(E1)*
Rich Mix *(E1)*
River Lounge *(E1)*
Rivington Place *(EC2)*
Spitalfields Market *(E1)*
St Andrew Holborn *(EC4)*
St Paul's Cathedral *(EC4)*
Sugar Quay *(EC3)*
30 St Mary Axe *(EC3)*
Troxy *(E1)*

Outside London

Ascot Racecourse *(Berks)*
Brighton Pier *(Brighton)*
The Conservatory at Painshill Park *(Surrey)*
Elstree Film Studio *(Herts)*
Epsom Downs *(Surrey)*
Gate Street Barn *(Surrey)*
Ham Polo Club *(Richmond on Thames)*
Newbury Racecourse *(Berkshire)*
The Old Courtroom *(Brighton)*
Old Trafford (Manchester United) *(Manchester)*
The Pavilion *(Birmingham)*

Pinewood Studios *(Bucks)*
Queen's Eyot *(Berks)*
The Royal Pavilion *(Brighton)*
Scotland Street School Museum *(Glasgow)*
Temple Island *(Oxon)*

Clubs

Central

Adam Street *(WC2)*
Arts Club *(W1)*
Bar Soho *(W1)*
The Caledonian Club *(SW1)*
Carlton Club *(SW1)*
Cavalry & Guards Club *(W1)*
Century *(W1)*
Crazy Bear (Member's Club) *(WC2)*
East India Club *(SW1)*
Floridita *(W1)*
The Fox Club *(W1)*
Groucho Club *(W1)*
The Hospital Club *(WC2)*
Jewel Piccadilly *(W1)*
Lansdowne Club *(W1)*
Les Ambassadeurs *(W1)*
Mosimann's Dining Club *(SW1)*
National Liberal Club *(SW1)*
The New Cavendish Club *(W1)*
Oxford & Cambridge Club *(SW1)*
Paramount *(WC1)*
Poetry Society *(WC2)*
Ronnie Scotts *(W1)*
Royal Air Force Club *(W1)*
Royal Over-Seas League *(SW1)*
Soho House *(W1)*
St Stephen's Club *(SW1)*
The Kingly Club *(W1)*
229 The Venue *(W1)*
The Union Club *(W1)*
University Women's Club *(W1)*
The Village *(W1)*

West

Auriol Kensington Rowing Club *(W6)*
Beaufort House *(SW3)*
The Cobden Club *(W10)*
The Frontline Club *(W2)*
High Road House *(W4)*
Hurlingham Club *(SW6)*
London Corinthian Sailing Club *(W6)*
Ognisko *(SW7)*
Victory Services Club *(W2)*

South

Bank of England Sports Centre *(SW15)*
London Rowing Club *(SW15)*
Roehampton Club *(SW15)*

East

City of London Club *(EC2)*
The Little Ship Club *(EC4)*
Lloyds Club *(EC3)*
Loose Cannon *(EC4)*
Shoreditch House *(E1)*

Outside London

The Scotch Malt Whisky Society *(Edinburgh)*

Nightclubs

Central

Annabel's *(W1)*
Aura *(SW1)*
Bloomsbury Ballroom *(WC1)*
Café de Paris *(W1)*
Club 49 Soho *(W1)*
The London Hippodrome *(WC2)*
Maya *(W1)*
No 5 *(W1)*
Pacha *(SW1)*
The Penthouse *(WC2)*
The Red Room *(W1)*
The Red Rooms *(WC2)*
Ruby Blue *(WC2)*
Shadow Lounge *(W1)*
Sound London *(WC2)*
St Moritz *(W1)*
Studio Valbonne *(W1)*
Sway *(WC2)*
Tiger Tiger *(SW1)*
229 *(W1)*

West

Boujis *(SW7)*
Crazy Larry's *(SW10)*
Embargo 59 *(SW10)*
FireHouse *(SW7)*
The Roof Gardens *(W8)*
606 Club *(SW10)*

North

Egg *(N7)*
Electric Ballroom *(NW1)*
KOKO *(NW1)*

South

Cable *(SE1)*

Clapham Grand *(SW11)*
The Ministry of Sound *(SE1)*

East
Aquarium *(EC1)*
Fabric *(EC1)*

Wine bars

Central
Shampers *(W1)*
Vats *(WC1)*

South
Balls Brothers Hays *(SE1)*

East
Balls Brothers Minster *(EC3)*
Balls Brothers Lime *(EC3)*
Ochre *(EC4)*

Bar & Pubs

Central
The Antelope *(SW1)*
Audley *(W1)*
Babble *(W1)*
Cirque De Soir *(W1)*
Cittie of Yorke *(WC1)*
Detroit *(WC2)*
gem *(W1)*
The Golden Lion *(SW1)*
Jerusalem *(W1)*
Mahiki *(W1)*
Milk & Honey *(W1)*
The Player *(W1)*
Punk *(W1)*
Red *(W1)*
Schochu Lounge *(W1)*
Ship & Shovell *(WC2)*
06 St Chad's Place *(WC1)*
Thomas Cubitt *(SW1)*
Whisky Mist at Zeta *(W1)*
Yard *(W1)*
Zebrano (at the establishment) *(W1)*

West
Aragon House *(SW6)*
The Atlas *(SW6)*
Beach Blanket Babylon *(W11)*
Britannia *(W8)*
Coopers Arms *(SW3)*
Cross Keys *(SW3)*
JuJu *(SW3)*
Lonsdale *(W11)*
Paradise by Way of Kensal Green *(W10)*
Pig's Ear *(SW3)*
Serpentine Bar & Kitchen *(W2)*
Trailer Happiness *(W11)*

North
The Chapel Bar *(N1)*
The Driver *(N1)*
The Fellow *(N1)*
Lucky Voice Private Karaoke *(N1)*

South
Alma *(SW18)*
Artesian Well *(SW8)*
Babalou *(SW2)*
Bedford *(SW12)*
Crown & Greyhound *(SE21)*
George Inn *(SE1)*
Imbibe Bar *(SE1)*
Loft *(SW4)*
Lost Society *(SW8)*
North Pole *(SE10)*
The Old Thameside Inn *(SE1)*
Red Monkey *()*
Sugar Cane *(SW11)*
Trafalgar Tavern *(SE10)*

East
All Star Lanes (Brick Lane) *(E1)*
Bar Kick *(E1)*
Bedroom Bar *(EC2)*
The Book Club *(EC2)*
Boundary *(E2)*
Callooh Callay *(EC2)*
Cantaloupe *(EC2)*
Cape - St. Katharine Docks *(E1)*
Captain Kidd *(E1)*
Cargo *(EC2)*
Cinnamon Kitchen *(EC2)*
Clerkenwell House *(EC1)*
Crown Tavern *(EC1)*
Dickens Inn *(E1)*
$ *(EC1)*
DreamBagsJaguarShoes *(E2)*
Favela Chic *(EC2)*
Fluid *(EC1)*
Gun *(E14)*
The Lamb Tavern *(EC3)*
Loungelover *(E1)*
McQueen *(EC2)*
Three Kings of Clerkenwell *(EC1)*
Vertigo *(EC2)*

Restaurants

Central

Alain Ducasse at the Dorchester *(W1)*
Albannach *(WC2)*
Amaya *(SW1)*
Aqua London *(W1)*
Automat *(W1)*
Avenue Restaurant & Bar *(SW1)*
Axis *(WC2)*
Bam-Bou *(W1)*
Bank Restaurant & Zander Bar, Westminster *(SW1)*
Bellamy's *(W1)*
belowzero restaurant + lounge & ICEBAR LONDON *(W1)*
Benares *(W1)*
Bentleys Oyster Bar and Grill *(W1)*
Bistro 1 *(W1)*
Boisdale *(SW1)*
Boudin Blanc *(W1)*
Brasserie Roux *(SW1)*
Brasserie St Jacques *(SW1)*
Browns *(WC2)*
Café Emm *(W1)*
Cecconi's *(W1)*
Le Cercle *(SW1)*
Chez Gérard, Opera Terrace *(WC2)*
China Tang *(W1)*
Chor Bizarre *(W1)*
Chowki *(W1)*
Christopher's *(WC2)*
Chuen Cheng Ku *(W1)*
Cinnamon Club *(SW1)*
Clos Maggiore *(WC2)*
Cocoon *(W1)*
Corrigan's Mayfair *(W1)*
Crazy Bear (Restaurant) *(W1)*
Criterion Restaurant *(W1)*
Dean Street Townhouse *(W1)*
Dover Street Restaurant & Bar *(W1)*
Elena's L'Etoile *(W1)*
L'Escargot *(W1)*
Forge *(WC2)*
Galvin Bistrot de Luxe *(W1)*
Gay Hussar *(W1)*
Green's *(SW1)*
Greenhouse *(W1)*
Greig's Restaurant *(W1)*
Guinea Grill *(W1)*
Hakkasan *(W1)*
The Halkin *(SW1)*
Hard Rock Cafe *(W1)*
Heights Bar & Restaurant *(W1)*
Hush - Private Dining *(W1)*
Ivy *(WC2)*
Just St James *(SW1)*
Ken Lo's Memories of China *(SW1)*
Kettners *(W1)*
The Landau *(W1)*
Latium *(W1)*
Levant *(W1)*
Malabar Junction *(WC1)*
Marcus Wareing at the Berkeley *(SW1)*
Mews of Mayfair *(W1)*
Meza *(W1)*
Michael Moore *(W1)*
Mint Leaf *(SW1)*
Momo *(W1)*
Mr Chow *(SW1)*
Nobu Berkeley Street *(W1)*
Pantechnicon Rooms *(SW1)*
Pattersons's *(W1)*
Piccolino *(W1)*
Pied à Terre *(W1)*
Porte des Indes *(W1)*
Poule au Pot *(SW1)*
Quaglino's *(SW1)*
Quo Vadis Club *(W1)*
Rex Whistler (Tate Britain) *(SW1)*
Roux at Parliament Square *(SW1)*
Sartoria *(W1)*
Scott's *(W1)*
Shanghai Blues *(WC1)*
Shepherd's *(SW1)*
Signor Sassi *(SW1)*
Simpsons-in-the-Strand *(WC2)*
Sketch *(W1)*
Souk *(WC2)*
Square *(W1)*
Sumosan *(W1)*
Taman Gang *(W1)*
Tamarai *(WC2)*
Trouvaille *(W1)*
Tuttons *(WC2)*
2 Amici *(SW1)*
Umu *(W1)*
Vanilla *(W1)*
Vasco & Piero's Pavilion *(W1)*
Veeraswamy *(W1)*
Il Vicolo *(SW1)*
Vincent Rooms *(SW1)*
Volt Lounge *(SW1)*
Wiltons *(SW1)*
Zafferano *(SW1)*

West

Admiral Coddrington *(SW3)*
Babylon *(W8)*
Bel Canto *(W2)*
Belvedere *(W8)*
Blue Elephant *(SW6)*
Bluebird *(SW3)*
Borscht & Tears *(SW3)*
Brinkley's *(SW10)*
Cactus Blue *(SW3)*
Carvosso's *(W4 1)*
Cheyne Walk Brasserie *(SW3)*
Chutney Mary *(SW10)*
The Collection *(SW3)*
Le Colombier *(SW3)*
Da Mario *(SW7)*
Del' Aziz (Fulham) *(SW6)*
Del' Aziz (Westfield) *(W12)*
Dock Kitchen *(W10)*
E&O *(W11)*
Eight Over Eight *(SW3)*
First Floor Restaurant *(W11)*
Garden Bar and Grill *(W10)*
Henry J Beans *(SW3)*
Julie's Restaurant & Wine Bar *(W11)*
Launceston Place *(W8)*
Le Cafe Anglais *(W2)*
The Ledbury *(W11)*
Madsen Restaurant *(SW7)*
Notting Hill Brasserie *(W11)*
Osteria dell'Arancio *(SW10)*
Patio *(W12)*
Pissarro's on the River *(W4)*
PJ's Bar & Grill *(SW3)*
Poissonnerie de l'Avenue *(SW3)*
summerhouse *(W9)*
Le Suquet *(SW3)*
Tom Aikens *(SW3)*
Tom's Kitchen *(SW3)*
Troubadour *(SW5)*
Wine Gallery *(SW10)*
Zuma *(SW7)*

North

Del' Aziz (Swiss Cottage) *(NW3)*
Engineer *(NW1)*
Frederick's *(N1)*
Garden Café *(NW1)*
Gilgamesh *(NW1)*
Lemonia *(NW1)*
Morgan M *(N7)*
Odette's *(NW1)*
Pasha *(N1)*
Shaka Zulu *(NW1)*
Water House *(N1)*

South

Baltic *(SE1)*
The Battersea Barge *(SW8)*
Beauberry House *(SE21)*
Chez Bruce *(SW17)*
Del' Aziz (Bankside) *(SE1)*
Del' Aziz (Bermondsey) *(SE1)*
Depot *(SW14)*
Greenwich Park Bar & Grill *(SE10)*
Level 7 Restaurant, Tate Modern *(SE1)*
Oxo Tower *(SE1)*
Pont de la Tour *(SE1)*
Skylon *(SE1)*
Spread Eagle *(SE10)*
The White House *(SW4)*

East

L'Anima *(EC2)*
Balls Brothers Lime Street *(EC3)*
Beach Blanket Babylon *(E1)*
Bistrothèque *(E2)*
Bleeding Heart *(EC1)*
Bow Wine Vaults *(EC4)*
The Brickhouse *(E1)*
Café du Marché *(EC1)*
Coq d'Argent *(EC2)*
Dans Le Noir *(EC1)*
Don *(EC4)*
Galvin La Chapelle *(E1)*
Gow's Restaurant and Oyster Bar *(EC2)*
Great Eastern Dining Rooms *(EC2)*
Imperial City *(EC3)*
Kenza *(EC2)*
Lotus Chinese Floating Restaurant *(E14)*
Mint Leaf (City) *(EC2)*
1 Lombard Street Restaurant/Bar/Brasserie *(EC3)*
Pacific Oriental *(EC2)*
Piccolino - Exchange Square *(EC2)*
Pizza East *(E1)*
Plateau *(E14)*
Portal *(EC1)*
Prism *(EC3)*
Royal Exchange *(EC3)*
Sauterelle *(EC3)*
Smith's of Smithfield *(EC1)*
St John *(EC1)*
Sweetings *(EC4)*
Les Trois Garçons *(EC2)*
Wapping Food *(E1)*

Outside London
Rock & Rose *(TW9)*

Hotels

Central
The Academy *(WC1)*
Ambassadors Bloomsbury *(WC1)*
Athenaeum Hotel *(W1)*
The Berkeley *(SW1)*
Brown's Hotel *(W1)*
The Cadogan *(SW1)*
Cavendish *(SW1)*
Charlotte Street Hotel *(W1)*
Chesterfield Mayfair *(W1)*
City Inn Westminster *(SW1)*
Claridge's *(W1)*
Connaught *(W1)*
Courthouse Hotel Kempinski *(W1)*
Covent Garden Hotel *(WC2)*
Cumberland Hotel *(W1)*
The Dorchester *(W1)*
Dukes Hotel *(SW1)*
The Goring *(SW1)*
Grand Trafalgar Square *(WC2)*
Grange Holborn *(WC1)*
The Grosvenor House Hotel *(W1)*
Hampshire Hotel *(WC2)*
Haymarket Hotel *(SW1)*
Hilton on Park Lane *(W1)*
InterContinental London *(W1)*
Jumeirah Carlton Tower *(SW1)*
Kingsway Hall Hotel *()*
The Lanesborough *(SW1)*
London Marriott *(W1)*
Mandarin Oriental Hyde Park *(SW1)*
Mandeville Hotel *(W1)*
The Mayfair *(W1)*
Le Meridien Piccadilly *(W1)*
The Metropolitan *(W1)*
Millennium London Mayfair *(W1)*
One Aldwych *(WC2)*
Park Inn London Russell Square *(WC1)*
The Park Lane Hotel *(W1)*
Portman Hotel *(W1)*
The Private Rooms at Buckingham Gate *(SW1)*
Radisson Edwardian Berkshire Hotel *(W1)*
Renaissance London Chancery Court Hotel *(WC1)*
The Ritz *(W1)*
Royal Horseguards *(SW1)*
Rubens *(SW1)*
Savoy *(WC2)*
Sheraton Park Tower *(SW1)*
Sofitel London St James *(SW1)*
Soho Hotel *(W1)*
St James's Club & Hotel *(SW1)*
St Martin's Lane Hotel *(WC2)*
The Stafford *(SW1)*
Swissôtel The Howard, London *(WC2)*
Thistle Charing Cross Hotel *(WC2)*
The Trafalgar *(SW1)*
Waldorf Hotel *(WC2)*
Washington *(W1)*

West
Baglioni Hotel *(SW7)*
The Bentley Hotel *(SW7)*
The Capital *(SW3)*
Chiswick Moran Hotel *(W4)*
The Hempel *(W2)*
London Metropole *(W2)*
The Milestone Hotel & Apartments *(W8)*
Millennium Gloucester Hotel *(SW7)*
Number Sixteen *(SW7)*
Royal Garden Hotel *(W8)*
Royal Lancaster *(W2)*
Vanderbilt Hotel *(SW7)*
Wyndham Grand London *(SW10)*

North
Crown Moran Hotel *(NW2)*
Holiday Inn, Camden Lock *()*
Landmark *(NW1)*
MIC Hotel & Conference Centre *(NW1)*

South
Bermondsey Square *(SE1)*
Cannizaro House *(SW19)*
Hotel Rafayel *(SW11)*
Hotel Verta *(SW11)*
London Marriott Hotel, County Hall *(SE1)*
Park Plaza County Hall *(SE1)*
Park Plaza Westminster *(SE1)*
Pestana Chelsea Bridge *(SW8)*
Riverbank Park Plaza *(SE1)*

East
Andaz *(EC2)*
Apex City of London Hotel *(EC3)*
City Hotel *(E1)*
Crowne Plaza London - The City *(EC4)*

Four Seasons Canary Wharf *(E14)*
Grange St Paul's *(EC4)*
The Guoman Tower *(E1)*
Hilton London Canary Wharf *(E14)*
Hoxton Hotel *()*
Malmaison Hotel *(EC1)*
The Zetter Hotel *(EC1)*

Outside London

Aviator *(Hampshire)*
Bingham *(Surrey)*
The Carlton Mitre Hotel *(Surrey)*
Cliveden *(Berks)*
Holiday Inn, Brentford Lock *()*
The Lowry *(Manchester)*
The Petersham *(Surrey)*
Stoke Place *(Buckinghamshire)*

Conference centres

Central

Altitude 360 *(SW1)*
Broadway House *(SW1)*
The CBI Conference Centre *(WC1)*
Church House *(SW1)*
IET London: Savoy Place *(WC2)*
The Langley *(WD17)*
The Lincoln Centre *(WC2)*
The Mary Sumner House *(SW1)*
Mary Ward House *(WC1)*
No. 11 Cavendish Square *(W1)*
Park Crescent Conference Centre *(W1)*
Portland Place Conference Centre *(W1)*
The Research House *(W1)*
76 Portland Place *(W1)*
Sixteen Park Crescent *(W1)*
St Paul's Church *(W1)*
Trafalgar Events *(WC2)*

West

Kensington Conference & Events Centre *(W8)*
Mayfair Conference Centre *(W2)*

North

Arts Depot *(N12)*
Kings Place *(N1)*
London Zoo *(NW1)*

South

15 Hatfields *(SE1)*
Southwark Cathedral *(SE1)*

East

America Square Conference Centre *(EC3)*
The City Presentation Centre *(EC1)*
City University *(EC1)*
Hatton *(EC1)*
Holborn Bars *(EC1)*
Inmarsat *(EC1)*
Mermaid Conference & Events Centre *(EC4)*
The Old Sessions House *(EC1)*
Royal Statistical Society *(EC1)*

Outside London

Edinburgh International Conference Centre *(Edinburgh)*
The International Convention Centre *(Birmingham)*
Manchester Central *(Manchester)*

Boat charter

West

Floating Boater *(W2)*

South

City Cruises *(SE16)*
Thames Luxury Charters *(SW15)*

East

All Hallows *(EC3)*
Sailing Barge Will *(E1)*

Spas

West

Relax BBC *(W12)*

Stadiums

West

Chelsea Football Club *(SW6)*

North

Tottenham Hotspur *(N17)*

South

IndigO2 *(SE10)*

Outside London

Aston Villa Hospitality and Events *(Birmingham)*
Everton FC *(Liverpool)*
Liverpool FC *(Liverpool)*
Twickenham Experience *(Middx)*

VENUES LICENSED FOR WEDDINGS

Central

Adam Street *(WC2)*
Arndale House *(WC2)*
Arts Club *(W1)*
Athenaeum Hotel *(W1)*
Avenue Restaurant & Bar *(SW1)*
Axis *(WC2)*
BAFTA, 195 Piccadilly *(W1)*
Banqueting House *(SW1)*
belowzero restaurant + lounge & ICEBAR LONDON *(W1)*
Benares *(W1)*
The Berkeley *(SW1)*
Bloomsbury Ballroom *(WC1)*
BMA House *(WC1)*
Brasserie Roux *(SW1)*
British Acadamy *(SW1)*
Brown's Hotel *(W1)*
Browns *(WC2)*
The Cadogan *(SW1)*
Café de Paris *(W1)*
The Caledonian Club *(SW1)*
Carlton Club *(SW1)*
The CBI Conference Centre *(WC1)*
Century *(W1)*
Chandos House *(W1)*
Cinnamon Club *(SW1)*
City Inn Westminster *(SW1)*
Claridge's *(W1)*
The Commonwealth Club *(WC2)*
Connaught *(W1)*
Courthouse Hotel Kempinski *(W1)*
Criterion Restaurant *(W1)*
Cumberland Hotel *(W1)*
Dartmouth House *(W1)*
Dominion Theatre *(W1)*
The Dorchester *(W1)*
Dukes Hotel *(SW1)*
Forbes House *(SW1)*
Fortnum & Mason *(W1)*
The Foundling Museum *(WC1)*
Goodenough College *(WC1)*
The Goring *(SW1)*
Grand Connaught Rooms *(WC2)*
Grand Trafalgar Square *(WC2)*
Gray's Inn *(WC1)*
The Grosvenor House Hotel *(W1)*
Groucho Club *(W1)*
Haymarket Hotel *(SW1)*
Hilton on Park Lane *(W1)*
RS Hispaniola *(WC2)*
Home House *(W1)*
Hospital *(WC2)*
ICA *(SW1)*
IET London: Savoy Place *(WC2)*
Institute of Directors *(SW1)*
InterContinental London *(W1)*
Jumeirah Carlton Tower *(SW1)*
Kingsway Hall Hotel *(WC2)*
The Lanesborough *(SW1)*
Lansdowne Club *(W1)*
The Law Society *(WC2)*
London Marriott *(W1)*
London Palladium *(W1)*
Mandarin Oriental Hyde Park *(SW1)*
Marcus Wareing at the Berkeley *(SW1)*
The Mayfair *(W1)*
Le Meridien Piccadilly *(W1)*
The Metropolitan *(W1)*
Millennium London Mayfair *(W1)*
Mint Leaf *(SW1)*
Momo *(W1)*
Mosimann's Dining Club *(SW1)*
National Liberal Club *(SW1)*
The New Cavendish Club *(W1)*
New Players Theatre *(WC2)*
No 4 Hamilton Place *(W1)*
One Aldwych *(WC2)*
One Great George Street *(SW1)*
One Whitehall Place *(SW1)*
One Wimpole Street *(W1)*
Pacha *(SW1)*
Paramount *(WC1)*
Park Inn London Russell Square *(WC1)*
The Park Lane Hotel *(W1)*
Portman Hotel *(W1)*
The Private Rooms at Buckingham Gate *(SW1)*
Renaissance London Chancery Court Hotel *(WC1)*
The Ritz *(W1)*
Royal Horseguards *(SW1)*
Royal Institution of Great Britain *(W1)*
Royal Society of Arts *(WC2)*
Rubens *(SW1)*
Savoy *(WC2)*
76 Portland Place *(W1)*
Sheraton Park Tower *(SW1)*
Simpsons-in-the-Strand *(WC2)*
Sketch *(W1)*
Sofitel London St James *(SW1)*

Soho Hotel *(W1)*
Soho House *(W1)*
Somerset House *(WC2)*
Spencer House *(W1)*
St Martin In The Fields *(WC2)*
St Martin's Lane Hotel *(WC2)*
St Mary's Church *(W1)*
St Stephen's Club *(SW1)*
The Stafford *(SW1)*
Swissôtel The Howard, London *(WC2)*
Theatre Royal, Drury Lane *(WC2)*
30 Pavilion Road *(SW1)*
Thistle Charing Cross Hotel *(WC2)*
28 Portland Place *(W1)*
229 The Venue *(W1)*
229 *(W1)*
University Women's Club *(W1)*
Volt Lounge *(SW1)*
Waldorf Hotel *(WC2)*
HQS Wellington *(WC2)*

West

Auriol Kensington Rowing Club *(W6)*
Baglioni Hotel *(SW7)*
The Bentley Hotel *(SW7)*
Bluebird *(SW3)*
The Capital *(SW3)*
Chelsea Old Town Hall *(SW3)*
Chelsea Football Club *(SW6)*
Chiswick House *(W4)*
Chiswick Moran Hotel *(W4)*
Chutney Mary *(SW10)*
The Collection *(SW3)*
Cross Keys *(SW3)*
Ealing Town Hall *(W5)*
Fulham Palace *(SW6)*
Fulham Town Hall *(SW6)*
The Hempel *(W2)*
Hurlingham Club *(SW6)*
Kensington Conference & Events Centre *(W8)*
Kensington Palace *(W8)*
London Metropole *(W2)*
Louise Blouin Foundation *(W11)*
The Milestone Hotel & Apartments *(W8)*
Millennium Gloucester Hotel *(SW7)*
Number Sixteen *(SW7)*
Orangery (Holland Park) *(W8)*
Orangery (Kensington Palace) *(W8)*
Pitzhanger Manor *(W5)*
The Queen's Club *(W14)*
The Roof Gardens *(W8)*
Royal Garden Hotel *(W8)*
Royal Geographical Society *(SW7)*
Royal Hospital Chelsea *(SW3)*
Royal Lancaster *(W2)*
Trailfinders Sports Club *(W13)*
Wyndham Grand London *(SW10)*

North

Alexandra Palace & Park *(N22)*
Alexandra Palace Ice Rink *(N22)*
Avenue House *(N3)*
Burgh House *(NW3)*
Crown Moran Hotel *(NW2)*
The Decorium *(N22)*
Frederick's *(N1)*
Highgate School *(N6)*
Holiday Inn, Camden Lock *(NW1)*
Hoxton Hall *(N1)*
Landmark *(NW1)*
Lauderdale House *(N6)*
London Zoo *(NW1)*
The Magic Circle Headquarters *(NW1)*
MIC Hotel & Conference Centre *(NW1)*
One Marylebone Road *(NW1)*
Royal College of Physicians *(NW1)*
Tottenham Hotspur *(N17)*
South
Alma *(SW18)*
BAC *(SW11)*
Bank of England Sports Centre *(SW15)*
The Battersea Barge *(SW8)*
Battersea Park *(SW11)*
Beauberry House *(SE21)*
HMS Belfast *(SE1)*
Bermondsey Square *(SE1)*
Blackheath Concert Halls *(SE3)*
Cannizaro House *(SW19)*
City Cruises *(SE16)*
Clapham Grand *(SW11)*
The Coronet *(SE1)*
Delfina Galleries *(SE1)*
Design Museum *(SE1)*
Devonport House *(SE10)*
Dulwich College *(SE21)*
Dulwich Picture Gallery *(SE21)*
Eltham Palace *(SE9)*
Firepower - The Royal Artillery Museum *(SE18)*
George Inn *(SE1)*
Glaziers' Hall *(SE1)*
The Golden Hinde *(SE1)*

Le Gothique *(SW18)*
Greenwich Park Bar & Grill *(SE10)*
Greenwich Yacht Club *(SE10)*
Guy's Hospital *(SE1)*
Horniman Museum *(SE23)*
Hotel Rafayel *(SW11)*
Hotel Verta *(SW11)*
Jerwood Space *(SE1)*
King's College School *(SW19)*
Kingswood House *(SE21)*
London Eye *(SE1)*
London Film Museum *(SE1)*
London Marriott Hotel, County Hall *(SE1)*
London Rowing Club *(SW15)*
London Wetland Centre *(SW13)*
National Maritime Museum *(SE10)*
National Theatre *(SE1)*
Old Royal Naval College *(SE10)*
The Oval *(SE11)*
Park Plaza County Hall *(SE1)*
Park Plaza Westminster *(SE1)*
Parkstead House *(SW15)*
The Pump House Gallery *(SW11)*
Queen's House *(SE10)*
Riverbank Park Plaza *(SE1)*
Roehampton Club *(SW15)*
Siobhan Davies Studios *(SE1)*
Southbank Centre *(SE1)*
Southwark Cathedral *(SE1)*
Swan at the Globe at Shakespeare's Globe *(SE1)*
Tower Bridge *(SE1)*
Trafalgar Tavern *(SE10)*
Tudor Barn Eltham *(SE9)*
Vinopolis: The Venue *(SE1)*
Wandsworth Civic Suite *(SW18)*
Winchester House *(SW15)*

East

Andaz *(EC2)*
Barbican Art Gallery *(EC2)*
Barbican Centre *(EC2)*
The Brewery *(EC1)*
City Hotel *(E1)*
City of London Club *(EC2)*
Clerkenwell House *(EC1)*
Crowne Plaza London - The City *(EC4)*
Docklands Sailing & Watersports Centre *(E14)*
East Wintergarden *(E14)*
ExCeL London *(E16)*
Four Seasons Canary Wharf *(E14)*
Gibson Hall *(EC2)*
Goldsmiths' Hall *(EC2)*
Grange St Paul's *(EC4)*
The Guoman Tower *(E1)*
The HAC *(EC1)*
Hilton London Canary Wharf *(E14)*
Hoxton Hotel *()*
Inner Temple *(EC4)*
Innholders' Hall *(EC4)*
Ironmongers' Hall *(EC2)*
The Little Ship Club *(EC4)*
McQueen *(EC2)*
Merchant Taylors' Hall *(EC2)*
Middle Temple Hall *(EC4)*
Mile End Park Ecology Pavilion *(E3)*
Old Finsbury Town Hall *(EC1)*
Plaisterers' Hall *(EC2)*
Plateau *(E14)*
Rich Mix *(E1)*
Shoreditch Town Hall *(EC1)*
Skinners' Hall *(EC4)*
St Andrew Holborn *(EC4)*
Stationers' Hall *(EC4)*
Sutton House *(E9)*
Tab Centre *(E2)*
30 St Mary Axe *(EC3)*
Trinity House *(EC3)*
Troxy *(E1)*
V&A Museum of Childhood *(E2)*
Watermen's Hall *(EC3)*

Outside London

Addington Palace *(Surrey)*
Ascot Racecourse *(Berks)*
Assembly Rooms *(Bath)*
Aston Villa Hospitality and Events *(Birmingham)*
Bingham *(Surrey)*
Blenheim Palace *(Oxon)*
Brighton Pier *(Brighton)*
Brocket Hall *(Herts)*
Cardiff City Hall *(Cardiff)*
The Carlton Mitre Hotel *(Surrey)*
Cliveden *(Berks)*
East Hampstead Park Conference Centre *(Berks)*
Epsom Downs *(Surrey)*
Everton FC *(Liverpool)*
Forty Hall *(Middx)*
Gate Street Barn *(Surrey)*
SS Great Britain *(Bristol)*
Great Fosters *(Surrey)*
Guildhall *(Bath)*
Ham House & Garden *(Surrey)*
Ham Polo Club *(Richmond on Thames)*
Hampton Court Palace *(Surrey)*
Harrow School *(Middx)*

Hatfield House *(Herts)*
Hever Castle *(Kent)*
Holiday Inn, Brentford Lock *(NW1)*
Hopetoun House *(Edinburgh)*
Kew Gardens *(Surrey)*
Lainston House *(Winchester)*
The Langley *(Herts)*
Liverpool FC *(Liverpool)*
The Lowry *(Manchester)*
Manchester Central *(Manchester)*
Manchester Town Hall *(Manchester)*
Marble Hill House *(Surrey)*
Museum of Flight *(Edinburgh)*
Museum of Science and Industry *(Manchester)*
Newbury Racecourse *(Berkshire)*
Newstead Abbey *(Nottingham)*
Old Trafford (Manchester United) *(Manchester)*
Osterley Park & House *(Middx)*
The Pavilion *(Birmingham)*
The Petersham *(Surrey)*
Philharmonic Hall *(Liverpool)*
Pinewood Studios *(Bucks)*
Pump Room and Roman Baths *(Bath)*
River & Rowing Museum *(Oxon)*
Royal Armouries *(Leeds)*
The Royal Pavilion *(Brighton)*
The Scotch Malt Whisky Society *(Edinburgh)*
Spring Grove House *(Middx)*
St George's Hall *(Liverpool)*
St. Mungo Museum of Religious Life and Art *(Glasgow)*
Stoke Place *(Buckinghamshire)*
Surgeon's Hall Complex *(Edinburgh)*
Syon Park *(Middx)*
Liverpool Town Hall *(Liverpool)*
Twickenham Experience *(Middx)*
Victoria Art Gallery *(Bath)*
Waddesdon Manor, The Dairy *(Bucks)*
Warwick Castle *(Warwickshire)*
Whipsnade Wild Animal Park *(Beds)*
Wollaton Hall *(Nottingham)*

VENUES WITH HIRER'S CHOICE OF CATERER

Central

Aldwych Theatre *(WC2)*
Ambassadors Theatre *(WC2)*
Arts Club *(W1)*
Artworkers Guild, The *(WC1)*
Athenaeum Hotel *(W1)*
Bloomsbury Ballroom *(WC1)*
Il Bottaccio *(SW1)*
Canning House *(SW1)*
The Charles Dickens Museum *(WC1)*
Cochrane Theatre *(WC1)*
Conway Hall *(WC1)*
Coram's Fields *(WC1)*
Covent Garden Market *(WC2)*
Duchess Theatre *(WC2)*
Fitzroy Square *(W1)*
Freemason's Hall *(WC2)*
Gallery Soho *(WC2)*
Grand Connaught Rooms *(WC2)*
Guards Museum *(SW1)*
Haymarket Theatre *(SW1)*
Hellenic Centre *(W1)*
International Coffee Organisation *(W1)*
Lincoln's Inn (Honourable Society of) *(WC2)*
The London Hippodrome *(WC2)*
London Scottish *(SW1)*
Lyceum Theatre *(WC2)*
Mall Galleries *(SW1)*
The Mary Sumner House *(SW1)*
Maya *(W1)*
No 5 *(W1)*
The October Gallery *(WC1)*
The Penthouse *(WC2)*
Photographers' Gallery *(W1)*
The Red Rooms *(WC2)*
Royal Horseguards *(SW1)*
7 Rifles Battalion *(W1)*
Shaftesbury Theatre *(WC2)*
SixtyOne Whitehall *(SW1)*
St Mary's Church *(W1)*
St Moritz *(W1)*
St Paul's Church *(W1)*
The Strand Gallery *(WC2)*
Studio Valbonne *(W1)*
Thomas Goode *(W1)*
The Vinyl Factory *(W1)*
Westminster Boating Base *(SW1)*

Westminster Cathedral Hall *(SW1)*

West

Apartment 195 *(SW3)*
Bel Canto *(W2)*
Boujis *(SW7)*
Brompton Oratory *(SW7)*
Bush Hall *(W12)*
Crazy Larry's *(SW10)*
Embargo 59 *(SW10)*
First Bowl Queensway *(W2)*
First Floor Restaurant *(W11)*
Fulham Town Hall *(SW6)*
Gunnersbury Park *(W3)*
Hammersmith Town Hall *(W6)*
Institut Français *(SW7)*
Louise Blouin Foundation *(W11)*
Philbeach Hall *(SW5)*
Pitzhanger Manor *(W5)*
Porchester Centre *(W2)*
Proud Chelsea *(SW3)*
Royal College of Art *(SW7)*
St Peter's Hall *(W11)*
Trailer Happiness *(W11)*
20th Century Theatre *(W11)*
Worx *(SW6)*

North

Alexandra Palace Ice Rink *(N22)*
Avenue House *(N3)*
Circus Space *(N1)*
The Decorium *(N22)*
Egg *(N7)*
Electric Ballroom *(NW1)*
Estorick Collection *(N1)*
Freud Museum *(NW3)*
Highgate School *(N6)*
The House *(NW1)*
Hoxton Hall *(N1)*
New End Theatre *(NW3)*
The Pirate Castle *(NW1)*
Proud Camden *(NW1)*
Tricycle Theatre *(NW6)*

South

BAC *(SW11)*
Bankside Gallery *(SE1)*
Battersea Park *(SW11)*
Blackheath Concert Halls *(SE3)*
Cable *(SE1)*
Chatham Hall *(SW11)*
City Hall - London's Living Room *(SE1)*
Clapham Grand *(SW11)*
The Coronet *(SE1)*
Earlsfield Library *(SW18)*
Goldsmiths College *(SE14)*
Greenwich Theatre *(SE10)*
King's College School *(SW19)*
Kingswood House *(SE21)*
LABAN *(SE8)*
Loft *(SW4)*
London Studios *(SE1)*
The Ministry of Sound *(SE1)*
Old Operating Theatre, Museum & Herb Garret *(SE1)*
Polka Theatre for Children *(SW19)*
The Pump House Gallery *(SW11)*
Riverbank Park Plaza *(SE1)*
Siobhan Davies Studios *(SE1)*
Thames Luxury Charters *(SW15)*
Wandsworth Civic Suite *(SW18)*
Winston Churchill's Britain at War *(SE1)*

East

AOP Gallery (The Association of Photographers) *(EC2)*
Aquarium *(EC1)*
Barnard's Inn Hall *(EC1)*
Candid Arts Trust, The *(EC1)*
Carpenters' Hall *(EC2)*
City Hotel *(E1)*
The E Rejuvenation Centre *(E1)*
Fabric *(EC1)*
Inner Temple *(EC4)*
Middle Temple Hall *(EC4)*
Mile End Park Ecology Pavilion *(E3)*
Newham City Farm *(E16)*
Old Truman Brewery *(E1)*
Prenelle Gallery *(E14)*
Queen Mary Students' Union *(E1)*
The Rag Factory *(E1)*
Rivington Place *(EC2)*
Royal Exchange *(EC3)*
Sailing Barge Will *(E1)*
Shoreditch Town Hall *(EC1)*
SPACE *(E8)*
Space *(E14)*
St Andrew Holborn *(EC4)*
St Botolph's Hall *(EC2)*
St Bride Foundation *(EC4)*
St John's Gate *(EC1)*
Troxy *(E1)*

Outside London

Addington Palace *(Surrey)*
Blenheim Palace *(Oxon)*
The Conservatory at Painshill Park *(Surrey)*
Forty Hall *(Middx)*

Guildhall *(Bath)*
Kew Bridge Steam Museum *(Middx)*
The Langley *(Herts)*
Philarmonic Hall *(Liverpool)*
Spring Grove House *(Middx)*
Victoria Art Gallery *(Bath)*
Wollaton Hall *(Nottingham)*

VENUES WITH AN OUTSIDE AREA

Central

The Academy *(WC1)*
Aqua London *(W1)*
Arts Club *(W1)*
Aura *(SW1)*
Bam-Bou *(W1)*
Bank Restaurant & Zander Bar, Westminster *(SW1)*
Bar Soho *(W1)*
belowzero restaurant + lounge & ICEBAR LONDON *(W1)*
Benjamin Franklin House *(WC2)*
Bentleys Oyster Bar and Grill *(W1)*
Berry Bros. & Rudd *(SW1)*
BMA House *(WC1)*
Boisdale *(SW1)*
The Caledonian Club *(SW1)*
Cavalry & Guards Club *(W1)*
Century *(W1)*
Chandos House *(W1)*
The Charles Dickens Museum *(WC1)*
Chesterfield Mayfair *(W1)*
Chez Gérard, Opera Terrace *(WC2)*
City Inn Westminster *(SW1)*
Coram's Fields *(WC1)*
Courtauld Gallery *(WC2)*
Courthouse Hotel Kempinski *(W1)*
Covent Garden Market *(WC2)*
Dartmouth House *(W1)*
Dukes Hotel *(SW1)*
Forbes House *(SW1)*
Forge *(WC2)*
45 Millbank *(SW1)*
The Foundling Museum *(WC1)*
The Golden Lion *(SW1)*
The Goring *(SW1)*
Grand Trafalgar Square *(WC2)*
Gray's Inn *(WC1)*
Greig's Restaurant *(W1)*
Guards Museum *(SW1)*
Hard Rock Cafe *(W1)*
RS Hispaniola *(WC2)*
Home House *(W1)*
Hospital *(WC2)*
House of St Barnabas *(W1)*
ICA *(SW1)*
The Imagination Gallery *(WC1)*
Jewel Piccadilly *(W1)*
Kingsway Hall Hotel *()*
Lancaster House *(SW1)*
Lansdowne Club *(W1)*
Les Ambassadeurs *(W1)*
Lincoln's Inn (Honourable Society of) *(WC2)*
Local Government House *(SW1)*
Malabar Junction *(WC1)*
Mandarin Oriental Hyde Park *(SW1)*
Mandeville Hotel *(W1)*
Mary Ward House *(WC1)*
Maya *(W1)*
Le Meridien Piccadilly *(W1)*
Mews of Mayfair *(W1)*
Momo *(W1)*
National Liberal Club *(SW1)*
The New Cavendish Club *(W1)*
No 4 Hamilton Place *(W1)*
No 5 *(W1)*
The October Gallery *(WC1)*
One Whitehall Place *(SW1)*
Pacha *(SW1)*
Park Crescent Conference Centre *(W1)*
Parliament Square (RICS) *(SW1)*
Piccolino *(W1)*
Portland Place Conference Centre *(W1)*
The Private Rooms at Buckingham Gate *(SW1)*
Queen Elizabeth II Conference Centre *(SW1)*
The Red Room *(W1)*
Renaissance London Chancery Court Hotel *(WC1)*
The Ritz *(W1)*
Royal Horseguards *(SW1)*
Royal Institute of British Architects *(W1)*
Royal Opera House *(WC2)*
Royal Over-Seas League *(SW1)*
Savile Club *(W1)*
76 Portland Place *(W1)*
Shampers *(W1)*
Sheraton Park Tower *(SW1)*
Soho House *(W1)*
Somerset House *(WC2)*

Spencer House *(W1)*
St Martin In The Fields *(WC2)*
St Martin's Lane Hotel *(WC2)*
St Stephen's Club *(SW1)*
The Strand Gallery *(WC2)*
Sway *(WC2)*
Swissôtel The Howard, London *(WC2)*
The Kingly Club *(W1)*
33 Portland Place *(W1)*
Thomas Cubitt *(SW1)*
Tiger Tiger *(SW1)*
The Trafalgar *(SW1)*
Trouvaille *(W1)*
28 Portland Place *(W1)*
229 The Venue *(W1)*
229 *(W1)*
The Union Club *(W1)*
University Women's Club *(W1)*
Vats *(WC1)*
The Village *(W1)*
The Vinyl Factory *(W1)*
Volt Lounge *(SW1)*
Washington *(W1)*
HQS Wellington *(WC2)*
Wellington Arch *(W1)*
Westminster Abbey Garden *(SW1)*
Westminster Boating Base *(SW1)*

West

Aragon House *(SW6)*
Auriol Kensington Rowing Club *(W6)*
Babylon *(W8)*
Baglioni Hotel *(SW7)*
Beach Blanket Babylon *(W11)*
Bluebird *(SW3)*
Borscht & Tears *(SW3)*
Boujis *(SW7)*
Brinkley's *(SW10)*
Bush Hall *(W12)*
Cactus Blue *(SW3)*
The Chelsea Gardener *(SW3)*
Chelsea Physic Garden *(SW3)*
Chelsea Football Club *(SW6)*
Chiswick House *(W4)*
Chiswick Moran Hotel *(W4)*
Conservatory at Chelsea *(SW3)*
Coopers Arms *(SW3)*
Crazy Larry's *(SW10)*
Del' Aziz (Fulham) *(SW6)*
Del' Aziz (Westfield) *(W12)*
E&O *(W11)*
Embargo 59 *(SW10)*
FireHouse *(SW7)*
Floating Boater *(W2)*
Fulham House *(SW6)*
Fulham Palace *(SW6)*
Garden Bar and Grill *(W10)*
Gunnersbury Park *(W3)*
Hammersmith Town Hall *(W6)*
The Hempel *(W2)*
Henry J Beans *(SW3)*
High Road House *(W4)*
Hurlingham Club *(SW6)*
Imperial College London *(SW7)*
The Irish Centre *(W6)*
Jasmine Studios *(W6)*
Kensington Palace *(W8)*
Kent House Knightsbridge *(SW7)*
The Ledbury *(W11)*
Leighton House Museum *(W14)*
Linden House *(W6)*
London Corinthian Sailing Club *(W6)*
Lowiczanka Restaurant *(W6)*
Madsen Restaurant *(SW7)*
Millennium Gloucester Hotel *(SW7)*
National Army Museum *(SW3)*
Natural History Museum *(SW7)*
Number Sixteen *(SW7)*
Ognisko *(SW7)*
Orangery (Holland Park) *(W8)*
Orangery (Kensington Palace) *(W8)*
Paradise by Way of Kensal Green *(W10)*
Pitzhanger Manor *(W5)*
Proud Chelsea *(SW3)*
The Queen's Club *(W14)*
Riverside Studios *(W6)*
The Roof Gardens *(W8)*
Royal College of Music *(SW7)*
Royal Geographical Society *(SW7)*
Royal Hospital Chelsea *(SW3)*
Serpentine Bar & Kitchen *(W2)*
Serpentine Gallery *(W2)*
St Peter's Hall *(W11)*
Trailfinders Sports Club *(W13)*
Victoria and Albert Museum *(SW7)*
Wine Gallery *(SW10)*
Worx *(SW6)*
Zuma *(SW7)*

North

Alexandra Palace & Park *(N22)*
Avenue House *(N3)*
Burgh House *(NW3)*
Canonbury Academy *(N1)*
Cecil Sharp House *(NW1)*
The Chapel Bar *(N1)*

Circus Space *(N1)*
The Decorium *(N22)*
Del' Aziz (Swiss Cottage) *(NW3)*
The Driver *(N1)*
Egg *(N7)*
Electric Ballroom *(NW1)*
Engineer *(NW1)*
Estorick Collection *(N1)*
The Fellow *(N1)*
Frederick's *(N1)*
Freud Museum *(NW3)*
Garden Café *(NW1)*
Highgate School *(N6)*
Holiday Inn, Camden Lock *(NW1)*
Jongleurs at Camden Lock *(NW1)*
Kenwood House (Old Kitchen) *(NW3)*
Kings Place *(N1)*
KOKO *(NW1)*
Lauderdale House *(N6)*
Lemonia *(NW1)*
London Canal Museum *(N1)*
London Zoo *(NW1)*
Lord's Cricket Ground *(NW8)*
Odette's *(NW1)*
One Marylebone Road *(NW1)*
The Pirate Castle *(NW1)*
Proud Camden *(NW1)*
Regent's College *(NW1)*
Roundhouse *(NW1)*
Royal Air Force Museum *(NW9)*
Tottenham Hotspur *(N17)*
University of Westminster *(NW1)*
Water House *(N1)*

South

Artesian Well *(SW8)*
Balls Brothers *(SE1)*
Baltic *(SE1)*
Bank of England Sports Centre *(SW15)*
Bankside Gallery *(SE1)*
The Battersea Barge *(SW8)*
Battersea Evolution *(SW11)*
Battersea Park *(SW11)*
Beauberry House *(SE21)*
Bermondsey Square *(SE1)*
BFI Southbank *(SE1)*
Cable *(SE1)*
Cannizaro House *(SW19)*
City Cruises *(SE16)*
City Hall - London's Living Room *(SE1)*
Clapham Grand *(SW11)*
Coin Street Neighbourhood Centre *(SE1)*
Common Ground Cafe & Bar *(SW18)*
The Coronet *(SE1)*
Cutty Sark *(SE10)*
Del' Aziz (Bankside) *(SE1)*
Del' Aziz (Bermondsey) *(SE1)*
Delfina Galleries *(SE1)*
Depot *(SW14)*
Design Museum *(SE1)*
Devonport House *(SE10)*
Dulwich College *(SE21)*
Dulwich Picture Gallery *(SE21)*
Eltham Palace *(SE9)*
Firepower - The Royal Artillery Museum *(SE18)*
The Garden Museum *(SE1)*
The Golden Hinde *(SE1)*
Goldsmiths College *(SE14)*
Le Gothique *(SW18)*
Greenwich Park Bar & Grill *(SE10)*
Greenwich Yacht Club *(SE10)*
Hayward Gallery *(SE1)*
Horniman Museum *(SE23)*
Hotel Rafayel *(SW11)*
Hotel Verta *(SW11)*
Jerwood Space *(SE1)*
Kingswood House *(SE21)*
LABAN *(SE8)*
The London Dungeon *(SE1)*
London Film Museum *(SE1)*
London Marriott Hotel, County Hall *(SE1)*
London Rowing Club *(SW15)*
London Wetland Centre *(SW13)*
Lost Society *(SW8)*
The Ministry of Sound *(SE1)*
Mosimann's Academy *(SW11)*
National Maritime Museum *(SE10)*
National Theatre *(SE1)*
Old Royal Naval College *(SE10)*
The Old Thameside Inn *(SE1)*
The 108 *(SE10)*
The Oval *(SE11)*
Park Plaza County Hall *(SE1)*
Parkstead House *(SW15)*
Pestana Chelsea Bridge *(SW8)*
Polka Theatre for Children *(SW19)*
The Pump House Gallery *(SW11)*
Queen's House *(SE10)*
Riverbank Park Plaza *(SE1)*
Roehampton Club *(SW15)*
Royal Observatory *(SE10)*
Simon Drake's House of Magic *(SE1)*
Siobhan Davies Studios *(SE1)*
South London Gallery *(SE5)*

Southbank Centre *(SE1)*
Southwark Cathedral *(SE1)*
St Thomas' Hospital *(SE1)*
Swan at the Globe at Shakespeare's Globe *(SE1)*
Thames Luxury Charters *(SW15)*
Tudor Barn Eltham *(SE9)*
Vinopolis: The Venue *(SE1)*
The White House *(SW4)*
Winchester House *(SW15)*

East

Apex City of London Hotel *(EC3)*
Apothecaries' Hall *(EC4)*
Balls Brothers Minster Pavement *(EC3)*
Barber-Surgeons' Hall *(EC2)*
Barnard's Inn Hall *(EC1)*
Bishopsgate Institute *(EC2)*
Bistrothèque *(E2)*
Bleeding Heart *(EC1)*
Broadgate Estates *(EC2)*
Candid Arts Trust, The *(EC1)*
Cannon Bridge Roof Garden *(EC4)*
Captain Kidd *(E1)*
Cargo *(EC2)*
Christ Church Spitalfields *(E1)*
Cinnamon Kitchen *(EC2)*
City Hotel *(E1)*
City of London Club *(EC2)*
Coq d'Argent *(EC2)*
Crown Tavern *(EC1)*
Crypt *(EC1)*
Drapers' Hall *(EC2)*
East Wintergarden *(E14)*
ExCeL London *(E16)*
Fabric *(EC1)*
Favela Chic *(EC2)*
Fishmongers' Hall *(EC4)*
Fluid *(EC1)*
Forman's Fish Island *(E3)*
Four Seasons Canary Wharf *(E14)*
Galvin La Chapelle *(E1)*
Geffrye Museum *(E2)*
Gibson Hall *(EC2)*
Grange St Paul's *(EC4)*
Grocers' Hall *(EC2)*
Gun *(E14)*
Haberdashers' Hall *(EC1)*
The HAC *(EC1)*
Hatton *(EC1)*
Hoxton Hotel *(EC2)*
Inner Temple *(EC4)*
The Lamb Tavern *(EC3)*
Leven is Strijd *(E14)*
The Little Ship Club *(EC4)*
Lotus Chinese Floating Restaurant *(E14)*
LSO St Luke's *(EC1)*
McQueen *(EC2)*
Merchant Taylors' Hall *(EC2)*
Middle Temple Hall *(EC4)*
Mile End Park Ecology Pavilion *(E3)*
Miller's House *(E3)*
Museum of London *(EC2)*
Newham City Farm *(E16)*
Old Billingsgate *(EC3)*
Old Truman Brewery *(E1)*
Pewterers' Hall *(EC2)*
Piccolino - Exchange Square *(EC2)*
Plaisterers' Hall *(EC2)*
Plateau *(E14)*
Prenelle Gallery *(E14)*
HMS President *(EC4)*
Proud Cabaret *(EC3)*
Queen Mary Students' Union *(E1)*
The Rag Factory *(E1)*
The Regalia *(EC4)*
River Lounge *(E1)*
Rivington Place *(EC2)*
Sailing Barge Will *(E1)*
Salters' Hall *(EC2)*
Skinners' Hall *(EC4)*
SPACE *(E8)*
Space *(E14)*
SS Robin *(E14)*
St Andrew Holborn *(EC4)*
St Bartholomew's Hospital *(EC1)*
St Botolph's Hall *(EC2)*
St Bride Foundation *(EC4)*
Stationers' Hall *(EC4)*
Sugar Quay *(EC3)*
Sutton House *(E9)*
Tab Centre *(E2)*
Tallow Chandlers' Hall *(EC4)*
HM Tower of London *(EC3)*
Trinity House *(EC3)*
V&A Museum of Childhood *(E2)*
Wapping Food *(E1)*
The Zetter Hotel *(EC1)*

Outside London

Addington Palace *(Surrey)*
Ascot Racecourse *(Berks)*
Assembly Rooms *(Bath)*
Aston Villa Hospitality and Events *(Birmingham)*
Aviator *(Hampshire)*
Bingham *(Surrey)*
Blenheim Palace *(Oxon)*
Brighton Pier *(Brighton)*

Brocket Hall *(Herts)*
The Carlton Mitre Hotel *(Surrey)*
Chessington World of Adventures *(Surrey)*
Cliveden *(Berks)*
The Conservatory at Painshill Park *(Surrey)*
East Hampstead Park Conference Centre *(Berks)*
Epsom Downs *(Surrey)*
Eton College (Dorney Lake) *(Berks)*
Everton FC *(Liverpool)*
Gate Street Barn *(Surrey)*
Great Fosters *(Surrey)*
Ham House & Garden *(Surrey)*
Ham Polo Club *(Richmond on Thames)*
Hampton Court Palace *(Surrey)*
Harrow School *(Middx)*
Hatfield House *(Herts)*
Hever Castle *(Kent)*
Holiday Inn, Brentford Lock *(Brentford)*
Hopetoun House *(Edinburgh)*
Imperial War Museum North *(Manchester)*
Edinburgh International Conference Centre *(Edinburgh)*
The International Convention Centre *(Birmingham)*
Kew Bridge Steam Museum *(Middx)*
Kew Gardens *(Surrey)*
Kew Palace *(Surrey)*
Lainston House *(Winchester)*
The Langley *(Herts)*
Legoland Windsor *(Berks)*
The Lowry *(Manchester)*
Marble Hill House *(Surrey)*
Museum of Flight *(Edinburgh)*
Museum of Science and Industry *(Manchester)*
Newbury Racecourse *(Berkshire)*
Newstead Abbey *(Nottingham)*
Nottingham Castle *(Nottingham)*
Old Trafford (Manchester United) *(Manchester)*
Osterley Park & House *(Middx)*
The Pavilion *(Birmingham)*
Philharmonic Hall *(Liverpool)*
Pinewood Studios *(Bucks)*
Preston Manor *(Brighton)*
Queen's Eyot *(Berks)*
River & Rowing Museum *(Oxon)*
Royal Holloway College *(TW20)*
Royal Northen College of Music *(Manchester)*
RY Britannia *(Edinburgh)*
Spring Grove House *(Middx)*
St. Mungo Museum of Religious Life and Art *(Glasgow)*
Surgeon's Hall Complex *(Edinburgh)*
Syon Park *(Middx)*
Temple Island *(Oxon)*
Thorpe Park *(Surrey)*
Twickenham Experience *(Middx)*
Waddesdon Manor, The Dairy *(Bucks)*
Warwick Castle *(Warwickshire)*
West Wycombe Caves *(Bucks)*
Whipsnade Wild Animal Park *(Beds)*
Wollaton Hall *(Nottingham)*

VENUES WITH MARQUEE SITES

Central

Arts Club *(W1)*
Berry Bros. & Rudd *(SW1)*
Chandos House *(W1)*
The Charles Dickens Museum *(WC1)*
City Inn Westminster *(SW1)*
Courtauld Gallery *(WC2)*
Courthouse Hotel Kempinski *(W1)*
Covent Garden Market *(WC2)*
Goodenough College *(WC1)*
The Goring *(SW1)*
Gray's Inn *(WC1)*
Guards Museum *(SW1)*
Home House *(W1)*
Lancaster House *(SW1)*
Les Ambassadeurs *(W1)*
Lincoln's Inn (Honourable Society of) *(WC2)*
Mary Ward House *(WC1)*
Park Crescent Conference Centre *(W1)*
Queen Elizabeth II Conference Centre *(SW1)*
Royal Institute of British Architects *(W1)*
Somerset House *(WC2)*
Spencer House *(W1)*
The Strand Gallery *(WC2)*
Swissôtel The Howard, London *(WC2)*
229 The Venue *(W1)*
229 *(W1)*

Westminster Abbey Garden *(SW1)*
Westminster Boating Base *(SW1)*

West

Chelsea Physic Garden *(SW3)*
Chelsea Football Club *(SW6)*
Chiswick House *(W4)*
Conservatory at Chelsea *(SW3)*
Fulham Palace *(SW6)*
The Hempel *(W2)*
Imperial College London *(SW7)*
Jasmine Studios *(W6)*
Kensington Palace *(W8)*
Linden House *(W6)*
London Corinthian Sailing Club *(W6)*
Natural History Museum *(SW7)*
Ognisko *(SW7)*
Orangery (Holland Park) *(W8)*
Orangery (Kensington Palace) *(W8)*
Paradise by Way of Kensal Green *(W10)*
Royal College of Music *(SW7)*
Royal Geographical Society *(SW7)*
Serpentine Gallery *(W2)*
Trailfinders Sports Club *(W13)*
Worx *(SW6)*

North

Alexandra Palace & Park *(N22)*
Canonbury Academy *(N1)*
Cecil Sharp House *(NW1)*
Circus Space *(N1)*
Egg *(N7)*
Freud Museum *(NW3)*
Garden Café *(NW1)*
Highgate School *(N6)*
Regent's College *(NW1)*
Royal Air Force Museum *(NW9)*
University of Westminster *(NW1)*

South

Bank of England Sports Centre *(SW15)*
Battersea Park *(SW11)*
Beauberry House *(SE21)*
Cannizaro House *(SW19)*
Coin Street Neighbourhood Centre *(SE1)*
Design Museum *(SE1)*
Dulwich College *(SE21)*
Dulwich Picture Gallery *(SE21)*
Froebel College *(SW15)*
The Garden Museum *(SE1)*
Le Gothique *(SW18)*
Greenwich Yacht Club *(SE10)*
Horniman Museum *(SE23)*
King's College School *(SW19)*
LABAN *(SE8)*
London Film Museum *(SE1)*
London Rowing Club *(SW15)*
The Ministry of Sound *(SE1)*
National Maritime Museum *(SE10)*
National Theatre *(SE1)*
Old Royal Naval College *(SE10)*
Parkstead House *(SW15)*
The Pump House Gallery *(SW11)*
Queen's House *(SE10)*
Roehampton Club *(SW15)*
South London Gallery *(SE5)*
Southwark Cathedral *(SE1)*
St Thomas' Hospital *(SE1)*
Tudor Barn Eltham *(SE9)*
Winchester House *(SW15)*

East

Cannon Bridge Roof Garden *(EC4)*
Docklands Sailing & Watersports Centre *(E14)*
Favela Chic *(EC2)*
Fishmongers' Hall *(EC4)*
Gibson Hall *(EC2)*
Gun *(E14)*
The HAC *(EC1)*
Inner Temple *(EC4)*
Leven is Strijd *(E14)*
Merchant Taylors' Hall *(EC2)*
Middle Temple Hall *(EC4)*
Newham City Farm *(E16)*
Old Billingsgate *(EC3)*
Pewterers' Hall *(EC2)*
Planit Finsbury Square *(EC2)*
HMS President *(EC4)*
Queen Mary Students' Union *(E1)*
The Regalia *(EC4)*
Rivington Place *(EC2)*
Sugar Quay *(EC3)*
Tab Centre *(E2)*

Outside London

Addington Palace *(Surrey)*
Ascot Racecourse *(Berks)*
Aviator *(Hampshire)*
Bingham *(Surrey)*
Blenheim Palace *(Oxon)*
Brocket Hall *(Herts)*
Burrell Collection *(Glasgow)*
Chessington World of Adventures *(Surrey)*
Cliveden *(Berks)*
The Conservatory at Painshill

Park *(Surrey)*
East Hampstead Park Conference Centre *(Berks)*
Epsom Downs *(Surrey)*
Everton FC *(Liverpool)*
Gate Street Barn *(Surrey)*
Ham House & Garden *(Surrey)*
Ham Polo Club *(Richmond on Thames)*
Hampton Court Palace *(Surrey)*
Harrow School *(Middx)*
Hatfield House *(Herts)*
Hever Castle *(Kent)*
Hopetoun House *(Edinburgh)*
Imperial War Museum North *(Manchester)*
The International Convention Centre *(Birmingham)*
Kew Bridge Steam Museum *(Middx)*
Kew Gardens *(Surrey)*
Lainston House *(Winchester)*
Legoland Windsor *(Berks)*
Museum of Flight *(Edinburgh)*
Newbury Racecourse *(Berkshire)*
Nottingham Castle *(Nottingham)*
Osterley Park & House *(Middx)*
Pinewood Studios *(Bucks)*
Preston Manor *(Brighton)*
Queen's Eyot *(Berks)*
River & Rowing Museum *(Oxon)*
Royal Holloway College *(TW20)*
Stoke Place *(Buckinghamshire)*
Surgeon's Hall Complex *(Edinburgh)*
Syon Park *(Middx)*
Temple Island *(Oxon)*
Twickenham Experience *(Middx)*
Waddesdon Manor, The Dairy *(Bucks)*
Warwick Castle *(Warwickshire)*
Whipsnade Wild Animal Park *(Beds)*
Wollaton Hall *(Nottingham)*

Indexes
Room Capacities

CAPACITY LISTS

Note: particularly with hotels, it may be possible to divide rooms to provide a smaller space.

Function rooms listed by standing capacity
* largest entry for venue

£E

2500 Battersea Evolution SW11 *(Max*)*
1200 Hampton Court Palace KT8 *(Marquee*)*
800 The Royal Academy of Arts W1 *(Max*)*
700 Victoria and Albert Museum SW7 *(Dome* or John Madejski Garden)*
500 Blenheim Palace OX20 *(Max*)*
Stoke Place SL2 *(Max*)*
499 Liberty W1 *(Max*)*
450 Spencer House W1 *(Max*)*
400 Hampton Court Palace KT8 *(Great Hall)*
National Portrait Gallery WC2 *(c17 & c18 Galleries*)*
Stoke Place SL2 *(Ballroom)*
Victoria and Albert Museum SW7 *(Raphael Gallery)*
350 Blenheim Palace OX20 *(Orangery)*
Chiswick House W4 *(Pavillion Marquee*)*
Lancaster House SW1 *(Long Gallery*)*
National Portrait Gallery WC2 *(Contemporary Galleries)*
The Royal Academy of Arts W1 *(Fine Rms)*
Two Temple Place WC2 *(Max*)*
329 British Museum WC1 *(East Foyer* or West Foyer)*
300 Eltham Palace SE9 *(Great Hall*)*
Fishmongers' Hall EC4 *(Max*)*
Hampton Court Palace KT8 *(Cartoon Gallery)*
Tate Britain SW1 *(Gallery 9 , Manton Foyer or Sackler Octagon*)*
250 Boujis SW7 *(Max*)*
Victoria and Albert Museum SW7 *(Silver Galleries)*
220 Annabel's W1 *(Max*)*
200 Courtauld Gallery WC2 *(Max*)*
Hampton Court Palace KT8 *(Kings Guard Chamber)*
Stoke Place SL2 *(Lakeside)*
Two Temple Place WC2 *(The Great Hall)*
180 Blenheim Palace OX20 *(Marlborough)*
Spencer House W1 *(Dining Room or Great Rm)*
Two Temple Place WC2 *(Lower Gallery)*
150 Chiswick House W4 *(Cafe or First Floor (6 Rms))*
Cliveden SL6 *(Great Hall*)*
Hampton Court Palace KT8 *(Queen's Public Dining Rm)*
Home House W1 *(Front Parlour & Eating Room*)*
National Portrait Gallery WC2 *(Victorian Galleries)*
Royal Observatory SE10 *(Max*)*
Victoria and Albert Museum SW7 *(Paintings Gallery)*
125 Hampton Court Palace KT8 *(Great Watching Chamber)*
120 Kenwood House (The Orangery) NW3 *(Max*)*
Lancaster House SW1 *(State Dining Rm)*
Tate Britain SW1 *(Rex Whistler Restauran)*
100 Chiswick House W4 *(Domed Saloon)*
Eltham Palace SE9 *(Drawing Rm)*
Liberty W1 *(Cafe Liberty)*
Stoke Place SL2 *(Howard Vyse Rm)*
Victoria and Albert Museum SW7 *(Cast Court)*
80 Chiswick House W4 *(Conservatory)*
Hampton Court Palace KT8 *(William III's Banqueting House)*
Liberty W1 *(Fashion Show)*
National Portrait Gallery WC2 *(Tudor Gallery)*
Sir John Soane's Museum WC2 *(Max*)*
75 Cliveden SL6 *(French Dining Rm)*
60 Liberty W1 *(Champagne & Oyster Bar)*
50 Stoke Place SL2 *(Thomas Gray)*
Tate Britain SW1 *(Duffield Room)*
40 Liberty W1 *(Heritage Suite)*

£M-E

6000 Chessington World of Adventures KT9 *(Max*)*
3000 The Business Design Centre N1 *(Max*)*
Madame Tussauds NW1 *(Max*)*
2400 IndigO2 SE10 *(Max*)*
2300 Planit Finsbury Square EC2 *(Max*)*
2000 Grand Trafalgar Square WC2 *(Max*)*
The Grosvenor House Hotel W1 *(Great Rm*)*
Old Billingsgate EC3 *(Grand Hall, Mezzanine And Terrace*)*
Royal Lancaster W2 *(Max*)*
Science Museum SW7 *(Max*)*
1800 The Casino at the Empire WC2 *(Whole Venue*)*
Roundhouse NW1 *(Max*)*
1500 Chelsea Football Club SW6 *(Max*)*
Guildhall EC2 *(Max*)*
Parkstead House SW15 *(Parkstead Lawns*)*
Saatchi Gallery SW3 *(Max*)*
Sadler's Wells Theatre EC1 *(Max*)*
Somerset House WC2 *(Edmond J. Safra Fountain Court (with marquee)*)*
1400 Park Plaza Westminster SE1 *(Ballroom*)*
1250 Hilton on Park Lane W1 *(Grand Ballroom*)*
1200 Altitude 360 SW1 *(Max*)*
Hurlingham Club SW6 *(Max*)*
Inner Temple EC4 *(Garden*)*
Edinburgh International Conference Centre EH3 *(Cromdale Hall*)*
London Film Museum SE1 *(Museum*)*
Natural History Museum SW7 *(Central Hall*)*
The Park Lane Hotel W1 *(Ballroom*)*
1100 Old Trafford (Manchester United) M16 *(Manchester Suite*)*
1000 Cardiff City Hall CF10 *(Max*)*

The Dorchester W1 *(Ballroom*)*
East Wintergarden E14 *(Hall*)*
Gilgamesh NW1 *(Max*)*
Grange St Paul's EC4 *(Max*)*
Hurlingham Club SW6 *(Palm Court)*
Imperial War Museum London SE1 *(Main Exhibits Gallery*)*
InterContinental London W1 *(Max*)*
Landmark NW1 *(Grand Ballroom*)*
London Aquarium SE1 *(Max*)*
Madame Tussauds NW1 *(Tussauds - whole attraction)*
National Gallery of Scotland EH2 *(Max*)*
Royal Armouries LS10 *(Royal Armouries Hall*)*
Royal Exchange EC3 *(Exclusive Use*)*
Royal Opera House WC2 *(Paul Hamlyn Hall *)*
St George's Hall L1 *(The Great Hall*)*
Tussaud's Showdome NW1 *(Max*)*

900 Guildhall EC2 *(Great Hall)*
Old Billingsgate EC3 *(Vault)*
The 108 SE10 *(Max*)*
Smith's of Smithfield EC1 *(Max*)*
Southbank Centre SE1 *(Clore Ballroom* or Queen Elizabeth Hall foyer)*

850 The Grosvenor House Hotel W1 *(Ballroom)*
Edinburgh International Conference Centre EH3 *(Strathblane Hall)*
The Penthouse WC2 *(Max*)*

800 Aqua London W1 *(Max*)*
Broadgate Estates EC2 *(Max*)*
Forman's Fish Island E3 *(Floor 2*)*
Just St James SW1 *(Max*)*
London Studios SE1 *(Studio 1*)*
Queen Elizabeth II Conference Centre SW1 *(Benjamin Britten*)*
Royal Air Force Museum NW9 *(Historic Hangars*)*
Savoy WC2 *(Lancaster Rm*)*

750 National Maritime Museum SE10 *(Neptune's Court*)*
Science Museum SW7 *(Making The Modern World)*

715 Café de Paris W1 *(Max*)*

700 Andaz EC2 *(Max*)*
Goldsmiths' Hall EC2 *(Max*)*
Holiday Inn, Brentford Lock TW8 *(Waterfront Suite*)*
Imperial War Museum North M17 *(Max*)*
Jumeirah Carlton Tower SW1 *(Ballroom*)*
Merchant Taylors' Hall EC2 *(Great Hall*)*
Millennium London Mayfair W1 *(Ballroom*)*
Portman Hotel W1 *(Portman Ballroom*)*

650 The Business Design Centre N1 *(Gallery Hall)*
Hopetoun House EH30 *(Max*)*
Museum of Flight EH39 *(Concorde Experience*)*
One Mayfair W1 *(Grand Hall*)*
Sketch W1 *(Max*)*

640 Millennium Gloucester Hotel SW7 *(Orchard Suite*)*

600 Altitude 360 SW1 *(Altitude 360° or River Room)*
Cardiff City Hall CF10 *(Assembly Room)*
Forman's Fish Island E3 *(Max)*
Grand Trafalgar Square WC2 *(Ballroom)*
Guildhall EC2 *(Old Library)*
The Hempel W2 *(Max*)*
Inner Temple EC4 *(Marquee)*
Kew Gardens TW9 *(Marquee Site*)*
Lincoln's Inn (Honourable Society of) WC2 *(Great Hall*)*
London Studios SE1 *(Studio 2)*
Old Trafford (Manchester United) M16 *(International Suite)*
One Whitehall Place SW1 *(Max*)*
Plaisterers' Hall EC2 *(Great Hall*)*
Science Museum SW7 *(Energy Hall or Welcome Wing (Ground))*

550 Hilton on Park Lane W1 *(Wellington Ballroom)*
Somerset House WC2 *(River Terrace)*

500 Banqueting House SW1 *(Main Hall*)*
Bridgewater Hall M2 *(Circle Foyer*)*
Christie's SW1 *(Max*)*
15 Hatfields SE1 *(Ground Floor*)*
Firepower - The Royal Artillery Museum SE18 *(Max*)*
Goldsmiths' Hall EC2 *(Livery Hall)*
Grand Trafalgar Square WC2 *(Old Billiard Room)*
Liverpool FC L4 *(Reds Combined*)*
Madame Tussauds NW1 *(Tussauds - World Stage)*
Manchester Town Hall M60 *(Great Hall*)*
Mary Ward House WC1 *(Max*)*
Middle Temple Hall EC4 *(Hall*)*
Millennium Gloucester Hotel SW7 *(Sentosa Suite)*
Mint Leaf SW1 *(Max*)*
Natural History Museum SW7 *(Earth Galleries)*
Parkstead House SW15 *(Central Courtyard)*
Pestana Chelsea Bridge SW8 *(Max*)*
Porte des Indes W1 *(Max*)*
Renaissance London Chancery Court Hotel WC1 *(Max*)*
The Roof Gardens W8 *(Max*)*
Royal Albert Hall SW7 *(Gallery*)*
Royal Garden Hotel W8 *(Palace Suite*)*
Science Museum SW7 *(Flight Gallery)*
Skylon SE1 *(Max*)*
Sugar Quay EC3 *(Max*)*
Westminster Abbey Garden SW1 *(Max*)*

480 Old Royal Naval College SE10 *(Queen Mary Ante Rm*)*
Royal Opera House WC2 *(Amphitheatre Bar)*

450 Barbican Centre EC2 *(Max*)*
Cannon Bridge Roof Garden EC4 *(Max*)*
The Casino at the Empire WC2 *(Upper Level)*
Claridge's W1 *(Ballroom*)*
Cocoon W1 *(Restaurant*)*
Drapers' Hall EC2 *(Max*)*
15 Hatfields SE1 *(Boardroom)*
Hurlingham Club SW6 *(Boomhouse Suite or Quadrangle Suite)*
Mary Ward House WC1 *(Mary Ward Hall)*
Millennium Gloucester Hotel SW7 *(Max)*
1 Lombard Street Restaurant/Bar/Brasserie EC3 *(Max*)*
Pacific Oriental EC2 *(Max*)*

Royal College of Physicians NW1 *(Max*)*
33 Portland Place W1 *(Max*)*
440 Quaglino's SW1 *(Max*)*
400 Andaz EC2 *(Great Eastern)*
Aqua London W1 *(Nueva)*
Assembly Rooms BA1 *(Max*)*
The Berkeley SW1 *(Max*)*
BFI IMAX SE1 *(Ground Floor Foyer*)*
Il Bottaccio SW1 *(Max*)*
Broadgate Estates EC2 *(Arena)*
Churchill Museum and Cabinet War Rooms SW1 *(Max*)*
Circus Space N1 *(Max*)*
The Collection SW3 *(Max*)*
The Commonwealth Club WC2 *(Restaurant Level*)*
The Conservatory at Painshill Park KT11 *(Max*)*
Cumberland Hotel W1 *(Max*)*
Dover Street Restaurant & Bar W1 *(Max*)*
Ham House & Garden TW10 *(Max*)*
Hopetoun House EH30 *(Ballroom)*
Inner Temple EC4 *(Hall)*
Institute of Directors SW1 *(Max*)*
Kew Gardens TW9 *(Temperate House or The Orangery)*
Mandarin Oriental Hyde Park SW1 *(Ballroom*)*
Millennium Gloucester Hotel SW7 *(Conservatory)*
National Gallery of Scotland EH2 *(National Gallery or Royal Scottish Academy)*
National Museum of Wales CF10 *(Max*)*
No 5 W1 *(Max*)*
Nobu Berkeley Street W1 *(Max*)*
One Mayfair W1 *(Mezzanine)*
Pont de la Tour SE1 *(Max*)*
Royal Air Force Museum NW9 *(Battle Of Britain Hall)*
Royal Opera House WC2 *(Linbury Theatre)*
Savoy WC2 *(Abraham Lincoln & Manhattan Rms)*
Science Museum SW7 *(Level 1)*
Stationers' Hall EC4 *(Livery Hall*)*
Wallace Collection W1 *(Main Galleries*)*
Westminster Abbey Garden SW1 *(Abbey Cloisters)*
380 RY Britannia EH6 *(Max*)*
375 Banqueting House SW1 *(Undercroft)*
360 LSO St Luke's EC1 *(Jerwood Hall*)*
350 Clothworkers' Hall EC3 *(Max*)*
Dulwich Picture Gallery SE21 *(Garden & Gallery*)*
15 Hatfields SE1 *(Earth, Water, Air)*
Gray's Inn WC1 *(Max*)*
Haberdashers' Hall EC1 *(Max*)*
Harrods SW1 *(Max*)*
The Hempel W2 *(Zen Garden)*
Holiday Inn, Camden Lock NW1 *(The Glasshouse*)*
Hotel Rafayel SW11 *(Roof Terrace*)*
Hotel Verta SW11 *(Max*)*
The Imagination Gallery WC1 *(Atrium and Restaurant*)*
Institute of Directors SW1 *(Nash)*
Jumeirah Carlton Tower SW1 *(Acacia, Birch, Cedar And Conservatory)*
Liverpool FC L4 *(Champions Lounge)*
The Lowry M50 *(The Studio*)*
The Mayfair W1 *(Max*)*
Museum of Science and Industry M3 *(Air & Space Hall*)*
Natural History Museum SW7 *(Darwin Centre)*
Old Trafford (Manchester United) M16 *(Lounge Bars)*
One Whitehall Place SW1 *(Gladstone Library)*
Oxo Tower SE1 *(Brasserie or Restaurant*)*
Prism EC3 *(Max*)*
Royal Albert Hall SW7 *(Elgar Room)*
Royal Exchange EC3 *(Courtyard)*
Royal Hospital Chelsea SW3 *(Great Hall*)*
Sadler's Wells Theatre EC1 *(Lillian Bayliss Theatre)*
Savoy WC2 *(River Rm)*
Somerset House WC2 *(Embankment East)*
St Paul's Cathedral EC4 *(Crypt*)*
Tate Modern SE1 *(Cafe 2*)*
330 Guildhall EC2 *(Art Gallery or Livery Hall)*
320 BFI IMAX SE1 *(1st Floor Foyer)*
BMA House WC1 *(Great Hall* or Lutyens)*
Pump Room and Roman Baths BA1 *(Roman Baths*)*
Saatchi Gallery SW3 *(Gallery 3)*
312 Royal Air Force Museum NW9 *(Cosford Rm (Dermot Boyle Wing))*
300 Altitude 360 SW1 *(Millbank Media Center)*
America Square Conference Centre EC3 *(Ludgate Suite*)*
Andaz EC2 *(Gallery)*
Assembly Rooms BA1 *(Tea Room)*
Avenue Restaurant & Bar SW1 *(Max*)*
Barbican Centre EC2 *(Garden Rm)*
Bermondsey Square SE1 *(Max*)*
The Caledonian Club SW1 *(Max*)*
The Collection SW3 *(Mezzanine)*
Coq d'Argent EC2 *(Max*)*
Cutty Sark SE10 *(Max*)*
The E Rejuvenation Centre E1 *(Max*)*
Everton FC L4 *(Max*)*
Grange Holborn WC1 *(Max*)*
Hakkasan W1 *(Max*)*
Hatfield House AL9 *(Max*)*
Hospital WC2 *(Gallery*)*
Jerwood Space SE1 *(Gallery & Glasshouse*)*
Kensington Palace W8 *(Orangery*)*
Kent House Knightsbridge SW7 *(Sanctuary*)*
Kingsway Hall Hotel WC2 *(Max*)*
Landmark NW1 *(Drawing Rm)*
Level 7 Restaurant, Tate Modern SE1 *(Max*)*
The London Art House N1 *(Manor Garden Hall*)*
London Stock Exchange EC4 *(Forum (whole)*)*
London Zoo NW1 *(Max*)*
Madame Tussauds NW1 *(Tussauds Stardome 4D)*
Mary Ward House WC1 *(Brewer & Smith)*
Maya W1 *(Max*)*
Merchant Taylors' Hall EC2 *(Cloisters & Garden)*
National Gallery of Scotland EH2 *(Weston Link)*
Old Billingsgate EC3 *(Gallery)*
Old Trafford (Manchester United) M16 *(Trafford Suite)*
Orangery (Kensington Palace) W8 *(Max*)*
Pacific Oriental EC2 *(Ground Floor)*

Phyllis Court RG9 *(Ballroom*)*
Pump Room and Roman Baths BA1 *(Pump Room)*
River & Rowing Museum RG9 *(Max*)*
Royal Air Force Museum NW9 *(Locking Rm (Dermot Boyle Wing))*
Royal Hospital Chelsea SW3 *(Max)*
Royal Opera House WC2 *(Ashton Studio)*
Saatchi Gallery SW3 *(Gallery 1, 5, 7, 8, 12)*
Skinners' Hall EC4 *(Banqueting Hall*)*
Surgeon's Hall Complex EH8 *(Quincentenary Main Hall*)*
Tate Modern SE1 *(Tate Modern Restaurant)*
HM Tower of London EC3 *(New Armouries*)*
Wallace Collection W1 *(Courtyard)*
Warwick Castle CV34 *(Central Courtyard*)*

290 The Hospital Club WC2 *(The Gallery (North & South together)*)*

280 The Law Society WC2 *(The Common Room*)*
London Zoo NW1 *(Prince Albert Suite)*
Saatchi Gallery SW3 *(Gallery 2, 4, 6, 9, 11)*

270 Liverpool Town Hall L2 *(Large Ballroom*)*

260 Saatchi Gallery SW3 *(Gallery 10)*
30 St Mary Axe EC3 *(39th & 40th Floor*)*

250 Apothecaries' Hall EC4 *(Max*)*
Arndale House WC2 *(Max*)*
Assembly Rooms BA1 *(Octagon)*
Belvedere W8 *(Max*)*
The Caledonian Club SW1 *(Johnnie Walker Music Room)*
Churchill Museum and Cabinet War Rooms SW1 *(HCA Auditorium)*
City Hall - London's Living Room SE1 *(Max*)*
The Commonwealth Club WC2 *(Auditorium or Reception Area)*
The Dorchester W1 *(Orchid)*
Everton FC L4 *(The People's Club)*
FACT L1 *(Max*)*
Geffrye Museum E2 *(Restaurant & Galleries*)*
Grocers' Hall EC2 *(Max*)*
The Grosvenor House Hotel W1 *(Court Suite)*
Guildhall EC2 *(Crypt East or Crypt West)*
Guildhall BA1 *(Banqueting Room*)*
Hever Castle TN8 *(GuthriePavillion*)*
Hopetoun House EH30 *(Adam Stables)*
The Imagination Gallery WC1 *(Gallery)*
Landmark NW1 *(Empire Rm)*
Legoland Windsor SL4 *(Max*)*
Lincoln's Inn (Honourable Society of) WC2 *(Old Hall)*
London Zoo NW1 *(Animal Houses)*
The Lowry M50 *(Quays Bar)*
Madame Tussauds NW1 *(A-list Party)*
Mandarin Oriental Hyde Park SW1 *(Carlyle Suite)*
Mercers' Hall EC2 *(Max*)*
The Merchants Hall EH2 *(The Hall*)*
Museum of Science and Industry M3 *(Power Hall)*
National Museum of Wales CF10 *(Art Galleries)*
Newstead Abbey NG15 *(Max*)*
Nottingham Castle NG1 *(Long Gallery*)*
One Whitehall Place SW1 *(Reading And Writing Rms (Sold In Conjunction With Gladstone Library) or Whitehall Suite)*
Oxo Tower SE1 *(Max)*
The Park Lane Hotel W1 *(Tudor Rose Rm)*
Plaisterers' Hall EC2 *(Livery Hall)*
Royal Air Force Museum NW9 *(Halton Gallery or Milestones Of Flight)*
RY Britannia EH6 *(State Apartments)*
Saddlers' Hall EC2 *(The Great Hall*)*
Salters' Hall EC2 *(Garden*)*
Science Museum SW7 *(Exploring Space)*
Siobhan Davies Studios SE1 *(Max*)*
Sketch W1 *(Gallery)*
Smith's of Smithfield EC1 *(Top Floor)*
Southbank Centre SE1 *(Level 5 Function Room)*
Stationers' Hall EC4 *(Garden)*
Swissôtel The Howard, London WC2 *(Swiss Chalet*)*
Tower Bridge SE1 *(Walkways*)*
HM Tower of London EC3 *(White Tower)*
The Trafalgar SW1 *(Rockwell*)*
Wallace Collection W1 *(Great Gallery)*

245 Le Meridien Piccadilly W1 *(Georgian Suites*)*

240 30 Pavilion Road SW1 *(Max*)*

225 Club 49 Soho W1 *(Max*)*

220 Forman's Fish Island E3 *(Floor 1)*
Great Fosters TW20 *(Max*)*
Haymarket Hotel SW1 *(Pool Area*)*
Imperial War Museum London SE1 *(Cinema)*
The London Dungeon SE1 *(Whole Attraction*)*
London Film Museum SE1 *(Riverside Room 1)*
Royal Opera House WC2 *(Crush Room)*
Somerset House WC2 *(The Courtauld Gallery)*
Taman Gang W1 *(Max*)*
Volt Lounge SW1 *(Max*)*
HQS Wellington WC2 *(Max*)*

210 The Law Society WC2 *(The Reading Room)*

200 Arts Club W1 *(Dining Rm*)*
BFI Southbank SE1 *(Delegate Centre*)*
Brocket Hall AL8 *(Ball Room*)*
Burrell Collection G43 *(Max*)*
Cardiff City Hall CF10 *(Ferrier Hall or Marble Hall)*
Chesterfield Mayfair W1 *(The Royal Suite*)*
Claridge's W1 *(Drawing Rm, French Salon)*
Connaught W1 *(Ball Room*)*
Estorick Collection N1 *(Max*)*
FireHouse SW7 *(Max*)*
Forbes House SW1 *(Max*)*
The Foundling Museum WC1 *(Max*)*
Four Seasons Canary Wharf E14 *(Ballroom*)*
Grand Trafalgar Square WC2 *(Annex)*
Hilton on Park Lane W1 *(Coronation Suite)*
Hospital WC2 *(Dining Rm)*
The Hospital Club WC2 *(First Floor Bar & Restaurant)*
Hurlingham Club SW6 *(Murgrave Theatre, Napier Room or Rongelagh Room)*
Imperial War Museum North M17 *(Watershard Cafe)*
Inner Temple EC4 *(Parliament Chamber)*
Innholders' Hall EC4 *(Dining Hall*)*
Just St James SW1 *(Just The Gallery)*
Kensington Palace W8 *(State Apartments)*
Liverpool FC L4 *(European Lounge)*
Local Government House SW1 *(Bevan Hall*)*
London Marriott Hotel, County Hall SE1 *(County Hall Suite*)*

Manchester Town Hall M60 *(Banqueting Hall)*
Le Meridien Piccadilly W1 *(Edwardian Suite, Terrace Restaurant or The Oak Room)*
Mint Leaf (City) EC2 *(Max*)*
Momo W1 *(Max*)*
No. 11 Cavendish Square W1 *(The Conservatory & Courtyard Garden*)*
One Wimpole Street W1 *(Max*)*
Parkstead House SW15 *(Manresa Hall)*
Queen's House SE10 *(Great Hall*)*
River & Rowing Museum RG9 *(Rowing Gallery)*
Roehampton Club SW15 *(Max*)*
Roundhouse NW1 *(Circle Bar or Torquils Bar)*
Roux at Parliament Square SW1 *(Max*)*
Royal Armouries LS10 *(Nelson Bistro or Wellington Suite)*
Royal Exchange EC3 *(Mezzanine Bar)*
Royal Hospital Chelsea SW3 *(State Apartments)*
Royal Opera House WC2 *(Amphi Restaurant)*
The Royal Pavilion BN1 *(Banqueting Room*)*
Salters' Hall EC2 *(Mail Hall)*
Shoreditch House E1 *(Roof Top Bar (Members Only)*)*
Skinners' Hall EC4 *(Roof Garden)*
Somerset House WC2 *(Portico Rooms or Seamen's Hall)*
Surgeon's Hall Complex EH8 *(Playfair Hall)*
Swissôtel The Howard, London WC2 *(Fitzalan Suite)*
Thistle Charing Cross Hotel WC2 *(Betjeman*)*
Waddesdon Manor, The Dairy HP18 *(Terrace*)*

190 Sadler's Wells Theatre EC1 *(Cable & Wireless)*

180 Aqua London W1 *(Kyoto)*
Hatfield House AL9 *(Riding School)*
The Lanesborough SW1 *(Belgravia*)*
Mosimann's Dining Club SW1 *(Max*)*
The Queen's Club W14 *(The Presidents Room*)*
The Ritz W1 *(Max*)*
Roundhouse NW1 *(Dr. Martens Free DM Studio)*
Royal Albert Hall SW7 *(Arena Foyers)*
Sadler's Wells Theatre EC1 *(Mezzanine Wood)*
Soho Hotel W1 *(Max*)*
St Martin's Lane Hotel WC2 *(The Studio*)*
HQS Wellington WC2 *(Court Rm)*

175 15 Hatfields SE1 *(Earth, Water)*

170 BMA House WC1 *(Paget Room)*
The Foundling Museum WC1 *(Picture Gallery option 1)*

160 Andaz EC2 *(Bishopsgate & Chancery)*
BMA House WC1 *(Courtyard Suite)*
Holborn Bars EC1 *(Waterhouse*)*
Hush - Private Dining W1 *(Max*)*
Institute of Directors SW1 *(Burton)*
Stationers' Hall EC4 *(Court Rm)*

150 Aviator GU14 *(Max*)*
Babylon W8 *(Max*)*
Barbican Centre EC2 *(Conservatory Terrace)*
The Bentley Hotel SW7 *(Max*)*
Bingham TW10 *(The Garden Room Exclusive*)*
BMA House WC1 *(Black Suite or Snow Room)*
Carlton Club SW1 *(Max*)*
The Casino at the Empire WC2 *(Face 2 Face or Shadow Bar)*
Chandos House W1 *(Max*)*
Churchill Museum and Cabinet War Rooms SW1 *(Harmsworth Room)*
Clothworkers' Hall EC3 *(Reception Rm)*
Crazy Bear (Member's Club) WC2 *(Max*)*
Cumberland Hotel W1 *(Blue 3&4 Combined)*
Dover Street Restaurant & Bar W1 *(Lower Bar)*
FACT L1 *(Bar)*
Fortnum & Mason W1 *(St James's Rm*)*
The Foundling Museum WC1 *(Picture Gallery option 2)*
Gallery of Modern Art G1 *(Gallery 1*)*
Goldsmiths' Hall EC2 *(Drawing Rm & Exhibition Rm or Exhibition Room)*
Gray's Inn WC1 *(Large Pension Rm or Spy Room)*
The Halkin SW1 *(Max*)*
Hopetoun House EH30 *(Tapestry Room)*
Hospital WC2 *(Studio)*
The Hospital Club WC2 *(TV Studio)*
Hotel Rafayel SW11 *(3rd Floor Event Space)*
Institute of Directors SW1 *(Waterloo)*
Kensington Palace W8 *(Queens Gallery)*
Kew Gardens TW9 *(Cambridge Cottage)*
Launceston Place W8 *(Max*)*
Leighton House Museum W14 *(Max*)*
Les Ambassadeurs W1 *(Max*)*
London Capital Club EC4 *(The Oriental Room*)*
LSO St Luke's EC1 *(Crypt Café)*
Mandarin Oriental Hyde Park SW1 *(Rosebery Rms)*
Mary Ward House WC1 *(Lethaby Room)*
The Metropolitan W1 *(Met Bar*)*
National Maritime Museum SE10 *(Peter Harrison Planetarium, Royal Observatory or The Queen's House)*
Newstead Abbey NG15 *(The Cloisters)*
No. 11 Cavendish Square W1 *(The Burdett Theatre)*
Nottingham Castle NG1 *(Cafe)*
Old Royal Naval College SE10 *(King William Restaurant)*
Pacific Oriental EC2 *(Mezzanine Floor)*
Philharmonic Hall L1 *(Grand Foyer Bar* or Rodewald Suite)*
Royal Air Force Museum NW9 *(Art Gallery)*
Royal Albert Hall SW7 *(Max)*
Royal College of Pathologists SW1 *(Max*)*
Science Museum SW7 *(Director's Suite)*
Serpentine Gallery W2 *(Max*)*
Sheraton Park Tower SW1 *(Trianon Rm*)*
Smith's of Smithfield EC1 *(Wine Room)*
Southbank Centre SE1 *(St Paul's Roof Pavilion or Weston Roof Pavilion)*
Swissôtel The Howard, London WC2 *(Temple Garden)*
Tate Modern SE1 *(East Room or Starr Foyer)*
Thomas Goode W1 *(Max*)*
Victoria Art Gallery BA2 *(Max*)*
Volt Lounge SW1 *(Restaurant)*
Waddesdon Manor, The Dairy HP18 *(West Hall)*

Westminster Abbey Garden SW1 *(Museum)*
Wollaton Hall NG8 *(Cafe or Great Hall*)*

140 America Square Conference Centre EC3 *(Fleet Suite)*
The Carlton Mitre Hotel KT8 *(Pavilion*)*
The Law Society WC2 *(Six Clerks Restaurant/Bar)*
Merchant Taylors' Hall EC2 *(Drawing Rm or Parlour)*
Royal College of Physicians NW1 *(Platt Rm)*

130 America Square Conference Centre EC3 *(Aldgate & Bishopsgate Suites)*
The Foundling Museum WC1 *(Picture Gallery option 3)*
Grange Holborn WC1 *(Orion Suite)*
Guildhall BA1 *(Brunswick Room)*
High Road House W4 *(Downstairs*)*
Hotel Rafayel SW11 *(Penthouse)*
LABAN SE8 *(Max* or Max)*
The Law Society WC2 *(Old Council Chamber)*
Phyllis Court RG9 *(Grandstand Pavilion)*
RY Britannia EH6 *(The Royal Deck)*
Liverpool Town Hall L2 *(Small Ballroom)*

125 Armourers' & Braisers' Hall EC2 *(Max*)*
Middle Temple Hall EC4 *(Parliament Chamber)*

120 Baltic Exchange EC3 *(Max*)*
Cannizaro House SW19 *(Viscount Melville Suite*)*
Canonbury Academy N1 *(Max*)*
The Casino at the Empire WC2 *(Flame)*
Claridge's W1 *(French Salon or Mirror Room)*
Devonport House SE10 *(Max*)*
The Dorchester W1 *(Crystal)*
Drapers' Hall EC2 *(Court Dining)*
Hampshire Hotel WC2 *(Penthouse*)*
Haymarket Hotel SW1 *(Shooting Gallery)*
The Hempel W2 *(No 17)*
Imperial War Museum London SE1 *(Conference Room)*
Inner Temple EC4 *(Luncheon Rm)*
Ivy WC2 *(Max*)*
Kent House Knightsbridge SW7 *(The Rutland Room)*
The Law Society WC2 *(Strand/Fleet/Bell Suites)*
Manchester Town Hall M60 *(Conference Hall)*
National Liberal Club SW1 *(David Lloyd George*)*
Newstead Abbey NG15 *(The West Front Suite)*
The Park Lane Hotel W1 *(Oak Rm)*
Park Plaza County Hall SE1 *(Max*)*
Pump Room and Roman Baths BA1 *(Terrace)*
Queen's House SE10 *(Orangery Suite)*
Rex Whistler (Tate Britain) SW1 *(Max*)*
Shoreditch House E1 *(Biscuit Tin)*
Skinners' Hall EC4 *(Old Court Rm)*
St. Mungo Museum of Religious Life and Art G4 *(Max*)*
Surgeon's Hall Complex EH8 *(Reception Room)*
Tate Modern SE1 *(Members Room)*
30 Pavilion Road SW1 *(Ballroom or Stone Hall)*
HQS Wellington WC2 *(Model Rm)*
Westminster Abbey Garden SW1 *(St Catherine's Chapel Garden)*

110 The Commonwealth Club WC2 *(Seminar Room)*
The Foundling Museum WC1 *(Picture Gallery option 4)*
Royal Opera House WC2 *(Macmillan)*
28 Portland Place W1 *(Heggie Rm*)*
Waddesdon Manor, The Dairy HP18 *(Winter Garden)*

100 Andaz EC2 *(Fenchurch)*
Apex City of London Hotel EC3 *(Max*)*
Arts Club W1 *(Bar & Conservatory or Garden Rm)*
Aviator GU14 *(1 & 2)*
Baglioni Hotel SW7 *(Max*)*
Belvedere W8 *(Top level)*
Bermondsey Square SE1 *(Terrace)*
Berry Bros. & Rudd SW1 *(The Cellars*)*
BMA House WC1 *(Harvey)*
Café de Paris W1 *(VIP Rm)*
The Caledonian Club SW1 *(Oval Room & Terrace or Smoking Room)*
Cavendish SW1 *(Alto*)*
The Commonwealth Club WC2 *(Conference Room)*
The Dorchester W1 *(Park Suite)*
Dukes Hotel SW1 *(Marlborough Suite*)*
FACT L1 *(The Cafe)*
The Foundling Museum WC1 *(Picture Gallery option 5)*
Four Seasons Canary Wharf E14 *(River Rm)*
Grand Trafalgar Square WC2 *(Salon or Victoria)*
Grocers' Hall EC2 *(Piper Rm)*
Guildhall EC2 *(Basinghall Suite)*
Hever Castle TN8 *(Castle Dining Hall or Tudor Suite)*
Hurlingham Club SW6 *(Terrace Room)*
Lincoln's Inn (Honourable Society of) WC2 *(Old Court Room)*
The London Art House N1 *(Baroque Hall)*
Mary Ward House WC1 *(Voysey Room)*
Middle Temple Hall EC4 *(Prince's Room)*
Millennium London Mayfair W1 *(Mayfair Suite)*
Miller's House E3 *(Max*)*
Museum of Science and Industry M3 *(Manchester Science)*
Newstead Abbey NG15 *(The Great Hall or The Orangery)*
No. 11 Cavendish Square W1 *(Friends' Lounge)*
One Aldwych WC2 *(Private Rms 1&2*)*
One Wimpole Street W1 *(The Wimpole Rm)*
Parkstead House SW15 *(Loyola Room or Richmond Room)*
Phyllis Court RG9 *(Finlay)*
The Queen's Club W14 *(Committee Room)*
The Ritz W1 *(Marie Antoinette Suite or Music Room)*
Roehampton Club SW15 *(Garden Rm)*
Royal Armouries LS10 *(Tower Gallery)*
Royal Garden Hotel W8 *(Kensington Suite or York Suite)*
Royal Northen College of Music M13 *(Lord Rhodes Room*)*
Salters' Hall EC2 *(Court Rm)*
The Sanctuary WC2 *(Max*)*

Skinners' Hall EC4 *(Outer Hall)*
Somerset House WC2 *(Navy Board Rooms or Terrace Rooms)*
SS Robin E14 *(Max*)*
St Paul's Cathedral EC4 *(Wren Suite)*
Stationers' Hall EC4 *(Stock Rm)*
Surgeon's Hall Complex EH8 *(Fellows Library)*
Swissôtel The Howard, London WC2 *(Arundel Suite)*
Thistle Charing Cross Hotel WC2 *(Regency Rm)*
HM Tower of London EC3 *(Royal Fusiliers Association Rm)*
28 Portland Place W1 *(Adam Suite, Harben Suite or Sainsbury's Rm)*
Vertigo EC2 *(Max*)*
Victoria Art Gallery BA2 *(Upper Gallery)*
Wax Chandlers' Hall EC2 *(Great Rm*)*
Westminster Abbey Garden SW1 *(Cheney Gates)*
Wollaton Hall NG8 *(Willoby Room)*

90 America Square Conference Centre EC3 *(Newgate Suite)*
BMA House WC1 *(Garden Room or Prince's Room)*
Chandos House W1 *(Terrace)*
Dulwich Picture Gallery SE21 *(Gallery Cafe)*
52-53 Russell Square WC1 *(Room 1*)*
The Foundling Museum WC1 *(Picture Gallery option 6)*
Ham House & Garden TW10 *(Orangery)*
London Marriott Hotel, County Hall SE1 *(King George V)*
Le Meridien Piccadilly W1 *(Adams Suite)*
Portman Hotel W1 *(Montagu Suite)*
The Royal Pavilion BN1 *(Great Kitchen)*
Tom Aikens SW3 *(Max*)*

85 Royal Academy of Engineering SW1 *(F2*)*

80 America Square Conference Centre EC3 *(Bishopsgate Suite)*
Apex City of London Hotel EC3 *(City Suite)*
Arts Club W1 *(Drawing Rm)*
Aviator GU14 *(Sky Lounge)*
The Casino at the Empire WC2 *(Icon Bar & Terrace)*
Chesterfield Mayfair W1 *(The Conservatory)*
Christopher's WC2 *(Max*)*
FACT L1 *(The Box)*
Fan Museum SE10 *(Max*)*
Fortnum & Mason W1 *(Burlington Room)*
Hush - Private Dining W1 *(Zanzibar)*
Imperial War Museum North M17 *(The Niveskind)*
Inner Temple EC4 *(Smoking Room)*
Institute of Directors SW1 *(St James's I or Trafalgar II/St James II)*
Kensington Palace W8 *(Sunken Garden)*
The Lanesborough SW1 *(Wellington Rm)*
Lloyds Club EC3 *(Max*)*
The Merchants Hall EH2 *(The Court Room & Crush Hall)*
The Metropolitan W1 *(White Room)*
Millennium London Mayfair W1 *(Waterloo Rm)*
Momo W1 *(Kemia Bar)*
Mosimann's Academy SW11 *(Max*)*
Mosimann's Dining Club SW1 *(Mappin & Webb Rm)*
One Whitehall Place SW1 *(Meston Suite or River Rm)*
One Wimpole Street W1 *(Max Rayne Foyer)*
Prism EC3 *(Bar)*
The Queen's Club W14 *(Club Restaurant)*
Quo Vadis Club W1 *(Max*)*
Saddlers' Hall EC2 *(The Livery Room)*
Sartoria W1 *(Combined Rooms*)*
Sketch W1 *(Glade)*
St James's Club & Hotel SW1 *(Max*)*
30 Pavilion Road SW1 *(Library)*
Tower Bridge SE1 *(Engine Rms)*
HM Tower of London EC3 *(Jewel House or Upper Wakefield Tower)*
Wellington Arch W1 *(Max*)*

76 Dulwich Picture Gallery SE21 *(Linbury Rm)*

75 Café de Paris W1 *(Blue Bar)*
Haberdashers' Hall EC1 *(Court Rm)*
London Film Museum SE1 *(Jubilee)*
Middle Temple Hall EC4 *(Queen's Rm)*
Millennium London Mayfair W1 *(Manhattan Suite)*
The Stafford SW1 *(The Cellar*)*

70 America Square Conference Centre EC3 *(Walbrook Suite)*
Cannizaro House SW19 *(Queen Elizabeth Rm)*
The Casino at the Empire WC2 *(FuLuShou)*
Chandos House W1 *(Duke Rm, First Floor or Robert Adam Rm, Ground Floor)*
The Commonwealth Club WC2 *(Craven Room or Thorne Rm)*
Fan Museum SE10 *(Museum or Orangery)*
The Fox Club W1 *(Max*)*
Imperial War Museum London SE1 *(Upper Boardroom)*
London Zoo NW1 *(Mappin Pavilion)*
Mandarin Oriental Hyde Park SW1 *(Balfour Rm)*
Merchant Taylors' Hall EC2 *(Courtroom)*
National Liberal Club SW1 *(Lady Violet)*
The Petersham TW10 *(River Rm* or Terrace Suite)*
St Martin's Lane Hotel WC2 *(The Backroom)*
Thistle Charing Cross Hotel WC2 *(Canterbury Rm)*
The Trafalgar SW1 *(Roof Garden)*
28 Portland Place W1 *(Adam's Rm or Harben Rm)*

68 Wax Chandlers' Hall EC2 *(Courtroom)*

65 Dover Street Restaurant & Bar W1 *(Upper Bar)*
Hampshire Hotel WC2 *(Digital Projection Suite)*
The Hospital Club WC2 *(Bellini Bar & Lounge)*
The Scotch Malt Whisky Society EH2 *(North View*)*

60 Aqua London W1 *(Nueva Private Area With Terrace)*
Bam-Bou W1 *(Red Bar*)*
The Caledonian Club SW1 *(Library or Stuart Room)*
Canonbury Academy N1 *(Queen Elizabeth)*
Charlotte Street Hotel W1 *(Rm1*)*
Claridge's W1 *(Kensington)*
The Dorchester W1 *(Pavilion)*
52-53 Russell Square WC1 *(Room 2)*
Geffrye Museum E2 *(Art rooms)*

Grange Holborn WC1 *(Orion A-D)*
Guildhall BA1 *(Kaposvar Room)*
Hayward Gallery SE1 *(Max*)*
Kensington Palace W8 *(1A)*
Kew Palace TW9 *(Max*)*
Landmark NW1 *(Tower Suite)*
The Lanesborough SW1 *(Westminster Rm)*
Liverpool FC L4 *(Directors Lounge)*
London Capital Club EC4 *(Boardroom)*
Merchant Taylors' Hall EC2 *(Kings Gallery)*
Mint Leaf (City) EC2 *(Mezzanine)*
Mosimann's Dining Club SW1 *(Parmigiani Fleurier Rm)*
1 Lombard Street Restaurant/Bar/Brasserie EC3 *(Private Room)*
The Park Lane Hotel W1 *(Balcony Suite or Orchard Suite)*
Phyllis Court RG9 *(Thames Room)*
Portland Place Conference Centre W1 *(Max*)*
Quaglino's SW1 *(Private Room 1)*
Royal Opera House WC2 *(Conservatory, Lambert Studio or Trust Rooms)*
Saddlers' Hall EC2 *(The Court Room)*
Sheraton Park Tower SW1 *(Venture Rm)*
Skylon SE1 *(Bar)*
Southbank Centre SE1 *(Level 3 Function Room or Sunley Pavilion)*
St James's Club & Hotel SW1 *(Mayfair Suite)*
Temple Island RG9 *(Max*)*
Liverpool Town Hall L2 *(Reception Rooms)*
Waddesdon Manor, The Dairy HP18 *(Manor Restaurant)*

55 Four Seasons Canary Wharf E14 *(City Rm)*
Hospital WC2 *(Forest Rm)*

50 America Square Conference Centre EC3 *(Aldgate Suite)*
Apex City of London Hotel EC3 *(Geneva)*
Apothecaries' Hall EC4 *(Courtroom or Parlour)*
Aviator GU14 *(4 & 5)*
Bridgewater Hall M2 *(Charles Halle)*
The Caledonian Club SW1 *(Selkirk Room)*
Carlton Club SW1 *(Cabinet Rm)*
Churchill Museum and Cabinet War Rooms SW1 *(Switch Room)*
Coram's Fields WC1 *(Venue 1*)*
Corrigan's Mayfair W1 *(Lindsay Room*)*
Covent Garden Hotel WC2 *(Max*)*
Geffrye Museum E2 *(Lecture room)*
The Halkin SW1 *(Private Dining Rm)*
The Hospital Club WC2 *(Forest Room (Private Dining Room))*
Hotel Rafayel SW11 *(Havana Dreams)*
The House NW1 *(Max*)*
Kent House Knightsbridge SW7 *(The Library)*
The London Art House N1 *(Egyptian Room or Orangery)*
LSO St Luke's EC1 *(Clore Gamelan Room)*
Marble Hill House TW1 *(Great Room or Tetra Hall*)*
Merchant Taylors' Hall EC2 *(Library)*
The Metropolitan W1 *(Met Space)*
The Milestone Hotel & Apartments W8 *(Windsor Suite*)*
Mint Leaf (City) EC2 *(Lounge)*
No 5 W1 *(Rooftop Terrace)*
Old Royal Naval College SE10 *(Admiral's House)*
One Aldwych WC2 *(Private Rm 3)*
One Wimpole Street W1 *(Garden Rm)*
The Park Lane Hotel W1 *(Mirror Rm)*
Parkstead House SW15 *(Cluttons Corridor)*
Plaisterers' Hall EC2 *(Humber Room)*
Pump Room and Roman Baths BA1 *(Kingston Room)*
Royal Exchange EC3 *(PDR)*
Royal Garden Hotel W8 *(Bertie's Bar)*
Royal Horseguards SW1 *(The Terrace or The Thames Suite*)*
Sadler's Wells Theatre EC1 *(Fonteyn Rm or Kahn Theatre)*
Shoreditch House E1 *(Biscuit Pin)*
The Stafford SW1 *(Panel Rm & Sutherland Rm)*
The Trafalgar SW1 *(Boardroom)*
Volt Lounge SW1 *(Crystal Room)*
HQS Wellington WC2 *(Committee Rm)*

48 Hotel Verta SW11 *(Vertillon)*

45 The Fox Club W1 *(Restaurant)*
Haymarket Hotel SW1 *(Private Room 2)*
London Marriott Hotel, County Hall SE1 *(Queen Mary)*
The Milestone Hotel & Apartments W8 *(Cheneston's Restaurant)*
Tower Bridge SE1 *(North Tower Lounge (day-time Only))*

40 The Academy WC1 *(Max*)*
Apex City of London Hotel EC3 *(New York)*
Arndale House WC2 *(4th Floor Conference Rm)*
Aviator GU14 *(1, 2 or Deli)*
The Berkeley SW1 *(Mulberry)*
Bridgewater Hall M2 *(Green Room)*
Café de Paris W1 *(Red Bar)*
The Capital SW3 *(Cadogan or Eaton Suite*)*
Chandos House W1 *(Duchess Rm, First Floor or James Adam Rm, Ground Floor)*
Chesterfield Mayfair W1 *(The Library)*
Churchill Museum and Cabinet War Rooms SW1 *(Learning Suite)*
Clos Maggiore WC2 *(Max*)*
Connaught W1 *(Regency Room)*
Crazy Bear (Member's Club) WC2 *(Private Lounge or Dining Room)*
The Dorchester W1 *(Penthouse)*
The Fox Club W1 *(Elizabeth Armistead Room)*
Grand Trafalgar Square WC2 *(Entrance Hall)*
Hilton on Park Lane W1 *(Argyll Suite or Serpentine Suite)*
The Hospital Club WC2 *(Games Room)*
Institute of Directors SW1 *(St James's II)*
LABAN SE8 *(Foyer)*
The Lowry M50 *(South Room)*
Motcomb's Townhouse SW1 *(Max*)*
Parkstead House SW15 *(Bessborough Room, Ponsonby Room or Ruskin Room)*
Philharmonic Hall L1 *(Green Room)*
Portland Place Conference Centre W1 *(Tavistock/Grosvenor)*
Prism EC3 *(Library)*
Royal Albert Hall SW7 *(Prince Of Wales)*
Sartoria W1 *(Private Rm 1 or Private Rm 2)*
Sheraton Park Tower SW1 *(Discovery Rm or Inspiration Rm)*
The Stafford SW1 *(Sutherland Rm)*
The Trafalgar SW1 *(Strategy)*

35 Haymarket Hotel SW1 *(Private Room 1)*
The Law Society WC2 *(Six Clerks Room or The Old Bookshop)*
The Petersham TW10 *(Cellars)*
Pont de la Tour SE1 *(Private Dining)*
Portland Place Conference Centre W1 *(Regent)*

30 Andaz EC2 *(Moorgate & Monument)*
Arts Club W1 *(Board Rm)*
The Carlton Mitre Hotel KT8 *(Cardinal Wolsey)*
Coram's Fields WC1 *(Venue 2)*
Gray's Inn WC1 *(Small Pension Rm)*
Imperial War Museum London SE1 *(Lower Boardroom)*
Institute of Directors SW1 *(Trafalgar I)*
The Landau W1 *(Postillion (Private Dining Rm)*)*
The London Art House N1 *(Picasso Room)*
Mary Ward House WC1 *(Boardroom)*
Number Sixteen SW7 *(Max*)*
The Park Lane Hotel W1 *(Drawing Rm)*
The Queen's Club W14 *(Board Room)*
Royal Albert Hall SW7 *(Royal Retiring)*
The Stafford SW1 *(Pink & Argyll Rm)*

25 Charlotte Street Hotel W1 *(Rm 2)*
Claridge's W1 *(Board Rm or St James's)*
The Hospital Club WC2 *(The Library & Terrace)*
Hurlingham Club SW6 *(Reading Room)*
The London Art House N1 *(Albert Moore Lounge or Bauhaus Room)*
LSO St Luke's EC1 *(Clore Rooms 1 & 2)*
Millennium London Mayfair W1 *(Kendal)*
Mosimann's Dining Club SW1 *(Stapleford Rm)*
Volt Lounge SW1 *(Cognac Room)*

24 The Capital SW3 *(Sitting Room)*
The Hempel W2 *(The Portland Room)*
Inner Temple EC4 *(Committee Rm)*
No. 11 Cavendish Square W1 *(President's Room)*
Pont de la Tour SE1 *(Semi-Private Wine Cellar)*
Portland Place Conference Centre W1 *(Chiswick)*

20 The Academy WC1 *(Boardroom)*
Aviator GU14 *(4 /5)*
Dukes Hotel SW1 *(Sheridan Rm)*
The Fox Club W1 *(Drawing Room)*
Grand Trafalgar Square WC2 *(Smaller Meeting Rooms)*
Quaglino's SW1 *(Private Room 2)*
The Queen's Club W14 *(Real Tennis Museum)*
Royal Albert Hall SW7 *(Henry Cole)*
The Scotch Malt Whisky Society EH2 *(Oval Room)*
St James's Club & Hotel SW1 *(Library)*
St Paul's Cathedral EC4 *(Temple Bar)*
Tower Bridge SE1 *(Bridge Master's Dining Rm)*
Volt Lounge SW1 *(Diamond Room)*

18 The Hospital Club WC2 *(The Rocket Meeting Room)*
The Scotch Malt Whisky Society EH2 *(Hunter Room)*

17 The Milestone Hotel & Apartments W8 *(Conservatory)*

16 LABAN SE8 *(Conference Room)*
No. 11 Cavendish Square W1 *(Treasurer's Room)*
Portland Place Conference Centre W1 *(Saville Suite)*

15 Aviator GU14 *(3 or 6)*
The Milestone Hotel & Apartments W8 *(Map Rm)*

12 The Milestone Hotel & Apartments W8 *(Oratory)*

8 LABAN SE8 *(Conference Room)*
The Scotch Malt Whisky Society EH2 *(Library)*

£M

20000 Earls Court & Olympia SW5 *(Earl's Court 1*)*

10250 Alexandra Palace & Park N22 *(Great Hall*)*

7000 Earls Court & Olympia SW5 *(Olympia Grand)*
Thorpe Park KT16 *(Max*)*

6000 Earls Court & Olympia SW5 *(Earl's Court 2)*

5000 Battersea Park SW11 *(Max*)*

4000 Earls Court & Olympia SW5 *(Olympia National)*

2500 Alexandra Palace & Park N22 *(West Hall)*

2160 The Coronet SE1 *(Max*)*

2000 Earls Court & Olympia SW5 *(Brompton Hall)*
Syon Park TW8 *(Lime Ave. Marquee*)*

1770 Tiger Tiger SW1 *(Max*)*

1750 Alexandra Palace Ice Rink N22 *(Max*)*

1550 Ascot Racecourse SL5 *(Max*)*

1500 KOKO NW1 *(Max*)*
London Metropole W2 *(King's Suite or Monarch Suite*)*

1250 Vinopolis: The Venue SE1 *(Max*)*

1200 Namco Station SE1 *(Max*)*

1150 Twickenham Experience TW1 *(Max*)*

1000 Blackheath Concert Halls SE3 *(Max*)*
The Brewery EC1 *(Porter Tun*)*
Central Hall Westminster SW1 *(Great Hall*)*
The Decorium N22 *(Max*)*
Epsom Downs KT18 *(Oaks Hall*)*
Grand Connaught Rooms WC2 *(Grand Hall*)*
Hamleys W1 *(Max*)*
Harrow School HA1 *(Max*)*
London Marriott W1 *(Westminster Suite*)*
Museum of Transport G3 *(Max*)*
Newbury Racecourse RG14 *(Grandstand Ground Floor*)*
Pacha SW1 *(Max*)*
Shaka Zulu NW1 *(Max*)*
Sound London WC2 *(Max*)*
Syon Park TW8 *(South Lawn Marquee)*
Thames Luxury Charters SW15 *(Dixie Queen (static)*)*

900 Lord's Cricket Ground NW8 *(Nursery Pavilion*)*
Newbury Racecourse RG14 *(Max)*
Wyndham Grand London SW10 *(The Grand Room*)*

850 Bloomsbury Ballroom WC1 *(Max*)*
Congress Centre WC1 *(Max*)*

800 Aston Villa Hospitality and Events B6 *(Holte Suite*)*
Beach Blanket Babylon E1 *(Max*)*
Epsom Downs KT18 *(Max)*
Jongleurs at Camden Lock NW1 *(Max*)*
London Eye SE1 *(Max*)*
Royal Courts of Justice WC2 *(Max*)*
Vinopolis: The Venue SE1 *(Great Halls)*

750 Addington Palace CR0 *(Max*)*
The Langley WD17 *(Ruby Suite*, Sapphire Suite or Topaz Suite)*
Theatre Royal, Drury Lane WC2 *(Max*)*

700 The Brewery EC1 *(King George III)*
Newbury Racecourse RG14 *(Grandstand First Floor or Grandstand Second Floor)*
Pacha SW1 *(Main Rm)*
Waldorf Hotel WC2 *(Max*)*

660 Riverbank Park Plaza SE1 *(Max*)*

650 Blue Elephant SW6 *(Max*)*
Bluebird SW3 *(Max*)*
Church House SW1 *(Max*)*

600 Aston Villa Hospitality and Events B6 *(Trinity and 82 Lounge)*
Brighton Pier BN2 *(Max*)*
Christ Church Spitalfields E1 *(Max*)*
Kensington Conference & Events Centre W8 *(Max*)*
Lloyd's of London EC3 *(Banqueting Suite*)*
London Metropole W2 *(Palace Suite)*
One Moorgate Place EC2 *(Great Hall*)*
The Oval SE11 *(Max*)*
Park Crescent Conference Centre W1 *(Max*)*
St Mary's Church W1 *(Max*)*
Thorpe Park KT16 *(Lake View Events Zone)*

565 Whipsnade Wild Animal Park LU6 *(Max*)*

560 Baltic SE1 *(Max*)*

550 Bloomsbury Ballroom WC1 *(Ballroom)*
Chelsea Physic Garden SW3 *(Garden*)*
Church House SW1 *(Assembly Hall)*
Museum of London EC2 *(Sackler Hall *)*
Ruby Blue WC2 *(Max*)*

540 London Marriott W1 *(Whitehall Suite)*

520 Thames Luxury Charters SW15 *(Dixie Queen (cruising))*

500 All Star Lanes (Brick Lane) E1 *(Max*)*
Aquarium EC1 *(Max*)*
Beauberry House SE21 *(Max*)*
Central Hall Westminster SW1 *(Lecture Hall or Library)*
Conservatory at Chelsea SW3 *(Max*)*
Covent Garden Market WC2 *(Max*)*
Delfina Galleries SE1 *(Max*)*
Earls Court & Olympia SW5 *(Olympia Conference Centre)*
Gibson Hall EC2 *(Max*)*
Glaziers' Hall SE1 *(Max*)*
Grand Connaught Rooms WC2 *(Edinburgh)*
Guards Museum SW1 *(Marquee*)*
The Guoman Tower E1 *(Max*)*
London Transport Museum WC2 *(Max*)*
Lord's Cricket Ground NW8 *(Thomas Lord Suite)*
Louise Blouin Foundation W11 *(Ground Gallery*)*
Plateau E14 *(Max*)*
Regent's College NW1 *(Gardens*)*
Simpsons-in-the-Strand WC2 *(Max*)*
SPACE E8 *(Max*)*
Studio Valbonne W1 *(Max*)*
Washington W1 *(Max*)*

480 IET London: Savoy Place WC2 *(Max*)*

470 The Cobden Club W10 *(Max*)*

450 Aston Villa Hospitality and Events B6 *(1874)*
Barbican Art Gallery EC2 *(Max*)*
HMS Belfast SE1 *(Max*)*
Ealing Town Hall W5 *(Max*)*
Paramount WC1 *(Level 31*)*
Park Crescent Conference Centre W1 *(The Theatre)*
Ruby Blue WC2 *(Main Bar)*
Swan at the Globe at Shakespeare's Globe SE1 *(Max*)*
Vinopolis: The Venue SE1 *(The Mezzanine)*
The Vinyl Factory W1 *(Max*)*

411 Floridita W1 *(Max*)*

400 Albannach WC2 *(Max*)*
Alexandra Palace & Park N22 *(Palace Restaurant)*
Bank of England Sports Centre SW15 *(Terrace Room *)*
Benares W1 *(Main Restaurant*)*
The Coliseum WC2 *(Max*)*
Elstree Film Studio WD6 *(Max*)*
Epsom Downs KT18 *(The Blue Riband Room or The Diomed Suit)*
Gibson Hall EC2 *(Garden)*
Hard Rock Cafe W1 *(Max*)*
Highgate School N6 *(Dining Hall*)*
Hop Exchange SE1 *(Max*)*
House of St Barnabas W1 *(Max*)*
Jasmine Studios W6 *(Max*)*
Lloyd's of London EC3 *(1688)*
One Great George Street SW1 *(Great Hall*)*
The Regalia EC4 *(Max*)*
Royal Institute of British Architects W1 *(Florence Hall*)*
Shanghai Blues WC1 *(Max*)*
Southwark Cathedral SE1 *(The Courtyard*)*
Theatre Royal, Drury Lane WC2 *(Grand Saloon)*
Tottenham Hotspur N17 *(Pat Jennings Lounge*)*
V&A Museum of Childhood E2 *(Max*)*

350 Adam Street WC2 *(Max*)*
All Star Lanes (Brick Lane) E1 *(Main Hall)*
BAFTA, 195 Piccadilly W1 *(David Lean Room*)*
Beaufort House SW3 *(Max*)*
HMS Belfast SE1 *(Quarter Deck (Summer Evenings))*
Cantaloupe EC2 *(Max*)*
Carpenters' Hall EC2 *(Max*)*
Dartmouth House W1 *(Max*)*
Delfina Galleries SE1 *(Exhibition Gallery)*
Harrow School HA1 *(Shepherd Churchill Hall)*
ICA SW1 *(Theatre*)*
Imperial City EC3 *(Max*)*
Mews of Mayfair W1 *(Max*)*
National Theatre SE1 *(Lyttelton Exhibition Level*)*
Newbury Racecourse RG14 *(Hennessy Suite)*
One Marylebone Road NW1 *(Max*)*
Portal EC1 *(Max*)*
Vinopolis: The Venue SE1 *(The European Odysey)*

320 The Coliseum WC2 *(Sky Bar)*
Thames Luxury Charters SW15 *(Erasmus)*

300 Beach Blanket Babylon E1 *(Cocktail Bar)*
Blakemore House Conference and Wedding Venue SG4 *(Garden Room*)*
Cavalry & Guards Club W1 *(Max*)*
Cittie of Yorke WC1 *(Max*)*

City of London Club EC2 *(Main Dining Rm*)*
Crown Moran Hotel NW2 *(Max*)*
Eton College (Dorney Lake) SL4 *(Max*)*
Inmarsat EC1 *(Max*)*
The Insurance Hall EC2 *(Max*)*
Kenza EC2 *(Max*)*
Lord's Cricket Ground NW8 *(Long Room)*
Louise Blouin Foundation W11 *(Third Floor)*
Mahiki W1 *(Max*)*
National Army Museum SW3 *(Art Gallery*)*
Newbury Racecourse RG14 *(Berkshire Stand Concourse)*
No 4 Hamilton Place W1 *(Bill Boeing Rm*)*
Pinewood Studios SL0 *(Ballroom*)*
The Private Rooms at Buckingham Gate SW1 *(Edwardian I*)*
Royal College of Music SW7 *(Max*)*
Savile Club W1 *(Max*)*
Shadow Lounge W1 *(Max*)*
South London Gallery SE5 *(Max*)*
St Bartholomew's Hospital EC1 *(Max*)*
Tottenham Hotspur N17 *(Box Holders' West)*
Twickenham Experience TW1 *(Spirit Of Rugby)*
Wapping Food E1 *(Max*)*
Winchester House SW15 *(River Lawn*)*

290 Aston Villa Hospitality and Events B6 *(McGregors Suite)*

280 Lonsdale W11 *(Max*)*
Meza W1 *(Max*)*

275 Concrete E1 *(Max*)*

270 belowzero restaurant + lounge & ICEBAR LONDON W1 *(Max*)*

260 IET London: Savoy Place WC2 *(Riverside Room)*
Lost Society SW8 *(Max*)*
St John's Gate EC1 *(Max*)*

255 The British Library NW1 *(Max*)*

250 Amadeus Centre W9 *(Lower Hall*)*
Ambassadors Bloomsbury WC1 *(Enterprise*)*
Bank Restaurant & Zander Bar, Westminster SW1 *(Max*)*
Barber-Surgeons' Hall EC2 *(Max*)*
Blackheath Concert Halls SE3 *(Recital Rm)*
Brighton Pier BN2 *(Horatio's Bar or Restaurant)*
Butchers' Hall EC1 *(Max*)*
The CBI Conference Centre WC1 *(Concourse*)*
Central Hall Westminster SW1 *(Aldars Gate)*
Century W1 *(Rose Langton Room*)*
Cinnamon Club SW1 *(Max*)*
The City Presentation Centre EC1 *(Max*)*
Coin Street Neighbourhood Centre SE1 *(Max Nasatyr Room* or Neighbourhood Room)*
Criterion Restaurant W1 *(Max*)*
Crowne Plaza London - The City EC4 *(Bridewell Room*)*
Design Museum SE1 *(Riverside Hall*)*
DreamBagsJaguarShoes E2 *(Max*)*
East Hampstead Park Conference Centre RG40 *(Max*)*
East India Club SW1 *(Max*)*
45 Millbank SW1 *(The Banqueting Hall*)*
Forty Hall EN2 *(Max*)*
Fulham Palace SW6 *(Marquee*)*
Goodenough College WC1 *(Great Hall*)*
The Goring SW1 *(Goring Garden*)*
Groucho Club W1 *(Max*)*
Ham Polo Club TW10 *(Max*)*
Hellenic Centre W1 *(Great Hall*)*
Ironmongers' Hall EC2 *(Max*)*
Kensington Conference & Events Centre W8 *(Small Hall)*
Lansdowne Club W1 *(Ballroom*)*
London Marriott W1 *(Belgrave Rm)*
Lord's Cricket Ground NW8 *(Pavilion Roof Terrace (May-Sep))*
Louise Blouin Foundation W11 *(Second Floor)*
Painters' Hall EC4 *(Max*)*
Royal Air Force Club W1 *(Ballroom*)*
Royal Society of Arts WC2 *(Max*)*
St Thomas' Hospital SE1 *(Governor's Hall*)*
The Vinyl Factory W1 *(Gallery)*

240 HMS Belfast SE1 *(Ship Co's Dining Hall)*
Bloomsbury Ballroom WC1 *(Crush Bar)*
Church House SW1 *(Harvey Goodwin Suite)*
City Cruises SE16 *(Mayflower Garden*)*
The Fashion and Textile Museum SE1 *(Max*)*
Whisky Mist at Zeta W1 *(Max*)*

235 Thames Luxury Charters SW15 *(Elizabethan)*

230 Church House SW1 *(Hoare Memorial Hall)*
Gibson Hall EC2 *(Garden Rm)*
Royal Court Theatre SW1 *(Cafe Bar*)*

220 Ealing Town Hall W5 *(Princes Room)*
Park Inn London Russell Square WC1 *(Max*)*
Ronnie Scotts W1 *(Max*)*
Royal Society of Arts WC2 *(Vaults)*
Tottenham Hotspur N17 *(Bill Nicholson Suite or The Goalmouth)*

210 Aura SW1 *(Max*)*

200 Addington Palace CR0 *(Great Hall)*
Aldwych Theatre WC2 *(Bar*)*
Alexandra Palace & Park N22 *(Londesborough Rm)*
AOP Gallery (The Association of Photographers) EC2 *(Max*)*
Aston Villa Hospitality and Events B6 *(Directors or The Corner Flag)*
Automat W1 *(Max*)*
Axis WC2 *(Max*)*
Beach Blanket Babylon W11 *(Bar Area*)*
Bedford SW12 *(Ballroom*)*
Blakemore House Conference and Wedding Venue SG4 *(Rosemary Room)*
Bluebird SW3 *(Beaufort & Gallery Room)*
Boundary E2 *(Max*)*
The Brickhouse E1 *(Max*)*
Britannia W8 *(Max*)*
Chiswick Moran Hotel W4 *(Max*)*
City Cruises SE16 *(Eltham)*
City Inn Westminster SW1 *(Private Dining*)*
City of London Club EC2 *(Drawing Rm)*
The Cobden Club W10 *(Second Floor)*
The Coliseum WC2 *(Balcony)*
Courthouse Hotel Kempinski W1 *(Max*)*
Crypt EC1 *(Max*)*

Delfina Galleries SE1 *(Café Gallery)*
Design Museum SE1 *(Design Museum Space)*
Dolphin House SW1 *(Bar*)*
Dominion Theatre W1 *(The Studio*)*
Farmers' & Fletchers' Hall EC1 *(Max*)*
Frederick's N1 *(Max*)*
The Garden Museum SE1 *(Max*)*
Great Eastern Dining Rooms EC2 *(Max*)*
Greenwich Yacht Club SE10 *(Max*)*
Guards Museum SW1 *(Museum)*
Harrow School HA1 *(Old Harrovian Rm)*
Hatton EC1 *(Max*)*
International Coffee Organisation W1 *(Max*)*
Jerusalem W1 *(Max*)*
Kenwood House (Old Kitchen) NW3 *(The Brew House*)*
London Canal Museum N1 *(1st Floor*)*
London Metropole W2 *(Windsor Suite)*
London Palladium W1 *(Max*)*
London Wetland Centre SW13 *(Waters Edge Rm*)*
National Theatre SE1 *(Terrace Bar & Food)*
Newbury Racecourse RG14 *(Long Room or Paddoc View)*
No 4 Hamilton Place W1 *(Argyll Rm & Terrace)*
The Old Sessions House EC1 *(Westminster*)*
One Birdcage Walk SW1 *(Library or Marble Hall/gallery*)*
One Marylebone Road NW1 *(Soane Hall)*
Pacha SW1 *(Funky Rm)*
Pissarro's on the River W4 *(Max*)*
Pitzhanger Manor W5 *(Gallery*)*
Preston Manor BN1 *(Lawns*)*
Queen's Eyot SL6 *(Marquee*)*
SixtyOne Whitehall SW1 *(Duke of Wellington Rm*)*
Sofitel London St James SW1 *(Westminister*)*
Soho House W1 *(Max*)*
SPACE E8 *(Gallery 1)*
St Andrew Holborn EC4 *(Church*)*
St John's Gate EC1 *(Chapter Hall)*
St Stephen's Club SW1 *(Queensborough Room*)*
Sumosan W1 *(Max*)*
Syon Park TW8 *(Great Conservatory)*
Tom's Kitchen SW3 *(Max*)*
Vinopolis: The Venue SE1 *(Academia, The Gallery or The New World Odyssey)*
The Vinyl Factory W1 *(Studio)*
Women's Library E1 *(Exhibition Hall*)*

180 Ambassadors Bloomsbury WC1 *(Prosper)*
BAFTA, 195 Piccadilly W1 *(Run Run Shaw/Mezzanine)*
belowzero restaurant + lounge & ICEBAR LONDON W1 *(Moose & Reindeer or Whole Venue)*
Brasserie Roux SW1 *(Private Room*)*
The Brewery EC1 *(Queen Charlotte Rm)*
Design Museum SE1 *(Contemporary Design Gallery)*
Fulham Palace SW6 *(Max)*
London Wetland Centre SW13 *(Observatory)*
Regent's College NW1 *(Herringham Hall)*
Rivington Place EC2 *(PS1*)*
Tottenham Hotspur N17 *(Centenary Lounge)*
Winchester House SW15 *(River Rm)*

172 The Geological Society of London W1 *(Lecture Theatre*)*

170 Epsom Downs KT18 *(Lammtarra Suit)*
Loungelover E1 *(Max*)*
Sofitel London St James SW1 *(Mayfair A&B)*

165 The Magic Circle Headquarters NW1 *(Max*)*

160 Lainston House SO21 *(Barn*)*

152 The Old Courtroom BN1 *(Max*)*

150 Aquarium EC1 *(Shark Bar)*
Beauberry House SE21 *(Function Rm/Balcony)*
Browns WC2 *(Courtroom 1*)*
Central Hall Westminster SW1 *(George Thomas)*
The Cobden Club W10 *(First Floor)*
Crown Moran Hotel NW2 *(Sala Rm)*
Crowne Plaza London - The City EC4 *(Bridewell 1)*
DreamBagsJaguarShoes E2 *(Basement)*
Epsom Downs KT18 *(Jockey Club Rm)*
Fulham Palace SW6 *(Great Hall)*
Gallery Soho WC2 *(Max*)*
The Garden Museum SE1 *(Garden)*
Goodenough College WC1 *(Large Common Room)*
Groucho Club W1 *(Soho Bar)*
RS Hispaniola WC2 *(Main Deck*)*
ICA SW1 *(Nash & Brandon Rms)*
Kenwood House (Old Kitchen) NW3 *(Old Kitchen)*
Kew Bridge Steam Museum TW8 *(The Grand Junction Engine House or The Steam Hall*)*
The Langley WD17 *(Conference Room)*
The Lincoln Centre WC2 *(Break-out Area*)*
Lloyd's of London EC3 *(Captain's Rm or Old Library)*
Lyceum Theatre WC2 *(Function Rm*)*
Mews of Mayfair W1 *(Lounge)*
MIC Hotel & Conference Centre NW1 *(Hilda Porter* or The Atrium)*
Museum of London EC2 *(City Gallery)*
Namco Station SE1 *(Private Party Area)*
One Great George Street SW1 *(Smeaton Rm)*
Orangery (Holland Park) W8 *(Max*)*
Pacha SW1 *(Terrace)*
Painters' Hall EC4 *(The Court Rm)*
Park Crescent Conference Centre W1 *(The Gulbekian Room)*
Pasha N1 *(Max*)*
Pewterers' Hall EC2 *(Max*)*
Piccolino W1 *(Max*)*
Pinewood Studios SL0 *(Pools Theatre)*
The Place WC1 *(Max*)*
Prenelle Gallery E14 *(Main Gallery* or Outer Deck)*
The Red Room W1 *(Max*)*
Royal Society of Arts WC2 *(Benjamin Franklin Rm)*
Royal Statistical Society EC1 *(Basement or Lecture Theatre*)*
Ruby Blue WC2 *(Restaurant)*
Scotland Street School Museum G5 *(Max*)*
Shaftesbury Theatre WC2 *(Bars*)*
Simon Drake's House of Magic SE1 *(Max*)*

Simpsons-in-the-Strand WC2 *(Bishops' Rm)*
Thames Luxury Charters SW15 *(Golden Salamander)*
Tottenham Hotspur N17 *(Gary Mabbutt Lounge or Steve Perryman Lounge)*
Vanderbilt Hotel SW7 *(Max*)*
Vanilla W1 *(Max*)*
Waterstone's W1 *(Max*)*
Winchester House SW15 *(Front Lawn)*

140 SS Great Britain BS1 *(Dining Saloon*)*
Mayfair Conference Centre W2 *(Max*)*

135 Parliament Square (RICS) SW1 *(Max*)*

130 All Star Lanes (Brick Lane) E1 *(Private Room)*
Heights Bar & Restaurant W1 *(Max*)*
Rubens SW1 *(Max*)*
St Andrew Holborn EC4 *(Courtroom)*
Tottenham Hotspur N17 *(Danny Blanchflower Suite)*

125 Brewers' Hall EC2 *(Max*)*

120 All Hallows EC3 *(Max*)*
All Star Lanes (Brick Lane) E1 *(Private Room)*
Aston Villa Hospitality and Events B6 *(Sky Lounge or The Park Suite)*
Audley W1 *(Max*)*
Beach Blanket Babylon W11 *(Private Room)*
HMS Belfast SE1 *(Gun Rm)*
Bluebird SW3 *(Gallery Room)*
The Brewery EC1 *(Sugar Rms)*
Café du Marché EC1 *(Max*)*
Chelsea Physic Garden SW3 *(Reception Room)*
Cheyne Walk Brasserie SW3 *(Max*)*
Church House SW1 *(Bishop Partridge Hall)*
Cittie of Yorke WC1 *(Cellar Bar)*
The Cobden Club W10 *(Ground Floor)*
Common Ground Cafe & Bar SW18 *(Max*)*
$ EC1 *(Lounge*)*
Freemason's Hall WC2 *(Max*)*
The Golden Hinde SE1 *(Max*)*
Horniman Museum SE23 *(With Marquee*)*
Imperial City EC3 *(Half Venue)*
The Insurance Hall EC2 *(Court Room)*
Jasmine Studios W6 *(Courtyard)*
London Palladium W1 *(Cinderella Bar)*
Mandeville Hotel W1 *(deVille Restaurant*)*
Menier Chocolate Factory SE1 *(Restaurant*)*
National Army Museum SW3 *(Lecture Theatre)*
National Theatre SE1 *(The Deck)*
One Marylebone Road NW1 *(Baccarat Room)*
Parliament Square (RICS) SW1 *(Council Chamber or Lecture Hall)*
Pitzhanger Manor W5 *(Max)*
The Player W1 *(Max*)*
River Lounge E1 *(Max*)*
Royal Air Force Club W1 *(Running Horse/Millennium Suite)*
Royal Institute of British Architects W1 *(Wren)*
Southwark Cathedral SE1 *(Garry Weston Library)*
Spring Grove House TW7 *(Max*)*
summerhouse W9 *(Max*)*
Swan at the Globe at Shakespeare's Globe SE1 *(Balcony Rm)*
Syon Park TW8 *(Syon Park House)*
Tallow Chandlers' Hall EC4 *(Livery Hall*)*
Thomas Cubitt SW1 *(Max*)*
Trinity House EC3 *(Court Rm* or Library)*
Washington W1 *(Richmond Suite)*
West Wycombe Caves HP14 *(Max*)*

115 The Kingly Club W1 *(Max*)*

110 Auriol Kensington Rowing Club W6 *(Max*)*
Beaufort House SW3 *(Champagne Bar)*
Chiswick Moran Hotel W4 *(Fairfax Room)*
Epsom Downs KT18 *(The Downs View Suit)*

100 Adam Street WC2 *(Gallery)*
Addington Palace CR0 *(Winter Garden)*
All Star Lanes (Brick Lane) E1 *(Private Room)*
Ambassadors Bloomsbury WC1 *(Innovate)*
Aquarium EC1 *(Lounge Bar)*
Athenaeum Hotel W1 *(Max*)*
Axis WC2 *(Private Rooms 1 & 2)*
Bank of England Sports Centre SW15 *(Balcony Bar or Green Room)*
Barber-Surgeons' Hall EC2 *(Reception Rm)*
Beaufort House SW3 *(Bar & Brasserie)*
HMS Belfast SE1 *(Wardroom and Anteroom)*
Bentleys Oyster Bar and Grill W1 *(Jameson Room*)*
Blakemore House Conference and Wedding Venue SG4 *(Thyme Room)*
Brighton Pier BN2 *(Glitter Ball Bar or Victoria Bar)*
Brown's Hotel W1 *(Clarendon*)*
Butchers' Hall EC1 *(Taurus Suite)*
Century W1 *(4th Floor)*
Chelsea Physic Garden SW3 *(Lecture Room)*
City Cruises SE16 *(Princess Rose)*
City of London Club EC2 *(Garden Rm)*
Criterion Restaurant W1 *(Semi Private Terrace)*
Dartmouth House W1 *(Churchill Rm or Courtyard)*
Dominion Theatre W1 *(The Gallery)*
Epsom Downs KT18 *(The Board Room)*
First Floor Restaurant W11 *(Bar or Restaurant*)*
45 Millbank SW1 *(Red Room)*
Founders' Hall EC1 *(Livery Hall*)*
The Frontline Club W2 *(Max*)*
The Goring SW1 *(Archive Rm)*
SS Great Britain BS1 *(Lecture Theatre)*
Groucho Club W1 *(Dining Rm)*
Hatton EC1 *(Onyx Restaurant)*
RS Hispaniola WC2 *(Upper Deck)*
Hoxton Hotel EC2 *(Lobby Bar*)*
IET London: Savoy Place WC2 *(Common Room, Faraday, Lancaster Room, Maxwell Suite or Thompson Room)*
London Corinthian Sailing Club W6 *(Ballroom*)*
London Palladium W1 *(Variety Bar)*
London Wetland Centre SW13 *(Gallery)*
Lord's Cricket Ground NW8 *(Media Centre)*
Mews of Mayfair W1 *(Cocktail Bar)*
Museum of London EC2 *(Garden Room or Terrace Gallery)*

The New Cavendish Club W1 *(Max*)*
Newbury Racecourse RG14 *(Fred Winter)*
No 4 Hamilton Place W1 *(Council Rm & Foyer)*
The Old Sessions House EC1 *(London Rm)*
One Great George Street SW1 *(Brunel Rm or Council Rm)*
One Moorgate Place EC2 *(Main Reception Rm)*
Osteria dell'Arancio SW10 *(Max*)*
Palace Theatre W1 *(D'Oyly Carte Bar*)*
Park Crescent Conference Centre W1 *(The Club Room)*
Pinewood Studios SL0 *(Hitchcock)*
Regent's College NW1 *(Knapp Gallery or Tuke Common Rm)*
SixtyOne Whitehall SW1 *(Library)*
SPACE E8 *(Gallery 2)*
St Andrew Holborn EC4 *(Crypt)*
Thames Luxury Charters SW15 *(Edwardian)*
Theatre Royal, Drury Lane WC2 *(Ballet Room)*
Tom's Kitchen SW3 *(Brasserie)*
Tottenham Hotspur N17 *(Box Holders' North)*
University Women's Club W1 *(Dining Room, Drawing Room* or Library)*
Watermen's Hall EC3 *(Freemen's Rm*)*
Winston Churchill's Britain at War SE1 *(Max*)*
Women's Library E1 *(Clore Mezzanine or Wash House)*

90 Avenue House N3 *(Drawing Rm* or Stephens Rm)*
belowzero restaurant + lounge & ICEBAR LONDON W1 *(Moose Dining Room)*
Carvosso's W4 1 *(Max*)*
Coopers' Hall EC2 *(Max*)*
Floridita W1 *(Havana Lounge)*
Freud Museum NW3 *(Max*)*
Pattersons's W1 *(Max*)*
St Stephen's Club SW1 *(Garden Room)*
Sweetings EC4 *(Max*)*
Vanderbilt Hotel SW7 *(Victoria & Albert)*
Water House N1 *(Max*)*

85 Chor Bizarre W1 *(Max*)*
Trailer Happiness W11 *(Max*)*

80 Adam Street WC2 *(Rehearsal Rm)*
Addington Palace CR0 *(Robing Room)*
All Star Lanes (Brick Lane) E1 *(Private Room)*
Aston Villa Hospitality and Events B6 *(The Players Lounge)*
Beauberry House SE21 *(Bar)*
Bellamy's W1 *(Max*)*
Benares W1 *(The Lounge)*
Blakemore House Conference and Wedding Venue SG4 *(Marjoram Room)*
Brown's Hotel W1 *(Niagara & Roosevelt combined)*
Café du Marché EC1 *(Rendezvous)*
City Cruises SE16 *(Westminster)*
The City Presentation Centre EC1 *(Theatre)*
Ealing Town Hall W5 *(Nelson Rm)*
Epsom Downs KT18 *(The Gallops Suit)*
Floating Boater W2 *(Prince Regent*)*
Fortune Theatre WC2 *(Bar*)*
Grand Connaught Rooms WC2 *(Penthouse)*
Haymarket Theatre SW1 *(Stalls Bar*)*
House of St Barnabas W1 *(Drawing Room)*
Hoxton Hotel EC2 *(Garden)*
Ironmongers' Hall EC2 *(Court Rm)*
Lansdowne Club W1 *(Shelburne Rm)*
London Wetland Centre SW13 *(Theatre)*
Mews of Mayfair W1 *(Restaurant)*
Meza W1 *(Atrium)*
National Army Museum SW3 *(Templer Centre)*
Newbury Racecourse RG14 *(Royal Box)*
The Old Sessions House EC1 *(Jailers Rm)*
One Birdcage Walk SW1 *(Council)*
Oxford & Cambridge Club SW1 *(Max*)*
Queen's Eyot SL6 *(Clubhouse)*
Royal Court Theatre SW1 *(Balcony Bar)*
Royal Statistical Society EC1 *(Council Chamber)*
Rubens SW1 *(Rembrandt Rm)*
Schochu Lounge W1 *(Max*)*
Sixteen Park Crescent W1 *(Max*)*
SixtyOne Whitehall SW1 *(Reading Rm)*
Sofitel London St James SW1 *(Piccadilly/Bloomsbury)*
Tottenham Hotspur N17 *(Highlights)*
Twickenham Experience TW1 *(Council Rm)*
Whisky Mist at Zeta W1 *(Lux Room)*
The Zetter Hotel EC1 *(New River Room*)*

75 Alexandra Palace & Park N22 *(Palm Court 5)*
Bedford SW12 *(Tavistock Room)*
Coin Street Neighbourhood Centre SE1 *(Rooftop Garden)*
Dominion Theatre W1 *(The Chaplin Suite)*
Don EC4 *(White Room*)*
House of St Barnabas W1 *(Chapel or Garden)*
Jongleurs at Camden Lock NW1 *(Roof Terrace)*
Relax BBC W12 *(Max*)*

70 belowzero restaurant + lounge & ICEBAR LONDON W1 *(Wolf Bar)*
Bluebird SW3 *(Beaufort Room)*
Brasserie St Jacques SW1 *(Max*)*
Browns WC2 *(Courtroom 2)*
The Cadogan SW1 *(Combined*)*
Cheyne Walk Brasserie SW3 *(Salon/lounge/bar)*
Cinnamon Club SW1 *(Private Room)*
First Floor Restaurant W11 *(Private Dining Rm 2)*
Floridita W1 *(Bar Constante)*
Groucho Club W1 *(Gennaro Rm)*
Kenza EC2 *(Private Dining)*
Lord's Cricket Ground NW8 *(Writing Rm)*
Mandeville Hotel W1 *(Bar)*
MIC Hotel & Conference Centre NW1 *(Epworth)*
No 4 Hamilton Place W1 *(Handley Page Rm or Sopwith Rm)*
One Moorgate Place EC2 *(Members' Rm)*
Paramount WC1 *(Viewing Gallery)*
PJ's Bar & Grill SW3 *(Max*)*
The Place WC1 *(Theatre Bar)*
Royal Institute of British Architects W1 *(Lutyens Rm)*
Soho House W1 *(Roof Deck)*
Watermen's Hall EC3 *(Court Rm)*

65 Tom's Kitchen SW3 *(First Floor Bar)*
60 Admiral Coddrington SW3 *(Bar* or Function Room)*
All Star Lanes (Brick Lane) E1 *(Private Room)*
belowzero restaurant + lounge & ICEBAR LONDON W1 *(ICEBAR LONDON)*
Bloomsbury Ballroom WC1 *(Long Bar)*
Cactus Blue SW3 *(Blue Room*)*
Cavalry & Guards Club W1 *(Waterloo Rm)*
Central Hall Westminster SW1 *(Dinsdale Young)*
Chartered Institute of Public Finance & Accountancy WC2 *(Conference Rm* or Council Chamber)*
Coopers Arms SW3 *(Max*)*
Coopers' Hall EC2 *(Court Rm)*
Crown Moran Hotel NW2 *(Barnet Rm)*
Dartmouth House W1 *(Small Drawing Rm)*
Don EC4 *(Bistro)*
Grand Connaught Rooms WC2 *(Durham)*
SS Great Britain BS1 *(Hayward Saloon)*
Green's SW1 *(Private Room*)*
Groucho Club W1 *(Mary-Lou)*
Lonsdale W11 *(Genevieve)*
Meza W1 *(Private Dining Room)*
Milk & Honey W1 *(Max*)*
One Birdcage Walk SW1 *(Hinton Rm or Napier)*
Piccolino W1 *(Private Room)*
Rubens SW1 *(Rubens Suite)*
South London Gallery SE5 *(Clore Studio)*
Southwark Cathedral SE1 *(Chapter Room, The JTW Room or The New Room)*
Sumosan W1 *(Private Room)*
Tallow Chandlers' Hall EC4 *(Parlour)*
Washington W1 *(Winchester)*
50 Addington Palace CR0 *(Dining Room or Wellington Room)*
All Star Lanes (Brick Lane) E1 *(Private Room)*
Axis WC2 *(Private Room 3)*
BAFTA, 195 Piccadilly W1 *(Gallery or Run Run Shaw)*
Beaufort House SW3 *(Private Dining)*
Bluebird SW3 *(Bluebird Room)*
Browns WC2 *(Courtroom 3)*
The Cadogan SW1 *(Salon Lillie)*
Chiswick Moran Hotel W4 *(Fairfax East or Fairfax West)*
Chutney Mary SW10 *(Private Room*)*
City of London Club EC2 *(Bar, Salisbury Rm or Salisbury Rm)*
Don EC4 *(Restaurant)*
Duchess Theatre WC2 *(Bar*)*
Elena's L'Etoile W1 *(Oscar Room*)*
Fulham Palace SW6 *(Dining Rm or Drawing Rm)*
Hellenic Centre W1 *(Boardroom)*
RS Hispaniola WC2 *(Board Rm)*
House of St Barnabas W1 *(Garden Room or Monro Room)*
Hoxton Hotel EC2 *(Larger Rooms)*
Leven is Strijd E14 *(Max*)*
Malmaison Hotel EC1 *(Max*)*
Mandeville Hotel W1 *(Red Room)*
MIC Hotel & Conference Centre NW1 *(Alice)*
Odeon Leicester Square WC2 *(Meeting Room*)*
Pinewood Studios SL0 *(Pine)*
The Private Rooms at Buckingham Gate SW1 *(Edwardian II)*
Radisson Edwardian Berkshire Hotel W1 *(Sonning Suite*)*
Royal Society of Arts WC2 *(Adelphi or Tavern Rm)*
Ruby Blue WC2 *(Conference)*
Sailing Barge Will E1 *(Max*)*
Spring Grove House TW7 *(Music Rm)*
St Thomas' Hospital SE1 *(Grand Committee Rm)*
Vanderbilt Hotel SW7 *(Edwardian)*
Il Vicolo SW1 *(Max*)*
Vinopolis: The Venue SE1 *(The Vineyard)*
Waldorf Hotel WC2 *(Aldwych Suite)*
48 The CBI Conference Centre WC1 *(Rms 1, 2 & 3)*
45 Avenue House N3 *(Salon)*
belowzero restaurant + lounge & ICEBAR LONDON W1 *(Reindeer Lounge Bar)*
Coopers' Hall EC2 *(Dining Rm)*
Mews of Mayfair W1 *(Art Gallery)*
The Private Rooms at Buckingham Gate SW1 *(Buckingham or Taj)*
Sofitel London St James SW1 *(Kensington)*
Washington W1 *(Fairfax)*
40 Addington Palace CR0 *(Empire Room)*
Alexandra Palace & Park N22 *(Palm Court 2/3)*
All Star Lanes (Brick Lane) E1 *(Private Room)*
Ambassadors Bloomsbury WC1 *(Create or Think)*
Aston Villa Hospitality and Events B6 *(The Champions Lounge)*
Audley W1 *(Upstairs Dining Room)*
Benares W1 *(Burton Room or The Berkeley Room)*
Benjamin Franklin House WC2 *(Franklin's Parlour* or Mrs Stevenson's Parlour)*
Blakemore House Conference and Wedding Venue SG4 *(Sage Room)*
Brasserie St Jacques SW1 *(Private Rooms)*
Christ Church Spitalfields E1 *(Old Vestry Rm)*
City of London Club EC2 *(City Room)*
Coin Street Neighbourhood Centre SE1 *(Fred Miller 1&2)*
Dominion Theatre W1 *(The Garland Suite)*
Freud Museum NW3 *(Marquee)*
House of St Barnabas W1 *(Bazelgette Room or Silk Room)*
Malmaison Hotel EC1 *(Mal 1)*
Mews of Mayfair W1 *(Private Dining Room)*
The Old Sessions House EC1 *(Recorder Rm)*
Parliament Square (RICS) SW1 *(Brussels Room)*
Pattersons's W1 *(Function Rm)*
Piccolino - Exchange Square EC2 *(Private Room*)*
Plateau E14 *(Private Dining Rm)*
Royal Society of Arts WC2 *(Romney)*
Shanghai Blues WC1 *(Private Dining Rm)*
St Bartholomew's Hospital EC1 *(Treasurer's Rm)*
Theatre Royal, Drury Lane WC2 *(Boardroom)*
Trinity House EC3 *(Luncheon Rm)*
Winchester House SW15 *(Library)*
Wyndham Grand London SW10 *(Albert Suite or Battersea)*
35 Floridita W1 *(Salon Rojo)*

One Moorgate Place EC2 *(Small Reception Rm)*
30 Admiral Coddrington SW3 *(Garden)*
Alexandra Palace & Park N22 *(Palm Court 4)*
All Star Lanes (Brick Lane) E1 *(Private Room)*
Ambassadors Bloomsbury WC1 *(Vision)*
Avenue House N3 *(Dining Rm)*
HMS Belfast SE1 *(Admiral's Quarters)*
Benjamin Franklin House WC2 *(Seminar Room)*
Church House SW1 *(Westminster)*
Coin Street Neighbourhood Centre SE1 *(Lil Patrick 1&2)*
Don EC4 *(Private Rm)*
Elena's L'Etoile W1 *(Elena's Room)*
First Floor Restaurant W11 *(Private Dining Rm 1)*
Floating Boater W2 *(Lapwing)*
Haymarket Theatre SW1 *(Oscar Wilde)*
Hoxton Hotel EC2 *(Room 3)*
Lansdowne Club W1 *(Findlay Rm)*
MIC Hotel & Conference Centre NW1 *(Wesley)*
One Great George Street SW1 *(Stephenson Rm)*
Prenelle Gallery E14 *(Library)*
Rivington Place EC2 *(Meeting Room)*
Royal Society of Arts WC2 *(Folkestone Rm)*
26 The Coliseum WC2 *(Royal Retiring Room)*
25 Alexandra Palace & Park N22 *(Palm Court 1)*
The Goring SW1 *(Drawing Rm)*
The Guoman Tower E1 *(Mortimer Suite)*
London Eye SE1 *(Per Capsule)*
Mews of Mayfair W1 *(La Cave)*
MIC Hotel & Conference Centre NW1 *(Norfolk or Whitfield)*
Noel Coward Theatre WC2 *(Sir Donald Albery Rm*)*
Oxford & Cambridge Club SW1 *(Edward VII)*
Royal Statistical Society EC1 *(New Meeting Rm)*
20 Addington Palace CR0 *(Chadwick Healey)*
Athenaeum Hotel W1 *(Ardmore)*
Benjamin Franklin House WC2 *(Outside Terrace)*
Browns WC2 *(Courtroom 4)*
The Cadogan SW1 *(Salon Oscar)*
Church House SW1 *(Jubilee)*
City of London Club EC2 *(Masterman/Wellington Rms)*
Dominion Theatre W1 *(The Milburn Suite)*
Elena's L'Etoile W1 *(Lounge Room)*
Farmers' & Fletchers' Hall EC1 *(Court Rm)*
Founders' Hall EC1 *(Parlour)*
IET London: Savoy Place WC2 *(Haslett Room)*
Imperial City EC3 *(Private Dining Rm)*
Lansdowne Club W1 *(Sun Rm)*
London Canal Museum N1 *(Meeting Rm)*
MIC Hotel & Conference Centre NW1 *(Exeter)*
The New Cavendish Club W1 *(Library)*
Painters' Hall EC4 *(Painted Chamber)*
The Scotch Malt Whisky Society EC1 *(Max*)*
Trinity House EC3 *(Reading Rm)*
Vanderbilt Hotel SW7 *(Harrington)*
Watermen's Hall EC3 *(The Parlour or The Silver Rm)*
The Zetter Hotel EC1 *(River Fleet Room)*
16 The Geological Society of London W1 *(Arthur Homes Rm)*
Newbury Racecourse RG14 *(Private Boxes)*
14 Zuma SW7 *(Private Rm*)*
12 Zuma SW7 *(Private Rm)*
10 Benjamin Franklin House WC2 *(Board Room)*
Elena's L'Etoile W1 *(Private Room)*
Noel Coward Theatre WC2 *(Royal Rm)*
The Private Rooms at Buckingham Gate SW1 *(Clarence)*
8 Noel Coward Theatre WC2 *(Wyndham Rm)*
The Private Rooms at Buckingham Gate SW1 *(Windsor)*
6 The Coliseum WC2 *(Harewood)*

£B-M

5000 ExCeL London E16 *(ICC Auditorium*)*
3000 The International Convention Centre B1 *(Hall 3*)*
2900 Debut London SE1 *(Max*)*
2000 Babalou SW2 *(Max*)*
Docklands Sailing & Watersports Centre E14 *(Max*)*
Trailfinders Sports Club W13 *(Max*)*
1850 The London Hippodrome WC2 *(Max*)*
1800 Fabric EC1 *(Max*)*
The Royal Horticultural Halls SW1 *(Lawrence Hall*)*
1500 Clapham Grand SW11 *(Max*)*
Spitalfields Market E1 *(Max*)*
Streatham Ice Arena SW16 *(Max*)*
Whitechapel Art Gallery E1 *(Max*)*
1200 Debut London SE1 *(Main)*
1190 ExCeL London E16 *(ICC Capital Suite)*
1125 ExCeL London E16 *(Platinum Suite)*
1100 Royal College of Art SW7 *(Max*)*
1000 Egg N7 *(Max*)*
Hammersmith Town Hall W6 *(Max*)*
Old Truman Brewery E1 *(Max*)*
828 University of London Union WC1 *(Max*)*
800 Kings Place N1 *(Max*)*
750 The HAC EC1 *(Prince Consort Rooms*)*
700 Crazy Larry's SW10 *(Max*)*
Goldsmiths College SE14 *(Max*)*
Proud Camden NW1 *(Max*)*
Shoreditch Town Hall EC1 *(Max*)*
The Village Underground EC2 *(Max*)*
650 Jewel Piccadilly W1 *(Max*)*
The Royal Horticultural Halls SW1 *(Lindley Hall)*
630 Porchester Centre W2 *(Max*)*
600 BAC SW11 *(Max*)*
Debut London SE1 *(Blue)*
Imperial College London SW7 *(Main Dining Hall*)*
Proud Camden NW1 *(Main Room Alone)*
Royal College of Art SW7 *(Henry Moore Gallery)*
520 Chelsea Old Town Hall SW3 *(Max*)*
500 Artesian Well SW8 *(Max*)*
Arts Depot N12 *(Main Auditorium*)*
Balls Brothers Minster Pavement EC3 *(Max*)*

Bishopsgate Institute EC2 *(Great Hall*)*
Cecil Sharp House NW1 *(Max*)*
Lotus Chinese Floating Restaurant E14 *(Max*)*
Mall Galleries SW1 *(Main Gallery*)*
Old Truman Brewery E1 *(Boiler House)*
Spitalfields Market E1 *(Areas 1-3)*
470 Bishopsgate Institute EC2 *(Max)*
450 Balls Brothers Lime Street EC3 *(Max*)*
Kings Place N1 *(Kings Place Art Gallery)*
London School of Economics WC2 *(Max*)*
Loose Cannon EC4 *(Max*)*
Mermaid Conference & Events Centre EC4 *(Max*)*
The Pavilion B6 *(Max*)*
420 Fulham Town Hall SW6 *(Max*)*
400 The Book Club EC2 *(Max*)*
Chelsea Old Town Hall SW3 *(Main Hall)*
Conway Hall WC1 *(Max*)*
Debut London SE1 *(Grey Arch or Red)*
Dulwich College SE21 *(Max*)*
Henry J Beans SW3 *(Max*)*
Mermaid Conference & Events Centre EC4 *(Auditorium)*
Royal Geographical Society SW7 *(Max*)*
350 Babble W1 *(Max*)*
Balls Brothers Lime Street EC3 *(Bar)*
Bush Hall W12 *(Max*)*
The Chelsea Gardener SW3 *(Max*)*
City Hotel E1 *(Max*)*
ecurie25 N1 *(Max*)*
Imperial College London SW7 *(Senior Common Rm)*
Music Room W1 *(Max*)*
HMS President EC4 *(Ball Rm*)*
Proud Cabaret EC3 *(Max*)*
Rich Mix E1 *(Max*)*
St Martin In The Fields WC2 *(Max*)*
Westminster Boating Base SW1 *(Max*)*
Worx SW6 *(Studio 2*)*
330 Kings Place N1 *(Battlebridge Room)*
McQueen EC2 *(Basement*)*
320 Kings Place N1 *(Hall Two)*
McQueen EC2 *(Ground Floor)*
308 Cochrane Theatre WC1 *(Bar*)*
300 Balls Brothers Minster Pavement EC3 *(Minster Suite)*
Bistrothèque E2 *(Max*)*
City University EC1 *(Max*)*
Debut London SE1 *(Hide Out)*
Embargo 59 SW10 *(Max*)*
Garden Café NW1 *(Max*)*
Goldsmiths College SE14 *(Bar Revolution)*
The International Convention Centre B1 *(Hall 8)*
The Irish Centre W6 *(Max*)*
Jewel Piccadilly W1 *(Jewel)*
King's College School SW19 *(Great Hall*)*
Le Cafe Anglais W2 *(Max*)*
London Scottish SW1 *(Max*)*
Mermaid Conference & Events Centre EC4 *(Blackfriars Rm or Clifford Rm)*
Ognisko SW7 *(Max*)*
Old Finsbury Town Hall EC1 *(Great Hall*)*
The Pavilion B6 *(Pearson Suite)*
Photographers' Gallery W1 *(Max*)*
The Rag Factory E1 *(Max*)*
Royal Institution of Great Britain W1 *(Max*)*
School of Pharmacy WC1 *(Max*)*
Serpentine Bar & Kitchen W2 *(Max*)*
7 Rifles Battalion W1 *(Max*)*
St Paul's Church W1 *(Max*)*
Tamarai WC2 *(Max*)*
Trafalgar Tavern SE10 *(Nelson Rm*)*
Victory Services Club W2 *(Carisbrooke Hall*)*
Worx SW6 *(Studio 1)*
260 Bishopsgate Institute EC2 *(Upper Hall)*
250 The Battersea Barge SW8 *(Max*)*
The Book Club EC2 *(Basement Bar)*
Favela Chic EC2 *(Max*)*
Fluid EC1 *(Max*)*
Guy's Hospital SE1 *(Governor's Hall*)*
The HAC EC1 *(Long Rm)*
King's College School SW19 *(Max)*
Kingswood House SE21 *(Max*)*
The Little Ship Club EC4 *(Max*)*
Royal College of Art SW7 *(Gulbenkian Galleries)*
Royal Over-Seas League SW1 *(Max*)*
Trailfinders Sports Club W13 *(Olympic Pavilion)*
The White House SW4 *(Max*)*
Yard W1 *(Max*)*
240 Cross Keys SW3 *(Max*)*
20th Century Theatre W11 *(Max*)*
230 Gow's Restaurant and Oyster Bar EC2 *(Max*)*
220 Aragon House SW6 *(Function Rm*)*
Fulham Town Hall SW6 *(Concert Hall)*
Mile End Park Ecology Pavilion E3 *(Max*)*
Old Truman Brewery E1 *(Bridge)*
The Strand Gallery WC2 *(Gallery With Marquee*)*
210 HMS President EC4 *(President Suite)*
200 BAC SW11 *(Lower Hall)*
Bankside Gallery SE1 *(Max*)*
Candid Arts Trust, The EC1 *(First Floor *)*
Canning House SW1 *(Max*)*
The Chapel Bar N1 *(Max*)*
Chez Gérard, Opera Terrace WC2 *(Max*)*
Detroit WC2 *(Max*)*
Dulwich College SE21 *(South Cloister)*
Greenwich Theatre SE10 *(Bar*)*
Jewel Piccadilly W1 *(Bar Blanca)*
King's College WC2 *(Great Hall*)*
Levant W1 *(Max*)*
Mermaid Conference & Events Centre EC4 *(River Rm)*
Ognisko SW7 *(Dining Rm)*
Oxford House E2 *(Max*)*
The Pavilion B6 *(Bar Area)*
Red W1 *(Max*)*
The Red Rooms WC2 *(Max*)*
Riverside Studios W6 *(Max*)*
Royal Holloway College TW20 *(Founder's Dining Hall or Picture Gallery*)*
School of Pharmacy WC1 *(Refectory)*
Shoreditch Town Hall EC1 *(Council Room)*
St Paul's Church W1 *(Church Area)*
Trailfinders Sports Club W13 *(Centenary Club)*
Tudor Barn Eltham SE9 *(Max*)*
University of Westminster NW1 *(Deep End or Old Cinema*)*
180 Guy's Hospital SE1 *(Robens Suite)*
Proud Camden NW1 *(South Gallery Alone)*

165 606 Club SW10 *(Max*)*
160 City University EC1 *(Northampton Suite)*
Froebel College SW15 *(Max*)*
Fulham House SW6 *(Max*)*
Lauderdale House N6 *(Lower Gallery*)*
150 Bedroom Bar EC2 *(Max*)*
Bloomsbury Theatre WC1 *(Foyer*)*
Cecil Sharp House NW1 *(Trefusis Hall)*
Chelsea Old Town Hall SW3 *(The Small Hall)*
Chowki W1 *(Max*)*
Dickens Inn E1 *(Max*)*
Dulwich College SE21 *(Lower Hall)*
Fitzroy Square W1 *(Max*)*
Gow's Restaurant and Oyster Bar EC2 *(Restaurant)*
Greenwich Playhouse SE10 *(Max*)*
Mermaid Conference & Events Centre EC4 *(Studio)*
The Pirate Castle NW1 *(Main Hall*)*
Polka Theatre for Children SW19 *(Max*)*
Red Monkey SW11 *(Max*)*
Royal College of Art SW7 *(Senior Common Room)*
Royal Geographical Society SW7 *(The Hall)*
St Botolph's Hall EC2 *(Max*)*
St Martin In The Fields WC2 *(The Gallery)*
Tab Centre E2 *(Main Hall*)*
University of London Union WC1 *(Bar 101)*
Victory Services Club W2 *(El Alamein Rm)*
140 Brompton Oratory SW7 *(St. Joseph's Hall*)*
Gun E14 *(Max*)*
Proud Chelsea SW3 *(Max*)*
The Strand Gallery WC2 *(Gallery)*
130 Da Mario SW7 *(Max*)*
120 The Charles Dickens Museum WC1 *(Max*)*
Chelsea Old Town Hall SW3 *(Cadogan Suite (Only with Main Hall))*
Cross Keys SW3 *(Gallery)*
Kings Place N1 *(St Pancras Room)*
HMS President EC4 *(Wardroom)*
06 St Chad's Place WC1 *(Max*)*
Space E14 *(Max*)*
St Martin In The Fields WC2 *(St Martins Hall)*
Troubadour SW5 *(Club*)*
110 Burgh House NW3 *(Max*)*
100 Apartment 195 SW3 *(Max*)*
Babalou SW2 *(Private Rm X 4)*
Bakers' Hall EC3 *(Max*)*
Balls Brothers Lime Street EC3 *(Restaurant)*
Balls Brothers Minster Pavement EC3 *(St Giles)*
Candid Arts Trust, The EC1 *(Basement)*
Le Cercle SW1 *(Max*)*
Dr Johnsons' House EC4 *(Max*)*
Forge WC2 *(Max*)*
George Inn SE1 *(Function Rm*)*
Imperial College London SW7 *(Council Rm)*
Institut Français SW7 *(Salon de Réception*)*
Jewel Piccadilly W1 *(The Ruby Room)*
King's College School SW19 *(Boathouse)*
Kingswood House SE21 *(Charles Suite)*
Linden House W6 *(Ballroom*)*
Mall Galleries SW1 *(East Gallery)*
McQueen EC2 *(Restaurant)*
Mermaid Conference & Events Centre EC4 *(Miles Rm)*
Old Finsbury Town Hall EC1 *(Council Chamber)*
Red W1 *(Downstairs)*
The Red Rooms WC2 *(VIP Room)*
Royal College of Art SW7 *(Entrance Gallery or Seminar Rm 1)*
Royal Institution of Great Britain W1 *(Georgian Rm or Library)*
7 Rifles Battalion W1 *(Club Bar)*
St Paul's Church W1 *(Blue Lounge)*
St Peter's Hall W11 *(Max*)*
Trafalgar Tavern SE10 *(Trafalgar Club)*
Tudor Barn Eltham SE9 *(Heritage Centre)*
Worx SW6 *(Studio 4)*
90 ExCeL London E16 *(Gallery Meeting Rooms)*
Lauderdale House N6 *(Long Gallery)*
Trouvaille W1 *(Max*)*
80 Bedroom Bar EC2 *(Function Room)*
Bistrothèque E2 *(Cabaret Rm)*
Canning House SW1 *(Library)*
Dulwich College SE21 *(Old Library)*
Fulham House SW6 *(Dining Rm)*
Gow's Restaurant and Oyster Bar EC2 *(Oyster Bar)*
Jewel Piccadilly W1 *(Velvet 1)*
London Scottish SW1 *(Dining Room)*
Mall Galleries SW1 *(North Gallery)*
New End Theatre NW3 *(Bar*)*
Old Finsbury Town Hall EC1 *(Yellow Room)*
Oxford House E2 *(Basement Gallery)*
Trafalgar Events WC2 *(Orange Room, Purple Room* or Red Room)*
75 Balls Brothers Minster Pavement EC3 *(St Claves or St Margaret's)*
Madsen Restaurant SW7 *(Max*)*
70 Artworkers Guild, The WC1 *(Gradidge Room*)*
The Little Ship Club EC4 *(Library)*
Proud Chelsea SW3 *(Single Floor)*
Royal Institution of Great Britain W1 *(Ante Rm)*
The Strand Gallery WC2 *(Single Floor)*
Tower Paintball SE1 *(Max*)*
Troubadour SW5 *(Gallery)*
Tuttons WC2 *(Max*)*
Victory Services Club W2 *(Grill Rm or Trafalgar Rm)*
65 Tab Centre E2 *(Balcony Space)*
60 The Antelope SW1 *(Max*)*
Bakers' Hall EC3 *(Court Rm)*
Bow Wine Vaults EC4 *(Max*)*
Cross Keys SW3 *(Room At The Top)*
Gunnersbury Park W3 *(Max*)*
The HAC EC1 *(Ante Room or Queen's Rm)*
Jewel Piccadilly W1 *(Velvet 2)*
Old Operating Theatre SE1 *(Max*)*
Pied à Terre W1 *(Max*)*
Trouvaille W1 *(Bar)*
55 Bishopsgate Institute EC2 *(Boardroom)*
50 Arts Depot N12 *(Dance Space)*
Artworkers Guild, The WC1 *(Master's Room (reception Hall))*
Candid Arts Trust, The EC1 *(Banquet Rm)*
City Hotel E1 *(Lane Suite Rm 3)*
George Inn SE1 *(Function Rm 2 or Old Bar)*
Hoxton Hall N1 *(Dance Studio*)*
Imperial College London SW7 *(Solar)*
Le Cafe Anglais W2 *(Private Room)*

The Pirate Castle NW1 *(Club Room)*
Scott's W1 *(Private Room*)*
Signor Sassi SW1 *(Private Room*)*
Tamarai WC2 *(Gallery)*
45 Pig's Ear SW3 *(Max*)*
Royal Over-Seas League SW1 *(Mountbatten)*
St Botolph's Hall EC2 *(Lower Hall)*
Tamarai WC2 *(Screening Room)*
40 The Clink SE1 *(Max*)*
Guy's Hospital SE1 *(Court Rm or Senior Staff Room)*
The Mary Sumner House SW1 *(Mary Sumner Rm*)*
Poetry Society WC2 *(Max*)*
Proud Camden NW1 *(Stables (each))*
Tab Centre E2 *(Richard Pearson Hall)*
Tamarai WC2 *(Dining Room or Lotus Lounge)*
Trafalgar Events WC2 *(Blue Room)*
37 Kings Place N1 *(Limehouse Room)*
35 Detroit WC2 *(Long Room, Crypt)*
32 Kings Place N1 *(Wenlock Room)*
30 Le Cercle SW1 *(Private Room)*
Galvin Bistrot de Luxe W1 *(Private Room*)*
Gun E14 *(Red Room)*
Old Finsbury Town Hall EC1 *(Wedding Room)*
Victory Services Club W2 *(Allenby Rm)*
Worx SW6 *(Studio 3)*
25 Apartment 195 SW3 *(Cellar)*
Red Monkey SW11 *(Karaoke Pod)*
20 The HAC EC1 *(Library & Boardroom)*
Kings Place N1 *(Horsfall Room)*
Madsen Restaurant SW7 *(Private Dining Room)*
Pied à Terre W1 *(Private Room)*
Victory Services Club W2 *(Chetwode Rm or Committee Rm)*
14 The Mary Sumner House SW1 *(Princess Helena)*

£B

2600 Troxy E1 *(Grand Hall*)*
1500 First Bowl Queensway W2 *(Max*)*
The Ministry of Sound SE1 *(Max*)*
1200 Electric Ballroom NW1 *(Max*)*
1000 Cable SE1 *(Max*)*
800 Wandsworth Civic Suite SW18 *(Max*)*
760 229 The Venue W1 *(Max*)*
229 W1 *(Max*)*
750 First Bowl Queensway W2 *(Ice Rink)*
650 Queen Mary Students' Union E1 *(Max*)*
620 229 The Venue W1 *(Venue 1)*
229 W1 *(Venue 1)*
548 gem W1 *(Max*)*
500 Cargo EC2 *(Max*)*
Kettners W1 *(Max*)*
Queen Mary College E1 *(The Octagon*)*
450 Cinnamon Kitchen EC2 *(Max*)*
400 Garden Bar and Grill W10 *(Max*)*
Paradise by Way of Kensal Green W10 *(Max*)*
Sway WC2 *(Max*)*
The Village W1 *(Max*)*
330 Clerkenwell House EC1 *(Max*)*
300 Bar Kick E1 *(Max*)*
Bar Soho W1 *(Max*)*
Cinnamon Kitchen EC2 *(Restaurant)*
JuJu SW3 *(Max*)*
King's Head Theatre N1 *(Max*)*
The Lamb Tavern EC3 *(Max*)*
The Old Thameside Inn SE1 *(Ground Floor*)*
Philbeach Hall SW5 *(Max*)*
Sway WC2 *(Crystal Lounge)*
Westminster Cathedral Hall SW1 *(Max*)*
264 Punk W1 *(Max*)*
260 Cape - St. Katharine Docks E1 *(Max*)*
Loft SW4 *(Max*)*
250 Del' Aziz (Bankside) SE1 *(Max*)*
Del' Aziz (Swiss Cottage) NW3 *(Max*)*
London Welsh Centre WC1 *(Max*)*
North Pole SE10 *(Max*)*
The Pump House Gallery SW11 *(Marquee*)*
The Village W1 *(Main Floor)*
Zebrano (at the establishment) W1 *(Max*)*
240 Del' Aziz (Bermondsey) SE1 *(Max*)*
220 JuJu SW3 *(Ground Floor)*
208 gem W1 *(Basement)*
200 Bar Soho W1 *(Ground Floor)*
Del' Aziz (Fulham) SW6 *(Max*)*
Garden Bar and Grill W10 *(Inside or Outside)*
Gate Street Barn GU5 *(Max*)*
Imbibe Bar SE1 *(Max*)*
Knightsbridge 145 SW1 *(Max*)*
Lucky Voice Private Karaoke N1 *(Max*)*
Ochre EC4 *(Max*)*
St Bride Foundation EC4 *(Bridewell Hall*)*
Three Kings of Clerkenwell EC1 *(Max*)*
180 Cirque De Soir W1 *(Max*)*
160 Cinnamon Kitchen EC2 *(Anise (bar))*
Clerkenwell House EC1 *(Ground Floor)*
150 Balls Brothers SE1 *(Max*)*
Callooh Callay EC2 *(Max*)*
Del' Aziz (Bankside) SE1 *(Downstairs)*
The Driver N1 *(1st Floor or Ground Floor*)*
First Bowl Queensway W2 *(Bowling Alley)*
London Rowing Club SW15 *(Long Rm*)*
The October Gallery WC1 *(Max*)*
The Old Thameside Inn SE1 *(Cellar Bar)*
229 W1 *(Venue 2)*
140 Lucky Voice Private Karaoke N1 *(Soho Branch)*
229 The Venue W1 *(Venue 2)*
130 Shampers W1 *(Max*)*
Sugar Cane SW11 *(Max*)*
Vats WC1 *(Max*)*
120 The Atlas SW6 *(Max*)*
Del' Aziz (Bermondsey) SE1 *(REstaurant)*
Del' Aziz (Fulham) SW6 *(Aziz)*
Del' Aziz (Westfield) W12 *(Max*)*
The Driver N1 *(2nd Floor or 3rd Floor)*
The Fellow N1 *(Max*)*
Garden Bar and Grill W10 *(Deck)*
Jacksons Lane N6 *(Studio 1*)*
St Moritz W1 *(Max*)*
Troxy E1 *(White Room)*
100 Bar Soho W1 *(Private Room)*
Chatham Hall SW11 *(Max*)*
Cinnamon Kitchen EC2 *(Terrace)*
Clerkenwell House EC1 *(Basement)*
Crown & Greyhound SE21 *(Private Rm (large)*)*
Crown Tavern EC1 *(Max*)*

Del' Aziz (Bankside) SE1 *(Upstairs)*
The Fellow N1 *(Black Door Cocktail Bar)*
The Golden Lion SW1 *(Max*)*
London Rowing Club SW15 *(Fairbairn Rm)*
The London Welsh Centre WC1 *(Bar)*
2 Amici SW1 *(Max*)*
229 W1 *(Gulbenkian Room)*
The Village W1 *(V Underground)*
90 Shampers W1 *(Restaurant (Ground Floor & Basement))*
80 Alma SW18 *(Max*)*
Cargo EC2 *(Restaurant)*
Clerkenwell House EC1 *(Upstairs)*
Del' Aziz (Fulham) SW6 *(Deli)*
The Driver N1 *(Roof Terrace)*
Greenwich Park Bar & Grill SE10 *(Max*)*
Jacksons Lane N6 *(Studio 2)*
JuJu SW3 *(Juju Lounge)*
The Old Thameside Inn SE1 *(Terrace)*
St Bride Foundation EC4 *(Farringdon Rm)*
70 Cirque De Soir W1 *(Basement)*
Del' Aziz (Bermondsey) SE1 *(Bar)*
65 Captain Kidd E1 *(Max*)*
60 Callooh Callay EC2 *(Private Area)*
London Rowing Club SW15 *(Balcony)*
Punk W1 *(VIP Room)*
Shampers W1 *(Downstairs Lounge)*
50 Callooh Callay EC2 *(Private Area)*
Crown Tavern EC1 *(Function Rm)*
Del' Aziz (Bermondsey) SE1 *(Deli)*
The Golden Lion SW1 *(Theatre Bar)*
Newham City Farm E16 *(Max*)*
St Bride Foundation EC4 *(Parssmore Edwards Rm)*
The Village W1 *(Boudoir)*
Vincent Rooms SW1 *(Private Room*)*
45 St Bride Foundation EC4 *(Salisbury Rm)*
2 Amici SW1 *(Private Room)*
40 London Rowing Club SW15 *(Members Rm)*
Ochre EC4 *(Function Rm)*
Shampers W1 *(Bar)*
St Bride Foundation EC4 *(Layton)*
30 Cirque De Soir W1 *(VIP)*
First Bowl Queensway W2 *(Karaoke Room 1)*
JuJu SW3 *(VIP)*
Ship & Shovell WC2 *(Max*)*
25 Callooh Callay EC2 *(Private Area)*
North Pole SE10 *(VIP)*
22 Michael Moore W1 *(Private Rooms*)*
20 The Fellow N1 *(Private Room)*
15 First Bowl Queensway W2 *(Karaoke Room 2)*
Lucky Voice Private Karaoke N1 *(Individual Pod)*
10 JuJu SW3 *(Booths)*

FUNCTION ROOMS LISTED BY SEATED CAPACITY

* largest entry for venue

£E

2500 Battersea Evolution SW11 *(Max*)*
400 Victoria and Albert Museum SW7 *(Raphael Gallery*)*
300 Blenheim Palace OX20 *(Max*)*
280 Hampton Court Palace KT8 *(Great Hall*)*
250 Chiswick House W4 *(Pavilion Marquee*)*
The Royal Academy of Arts W1 *(Max*)*
Victoria and Albert Museum SW7 *(Dome)*
230 National Portrait Gallery WC2 *(Max*)*
220 Fishmongers' Hall EC4 *(Max*)*
200 Eltham Palace SE9 *(Great Hall*)*
Stoke Place SL2 *(Max*)*
Tate Britain SW1 *(Gallery 9 *)*
180 Hampton Court Palace KT8 *(Cartoon Gallery)*
Stoke Place SL2 *(Ballroom)*
160 Annabel's W1 *(Max*)*
Blenheim Palace OX20 *(Orangery)*
150 Hampton Court Palace KT8 *(Kings Guard Chamber)*
Lancaster House SW1 *(Long Gallery*)*
126 Spencer House W1 *(Max*)*
120 Cliveden SL6 *(Terraced Dining Rm*)*
Tate Britain SW1 *(Sackler Octagon)*
Two Temple Place WC2 *(The Great Hall*)*
100 Hampton Court Palace KT8 *(Great Watching Chamber)*
National Portrait Gallery WC2 *(c17 & c18 Galleries or Victorian Galleries)*
The Royal Academy of Arts W1 *(Fine Rms)*
96 Chiswick House W4 *(First Floor (6 Rms))*
90 Spencer House W1 *(Great Rm)*
80 Blenheim Palace OX20 *(Marlborough)*
Chiswick House W4 *(Cafe)*
National Portrait Gallery WC2 *(Contemporary Galleries)*
Tate Britain SW1 *(Rex Whistler Restaurant)*
75 Lancaster House SW1 *(The Music Rm)*
72 Home House W1 *(Front Parlour & Eating Room*)*
70 Victoria and Albert Museum SW7 *(Paintings Gallery)*
60 Cliveden SL6 *(French Dining Rm)*
Eltham Palace SE9 *(Drawing Rm)*
Liberty W1 *(Cafe Liberty*)*
Royal Observatory SE10 *(Max*)*
Stoke Place SL2 *(Howard Vyse Rm)*
52 Lancaster House SW1 *(State Dining Rm)*
50 Courtauld Gallery WC2 *(Max*)*
Hampton Court Palace KT8 *(Queen's Public Dining Rm or William III's Banqueting House)*
Stoke Place SL2 *(Lakeside)*
48 Chiswick House W4 *(Domed Saloon)*
40 Tate Britain SW1 *(Duffield Room)*

30 Sir John Soane's Museum WC2 *(Max*)*
Stoke Place SL2 *(Thomas Gray)*
24 Cliveden SL6 *(Boudoir or Churchill Boardroom)*
20 Cliveden SL6 *(Macmillan Boardroom)*
Liberty W1 *(Heritage Suite)*
10 Eltham Palace SE9 *(Dining Rm)*

£M-E

4800 Manchester Central M2 *(Max*)*
3000 Manchester Central M2 *(Central 2)*
2500 The Business Design Centre N1 *(Max*)*
2000 The Grosvenor House Hotel W1 *(Great Rm*)*
1900 Royal Albert Hall SW7 *(Max*)*
1700 Old Billingsgate EC3 *(Grand Hall, Mezzanine And Terrace*)*
1250 Hilton on Park Lane W1 *(Max*)*
1200 Manchester Central M2 *(Central 1)*
Planit Finsbury Square EC2 *(Max*)*
1100 Saatchi Gallery SW3 *(Max*)*
1050 Royal Lancaster W2 *(Max*)*
1000 Fortnum & Mason W1 *(Max*)*
Grand Trafalgar Square WC2 *(Max*)*
Hilton on Park Lane W1 *(Grand Ballroom)*
Hurlingham Club SW6 *(Max*)*
Old Trafford (Manchester United) M16 *(Manchester Suite*)*
Park Plaza Westminster SE1 *(Ballroom*)*
Parkstead House SW15 *(Parkstead Lawns*)*
Roundhouse NW1 *(Max*)*
950 Old Trafford (Manchester United) M16 *(Max)*
930 Queen Elizabeth II Conference Centre SW1 *(Whittle & Fleming Rooms*)*
850 Edinburgh International Conference Centre EH3 *(Cromdale Hall*)*
800 Royal Armouries LS10 *(Royal Armouries Hall*)*
750 Chelsea Football Club SW6 *(Max*)*
704 Guildhall EC2 *(Great Hall*)*
700 InterContinental London W1 *(Max*)*
The Park Lane Hotel W1 *(Ballroom*)*
650 Museum of Flight EH39 *(Concorde Experience*)*
Natural History Museum SW7 *(Central Hall*)*
600 Old Billingsgate EC3 *(Vault)*
550 Grange St Paul's EC4 *(Max*)*
Holiday Inn, Brentford Lock TW8 *(Waterfront Suite*)*
Portman Hotel W1 *(Portman Ballroom*)*
Somerset House WC2 *(Edmond J. Safra Fountain Court (with marquee)*)*
504 IndigO2 SE10 *(Max*)*
500 Cardiff City Hall CF10 *(Assembly Room*)*
The Dorchester W1 *(Ballroom*)*
East Wintergarden E14 *(Hall*)*
Fortnum & Mason W1 *(Ground Floor or Lower Ground Floor)*
Gilgamesh NW1 *(Max*)*
The Grosvenor House Hotel W1 *(Ballroom)*
Edinburgh International Conference Centre EH3 *(Strathblane Hall)*
Landmark NW1 *(Grand Ballroom*)*
National Maritime Museum SE10 *(Neptune's Court*)*
Old Trafford (Manchester United) M16 *(International Suite)*
The 108 SE10 *(Max*)*
Savoy WC2 *(Lancaster Rm*)*
Science Museum SW7 *(Flight Gallery*)*
St George's Hall L1 *(The Great Hall*)*
480 Forman's Fish Island E3 *(Floor 2*)*
Old Royal Naval College SE10 *(Max*)*
470 Just St James SW1 *(Max*)*
450 BFI IMAX SE1 *(Auditorium*)*
Millennium Gloucester Hotel SW7 *(Orchard Suite*)*
Queen Elizabeth II Conference Centre SW1 *(Benjamin Britten)*
Royal Opera House WC2 *(Paul Hamlyn Hall *)*
444 Royal Air Force Museum NW9 *(Historic Hangars*)*
430 Science Museum SW7 *(Making The Modern World)*
420 Grand Trafalgar Square WC2 *(Ballroom)*
Millennium London Mayfair W1 *(Ballroom*)*
400 Forman's Fish Island E3 *(Max)*
Ham House & Garden TW10 *(Max*)*
Imperial War Museum London SE1 *(Main Exhibits Gallery*)*
Jumeirah Carlton Tower SW1 *(Ballroom*)*
Kew Gardens TW9 *(Marquee Site*)*
Royal Garden Hotel W8 *(Palace Suite*)*
Science Museum SW7 *(Level 1)*
Southbank Centre SE1 *(Clore Ballroom*)*
380 Banqueting House SW1 *(Main Hall*)*
Madame Tussauds NW1 *(Tussauds - World Stage*)*
370 Hurlingham Club SW6 *(Boomhouse Suite)*
Plaisterers' Hall EC2 *(Great Hall*)*
360 Renaissance London Chancery Court Hotel WC1 *(Max*)*
350 Altitude 360 SW1 *(Altitude 360°*)*
Guildhall EC2 *(Old Library)*
Liverpool FC L4 *(Champions Lounge*)*
London Studios SE1 *(Studio 1*)*
Millennium Gloucester Hotel SW7 *(Sentosa Suite)*
Pestana Chelsea Bridge SW8 *(Max*)*
Royal Exchange EC3 *(Exclusive Use*)*
Science Museum SW7 *(Welcome Wing (Ground))*
330 Imperial War Museum North M17 *(Max*)*
320 The Conservatory at Painshill Park KT11 *(Max*)*
Hurlingham Club SW6 *(Quadrangle Suite)*
310 Assembly Rooms BA1 *(Max*)*
300 Altitude 360 SW1 *(River Room)*
Circus Space N1 *(Max*)*
Cutty Sark SE10 *(Max*)*
Everton FC L4 *(The Marquee*)*
The Hempel W2 *(Zen Garden*)*
Hopetoun House EH30 *(Ballroom*)*
Lincoln's Inn (Honourable Society of) WC2 *(Great Hall*)*
Manchester Town Hall M60 *(Great Hall*)*
Middle Temple Hall EC4 *(Hall*)*
Millennium Gloucester Hotel SW7 *(Max)*
National Museum of Wales CF10 *(Grand Hall*)*
No. 11 Cavendish Square W1 *(The Burdett Theatre*)*
One Mayfair W1 *(Grand Hall*)*

Osterley Park & House TW7 *(Max*)*
Pacific Oriental EC2 *(Max*)*
Parkstead House SW15 *(Central Courtyard)*
Porte des Indes W1 *(Max*)*
Quaglino's SW1 *(Max*)*
Royal Albert Hall SW7 *(Gallery)*
Royal Opera House WC2 *(Linbury Theatre)*
Sadler's Wells Theatre EC1 *(Max*)*
Tussaud's Showdome NW1 *(Max*)*

290 Merchant Taylors' Hall EC2 *(Great Hall*)*

288 Barbican Centre EC2 *(Garden Rm*)*

280 The Lowry M50 *(The Studio*)*
Royal Air Force Museum NW9 *(Battle Of Britain Hall)*

275 Royal Hospital Chelsea SW3 *(Max*)*

272 Royal Hospital Chelsea SW3 *(Great Hall)*

260 Firepower - The Royal Artillery Museum SE18 *(Max*)*

250 Dover Street Restaurant & Bar W1 *(Max*)*
Inner Temple EC4 *(Hall*)*
Institute of Directors SW1 *(Nash*)*
Liverpool FC L4 *(European Lounge)*
LSO St Luke's EC1 *(Jerwood Hall*)*
Mandarin Oriental Hyde Park SW1 *(Ballroom*)*
The Mayfair W1 *(Max*)*
One Whitehall Place SW1 *(Gladstone Library* or Whitehall Suite)*
Phyllis Court RG9 *(Ballroom*)*
Royal Opera House WC2 *(Ashton Studio)*
Somerset House WC2 *(River Terrace)*
St Paul's Cathedral EC4 *(Crypt*)*
Sugar Quay EC3 *(Max*)*

240 Aqua London W1 *(Max*)*
Bridgewater Hall M2 *(Circle Foyer*)*
Claridge's W1 *(Ballroom*)*
Cumberland Hotel W1 *(Max*)*
Grand Trafalgar Square WC2 *(Old Billiard Room)*
Guildhall EC2 *(Livery Hall)*
Hilton London Canary Wharf E14 *(Max*)*
London Zoo NW1 *(Max*)*
Old Trafford (Manchester United) M16 *(Trafford Suite)*
HM Tower of London EC3 *(New Armouries*)*

232 Goldsmiths' Hall EC2 *(Livery Hall*)*

230 Andaz EC2 *(Max*)*
Surgeon's Hall Complex EH8 *(Quincentenary Main Hall*)*
Westminster Abbey Garden SW1 *(Max*)*

224 The Commonwealth Club WC2 *(Restaurant Level*)*
Drapers' Hall EC2 *(Max*)*

220 Andaz EC2 *(Great Eastern)*
Café de Paris W1 *(Max*)*
15 Hatfields SE1 *(Ground Floor*)*
Hakkasan W1 *(Max*)*
Holiday Inn, Camden Lock NW1 *(The Glasshouse*)*
Mary Ward House WC1 *(Mary Ward Hall*)*
Le Meridien Piccadilly W1 *(Georgian Suites*)*
Royal College of Physicians NW1 *(Max*)*

210 Liverpool Town Hall L2 *(Large Ballroom*)*

205 Stationers' Hall EC4 *(Livery Hall*)*

200 America Square Conference Centre EC3 *(Ludgate Suite*)*
The Berkeley SW1 *(Max*)*
BFI IMAX SE1 *(1st Floor Foyer or Ground Floor Foyer)*
BMA House WC1 *(Great Hall*)*
Il Bottaccio SW1 *(Max*)*
Clothworkers' Hall EC3 *(Max*)*
Four Seasons Canary Wharf E14 *(Ballroom*)*
Guildhall EC2 *(Crypt West)*
Guildhall BA1 *(Banqueting Room*)*
Hatfield House AL9 *(Max*)*
Hever Castle TN8 *(GuthriePavilion*)*
Hilton on Park Lane W1 *(Wellington Ballroom)*
Imperial War Museum North M17 *(Watershard Cafe)*
Kent House Knightsbridge SW7 *(Sanctuary*)*
Kew Gardens TW9 *(Temperate House or The Orangery)*
The London Art House N1 *(Manor Garden Hall*)*
London Studios SE1 *(Studio 2)*
London Zoo NW1 *(Prince Albert Suite)*
Mandarin Oriental Hyde Park SW1 *(Carlyle Suite)*
Mint Leaf SW1 *(Max*)*
National Liberal Club SW1 *(David Lloyd George*)*
Nobu Berkeley Street W1 *(Max*)*
Old Royal Naval College SE10 *(Queen Mary Ante Rm)*
1 Lombard Street Restaurant/Bar/Brasserie EC3 *(Max*)*
One Mayfair W1 *(Mezzanine)*
The Park Lane Hotel W1 *(Tudor Rose Rm)*
Royal Opera House WC2 *(Amphitheatre Bar)*
Saatchi Gallery SW3 *(Gallery 1, 5, 7, 8, 12 or Gallery 3)*
Savoy WC2 *(Abraham Lincoln & Manhattan Rms)*
Skylon SE1 *(Max*)*
Southbank Centre SE1 *(Queen Elizabeth Hall foyer)*
Tate Modern SE1 *(Cafe 2*)*
33 Portland Place W1 *(Max*)*

192 15 Hatfields SE1 *(Boardroom)*

190 The Grosvenor House Hotel W1 *(Court Suite)*

180 China Tang W1 *(Max*)*
Christie's SW1 *(Max*)*
The Collection SW3 *(Mezzanine*)*
Everton FC L4 *(The People's Club)*
Great Fosters TW20 *(Max*)*
Guildhall EC2 *(Crypt East)*
Harrods SW1 *(Max*)*
Jumeirah Carlton Tower SW1 *(Acacia, Birch, Cedar And Conservatory)*
Landmark NW1 *(Drawing Rm)*
The Law Society WC2 *(The Common Room*)*
London Aquarium SE1 *(Max*)*
Millennium Gloucester Hotel SW7 *(Conservatory)*
Natural History Museum SW7 *(Earth Galleries)*
Pacific Oriental EC2 *(Ground Floor)*
Pump Room and Roman Baths BA1 *(Max*)*
The Roof Gardens W8 *(Max*)*

Saatchi Gallery SW3 *(Gallery 2, 4, 6, 9, 11)*
176 RY Britannia EH6 *(Max*)*
175 Surgeon's Hall Complex EH8 *(Playfair Hall)*
170 Assembly Rooms BA1 *(Tea Room)*
Bridgewater Hall M2 *(Barbirolli)*
The Caledonian Club SW1 *(Johnnie Walker Music Room*)*
Cocoon W1 *(Max*)*
Kensington Palace W8 *(Max*)*
Museum of Science and Industry M3 *(Air & Space Hall*)*
Skinners' Hall EC4 *(Banqueting Hall*)*
168 Royal Air Force Museum NW9 *(Milestones Of Flight)*
Royal Armouries LS10 *(Wellington Suite)*
166 Liverpool Town Hall L2 *(Council Chamber)*
160 Arts Club W1 *(Max*)*
Avenue Restaurant & Bar SW1 *(Max*)*
Grange Holborn WC1 *(Max*)*
Grocers' Hall EC2 *(Max*)*
Mary Ward House WC1 *(Brewer & Smith)*
Le Meridien Piccadilly W1 *(Edwardian Suite)*
Pont de la Tour SE1 *(Max*)*
Pump Room and Roman Baths BA1 *(Pump Room)*
Saatchi Gallery SW3 *(Gallery 10)*
Shoreditch House E1 *(Roof Top Bar (Members Only)*)*
Southbank Centre SE1 *(Level 5 Function Room)*
Wallace Collection W1 *(Courtyard*)*
156 Cocoon W1 *(Restaurant)*
Mercers' Hall EC2 *(Max*)*
150 Arts Club W1 *(Dining Rm)*
Bam-Bou W1 *(Main Restaurant*)*
Banqueting House SW1 *(Undercroft)*
Brocket Hall AL8 *(Ball Room*)*
Burrell Collection G43 *(Max*)*
Cardiff City Hall CF10 *(Marble Hall)*
Coq d'Argent EC2 *(Max*)*
Gray's Inn WC1 *(Max*)*
Hospital WC2 *(Studio*)*
The Hospital Club WC2 *(TV Studio*)*
InterContinental London W1 *(Park Lane Events Suite)*
Kensington Palace W8 *(Orangery)*
Level 7 Restaurant, Tate Modern SE1 *(Max*)*
London Marriott Hotel, County Hall SE1 *(County Hall Suite*)*
Manchester Town Hall M60 *(Banqueting Hall)*
Le Meridien Piccadilly W1 *(Terrace Restaurant or The Oak Room)*
National Gallery of Scotland EH2 *(National Gallery*)*
Natural History Museum SW7 *(Darwin Centre)*
Old Billingsgate EC3 *(Gallery)*
One Whitehall Place SW1 *(Reading And Writing Rms (Sold In Conjunction With Gladstone Library))*
Orangery (Kensington Palace) W8 *(Max*)*
Oxo Tower SE1 *(Brasserie or Restaurant*)*
Parkstead House SW15 *(Manresa Hall)*
Sadler's Wells Theatre EC1 *(Lillian Bayliss Theatre or Mezzanine Wood)*
Salters' Hall EC2 *(Max*)*
Sartoria W1 *(Max*)*
Science Museum SW7 *(Exploring Space)*
Siobhan Davies Studios SE1 *(Max*)*
Sketch W1 *(Max*)*
Tate Modern SE1 *(Tate Modern Restaurant)*
Thistle Charing Cross Hotel WC2 *(Betjeman*)*
144 The Commonwealth Club WC2 *(Auditorium)*
15 Hatfields SE1 *(Earth, Water, Air)*
140 Aqua London W1 *(Nueva)*
Belvedere W8 *(Max*)*
The Dorchester W1 *(Orchid)*
Grand Trafalgar Square WC2 *(Annex)*
Grange Holborn WC1 *(Orion Suite)*
Hilton on Park Lane W1 *(Coronation Suite)*
Hopetoun House EH30 *(Adam Stables)*
The Hospital Club WC2 *(The Gallery (North & South together))*
Just St James SW1 *(Just The Gallery)*
Museum of Science and Industry M3 *(Max)*
National Gallery of Scotland EH2 *(Weston Link)*
Roehampton Club SW15 *(Max*)*
Sketch W1 *(Gallery)*
139 Saddlers' Hall EC2 *(The Great Hall*)*
132 Haberdashers' Hall EC1 *(Max*)*
130 Apothecaries' Hall EC4 *(Max*)*
Churchill Museum and Cabinet War Rooms SW1 *(HCA Auditorium*)*
Crazy Bear (Member's Club) WC2 *(Max*)*
Lincoln's Inn (Honourable Society of) WC2 *(Old Hall)*
Portman Hotel W1 *(Berkley. Gloucester & Bryanston Suite)*
Royal Opera House WC2 *(Amphi Restaurant)*
Smith's of Smithfield EC1 *(Top Floor*)*
Warwick Castle CV34 *(Great Hall*)*
129 Hotel Rafayel SW11 *(3rd Floor Event Space*)*
126 Grocers' Hall EC2 *(Piper Rm)*
125 Salters' Hall EC2 *(Mail Hall)*
120 Assembly Rooms BA1 *(Octagon)*
BMA House WC1 *(Paget Room)*
The Commonwealth Club WC2 *(Reception Area)*
Connaught W1 *(Ball Room*)*
Cumberland Hotel W1 *(Blue 3&4 Combined)*
Dover Street Restaurant & Bar W1 *(Lower Bar)*
Dulwich Picture Gallery SE21 *(Garden & Gallery*)*
Forbes House SW1 *(Max*)*
Fortnum & Mason W1 *(St James's Rm)*
Hatfield House AL9 *(Riding School)*
Hurlingham Club SW6 *(Napier Room or Rongelagh Room)*
Imperial War Museum London SE1 *(Cinema)*
Landmark NW1 *(Empire Rm)*
The Lanesborough SW1 *(Belgravia*)*
London Film Museum SE1 *(Riverside Room 1*)*
The Lowry M50 *(Terrace Rest.)*
The Merchants Hall EH2 *(The Hall*)*
Museum of Science and Industry M3 *(Power Hall)*
National Maritime Museum SE10 *(The Queen's House)*
Nottingham Castle NG1 *(Long Gallery*)*
Old Royal Naval College SE10 *(King William Restaurant)*

Pacific Oriental EC2 *(Mezzanine Floor)*
Prism EC3 *(Max*)*
The Queen's Club W14 *(The Presidents Room*)*
Queen's House SE10 *(Great Hall*)*
River & Rowing Museum RG9 *(Rowing Gallery*)*
Roux at Parliament Square SW1 *(Max*)*
Royal Air Force Museum NW9 *(Cosford Rm (Dermot Boyle Wing))*
Savoy WC2 *(Beaufort Rm or River Rm)*
Sheraton Park Tower SW1 *(Trianon Rm*)*
Somerset House WC2 *(Embankment East or Seamen's Hall)*
Swissôtel The Howard, London WC2 *(Fitzalan Suite*)*
30 Pavilion Road SW1 *(Ballroom or Stone Hall*)*
Tower Bridge SE1 *(Walkways*)*
Wallace Collection W1 *(Great Gallery or Main Galleries)*
Warwick Castle CV34 *(Restaurant)*
HQS Wellington WC2 *(Court Rm*)*

119 London Stock Exchange EC4 *(Max*)*

112 Skylon SE1 *(Grill)*

110 Babylon W8 *(Max*)*
The Carlton Mitre Hotel KT8 *(Max*)*
The Imagination Gallery WC1 *(Gallery*)*
National Maritime Museum SE10 *(Peter Harrison Planetarium)*
One Wimpole Street W1 *(Max*)*
Volt Lounge SW1 *(Max*)*
Waddesdon Manor, The Dairy HP18 *(West Hall*)*

108 Royal Garden Hotel W8 *(Kensington Suite)*

104 28 Portland Place W1 *(Harben Suite*)*

100 Aqua London W1 *(Kyoto)*
Armourers' & Braisers' Hall EC2 *(Max*)*
BMA House WC1 *(Snow Room)*
Cannon Bridge Roof Garden EC4 *(Max*)*
Cardiff City Hall CF10 *(Ferrier Hall)*
Chandos House W1 *(Max*)*
Chessington World of Adventures KT9 *(Max*)*
Chesterfield Mayfair W1 *(Max*)*
Churchill Museum and Cabinet War Rooms SW1 *(Harmsworth Room)*
City Hall - London's Living Room SE1 *(Max*)*
The E Rejuvenation Centre E1 *(Max*)*
The Foundling Museum WC1 *(Max*)*
Hospital WC2 *(Dining Rm)*
The Hospital Club WC2 *(First Floor Bar & Restaurant)*
Jerwood Space SE1 *(Gallery & Glasshouse*)*
LABAN SE8 *(Max* or Max)*
The Landau W1 *(The Landau*)*
Legoland Windsor SL4 *(Max*)*
Les Ambassadeurs W1 *(Max*)*
London Stock Exchange EC4 *(Forum (whole))*
Momo W1 *(Max*)*
Mosimann's Dining Club SW1 *(Max*)*
National Gallery of Scotland EH2 *(Royal Scottish Academy)*
No. 11 Cavendish Square W1 *(The Conservatory & Courtyard Garden)*
Nottingham Castle NG1 *(Cafe)*
Phyllis Court RG9 *(Grandstand Pavilion)*
The Ritz W1 *(Max*)*
River & Rowing Museum RG9 *(Thames Room)*
Royal Air Force Museum NW9 *(Halton Gallery or Locking Rm (Dermot Boyle Wing))*
Royal Albert Hall SW7 *(Arena Foyers)*
Royal Exchange EC3 *(Mezzanine Bar)*
Royal Opera House WC2 *(Crush Room or Macmillan)*
Taman Gang W1 *(Max*)*
Tate Modern SE1 *(East Room)*
30 St Mary Axe EC3 *(Max*)*
Thistle Charing Cross Hotel WC2 *(Regency Rm)*
Wollaton Hall NG8 *(Great Hall*)*

96 Cannizaro House SW19 *(Viscount Melville Suite*)*
Claridge's W1 *(Drawing Rm, French Salon or Mirror Room)*
Drapers' Hall EC2 *(Court Dining)*
Royal Hospital Chelsea SW3 *(State Apartments)*
RY Britannia EH6 *(State Dining Room)*
St Martin's Lane Hotel WC2 *(The Studio*)*
28 Portland Place W1 *(Adam Suite)*

95 Hurlingham Club SW6 *(Murgrave Theatre)*

94 Andaz EC2 *(Bishopsgate & Chancery)*

90 Barnard's Inn Hall EC1 *(Max*)*
Bingham TW10 *(The Garden Room Exclusive*)*
Carlton Club SW1 *(Max*)*
The Carlton Mitre Hotel KT8 *(Pavilion)*
Forman's Fish Island E3 *(Floor 1)*
The Foundling Museum WC1 *(Picture Gallery option 1)*
Holborn Bars EC1 *(Restaurant*)*
Inner Temple EC4 *(Parliament Chamber)*
London Zoo NW1 *(Raffles Suite)*
The Park Lane Hotel W1 *(Oak Rm)*
Philharmonic Hall L1 *(Max*)*
The Royal Pavilion BN1 *(Banqueting Room*)*
Stationers' Hall EC4 *(Court Rm)*
Surgeon's Hall Complex EH8 *(Reception Room)*

87 Innholders' Hall EC4 *(Dining Hall*)*

85 Hush - Private Dining W1 *(Max*)*

84 Claridge's W1 *(French Salon)*
Devonport House SE10 *(Max*)*
Royal Garden Hotel W8 *(York Suite)*

83 The Law Society WC2 *(Six Clerks Restaurant/Bar)*

80 Arndale House WC2 *(Max*)*
Belvedere W8 *(Top level)*
Bermondsey Square SE1 *(Max*)*
The Casino at the Empire WC2 *(Face 2 Face*)*
The Commonwealth Club WC2 *(Conference Room)*
Fortnum & Mason W1 *(Gallery Restaurant)*
The Foundling Museum WC1 *(Picture Gallery option 2)*
Guildhall EC2 *(Basinghall Suite)*
The Halkin SW1 *(Max*)*
Hotel Rafayel SW11 *(Max)*
Imperial War Museum North M17 *(The Niveskind)*
Institute of Directors SW1 *(Burton)*
Kew Gardens TW9 *(Cambridge Cottage)*
The Law Society WC2 *(Strand/Fleet/Bell Suites or The Reading Room)*
London Zoo NW1 *(Mappin Pavilion)*
LSO St Luke's EC1 *(Crypt Café)*

Madame Tussauds NW1 *(Tussauds - whole attraction)*
Manchester Town Hall M60 *(Conference Hall)*
Mary Ward House WC1 *(Lethaby Room)*
Merchant Taylors' Hall EC2 *(Drawing Rm or Parlour)*
Newstead Abbey NG15 *(The Great Hall* or The West Front Suite)*
No 5 W1 *(Max*)*
Notting Hill Brasserie W11 *(Max*)*
Park Plaza County Hall SE1 *(Max*)*
Parkstead House SW15 *(Loyola Room)*
Plaisterers' Hall EC2 *(Livery Hall)*
Portman Hotel W1 *(Montagu Suite)*
Pump Room and Roman Baths BA1 *(Terrace)*
Rex Whistler (Tate Britain) SW1 *(Max*)*
Royal Air Force Museum NW9 *(Art Gallery)*
Royal College of Pathologists SW1 *(Max*)*
RY Britannia EH6 *(The Royal Deck)*
Savoy WC2 *(Pinafore)*
Science Museum SW7 *(Director's Suite)*
Shoreditch House E1 *(Biscuit Tin)*
Somerset House WC2 *(Portico Rooms)*
Southbank Centre SE1 *(Weston Roof Pavilion)*
St. Mungo Museum of Religious Life and Art G4 *(Max*)*
Swissôtel The Howard, London WC2 *(Arundel Suite or Temple Garden)*
HM Tower of London EC3 *(White Tower)*
Liverpool Town Hall L2 *(Small Ballroom)*
Victoria Art Gallery BA2 *(Max*)*
Volt Lounge SW1 *(Restaurant)*
Wiltons SW1 *(Max*)*

77 Cavendish SW1 *(Alto*)*
Haberdashers' Hall EC1 *(Court Rm)*

76 Kensington Palace W8 *(Queens Gallery)*

75 The Casino at the Empire WC2 *(Flame)*

74 Skylon SE1 *(Restaurant)*

72 15 Hatfields SE1 *(Earth, Water)*
Millennium London Mayfair W1 *(Mayfair Suite)*

70 Andaz EC2 *(Fenchurch)*
The Bentley Hotel SW7 *(Max*)*
Corrigan's Mayfair W1 *(Exclusive Use*)*
Crazy Bear (Restaurant) W1 *(Max*)*
Everton FC L4 *(Dixie Dean Suite)*
The Foundling Museum WC1 *(Picture Gallery option 3)*
Geffrye Museum E2 *(Restaurant & Galleries*)*
Goldsmiths' Hall EC2 *(Drawing Rm & Exhibition Rm or Exhibition Room)*
Gray's Inn WC1 *(Large Pension Rm)*
Hampshire Hotel WC2 *(Penthouse*)*
The Imagination Gallery WC1 *(Atrium and Restaurant)*
Inner Temple EC4 *(Luncheon Rm)*
Le Meridien Piccadilly W1 *(Adams Suite)*
Middle Temple Hall EC4 *(Parliament Chamber)*
One Whitehall Place SW1 *(Meston Suite or River Rm)*
Phyllis Court RG9 *(Finlay)*
Poissonnerie de l'Avenue SW3 *(Max*)*
Sadler's Wells Theatre EC1 *(Cable & Wireless)*
Serpentine Gallery W2 *(Max*)*
Smith's of Smithfield EC1 *(Wine Room)*
Southbank Centre SE1 *(St Paul's Roof Pavilion)*
30 St Mary Axe EC3 *(39th & 40th Floor)*
Thomas Goode W1 *(Max*)*
HM Tower of London EC3 *(Royal Fusiliers Association Rm)*
Wollaton Hall NG8 *(Willoby Room)*

68 Wax Chandlers' Hall EC2 *(Great Rm*)*

66 Four Seasons Canary Wharf E14 *(River Rm)*

64 The Commonwealth Club WC2 *(Seminar Room)*
Hever Castle TN8 *(Tudor Suite)*
28 Portland Place W1 *(Heggie Rm)*

60 America Square Conference Centre EC3 *(Aldgate & Bishopsgate Suites, Fleet Suite or Walbrook Suite)*
Apex City of London Hotel EC3 *(City Suite*)*
Arts Club W1 *(Garden Rm)*
Berry Bros. & Rudd SW1 *(The Cellars*)*
The Caledonian Club SW1 *(Smoking Room)*
The Casino at the Empire WC2 *(FuLuShou or Shadow Bar)*
The Commonwealth Club WC2 *(Craven Room)*
Dans Le Noir EC1 *(Max*)*
The Dorchester W1 *(Crystal or Park Suite)*
Dukes Hotel SW1 *(Marlborough Suite*)*
FACT L1 *(The Box*)*
FireHouse SW7 *(Max*)*
The Foundling Museum WC1 *(Picture Gallery option 4)*
Geffrye Museum E2 *(Art rooms)*
Ham House & Garden TW10 *(Orangery)*
Hayward Gallery SE1 *(Max*)*
High Road House W4 *(Downstairs*)*
Hopetoun House EH30 *(Tapestry Room)*
Hotel Rafayel SW11 *(Penthouse)*
Hurlingham Club SW6 *(Terrace Room)*
Hush - Private Dining W1 *(Zanzibar)*
Imperial War Museum London SE1 *(Conference Room)*
Institute of Directors SW1 *(Waterloo)*
Ivy WC2 *(Max*)*
Kingsway Hall Hotel WC2 *(Max*)*
The Lanesborough SW1 *(Wellington Rm)*
Launceston Place W8 *(Max*)*
Leighton House Museum W14 *(Max*)*
Local Government House SW1 *(Max*)*
The London Art House N1 *(Baroque Hall)*
London Capital Club EC4 *(The Oriental Room*)*
London Marriott Hotel, County Hall SE1 *(King George V)*
Mandarin Oriental Hyde Park SW1 *(Rosebery Rms)*
Mary Ward House WC1 *(Voysey Room)*
Millennium London Mayfair W1 *(Manhattan Suite or Waterloo Rm)*
Mint Leaf SW1 *(Private Rm)*
Mint Leaf (City) EC2 *(Mezzanine*)*
National Maritime Museum SE10 *(Royal Observatory)*
The Park Lane Hotel W1 *(Balcony Suite)*

Parkstead House SW15 *(Bessborough Room or Ponsonby Room)*
The Ritz W1 *(Music Room)*
Roehampton Club SW15 *(Garden Rm)*
Royal Armouries LS10 *(Tower Gallery)*
Sauterelle EC3 *(Max*)*
Skinners' Hall EC4 *(Old Court Rm)*
Somerset House WC2 *(Navy Board Rooms)*
St Paul's Cathedral EC4 *(Wren Suite)*
Stationers' Hall EC4 *(Stock Rm)*
The Trafalgar SW1 *(Rockwell*)*
Waddesdon Manor, The Dairy HP18 *(Manor Restaurant or Winter Garden)*

57 Dyers' Hall EC4 *(Max*)*

56 Fortnum & Mason W1 *(Burlington Room)*
28 Portland Place W1 *(Sainsbury's Rm)*

55 The Law Society WC2 *(Old Council Chamber)*
Surgeon's Hall Complex EH8 *(Fellows Library)*

54 The Caledonian Club SW1 *(Stuart Room)*

52 Tom Aikens SW3 *(Max*)*

50 Aviator GU14 *(1 & 2* or Sky Lounge)*
Baglioni Hotel SW7 *(Max*)*
BMA House WC1 *(Prince's Room)*
Brocket Hall AL8 *(Dining Room)*
The Casino at the Empire WC2 *(Icon Bar & Terrace)*
Chandos House W1 *(Duke Rm, First Floor)*
Chesterfield Mayfair W1 *(The Royal Suite)*
Churchill Museum and Cabinet War Rooms SW1 *(Learning Suite)*
Claridge's W1 *(Kensington)*
Dover Street Restaurant & Bar W1 *(Upper Bar)*
Dulwich Picture Gallery SE21 *(Gallery Cafe or Linbury Rm)*
FACT L1 *(The Cafe)*
Fortnum & Mason W1 *(Wine Bar)*
The Foundling Museum WC1 *(Picture Gallery option 5)*
Geffrye Museum E2 *(Lecture room)*
Goldsmiths' Hall EC2 *(Court Luncheon Room)*
Imperial War Museum London SE1 *(Upper Boardroom)*
Institute of Directors SW1 *(St James's I or Trafalgar II/St James II)*
Kent House Knightsbridge SW7 *(The Rutland Room)*
London Stock Exchange EC4 *(Forum 1)*
Marcus Wareing at the Berkeley SW1 *(Max*)*
Maya W1 *(Max*)*
Merchant Taylors' Hall EC2 *(Courtroom)*
The Merchants Hall EH2 *(The Court Room & Crush Hall)*
The Metropolitan W1 *(White Room*)*
Mint Leaf (City) EC2 *(Lounge)*
Mosimann's Academy SW11 *(Max*)*
Mosimann's Dining Club SW1 *(Mappin & Webb Rm)*
Newstead Abbey NG15 *(The Orangery)*
Old Royal Naval College SE10 *(Admiral's House)*
One Aldwych WC2 *(Private Rms 1&2*)*
One Wimpole Street W1 *(Garden Rm or The Wimpole Rm)*
Parkstead House SW15 *(Richmond Room)*
Phyllis Court RG9 *(Thames Room)*
The Queen's Club W14 *(Committee Room)*
Queen's House SE10 *(Orangery Suite)*
Sadler's Wells Theatre EC1 *(Kahn Theatre)*
Salters' Hall EC2 *(Court Rm)*
Savoy WC2 *(Gondoliers)*
Science Museum SW7 *(Dana Centre)*
Sketch W1 *(Glade)*
Soho Hotel W1 *(Max*)*
Somerset House WC2 *(Terrace Rooms or The Courtauld Gallery)*
SS Robin E14 *(Max*)*
St George's Hall L1 *(Cockerel Room)*
Thistle Charing Cross Hotel WC2 *(Canterbury Rm)*

48 Royal Horseguards SW1 *(The Thames Suite*)*
Sartoria W1 *(Combined Rooms)*
The Scotch Malt Whisky Society EH2 *(North View*)*
St Martin's Lane Hotel WC2 *(The Backroom)*

45 The Halkin SW1 *(Private Dining Rm)*
The Queen's Club W14 *(Club Restaurant)*
Sketch W1 *(Lecture Rm)*

44 Cavendish SW1 *(Electra)*
Quaglino's SW1 *(Private Room 1)*
The Stafford SW1 *(The Cellar*)*

42 The Park Lane Hotel W1 *(Orchard Suite)*

40 America Square Conference Centre EC3 *(Newgate Suite)*
Apothecaries' Hall EC4 *(Courtroom or Parlour)*
Aqua London W1 *(Nueva Private Area With Terrace)*
Baltic Exchange EC3 *(Max*)*
Bridgewater Hall M2 *(Charles Halle)*
Cannizaro House SW19 *(Queen Elizabeth Rm)*
Chandos House W1 *(Duchess Rm, First Floor)*
Christopher's WC2 *(Max*)*
The Commonwealth Club WC2 *(Thorne Rm)*
Crazy Bear (Member's Club) WC2 *(Private Lounge or Dining Room)*
Estorick Collection N1 *(Max*)*
The Foundling Museum WC1 *(Picture Gallery option 6)*
Grand Trafalgar Square WC2 *(Salon or Victoria)*
Haymarket Hotel SW1 *(Shooting Gallery*)*
Hever Castle TN8 *(Castle Dining Hall)*
Kensington Palace W8 *(1A)*
Kent House Knightsbridge SW7 *(The Library)*
The Lanesborough SW1 *(Westminster Rm)*
Lincoln's Inn (Honourable Society of) WC2 *(Old Court Room)*
Liverpool FC L4 *(Directors Lounge)*
London Stock Exchange EC4 *(Forum 2)*
LSO St Luke's EC1 *(Clore Gamelan Room)*
The Milestone Hotel & Apartments W8 *(Cheneston's Restaurant or Windsor Suite*)*
National Museum of Wales CF10 *(Oriel Suite)*
1 Lombard Street Restaurant/Bar/Brasserie EC3 *(Private Room)*
One Wimpole Street W1 *(Max Rayne Foyer)*
The Park Lane Hotel W1 *(Mirror Rm)*
Portland Place Conference Centre W1 *(Max*)*

Pump Room and Roman Baths BA1 *(Kingston Room)*
Royal Academy of Engineering SW1 *(F2*)*
Royal Opera House WC2 *(Lambert Studio or Trust Rooms)*
The Royal Pavilion BN1 *(Great Kitchen)*
Southbank Centre SE1 *(Level 3 Function Room or Sunley Pavilion)*
St James's Club & Hotel SW1 *(Mayfair Suite*)*
The Stafford SW1 *(Panel Rm & Sutherland Rm)*
Temple Island RG9 *(Max*)*
Tower Bridge SE1 *(Engine Rms)*
HM Tower of London EC3 *(Upper Wakefield Tower)*
28 Portland Place W1 *(Adam's Rm or Harben Rm)*
Victoria Art Gallery BA2 *(Upper Gallery)*
Wallace Collection W1 *(Dining Rm)*

36 The Caledonian Club SW1 *(Selkirk Room)*
Carlton Club SW1 *(Cabinet Rm)*
Landmark NW1 *(Tower Suite)*
The London Art House N1 *(Egyptian Room or Orangery)*
Wellington Arch W1 *(Max*)*

35 The Hospital Club WC2 *(Forest Room (Private Dining Room))*
London Zoo NW1 *(Bartlett Room)*
Pont de la Tour SE1 *(Semi-Private Wine Cellar)*
Savoy WC2 *(Mikado)*

34 The Dorchester W1 *(Pavilion)*

32 Apex City of London Hotel EC3 *(Geneva)*
Hampshire Hotel WC2 *(Digital Projection Suite)*
Motcomb's Townhouse SW1 *(Max*)*
Notting Hill Brasserie W11 *(Semi-Private Areas By Bar)*
Royal Albert Hall SW7 *(Henry Cole)*
Wax Chandlers' Hall EC2 *(Courtroom)*

30 Alain Ducasse at the Dorchester W1 *(Salon Park Lane*)*
Bridgewater Hall M2 *(Green Room)*
The Caledonian Club SW1 *(Library)*
Canonbury Academy N1 *(Queen Elizabeth*)*
Chandos House W1 *(Robert Adam Rm, Ground Floor or Terrace Rm)*
Churchill Museum and Cabinet War Rooms SW1 *(Switch Room)*
Corrigan's Mayfair W1 *(Lindsay Room)*
Fan Museum SE10 *(Orangery*)*
The Foundling Museum WC1 *(Court Room option 1)*
Four Seasons Canary Wharf E14 *(City Rm)*
The Fox Club W1 *(Elizabeth Armistead Room*)*
Grange Holborn WC1 *(Orion A-D)*
Haymarket Hotel SW1 *(Pool Area, Private Room 1 or Private Room 2)*
The Hempel W2 *(No 17)*
Hospital WC2 *(Forest Rm)*
Institute of Directors SW1 *(Trafalgar 1)*
Kew Palace TW9 *(Max*)*
The Law Society WC2 *(Six Clerks Room or The Old Bookshop)*
Mandarin Oriental Hyde Park SW1 *(Balfour Rm)*
Merchant Taylors' Hall EC2 *(Library)*
The Metropolitan W1 *(Met Space)*
National Liberal Club SW1 *(Lady Violet)*
National Museum of Wales CF10 *(Court Room)*
One Aldwych WC2 *(Private Rm 3)*
Parkstead House SW15 *(Ruskin Room)*
Royal Albert Hall SW7 *(Prince Of Wales)*
Royal Horseguards SW1 *(The Terrace)*
Royal Opera House WC2 *(Conservatory)*
Sadler's Wells Theatre EC1 *(Fonteyn Rm)*
Sheraton Park Tower SW1 *(Venture Rm)*
Skylon SE1 *(Bar)*
Volt Lounge SW1 *(Crystal Room)*
Wallace Collection W1 *(State Rm)*
HQS Wellington WC2 *(Model Rm)*

28 Charlotte Street Hotel W1 *(Rm1*)*
Chesterfield Mayfair W1 *(The Conservatory)*
Covent Garden Hotel WC2 *(Max*)*
Royal Academy of Engineering SW1 *(G1)*
Saddlers' Hall EC2 *(The Court Room)*
30 Pavilion Road SW1 *(Library)*
The Trafalgar SW1 *(Boardroom)*

27 The Fox Club W1 *(Max)*
Innholders' Hall EC4 *(Old Court Rm)*

26 Andaz EC2 *(Moorgate & Monument)*
Arts Club W1 *(Drawing Rm)*
Baltic Exchange EC3 *(Boardroom)*
Christopher's WC2 *(Small Dining Rm)*
The Petersham TW10 *(Terrace Suite*)*
Royal Exchange EC3 *(PDR)*

25 Aviator GU14 *(4 & 5)*
East Wintergarden E14 *(Promenade Room)*
The Fox Club W1 *(Restaurant)*
Guildhall BA1 *(Kaposvar Room)*
Philharmonic Hall L1 *(Green Room)*

24 Apex City of London Hotel EC3 *(New York)*
Arndale House WC2 *(4th Floor Conference Rm)*
The Capital SW3 *(Cadogan*)*
Connaught W1 *(Regency Room)*
Dover Street Restaurant & Bar W1 *(Alcove)*
Imperial War Museum London SE1 *(Lower Boardroom)*
Institute of Directors SW1 *(St James's II)*
Lloyds Club EC3 *(Max*)*
The London Art House N1 *(Picasso Room)*
The Lowry M50 *(South Room)*
Mosimann's Dining Club SW1 *(Parmigiani Fleurier Rm)*
No 5 W1 *(Private Dining Rm)*
No. 11 Cavendish Square W1 *(President's Room)*
The Park Lane Hotel W1 *(Drawing Rm)*
Portman Hotel W1 *(Library)*
Quo Vadis Club W1 *(Max*)*
The Ritz W1 *(William Kent Room)*
Sartoria W1 *(Private Rm 1 or Private Rm 2)*
Smith's of Smithfield EC1 *(Private Rm 1)*
The Stafford SW1 *(Sutherland Rm)*
Thomas Goode W1 *(Chairman's Rm)*

23 Clos Maggiore WC2 *(Max*)*

22 The Berkeley SW1 *(Tattersalls)*
Middle Temple Hall EC4 *(Queen's Rm)*
The Park Lane Hotel W1 *(Smart Rms)*
Salters' Hall EC2 *(Dining Rm)*
Sheraton Park Tower SW1 *(Inspiration Rm)*
Stationers' Hall EC4 *(Ante Rm)*

20 Armourers' & Braisers' Hall EC2 *(Court Rm)*

Aviator GU14 *(1 or 2)*
Bingham TW10 *(Garden Room 1, Garden Room 2 or Garden Room 3)*
Brocket Hall AL8 *(Family Dining Room)*
Chandos House W1 *(James Adam Rm, Ground Floor)*
The Foundling Museum WC1 *(Court Room option 2)*
Grand Trafalgar Square WC2 *(Westminster)*
Hilton on Park Lane W1 *(Argyll Suite or Serpentine Suite)*
LABAN SE8 *(Meeting Room)*
Launceston Place W8 *(Semi-Private Hire)*
London Capital Club EC4 *(Boardroom)*
London Marriott Hotel, County Hall SE1 *(Queen Mary)*
London Zoo NW1 *(Council Room)*
LSO St Luke's EC1 *(Clore Rooms 1 & 2)*
Mary Ward House WC1 *(Boardroom)*
Poissonnerie de l'Avenue SW3 *(Private Room)*
Pont de la Tour SE1 *(Private Dining)*
Prism EC3 *(Library)*
The Queen's Club W14 *(Board Room)*
Roundhouse NW1 *(Circle Bar or Torquils Bar)*
Royal Academy of Engineering SW1 *(F1)*
Royal Albert Hall SW7 *(Royal Retiring)*
Royal Astronomical Society W1 *(Max*)*
Royal College of Radiologists W1 *(Council Room*)*
Tower Bridge SE1 *(North Tower Lounge (day-time Only))*
HM Tower of London EC3 *(St Thomas's Tower)*
The Trafalgar SW1 *(Strategy)*
Wiltons SW1 *(Private Room)*

18 Alain Ducasse at the Dorchester W1 *(Max)*
The Berkeley SW1 *(Mulberry)*
Chesterfield Mayfair W1 *(The Library)*
China Tang W1 *(Library, Private Rms 2/3 or Private Rm 1)*
Millennium London Mayfair W1 *(Grosvenor Suite)*
The Scotch Malt Whisky Society EH2 *(Hunter Room)*
Shoreditch House E1 *(Snug (Members Only))*

16 Aqua London W1 *(Nueva Private Glass Dining Room)*
The Commonwealth Club WC2 *(Glass Dining Rm)*
The Dorchester W1 *(Penthouse)*
The Hempel W2 *(The Portland Room)*
Hush - Private Dining W1 *(Tangiers)*
The Landau W1 *(Postillion (Private Dining Rm))*
The London Art House N1 *(Albert Moore Lounge or Bauhaus Room)*
No. 11 Cavendish Square W1 *(Treasurer's Room)*
The Petersham TW10 *(Cellars)*
Portland Place Conference Centre W1 *(Saville Suite)*
Quaglino's SW1 *(Private Room 2)*
Sadler's Wells Theatre EC1 *(Cripplegate or Sackler)*
Sheraton Park Tower SW1 *(Discovery Rm)*
Skinners' Hall EC4 *(Commitee Room)*
St James's Club & Hotel SW1 *(Library)*
The Stafford SW1 *(Pink & Argyll Rm)*
30 St Mary Axe EC3 *(Private Dining Room 3)*

15 The Academy WC1 *(Boardroom*)*
Gray's Inn WC1 *(Small Pension Rm)*
Volt Lounge SW1 *(Cognac Room)*

14 L'Anima EC2 *(Max*)*
Aviator GU14 *(Boardroom or Deli)*
Berry Bros. & Rudd SW1 *(Townhouse)*
Cavendish SW1 *(Cirrus or Stratus)*
Claridge's W1 *(Board Rm or St James's)*
Cocoon W1 *(Private Dining Room)*
The Commonwealth Club WC2 *(Boardroom)*
High Road House W4 *(Upstairs)*
The Hospital Club WC2 *(The Rocket Meeting Room)*
Hurlingham Club SW6 *(Reading Room)*
Edinburgh International Conference Centre EH3 *(Soutra Room)*
Jumeirah Carlton Tower SW1 *(Maple or The Boardroom)*
The Milestone Hotel & Apartments W8 *(Conservatory)*
Mosimann's Dining Club SW1 *(Bentley Rm)*
One Wimpole Street W1 *(Cavendish Boardroom)*
Royal College of Radiologists W1 *(Robens Room)*
The Scotch Malt Whisky Society EH2 *(Oval Room)*
Shoreditch House E1 *(Private Dining Room (Members Only))*
St Martin's Lane Hotel WC2 *(Board Rm)*
Waddesdon Manor, The Dairy HP18 *(Dieppe)*

12 Alain Ducasse at the Dorchester W1 *(Salon Prive)*
Arts Club W1 *(Board Rm)*
Aviator GU14 *(3, 4 /5 or 6)*
Babylon W8 *(Private Rm)*
The Bentley Hotel SW7 *(Daniel)*
The Capital SW3 *(Eaton Suite)*
Charlotte Street Hotel W1 *(Rm 2)*
Corrigan's Mayfair W1 *(Chef's Table)*
The Dorchester W1 *(Boardroom)*
Dukes Hotel SW1 *(Sheridan Rm)*
Galvin La Chapelle E1 *(Max*)*
The Hospital Club WC2 *(Games Room or The Library & Terrace)*
Hotel Rafayel SW11 *(Board Room)*
The House NW1 *(Max*)*
The Lanesborough SW1 *(Wine Cellar)*
London Marriott Hotel, County Hall SE1 *(Boardroom)*
Marcus Wareing at the Berkeley SW1 *(Private Dining (pomorol Room)*
Millennium London Mayfair W1 *(Kendal)*
National Liberal Club SW1 *(Lawrence Robson Room)*
The Queen's Club W14 *(Real Tennis Museum)*
Royal Horseguards SW1 *(The London)*
Skinners' Hall EC4 *(Parlour)*
Smith's of Smithfield EC1 *(Private Rm 2)*
St Paul's Cathedral EC4 *(Temple Bar)*
30 St Mary Axe EC3 *(Private Dining Rooms 2 & 4)*
Tower Bridge SE1 *(Bridge Master's Dining Rm)*
Umu W1 *(Max*)*

10 Aqua London W1 *(Kyoto Private Glass Dining Room)*
The Berkeley SW1 *(Knightsbridge)*

The Capital SW3 *(Sitting Room)*
Cavendish SW1 *(Nimbus)*
Connaught W1 *(Georgian Room)*
The Foundling Museum WC1 *(Court Room option 3)*
The Fox Club W1 *(Drawing Room)*
Launceston Place W8 *(Chef's Office)*
Local Government House SW1 *(Meeting Rooms)*
London Stock Exchange EC4 *(Recess 1)*
London Zoo NW1 *(Darwin Room)*
Merchant Taylors' Hall EC2 *(Committee Rm)*
Mosimann's Dining Club SW1 *(Stapleford Rm)*
Number Sixteen SW7 *(Max*)*
River & Rowing Museum RG9 *(Henley Room)*
St James's Club & Hotel SW1 *(Wellington Board Room)*
Tom Aikens SW3 *(Private Dining Room)*
Volt Lounge SW1 *(Diamond Room)*
9 Gray's Inn WC1 *(Seminar Rm)*
8 The Caledonian Club SW1 *(Morrison Room)*
The Milestone Hotel & Apartments W8 *(Map Rm or Oratory)*
Millennium London Mayfair W1 *(Boardroom 2 & 3)*
Saddlers' Hall EC2 *(The Warden's Room)*
The Scotch Malt Whisky Society EH2 *(Library)*
St James's Club & Hotel SW1 *(Granville)*
30 St Mary Axe EC3 *(Private Dining Rooms 1 & 5)*
7 Alain Ducasse at the Dorchester W1 *(Table Lumiere)*
6 Wax Chandlers' Hall EC2 *(Parlour)*
4 Mosimann's Dining Club SW1 *(Davidoff Rm)*
2 Mosimann's Dining Club SW1 *(Montblanc Rm)*

£M

8000 Earls Court & Olympia SW5 *(Earl's Court 1*)*
5000 Alexandra Palace & Park N22 *(Great Hall*)*
Earls Court & Olympia SW5 *(Earl's Court 2)*
4000 Earls Court & Olympia SW5 *(Olympia Grand)*
3000 Earls Court & Olympia SW5 *(Olympia National)*
2000 Alexandra Palace & Park N22 *(West Hall)*
Battersea Park SW11 *(Max*)*
1943 Odeon Leicester Square WC2 *(Screen 1*)*
1500 Earls Court & Olympia SW5 *(Brompton Hall)*
1278 Shaftesbury Theatre WC2 *(Max*)*
1100 Ascot Racecourse SL5 *(Max*)*
1000 London Metropole W2 *(King's Suite or Monarch Suite*)*
850 Harrow School HA1 *(Max*)*
Newbury Racecourse RG14 *(Max*)*
800 Lord's Cricket Ground NW8 *(Nursery Pavilion*)*
Twickenham Experience TW1 *(Max*)*
750 Addington Palace CR0 *(Marquee*)*
700 The Brewery EC1 *(Porter Tun*)*
Epsom Downs KT18 *(Oaks Hall*)*
650 The Decorium N22 *(Max*)*
600 Blackheath Concert Halls SE3 *(Max*)*
Epsom Downs KT18 *(Max)*
London Metropole W2 *(Palace Suite)*
Newbury Racecourse RG14 *(Grandstand Ground Floor)*
Royal Courts of Justice WC2 *(Max*)*
Shaka Zulu NW1 *(Max*)*
Syon Park TW8 *(Lime Ave. Marquee* or South Lawn Marquee)*
552 Aston Villa Hospitality and Events B6 *(Holte Suite*)*
London Marriott W1 *(Westminster Suite*)*
550 Grand Connaught Rooms WC2 *(Grand Hall*)*
The Langley WD17 *(Ruby Suite*, Sapphire Suite or Topaz Suite)*
Vinopolis: The Venue SE1 *(Great Halls*)*
540 Riverbank Park Plaza SE1 *(Max*)*
510 The Oval SE11 *(Max*)*
500 Aston Villa Hospitality and Events B6 *(Trinity and 82 Lounge)*
The Guoman Tower E1 *(Max*)*
Kensington Conference & Events Centre W8 *(Max*)*
Newbury Racecourse RG14 *(Grandstand Second Floor)*
Wyndham Grand London SW10 *(The Grand Room*)*
490 City Cruises SE16 *(Sightseeing on Riverliner*)*
460 Meza W1 *(Max*)*
420 Thames Luxury Charters SW15 *(Max*)*
400 Beauberry House SE21 *(Max*)*
Central Hall Westminster SW1 *(Great Hall*)*
Conservatory at Chelsea SW3 *(Max*)*
Royal College of Music SW7 *(Max*)*
Thames Luxury Charters SW15 *(Dixie Queen (cruising) or Dixie Queen (static))*
Thorpe Park KT16 *(Lake View Events Zone*)*
Whipsnade Wild Animal Park LU6 *(Max*)*
390 The Brewery EC1 *(King George III)*
389 Harrow School HA1 *(Ryan Theatre)*
380 Waldorf Hotel WC2 *(Adelphi Suite*)*
372 Church House SW1 *(Assembly Hall*)*
360 Alexandra Palace & Park N22 *(Palace Restaurant)*
Floridita W1 *(Max*)*
Louise Blouin Foundation W11 *(Ground Gallery*)*
350 Barbican Art Gallery EC2 *(Max*)*
Blue Elephant SW6 *(Max*)*
City Cruises SE16 *(Millennium of London)*
The Coronet SE1 *(Max*)*
Epsom Downs KT18 *(The Blue Riband Room)*
Harrow School HA1 *(Shepherd Churchill Hall)*
Lord's Cricket Ground NW8 *(Thomas Lord Suite)*
Museum of London EC2 *(Sackler Hall *)*
Vinopolis: The Venue SE1 *(The Mezzanine)*
340 Jongleurs at Camden Lock NW1 *(Max*)*
330 Lloyd's of London EC3 *(Banqueting Suite*)*
325 Chelsea Physic Garden SW3 *(Garden*)*
300 Congress Centre WC1 *(Max*)*
Crown Moran Hotel NW2 *(Max*)*

Epsom Downs KT18 *(The Diomed Suit)*
Freemason's Hall WC2 *(Max*)*
Gibson Hall EC2 *(Max*)*
Highgate School N6 *(Dining Hall*)*
St Mary's Church W1 *(Max*)*
Swan at the Globe at Shakespeare's Globe SE1 *(Max*)*
Twickenham Experience TW1 *(Spirit Of Rugby)*

280 Park Crescent Conference Centre W1 *(Max*)*
Pinewood Studios SL0 *(Ballroom*)*

270 Bank of England Sports Centre SW15 *(Terrace Room *)*
Simpsons-in-the-Strand WC2 *(Max*)*

260 Delfina Galleries SE1 *(Max*)*
One Great George Street SW1 *(Great Hall*)*

250 Aston Villa Hospitality and Events B6 *(1874)*
Beach Blanket Babylon E1 *(Max*)*
Bloomsbury Ballroom WC1 *(Max*)*
Christ Church Spitalfields E1 *(Max*)*
Delfina Galleries SE1 *(Exhibition Gallery)*
Ealing Town Hall W5 *(Max*)*
Elstree Film Studio WD6 *(Max*)*
Eton College (Dorney Lake) SL4 *(Max*)*
Grand Connaught Rooms WC2 *(Edinburgh)*
Guards Museum SW1 *(Marquee*)*
Hop Exchange SE1 *(Max*)*
IET London: Savoy Place WC2 *(Riverside Room*)*
KOKO NW1 *(Max*)*
London Metropole W2 *(Windsor Suite)*
Louise Blouin Foundation W11 *(Third Floor)*
One Moorgate Place EC2 *(Great Hall*)*
The Regalia EC4 *(Max*)*
Royal Institute of British Architects W1 *(Florence Hall*)*
Tottenham Hotspur N17 *(Pat Jennings Lounge*)*
V&A Museum of Childhood E2 *(Max*)*
The Vinyl Factory W1 *(Max*)*

240 Bluebird SW3 *(Max*)*
Glaziers' Hall SE1 *(Max*)*
International Coffee Organisation W1 *(Max*)*
Tiger Tiger SW1 *(Max*)*
Whisky Mist at Zeta W1 *(Max*)*

230 Hard Rock Cafe W1 *(Max*)*

220 Carpenters' Hall EC2 *(Max*)*
Goodenough College WC1 *(Great Hall*)*
Imperial City EC3 *(Max*)*
Lloyd's of London EC3 *(1688)*
Park Crescent Conference Centre W1 *(The Theatre)*
Ronnie Scotts W1 *(Max*)*

210 Ambassadors Bloomsbury WC1 *(Max*)*

204 BAFTA, 195 Piccadilly W1 *(David Lean Room*)*

200 All Star Lanes (Brick Lane) E1 *(Main Hall*)*
Beach Blanket Babylon E1 *(Restaurant)*
Central Hall Westminster SW1 *(Lecture Hall or Library)*
Earls Court & Olympia SW5 *(Olympia Conference Centre)*
Fulham Palace SW6 *(Marquee*)*
The Goring SW1 *(Goring Garden*)*
Kenza EC2 *(Max*)*
London Marriott W1 *(Belgrave Rm)*
Lord's Cricket Ground NW8 *(Long Room)*
Newbury Racecourse RG14 *(Berkshire Stand Concourse or Hennessy Suite)*
No 4 Hamilton Place W1 *(Bill Boeing Rm*)*
One Marylebone Road NW1 *(Soane Hall*)*
Plateau E14 *(Max*)*
Regent's College NW1 *(Gardens*)*
Ruby Blue WC2 *(Max*)*
Savile Club W1 *(Max*)*
Shanghai Blues WC1 *(Max*)*
South London Gallery SE5 *(Max*)*
St Thomas' Hospital SE1 *(Max*)*
Studio Valbonne W1 *(Max*)*
Vinopolis: The Venue SE1 *(The Gallery)*
Winchester House SW15 *(River Lawn*)*

190 45 Millbank SW1 *(The Banqueting Hall*)*
St Bartholomew's Hospital EC1 *(Max*)*

180 Amadeus Centre W9 *(Max*)*
Ambassadors Bloomsbury WC1 *(Enterprise)*
Ealing Town Hall W5 *(Princes Room)*
Forty Hall EN2 *(Max*)*
Hellenic Centre W1 *(Great Hall*)*
London Transport Museum WC2 *(Max*)*
Pacha SW1 *(Main Rm*)*
Sound London WC2 *(Max*)*

172 The Geological Society of London W1 *(Max*)*

170 76 Portland Place W1 *(Max*)*

164 London Marriott W1 *(Whitehall Suite)*

160 Blackheath Concert Halls SE3 *(Recital Rm)*
The Brewery EC1 *(Queen Charlotte Rm)*
Butchers' Hall EC1 *(Max*)*
Church House SW1 *(Harvey Goodwin Suite)*
Hatton EC1 *(Max*)*
The Insurance Hall EC2 *(Max*)*
Rubens SW1 *(Old Masters Restaurant*)*
Tottenham Hotspur N17 *(Bill Nicholson Suite)*

156 Alexandra Palace & Park N22 *(Londesborough Rm)*
Painters' Hall EC4 *(Max*)*

155 Mews of Mayfair W1 *(Max*)*

150 Bank Restaurant & Zander Bar, Westminster SW1 *(Max*)*
Church House SW1 *(Hoare Memorial Hall)*
Cinnamon Club SW1 *(Max*)*
Criterion Restaurant W1 *(Max*)*
Design Museum SE1 *(Max*)*
Ham Polo Club TW10 *(Max*)*
RS Hispaniola WC2 *(Main Deck*)*
Ironmongers' Hall EC2 *(Max*)*
Jasmine Studios W6 *(Max*)*
Lansdowne Club W1 *(Ballroom*)*
Museum of Transport G3 *(Max*)*
One Birdcage Walk SW1 *(Library*)*
Paramount WC1 *(Level 31*)*
Park Inn London Russell Square WC1 *(Max*)*
Queen's Eyot SL6 *(Marquee*)*
The Red Room W1 *(Max*)*
Ruby Blue WC2 *(Main Bar)*
Southwark Cathedral SE1 *(The Courtyard*)*
Syon Park TW8 *(Great Conservatory)*

Thames Luxury Charters SW15 (Erasmus)
Wapping Food E1 (Max*)
144 HMS Belfast SE1 (Max*)
140 Baltic SE1 (Max*)
Benares W1 (Main Restaurant*)
Bleeding Heart EC1 (Bleeding Heart (w/e Only)*)
Brasserie Roux SW1 (Private Room*)
Crowne Plaza London - The City EC4 (Bridewell Room*)
Dartmouth House W1 (Max*)
East India Club SW1 (Max*)
Epsom Downs KT18 (Jockey Club Rm)
SS Great Britain BS1 (Dining Saloon*)
Louise Blouin Foundation W11 (Second Floor)
National Army Museum SW3 (Art Gallery*)
The Private Rooms at Buckingham Gate SW1 (Edwardian I*)
Royal Air Force Club W1 (Ballroom*)
Thames Luxury Charters SW15 (Elizabethan)
136 Boundary E2 (Max*)
132 HMS Belfast SE1 (Ship Co's Dining Hall)
130 City Inn Westminster SW1 (Private Dining*)
The Coliseum WC2 (Max*)
Delfina Galleries SE1 (Café Gallery)
Lonsdale W11 (Max*)
The Magic Circle Headquarters NW1 (Max*)
Newbury Racecourse RG14 (Long Room)
Sofitel London St James SW1 (Westminister*)
St Andrew Holborn EC4 (Church*)
Tottenham Hotspur N17 (Centenary Lounge)
Washington W1 (Max*)
125 St Thomas' Hospital SE1 (Governor's Hall)
124 Winchester House SW15 (River Rm)
120 Addington Palace CR0 (Great Hall)
Aston Villa Hospitality and Events B6 (The Corner Flag)
Barber-Surgeons' Hall EC2 (Max*)
Bel Canto W2 (Max*)
Bleeding Heart EC1 (Max)
Cavalry & Guards Club W1 (Max*)
Chiswick Moran Hotel W4 (Max*)
City of London Club EC2 (Max*)
The Cobden Club W10 (First Floor*)
Common Ground Cafe & Bar SW18 (Max*)
Crown Moran Hotel NW2 (Sala Rm)
Crypt EC1 (Max*)
Design Museum SE1 (Riverside Hall)
Dominion Theatre W1 (The Studio*)
Farmers' & Fletchers' Hall EC1 (Max*)
Frederick's N1 (Max*)
The Garden Museum SE1 (Max*)
Groucho Club W1 (Max*)
Horniman Museum SE23 (With Marquee*)
Ken Lo's Memories of China SW1 (Max*)
Kenwood House (Old Kitchen) NW3 (Old Kitchen or The Brew House*)
Kew Bridge Steam Museum TW8 (The Steam Hall*)
Lainston House SO21 (Barn*)
London Canal Museum N1 (1st Floor*)
London Wetland Centre SW13 (Waters Edge Rm*)
MIC Hotel & Conference Centre NW1 (The Atrium*)
National Theatre SE1 (Terrace Bar & Food*)
No 4 Hamilton Place W1 (Argyll Rm & Terrace)
The Old Sessions House EC1 (Westminster*)
Pissarro's on the River W4 (Max*)
Portal EC1 (Max*)
Royal Society of Arts WC2 (Vaults*)
Ruby Blue WC2 (Restaurant)
Shadow Lounge W1 (Max*)
Syon Park TW8 (Syon Park House)
Theatre Royal, Drury Lane WC2 (Grand Saloon*)
Tottenham Hotspur N17 (Box Holders' West, Gary Mabbutt Lounge or Steve Perryman Lounge)
Trinity House EC3 (Library*)
114 Veeraswamy W1 (Max*)
110 Aston Villa Hospitality and Events B6 (Directors)
Automat W1 (Max*)
Beaufort House SW3 (Max*)
Bluebird SW3 (Beaufort & Gallery Room)
Chutney Mary SW10 (Max*)
City of London Club EC2 (Main Dining Rm)
East Hampstead Park Conference Centre RG40 (Max*)
Lloyd's of London EC3 (Captain's Rm)
Piccolino - Exchange Square EC2 (Max*)
Royal Society of Arts WC2 (Benjamin Franklin Rm)
St John EC1 (Max*)
108 Ambassadors Bloomsbury WC1 (Prosper)
100 AOP Gallery (The Association of Photographers) EC2 (Max*)
Axis WC2 (Max*)
belowzero restaurant + lounge & ICEBAR LONDON W1 (Moose & Reindeer* or Whole Venue)
The Brewery EC1 (Sugar Rms)
Browns WC2 (Courtroom 1*)
Central Hall Westminster SW1 (Aldars Gate)
Cittie of Yorke WC1 (Max*)
The Cobden Club W10 (Ground Floor or Second Floor)
Courthouse Hotel Kempinski W1 (Max*)
Dominion Theatre W1 (The Gallery)
Epsom Downs KT18 (Lammtarra Suit)
Greenwich Yacht Club SE10 (Max*)
Horniman Museum SE23 (Max)
Kensington Conference & Events Centre W8 (Small Hall)
Museum of London EC2 (City Gallery)
One Great George Street SW1 (Smeaton Rm)
Pewterers' Hall EC2 (Max*)
Piccolino W1 (Max*)
Pinewood Studios SL0 (Hitchcock or Pools Theatre)
Rivington Place EC2 (PS1*)
Royal Statistical Society EC1 (Lecture Theatre*)
SixtyOne Whitehall SW1 (Duke of Wellington Rm*)

Sofitel London St James SW1 *(Mayfair A&B)*
St John's Gate EC1 *(Chapter Hall*)*
St Stephen's Club SW1 *(Queensborough Room*)*
Sumosan W1 *(Max*)*
Tallow Chandlers' Hall EC4 *(Livery Hall*)*
Tottenham Hotspur N17 *(Danny Blanchflower Suite)*
Vinopolis: The Venue SE1 *(Academia)*
Waterstone's W1 *(Max*)*
Winchester House SW15 *(Front Lawn)*
95 Eight Over Eight SW3 *(Max*)*
90 Aura SW1 *(Max*)*
Brewers' Hall EC2 *(Max*)*
Church House SW1 *(Bishop Partridge Hall)*
The Coliseum WC2 *(Sky Bar)*
Epsom Downs KT18 *(The Downs View Suit)*
Fulham Palace SW6 *(Great Hall)*
Heights Bar & Restaurant W1 *(Max*)*
RS Hispaniola WC2 *(Upper Deck)*
Imperial City EC3 *(Half Venue)*
National Theatre SE1 *(The Deck)*
Rock & Rose TW9 *(Max*)*
Royal Court Theatre SW1 *(Cafe Bar*)*
Vanderbilt Hotel SW7 *(Victoria & Albert*)*
85 Century W1 *(4th Floor*)*
Osteria dell'Arancio SW10 *(Max*)*
Simon Drake's House of Magic SE1 *(Max*)*
84 E&O W11 *(Max*)*
80 Adam Street WC2 *(Max*)*
Amadeus Centre W9 *(Lower Hall)*
Auriol Kensington Rowing Club W6 *(Max*)*
Bellamy's W1 *(Max*)*
Boisdale SW1 *(Max*)*
Brown's Hotel W1 *(Niagara & Roosevelt combined*)*
The CBI Conference Centre WC1 *(Concourse or Methven*)*
Century W1 *(Rose Langton Room)*
Concrete E1 *(Max*)*
Crowne Plaza London - The City EC4 *(Bridewell 1)*
Dartmouth House W1 *(Churchill Rm)*
Dock Kitchen W10 *(Max*)*
45 Millbank SW1 *(Red Room)*
Gibson Hall EC2 *(Garden Rm)*
Goodenough College WC1 *(Large Common Room)*
Harrow School HA1 *(Old Harrovian Rm)*
London Corinthian Sailing Club W6 *(Ballroom*)*
Mayfair Conference Centre W2 *(Max*)*
The New Cavendish Club W1 *(Max*)*
Newbury Racecourse RG14 *(Fred Winter or Paddoc View)*
One Great George Street SW1 *(Brunel Rm or Council Rm)*
Orangery (Holland Park) W8 *(Max*)*
Parliament Square (RICS) SW1 *(Max*)*
Pattersons's W1 *(Max*)*
Pitzhanger Manor W5 *(Max*)*
The Place WC1 *(Max*)*
Spring Grove House TW7 *(Max*)*
Les Trois Garçons EC2 *(Max*)*
Vinopolis: The Venue SE1 *(The European Odyssey)*
Whisky Mist at Zeta W1 *(Lux Room)*
78 Coin Street Neighbourhood Centre SE1 *(Max Nasatyr Room* or Neighbourhood Room)*
Pasha N1 *(Max*)*
75 Chez Bruce SW17 *(Max*)*
$ EC1 *(Max*)*
Ealing Town Hall W5 *(Nelson Rm)*
First Floor Restaurant W11 *(Restaurant*)*
Founders' Hall EC1 *(Livery Hall*)*
ICA SW1 *(Nash & Brandon Rms*)*
Square W1 *(Max*)*
Vanilla W1 *(Max*)*
74 Cheyne Walk Brasserie SW3 *(Max*)*
Guinea Grill W1 *(Max*)*
73 Watermen's Hall EC3 *(Freemen's Rm*)*
72 Brown's Hotel W1 *(Clarendon)*
Water House N1 *(Max*)*
70 All Hallows EC3 *(Max*)*
Aston Villa Hospitality and Events B6 *(McGregors Suite)*
Avenue House N3 *(Drawing Rm*)*
belowzero restaurant + lounge & ICEBAR LONDON W1 *(Moose Dining Room)*
Central Hall Westminster SW1 *(George Thomas)*
Criterion Restaurant W1 *(Semi Private Terrace)*
Design Museum SE1 *(Design Museum Space)*
Hatton EC1 *(Onyx Restaurant)*
Lloyd's of London EC3 *(Old Library)*
Mandeville Hotel W1 *(deVille Restaurant*)*
Menier Chocolate Factory SE1 *(Restaurant*)*
Museum of London EC2 *(Terrace Gallery)*
One Birdcage Walk SW1 *(Marble Hall/gallery)*
Oxford & Cambridge Club SW1 *(Max*)*
Regent's College NW1 *(Herringham Hall)*
River Lounge E1 *(Max*)*
Scotland Street School Museum G5 *(Max*)*
St Andrew Holborn EC4 *(Courtroom)*
Swan at the Globe at Shakespeare's Globe SE1 *(Balcony Rm)*
Thames Luxury Charters SW15 *(Golden Salamander)*
Tom's Kitchen SW3 *(Brasserie*)*
University Women's Club W1 *(Dining Room, Drawing Room* or Library)*
Washington W1 *(Richmond Suite)*
69 Avenue House N3 *(Stephens Rm)*
68 Floridita W1 *(Havana Lounge)*
66 Bluebird SW3 *(Gallery Room)*
65 Butchers' Hall EC1 *(Taurus Suite)*
Cittie of Yorke WC1 *(Cellar Bar)*
Mews of Mayfair W1 *(Restaurant)*
64 City Cruises SE16 *(Eltham)*
The Ledbury W11 *(Max*)*
Tottenham Hotspur N17 *(Highlights)*
63 Ambassadors Bloomsbury WC1 *(Innovate)*
62 Beauberry House SE21 *(Function Rm/Balcony)*
60 Adam Street WC2 *(Gallery)*
Addington Palace CR0 *(Winter Garden)*
Aston Villa Hospitality and Events B6 *(Sky Lounge or The Players Lounge)*
Automat W1 *(Conservatory)*
Beach Blanket Babylon W11 *(Private Room*)*
HMS Belfast SE1 *(Gun Rm)*

Bentleys Oyster Bar and Grill W1 *(Jameson Room*)*
Brasserie St Jacques SW1 *(Max*)*
Cactus Blue SW3 *(Max*)*
Café du Marché EC1 *(Max*)*
Chelsea Physic Garden SW3 *(Reception Room)*
Chiswick Moran Hotel W4 *(Fairfax Room)*
Cinnamon Club SW1 *(Private Room)*
Crown Moran Hotel NW2 *(Barnet Rm)*
Epsom Downs KT18 *(The Board Room or The Gallops Suit)*
L'Escargot W1 *(Max*)*
Gallery Soho WC2 *(Max*)*
Great Eastern Dining Rooms EC2 *(Max*)*
Groucho Club W1 *(Dining Rm)*
Guards Museum SW1 *(Museum)*
House of St Barnabas W1 *(Max*)*
IET London: Savoy Place WC2 *(Faraday, Maxwell Suite or Thompson Room)*
Jongleurs at Camden Lock NW1 *(Roof Terrace)*
Julie's Restaurant & Wine Bar W11 *(Max*)*
Lord's Cricket Ground NW8 *(Writing Rm)*
Meza W1 *(Atrium)*
MIC Hotel & Conference Centre NW1 *(Hilda Porter)*
No 4 Hamilton Place W1 *(Council Rm & Foyer)*
Odeon Leicester Square WC2 *(Screens 2-6)*
The Old Sessions House EC1 *(Jailers Rm)*
One Marylebone Road NW1 *(Baccarat Room)*
Painters' Hall EC4 *(The Court Rm)*
Park Crescent Conference Centre W1 *(The Gulbekian Room)*
Prenelle Gallery E14 *(Main Gallery*)*
Queen's Eyot SL6 *(Clubhouse)*
Rivington Place EC2 *(PS2)*
Ruby Blue WC2 *(Balcony Bar)*
76 Portland Place W1 *(Herschel Room)*
SixtyOne Whitehall SW1 *(Library)*
South London Gallery SE5 *(Clore Studio)*
summerhouse W9 *(Max*)*
Thames Luxury Charters SW15 *(Edwardian)*
Trinity House EC3 *(Court Rm)*
Women's Library E1 *(Wash House*)*

57 Morgan M N7 *(Max*)*

56 Broadway House SW1 *(Council Chamber* or Westminister Suite)*
The Frontline Club W2 *(Max*)*
Kew Bridge Steam Museum TW8 *(The Gallery)*

55 Carvosso's W4 1 *(Max*)*
Chor Bizarre W1 *(Max*)*
House of St Barnabas W1 *(Chapel)*
Mandeville Hotel W1 *(Bar)*
Schochu Lounge W1 *(Max*)*

52 Floridita W1 *(Bar Constante)*

50 Admiral Coddrington SW3 *(Bar or Restaurant*)*
Athenaeum Hotel W1 *(Max*)*
Axis WC2 *(Private Rooms 1 & 2)*
BAFTA, 195 Piccadilly W1 *(Run Run Shaw/Mezzanine)*
Beaufort House SW3 *(Bar & Brasserie)*
HMS Belfast SE1 *(Wardroom and Anteroom)*
Chelsea Physic Garden SW3 *(Lecture Room)*
City Cruises SE16 *(Westminster)*
City of London Club EC2 *(Garden Rm)*
Dartmouth House W1 *(Small Drawing Rm)*
The Fashion and Textile Museum SE1 *(Max*)*
Fulham Palace SW6 *(Drawing Rm)*
Grand Connaught Rooms WC2 *(Durham or Penthouse)*
Ironmongers' Hall EC2 *(Court Rm)*
Kenza EC2 *(Private Dining)*
The Lincoln Centre WC2 *(Break-out Area*)*
London Palladium W1 *(Cinderella Bar* or Variety Bar)*
Lord's Cricket Ground NW8 *(Media Centre)*
One Birdcage Walk SW1 *(Napier)*
One Moorgate Place EC2 *(Main Reception Rm)*
Palace Theatre W1 *(D'Oyly Carte Bar*)*
Portal EC1 *(Glasshouse)*
Preston Manor BN1 *(Max*)*
Regent's College NW1 *(Tuke Common Rm)*
Royal Statistical Society EC1 *(Basement)*
Simpsons-in-the-Strand WC2 *(Bishops' Rm)*
Sofitel London St James SW1 *(Piccadilly/Bloomsbury)*
Southwark Cathedral SE1 *(Garry Weston Library)*
Spring Grove House TW7 *(Music Rm)*
Syon Park TW8 *(Private Dining Rm)*
Theatre Royal, Drury Lane WC2 *(Ballet Room)*
Thomas Cubitt SW1 *(Max*)*
Vanderbilt Hotel SW7 *(Edwardian)*
Vinopolis: The Venue SE1 *(The New World Odyssey)*
West Wycombe Caves HP14 *(Max*)*
The Zetter Hotel EC1 *(Zetter Restaurant*)*

48 Bank of England Sports Centre SW15 *(Balcony Bar or Green Room)*
Browns WC2 *(Courtroom 2)*
The CBI Conference Centre WC1 *(Rms 1, 2 & 3)*
One Birdcage Walk SW1 *(Council)*
Twickenham Experience TW1 *(Council Rm)*

46 Broadway House SW1 *(Stevenson)*
Guinea Grill W1 *(Restaurant)*
Women's Library E1 *(Clore Mezzanine)*

45 Albannach WC2 *(Max*)*
Beach Blanket Babylon W11 *(Bar Area)*
The Brickhouse E1 *(Second Floor*)*
Chartered Institute of Public Finance & Accountancy WC2 *(Max*)*
Don EC4 *(White Room*)*
Floating Boater W2 *(Prince Regent*)*
Il Vicolo SW1 *(Max*)*

44 Bleeding Heart EC1 *(Terrace Room)*
The Goring SW1 *(Archive Rm)*
Meza W1 *(Private Dining Room)*
Rubens SW1 *(Rembrandt Rm)*

43 First Floor Restaurant W11 *(Private Dining Rm 2)*

42 Soho House W1 *(Roof Deck*)*

40 Addington Palace CR0 *(Dining Room or Wellington Room)*
Aston Villa Hospitality and Events B6 *(The Park Suite)*

Bank Restaurant & Zander Bar, Westminster SW1 *(Private Rms (combined))*
Bluebird SW3 *(Beaufort Room)*
Brinkley's SW10 *(Max*)*
The British Library NW1 *(Max*)*
Browns WC2 *(Courtroom 3)*
Cactus Blue SW3 *(Blue Room)*
Chartered Institute of Public Finance & Accountancy WC2 *(Conference Rm or Council Chamber)*
City of London Club EC2 *(Salisbury Rm or Salisbury Rm)*
The Coliseum WC2 *(Balcony)*
Coopers Arms SW3 *(Max*)*
Dominion Theatre W1 *(The Chaplin Suite)*
Don EC4 *(Bistro)*
Gay Hussar W1 *(Max*)*
The Golden Hinde SE1 *(Max*)*
SS Great Britain BS1 *(Hayward Saloon)*
Groucho Club W1 *(Gennaro Rm or Mary-Lou)*
House of St Barnabas W1 *(Drawing Room or Soho Room)*
IET London: Savoy Place WC2 *(Common Room)*
The Insurance Hall EC2 *(Court Room)*
Lansdowne Club W1 *(Shelburne Rm)*
Museum of London EC2 *(Garden Room)*
Newbury Racecourse RG14 *(Royal Box)*
No 4 Hamilton Place W1 *(Handley Page Rm or Sopwith Rm)*
The Old Sessions House EC1 *(London Rm)*
One Birdcage Walk SW1 *(Hinton Rm)*
Park Crescent Conference Centre W1 *(The Club Room)*
Parliament Square (RICS) SW1 *(Lecture Hall)*
Piccolino W1 *(Private Room)*
PJ's Bar & Grill SW3 *(Max*)*
The Private Rooms at Buckingham Gate SW1 *(Buckingham or Edwardian II)*
Regent's College NW1 *(Knapp Gallery)*
Royal Institute of British Architects W1 *(Wren)*
Royal Statistical Society EC1 *(Council Chamber)*
Sailing Barge Will E1 *(Max*)*
76 Portland Place W1 *(Hooke Room)*
Sixteen Park Crescent W1 *(Max*)*
SixtyOne Whitehall SW1 *(Reading Rm)*
Tom's Kitchen SW3 *(First Floor Bar)*
Tottenham Hotspur N17 *(Box Holders' North)*

37 Watermen's Hall EC3 *(Court Rm)*

36 Green's SW1 *(Private Room*)*
Ruby Blue WC2 *(Conference)*
St Stephen's Club SW1 *(Garden Room)*

35 Avenue House N3 *(Salon)*
Bleeding Heart EC1 *(Red Room)*
The Brickhouse E1 *(Ground Floor)*
Café du Marché EC1 *(Rendezvous)*
Don EC4 *(Restaurant)*
Freud Museum NW3 *(Marquee*)*

34 Benjamin Franklin House WC2 *(Franklin's Parlour*)*
Julie's Restaurant & Wine Bar W11 *(Garden Rm)*
The Ledbury W11 *(Terrace)*

33 Beauberry House SE21 *(Bar)*
76 Portland Place W1 *(Phillips Room)*

32 Benares W1 *(The Lounge)*
Bluebird SW3 *(Mezzanine)*
The Cadogan SW1 *(Salon Lillie*)*
Carpenters' Hall EC2 *(Luncheon Rm)*
Chartered Institute of Public Finance & Accountancy WC2 *(Room 4)*
Chutney Mary SW10 *(Private Room)*
Coopers' Hall EC2 *(Dining Rm*)*
Elena's L'Etoile W1 *(Oscar Room*)*
Frederick's N1 *(Clarence Rm)*
Shepherd's SW1 *(Max*)*
Sumosan W1 *(Private Room)*

30 Addington Palace CR0 *(Empire Room)*
Admiral Coddrington SW3 *(Function Room)*
All Star Lanes (Brick Lane) E1 *(Private Room)*
Axis WC2 *(Private Room 3)*
BAFTA, 195 Piccadilly W1 *(Run Run Shaw)*
Baltic SE1 *(Private Rm)*
Benares W1 *(The Berkeley Room)*
Bleeding Heart EC1 *(Wine Cellar (No Seven))*
Bluebird SW3 *(Bluebird Room)*
Brinkley's SW10 *(Garden)*
Broadway House SW1 *(Abbey Room)*
Central Hall Westminster SW1 *(Dinsdale Young)*
Chiswick Moran Hotel W4 *(Fairfax East or Fairfax West)*
Church House SW1 *(Westminster)*
Le Colombier SW3 *(Max*)*
Dolphin House SW1 *(Restaurant*)*
L'Escargot W1 *(Private Rm 2)*
Fulham Palace SW6 *(Dining Rm)*
London Wetland Centre SW13 *(Bird Hide (Breakfast Only) or Gallery)*
Malmaison Hotel EC1 *(Mal 1*)*
MIC Hotel & Conference Centre NW1 *(Epworth)*
Odette's NW1 *(Conservatory*)*
The Old Sessions House EC1 *(Recorder Rm)*
Osteria dell'Arancio SW10 *(Upstairs)*
Parliament Square (RICS) SW1 *(Council Chamber)*
Royal Institute of British Architects W1 *(Lutyens Rm)*
Royal Society of Arts WC2 *(Tavern Rm)*
Shanghai Blues WC1 *(Private Dining Rm)*
Spread Eagle SE10 *(Max*)*
Sweetings EC4 *(Max*)*
Tallow Chandlers' Hall EC4 *(Parlour)*
Washington W1 *(Winchester)*
Wyndham Grand London SW10 *(Albert Suite or Battersea)*

28 First Floor Restaurant W11 *(Private Dining Rm 1)*
Guinea Grill W1 *(Boardroom)*
Mews of Mayfair W1 *(Private Dining Room)*
One Moorgate Place EC2 *(Members' Rm)*
Royal Society of Arts WC2 *(Adelphi)*

27 The Private Rooms at Buckingham Gate SW1 *(Taj)*

26 belowzero restaurant + lounge & ICEBAR LONDON W1 *(Reindeer Lounge Bar)*
Boisdale SW1 *(Back Bar)*
Hoxton Hotel EC2 *(Max*)*

25 Aston Villa Hospitality and Events B6 *(The Champions Lounge)*
BAFTA, 195 Piccadilly W1 *(Gallery)*
Benjamin Franklin House WC2 *(Mrs Stevenson's Parlour)*
Chor Bizarre W1 *(Private Rm 1)*

Christ Church Spitalfields E1 (Old Vestry Rm)
The Geological Society of London W1 (Council Room)
House of St Barnabas W1 (Bazelgette Room or Garden Room)
London Wetland Centre SW13 (Tower)
MIC Hotel & Conference Centre NW1 (Alice)
Odeon Leicester Square WC2 (Meeting Room)
Parliament Square (RICS) SW1 (Brussels Room)
Rock & Rose TW9 (Garden Room)
Royal Institute of British Architects W1 (Aston Webb)
Le Suquet SW3 (Private Rm*)
The Kingly Club W1 (Max*)

24 Coin Street Neighbourhood Centre SE1 (Fred Miller 1&2)
Dock Kitchen W10 (Private Room)
Don EC4 (Private Rm)
Glaziers' Hall SE1 (Master's Room)
Hellenic Centre W1 (Boardroom)
Julie's Restaurant & Wine Bar W11 (Banqueting Rm)
One Great George Street SW1 (Stephenson Rm)
Paramount WC1 (Red Room)
Plateau E14 (Private Dining Rm)
76 Portland Place W1 (Eddington Room or Gutherie Room)
Southwark Cathedral SE1 (Chapter Room or The New Room)
St Thomas' Hospital SE1 (Grand Committee Rm)
Veeraswamy W1 (Palmer Room)
Winchester House SW15 (Library)

22 Beaufort House SW3 (Private Dining)
Benares W1 (Burton Room)
Boisdale SW1 (Jacobite Room)
Broadway House SW1 (The Whittle Room)
Hoxton Hotel EC2 (Larger Rooms)
Leven is Strijd E14 (Max*)
One Birdcage Walk SW1 (Courses Rm)
Pattersons's W1 (Function Rm)
Piccolino - Exchange Square EC2 (Private Room)
Rubens SW1 (Rubens Suite)
Tom's Kitchen SW3 (Private Dining Room)

21 Broadway House SW1 (Lawrence)
Royal Court Theatre SW1 (Balcony Bar)

20 Addington Palace CR0 (Chadwick Healey)
Admiral Coddrington SW3 (Garden)
Albannach WC2 (Private Rm)
BAFTA, 195 Piccadilly W1 (Boardroom)
Bank Restaurant & Zander Bar, Westminster SW1 (Private Rms (x2))
HMS Belfast SE1 (Admiral's Quarters)
Brasserie St Jacques SW1 (Private Rooms)
Brinkley's SW10 (Private Rm 2)
Cavalry & Guards Club W1 (Waterloo Rm)
City of London Club EC2 (City Room)
E&O W11 (Private Dining Room)
East Hampstead Park Conference Centre RG40 (Windsor)
The Guoman Tower E1 (Mortimer Suite)
House of St Barnabas W1 (Silk Room)
London Palladium W1 (Hall Of Fame)
Lonsdale W11 (Genevieve)
Mandeville Hotel W1 (Red Room)
Radisson Edwardian Berkshire Hotel W1 (Sonning Suite*)
Rivington Place EC2 (Meeting Room)
Royal Institute of British Architects W1 (Council Chamber)
Royal Society of Arts WC2 (Romney)
76 Portland Place W1 (Ada Lovelace Room or Faraday Room)
Shaftesbury Theatre WC2 (Bars)
Sofitel London St James SW1 (Kensington)
South London Gallery SE5 (Double Height)
Southwark Cathedral SE1 (The JTW Room)
Theatre Royal, Drury Lane WC2 (Boardroom , Novello Suite or Royal Room)
Trinity House EC3 (Luncheon Rm)
Zafferano SW1 (Private Room*)

18 Ambassadors Bloomsbury WC1 (Create, Think or Vision)
Bleeding Heart EC1 (The Parlour (No Seven))
Brinkley's SW10 (Private Rm 3)
Chiswick Moran Hotel W4 (Westwood)
Farmers' & Fletchers' Hall EC1 (Court Rm)
Hoxton Hotel EC2 (Room 3)
MIC Hotel & Conference Centre NW1 (The Camden Room)
One Moorgate Place EC2 (Small Reception Rm)
Oxford & Cambridge Club SW1 (Edward VII)
Square W1 (Private Room)
St Bartholomew's Hospital EC1 (Treasurer's Rm)
St John EC1 (Private Room)
Wyndham Grand London SW10 (The Ballroom)

16 The Brickhouse E1 (Third)
Broadway House SW1 (Dartmouth Room)
Chez Bruce SW17 (Private Rm)
Crowne Plaza London - The City EC4 (The Board Room)
Don EC4 (Wine Study)
Elena's L'Etoile W1 (Elena's Room or Lounge Room)
Floating Boater W2 (Lapwing)
Frederick's N1 (Sussex Rm)
The Geological Society of London W1 (Arthur Homes Rm)
Lansdowne Club W1 (Findlay Rm)
Mews of Mayfair W1 (La Cave)
Poule au Pot SW1 (Max*)
Royal Statistical Society EC1 (New Meeting Rm)
Le Suquet SW3 (Private Rm)
Vanderbilt Hotel SW7 (Harrington)
Watermen's Hall EC3 (The Silver Rm)

15 Avenue House N3 (Balcony Rm)
Dominion Theatre W1 (The Garland Suite)
London Palladium W1 (Argyll Suite)
MIC Hotel & Conference Centre NW1 (Exeter, Norfolk or Wesley)
Rock & Rose TW9 (Private Room)
Trailer Happiness W11 (Max*)
Trinity House EC3 (Reading Rm)
Washington W1 (Fairfax)

14 Amaya SW1 (Silver Room*)
Benares W1 (Dover Room)
Bentleys Oyster Bar and Grill W1 (Crustacea Room)
Broadway House SW1 (Board Room)

City of London Club EC2 *(Masterman/Wellington Rms)*
Eight Over Eight SW3 *(Private Room)*
Ken Lo's Memories of China SW1 *(Private Rm 1)*
Malmaison Hotel EC1 *(Brasserie)*
MIC Hotel & Conference Centre NW1 *(Boardroom)*
Morgan M N7 *(Private Rm)*
Painters' Hall EC4 *(Painted Chamber)*
Pantechnicon Rooms SW1 *(Max*)*
Portal EC1 *(Adega Rm)*
Royal Society of Arts WC2 *(Folkestone Rm)*
Royal Statistical Society EC1 *(Old Meeting Rm)*
Spread Eagle SE10 *(Private Rm)*
Twickenham Experience TW1 *(Cellar)*

13 The Geological Society of London W1 *(William Buckland)*

12 Adam Street WC2 *(Dining Rm)*
Athenaeum Hotel W1 *(Ardmore)*
Broadway House SW1 *(Brunel Room)*
Browns WC2 *(Courtroom 4)*
The Cadogan SW1 *(Salon Oscar)*
Chartered Institute of Public Finance & Accountancy WC2 *(Room 5)*
Church House SW1 *(Jubilee)*
City Inn Westminster SW1 *(Sky Lounge)*
Crown Moran Hotel NW2 *(Brent/Camden Rm)*
Dean Street Townhouse W1 *(Max*)*
Gay Hussar W1 *(Second Floor)*
The Goring SW1 *(Drawing Rm)*
Hoxton Hotel EC2 *(Room 2)*
IET London: Savoy Place WC2 *(Haslett Room)*
Imperial City EC3 *(Private Dining Rm)*
Julie's Restaurant & Wine Bar W11 *(Moroccan Rm)*
Lansdowne Club W1 *(Sun Rm)*
London Canal Museum N1 *(Meeting Rm)*
MIC Hotel & Conference Centre NW1 *(Whitfield)*
The New Cavendish Club W1 *(Library)*
Parliament Square (RICS) SW1 *(New York/Hong Kong Rooms)*
Pinewood Studios SL0 *(Pine)*
Radisson Edwardian Berkshire Hotel W1 *(Sandhurst Suite)*
The Scotch Malt Whisky Society EC1 *(Max*)*
Sofitel London St James SW1 *(Boardroom & Private Dining Room)*
Vanderbilt Hotel SW7 *(Vanderbilt)*

11 Ken Lo's Memories of China SW1 *(Private Rm 2)*
76 Portland Place W1 *(Garnder Meeting)*

10 Bank Restaurant & Zander Bar, Westminster SW1 *(Mezzanine (semi-private))*
Benjamin Franklin House WC2 *(Board Room)*
Broadway House SW1 *(Carteret Room /St James's Room)*
Carvosso's W4 1 *(Smaller Private Rooms X 3)*
Chiswick Moran Hotel W4 *(Beverley Room or Sunset Room)*
City of London Club EC2 *(Hardwick Rm)*
Museum of London EC2 *(Terrace Boardroom)*
Newbury Racecourse RG14 *(Private Boxes)*
Palace Theatre W1 *(VIP Suite)*
Parliament Square (RICS) SW1 *(Dubai)*
The Private Rooms at Buckingham Gate SW1 *(Clarence)*
Southwark Cathedral SE1 *(The Tutu Room)*
Theatre Royal, Drury Lane WC2 *(Prince Of Wales Room)*
Les Trois Garçons EC2 *(Private Rm)*
Watermen's Hall EC3 *(The Parlour)*
The Zetter Hotel EC1 *(River Fleet Room)*

9 Elena's L'Etoile W1 *(Private Room)*

8 Brown's Hotel W1 *(Graham Bell Rm)*
The Coliseum WC2 *(Royal Retiring Room)*
Dominion Theatre W1 *(The Milburn Suite)*
Hoxton Hotel EC2 *(Room 1)*
Odette's NW1 *(Private Rm)*
Southwark Cathedral SE1 *(The ECB Room)*

6 Athenaeum Hotel W1 *(Apartments)*
The Private Rooms at Buckingham Gate SW1 *(Windsor)*

4 The Coliseum WC2 *(Harewood)*

£B-M

2060 The International Convention Centre B1 *(Hall 3*)*

900 The Royal Horticultural Halls SW1 *(Lawrence Hall*)*

800 Old Truman Brewery E1 *(Max*)*

790 Debut London SE1 *(Max*)*

630 The International Convention Centre B1 *(Hall 4)*

500 Clapham Grand SW11 *(Max*)*
Imperial College London SW7 *(Main Dining Hall*)*
Shoreditch Town Hall EC1 *(Max*)*

450 The HAC EC1 *(Prince Consort Rooms*)*
The London Hippodrome WC2 *(Max*)*
Porchester Centre W2 *(Max*)*

440 Royal Institution of Great Britain W1 *(Max*)*

424 City University EC1 *(Max*)*

420 The Royal Horticultural Halls SW1 *(Lindley Hall)*

400 BAC SW11 *(Max*)*
Crazy Larry's SW10 *(Max*)*
Debut London SE1 *(Grey Arch)*
Fulham Town Hall SW6 *(Max*)*
Hammersmith Town Hall W6 *(Max*)*
Lotus Chinese Floating Restaurant E14 *(Max*)*
Whitechapel Art Gallery E1 *(Max*)*

390 Debut London SE1 *(Main)*

370 Debut London SE1 *(Blue)*

360 Spitalfields Market E1 *(Max*)*

350 Royal College of Art SW7 *(Henry Moore Gallery*)*
The Village Underground EC2 *(Max*)*

320 The International Convention Centre B1 *(Hall 11)*

300 Cecil Sharp House NW1 *(Max*)*
Dulwich College SE21 *(Max*)*
Proud Camden NW1 *(Main Room Alone*)*

280 Proud Cabaret EC3 *(Max*)*

270 The International Convention Centre B1 *(Hall 8)*

250 City Hotel E1 *(Max*)*

Imperial College London SW7 *(Senior Common Rm)*
7 Rifles Battalion W1 *(Max*)*
240 Arts Depot N12 *(Main Auditorium*)*
Victory Services Club W2 *(Carisbrooke Hall*)*
230 St Paul's Church W1 *(Max*)*
220 Kings Place N1 *(Battlebridge Room*)*
University of London Union WC1 *(Max*)*
210 HMS President EC4 *(Ball Rm*)*
200 Bush Hall W12 *(Max*)*
Debut London SE1 *(Red)*
Dulwich College SE21 *(Great Hall)*
Garden Café NW1 *(Max*)*
Mall Galleries SW1 *(Main Gallery*)*
Old Finsbury Town Hall EC1 *(Great Hall*)*
Rich Mix E1 *(Max*)*
Royal Holloway College TW20 *(Founder's Dining Hall*)*
St Martin In The Fields WC2 *(Max*)*
Trafalgar Tavern SE10 *(Nelson Rm*)*
185 Conway Hall WC1 *(Max*)*
184 City University EC1 *(Northampton Suite)*
180 Balls Brothers Minster Pavement EC3 *(Minster Suite*)*
Chelsea Old Town Hall SW3 *(Main Hall*)*
King's College School SW19 *(Great Hall*)*
Lemonia NW1 *(Max*)*
London Scottish SW1 *(Max*)*
Loose Cannon EC4 *(Max*)*
The Pavilion B6 *(Pearson Suite*)*
Royal Over-Seas League SW1 *(Max*)*
175 King's College WC2 *(Great Hall*)*
172 The HAC EC1 *(Long Rm)*
170 Mermaid Conference & Events Centre EC4 *(Blackfriars Rm*)*
Trailfinders Sports Club W13 *(Olympic Pavilion*)*
160 Bistrothèque E2 *(Max*)*
Debut London SE1 *(Hide Out)*
The Irish Centre W6 *(Max*)*
Kings Place N1 *(Hall Two)*
Kingswood House SE21 *(Max*)*
St Paul's Church W1 *(Church Area)*
150 Bistrothèque E2 *(Restaurant)*
The Chelsea Gardener SW3 *(Max*)*
Chez Gérard, Opera Terrace WC2 *(Max*)*
Fulham Town Hall SW6 *(Concert Hall)*
London School of Economics WC2 *(Max*)*
Music Room W1 *(Max*)*
Ognisko SW7 *(Ballroom or Dining Rm*)*
Royal College of Art SW7 *(Gulbenkian Galleries)*
School of Pharmacy WC1 *(Max*)*
Serpentine Bar & Kitchen W2 *(Max*)*
Shoreditch Town Hall EC1 *(Council Room)*
Trailfinders Sports Club W13 *(Centenary Club)*
Tudor Barn Eltham SE9 *(Max*)*
Westminster Boating Base SW1 *(Max*)*
Worx SW6 *(Studio 2*)*
140 BAC SW11 *(Lower Hall)*
Cecil Sharp House NW1 *(Trefusis Hall)*
Fabric EC1 *(Max*)*
Le Gothique SW18 *(Max*)*
Le Cafe Anglais W2 *(Max*)*
135 606 Club SW10 *(Max*)*
130 Da Mario SW7 *(Max*)*
Docklands Sailing & Watersports Centre E14 *(Max*)*
Souk WC2 *(Max*)*
125 New Players Theatre WC2 *(Players Bar And Restaurant*)*
120 Chowki W1 *(Max*)*
Depot SW14 *(Max*)*
Dickens Inn E1 *(Max*)*
Dulwich College SE21 *(South Cloister)*
Levant W1 *(Max*)*
The Little Ship Club EC4 *(Max*)*
Riverside Studios W6 *(Max*)*
Royal Geographical Society SW7 *(Max*)*
Royal Holloway College TW20 *(Picture Gallery)*
Spitalfields Market E1 *(Areas 1-3)*
20th Century Theatre W11 *(Max*)*
University of Westminster NW1 *(Deep End*)*
110 The Book Club EC2 *(Max*)*
Guy's Hospital SE1 *(Robens Suite*)*
St Martin In The Fields WC2 *(St Martins Hall)*
Tab Centre E2 *(Main Hall*)*
100 Brompton Oratory SW7 *(St. Joseph's Hall*)*
Chelsea Old Town Hall SW3 *(The Small Hall)*
Engineer NW1 *(Max*)*
Froebel College SW15 *(Max*)*
Fulham House SW6 *(Max*)*
Gow's Restaurant and Oyster Bar EC2 *(Restaurant*)*
Lauderdale House N6 *(Max*)*
The Mary Sumner House SW1 *(Conference Hall*)*
Mermaid Conference & Events Centre EC4 *(River Rm)*
Oxford House E2 *(Max*)*
Proud Camden NW1 *(South Gallery Alone)*
Streatham Ice Arena SW16 *(Max*)*
Tamarai WC2 *(Max*)*
Worx SW6 *(Studio 1)*
90 Dulwich College SE21 *(Lower Hall)*
Guy's Hospital SE1 *(Governor's Hall)*
Kings Place N1 *(St Pancras Room)*
Lauderdale House N6 *(Lower Gallery)*
HMS President EC4 *(President Suite)*
Space E14 *(Max*)*
Victory Services Club W2 *(El Alamein Rm)*
80 The Battersea Barge SW8 *(Max*)*
Canning House SW1 *(Max*)*
Le Cercle SW1 *(Max*)*
The Chapel Bar N1 *(Max*)*
Detroit WC2 *(Max*)*
Favela Chic EC2 *(Max*)*
Fitzroy Square W1 *(Max*)*
Forge WC2 *(Max*)*
Old Truman Brewery E1 *(Bridge)*
HMS President EC4 *(Wardroom)*
Royal College of Art SW7 *(Senior Common Room)*
School of Pharmacy WC1 *(Refectory)*
St Botolph's Hall EC2 *(Max*)*
St Peter's Hall W11 *(Max*)*
77 Bakers' Hall EC3 *(Max*)*
75 Greenwich Theatre SE10 *(Bar*)*
74 Linden House W6 *(Ballroom*)*
72 Arts Depot N12 *(Dance Space)*
70 Bankside Gallery SE1 *(Max*)*

Cross Keys SW3 *(Max*)*
Embargo 59 SW10 *(Max*)*
Mermaid Conference & Events Centre EC4 *(Miles Rm or Studio)*
The Pirate Castle NW1 *(Main Hall*)*
Royal Institution of Great Britain W1 *(Library)*
St Paul's Church W1 *(Blue Lounge)*
Tudor Barn Eltham SE9 *(Heritage Centre)*
Victory Services Club W2 *(Grill Rm or Trafalgar Rm)*

65 Greenhouse W1 *(Max*)*

64 Imperial College London SW7 *(Council Rm)*

63 Theatre 503 at the Latchmere Pub SW11 *(Max*)*

60 Apartment 195 SW3 *(Max*)*
Balls Brothers Minster Pavement EC3 *(St Giles)*
Bistrothèque E2 *(Cabaret Rm)*
Cross Keys SW3 *(Restaurant)*
Greig's Restaurant W1 *(Max*)*
Kingswood House SE21 *(Charles Suite)*
Mall Galleries SW1 *(East Gallery)*
McQueen EC2 *(Restaurant*)*
Old Finsbury Town Hall EC1 *(Council Chamber)*
St Martin In The Fields WC2 *(The Gallery)*
Troubadour SW5 *(Club*)*
Vasco & Piero's Pavilion W1 *(Main Room*)*
Yard W1 *(Max*)*

55 Aragon House SW6 *(Max*)*

50 Bistrothèque E2 *(Private Room)*
Bow Wine Vaults EC4 *(Max*)*
Burgh House NW3 *(Max*)*
The Charles Dickens Museum WC1 *(Max*)*
George Inn SE1 *(Function Rm*)*
Gow's Restaurant and Oyster Bar EC2 *(Oyster Bar)*
Institut Français SW7 *(Salon de Réception*)*
Latium W1 *(Max*)*
The Little Ship Club EC4 *(Library)*
Photographers' Gallery W1 *(Max*)*
Proud Camden NW1 *(Covered Outdoor Café)*
Royal College of Art SW7 *(Seminar Rm 1)*
Tuttons WC2 *(Max*)*
The White House SW4 *(Max*)*

45 Greig's Restaurant W1 *(The Main Room)*
Trouvaille W1 *(Max*)*
Wine Gallery SW10 *(Max*)*

40 Balls Brothers Minster Pavement EC3 *(St Claves or St Margaret's)*
Chowki W1 *(Private Dining Area)*
Depot SW14 *(Outside Area)*
Fulham House SW6 *(Dining Rm)*
The HAC EC1 *(Ante Room or Queen's Rm)*
King's College School SW19 *(Boathouse)*
London Scottish SW1 *(Dining Room)*
Madsen Restaurant SW7 *(Max*)*
Old Finsbury Town Hall EC1 *(Yellow Room)*
Pied à Terre W1 *(Max*)*
Scott's W1 *(Private Room*)*
Trafalgar Tavern SE10 *(Trafalgar Club)*
Wine Gallery SW10 *(Private Rm 3)*

36 Vasco & Piero's Pavilion W1 *(Private Room)*

35 City Hotel E1 *(Lane Suite Rm 3)*
Cross Keys SW3 *(Room At The Top)*
Detroit WC2 *(Long Room, Crypt)*
Gunnersbury Park W3 *(Max*)*
Oxford House E2 *(Scott Rm)*
Pig's Ear SW3 *(Max*)*
Tab Centre E2 *(Richard Pearson Hall)*

32 Engineer NW1 *(Private Room 1)*
Royal Over-Seas League SW1 *(Mountbatten)*
Troubadour SW5 *(Gallery)*

30 The Antelope SW1 *(Max*)*
Dr Johnsons' House EC4 *(Max*)*
George Inn SE1 *(Function Rm 2)*
Kings Place N1 *(Limehouse Room)*
Linden House W6 *(Commodore's Rm)*
Mall Galleries SW1 *(North Gallery)*
Red Monkey SW11 *(Max*)*
Royal Institution of Great Britain W1 *(Georgian Rm)*
Signor Sassi SW1 *(Private Room*)*
Tuttons WC2 *(Larger Vault)*
Worx SW6 *(Studio 4)*

26 Bakers' Hall EC3 *(Court Rm)*
Le Cafe Anglais W2 *(Private Room)*
Royal Holloway College TW20 *(Large Boardroom)*
The White House SW4 *(Banquet Room)*

25 Candid Arts Trust, The EC1 *(Banquet Rm*)*
Guy's Hospital SE1 *(Court Rm)*
The Pirate Castle NW1 *(Club Room)*
Proud Camden NW1 *(Stables (each))*
Trafalgar Events WC2 *(Orange Room, Purple Room* or Red Room)*

24 The Mary Sumner House SW1 *(Mary Sumner Rm, Princess Elizabeth or Princess Victoria)*
Victory Services Club W2 *(Allenby Rm)*

22 Forge WC2 *(Private Room)*
Galvin Bistrot de Luxe W1 *(Private Room*)*
Wine Gallery SW10 *(Private Rm 2)*

20 Boudin Blanc W1 *(Max*)*
Engineer NW1 *(Mirror Rm)*
Guy's Hospital SE1 *(Senior Staff Room)*
Kings Place N1 *(Wenlock Room)*
Lemonia NW1 *(Private Room)*
HMS President EC4 *(Boardroom II)*
Tamarai WC2 *(Gallery or Screening Room)*
Tuttons WC2 *(Smaller Vault)*
Victory Services Club W2 *(Committee Rm)*
Wine Gallery SW10 *(Garden)*

18 Bishopsgate Institute EC2 *(Roseberry Room*)*
Greig's Restaurant W1 *(The Oak Room)*
The Research House W1 *(Studio 1* or Studio 2)*
Wine Gallery SW10 *(Private Rm 1)*

16 Artworkers Guild, The WC1 *(Gradidge Room*)*
The Book Club EC2 *(Private Dining Rm)*
The Mary Sumner House SW1 *(Princess Alexandra, Princess Beatrice or Princess Mary)*
The Research House W1 *(Studio 3)*
Troubadour SW5 *(Shackleton Room)*

15 Apartment 195 SW3 *(Cellar)*
Hoxton Hall N1 *(Max*)*
Tamarai WC2 *(Dining Room or Lotus Lounge)*
Trafalgar Events WC2 *(Blue Room)*
Trouvaille W1 *(Private Room)*

14 Boudin Blanc W1 *(Private Rm 2 (wine Cellar))*
The HAC EC1 *(Library & Boardroom)*
Victory Services Club W2 *(Chetwode Rm)*

12 Cecconi's W1 *(Private Room*)*
Le Cercle SW1 *(Private Room)*
The Mary Sumner House SW1 *(Princess Helena)*
Pied à Terre W1 *(Private Room)*
The Pirate Castle NW1 *(Meeting/activity Room)*
10 Greenhouse W1 *(Private Room)*
Greig's Restaurant W1 *(The Wine Room)*
Madsen Restaurant SW7 *(Private Dining Room)*
Royal Holloway College TW20 *(Small Boardroom)*
Worx SW6 *(Studio 3)*
8 HMS President EC4 *(Boardroom I)*
The White House SW4 *(Rockstar Room)*
6 Latium W1 *(Chef's Table)*
4 Bishopsgate Institute EC2 *(Townsend Gallery)*

£B

1050 Troxy E1 *(Grand Hall*)*
1016 Troxy E1 *(Max)*
520 Wandsworth Civic Suite SW18 *(Max*)*
400 Chuen Cheng Ku W1 *(Max*)*
350 Queen Mary Students' Union E1 *(Max*)*
300 Lowiczanka Restaurant W6 *(Max*)*
229 The Venue W1 *(Max*)*
250 229 W1 *(Venue 1*)*
220 Philbeach Hall SW5 *(Max*)*
229 The Venue W1 *(Venue 1)*
200 Kettners W1 *(Max*)*
The Ministry of Sound SE1 *(Max*)*
Sway WC2 *(Crystal Lounge*)*
Westminster Cathedral Hall SW1 *(Max*)*
180 Chuen Cheng Ku W1 *(Rm 1)*
Del' Aziz (Swiss Cottage) NW3 *(Max*)*
Queen Mary College E1 *(The Octagon*)*
170 Knightsbridge 145 SW1 *(Max*)*
160 Garden Bar and Grill W10 *(Max*)*
150 The London Welsh Centre WC1 *(Max*)*
The Pump House Gallery SW11 *(Marquee*)*
Sway WC2 *(Max)*
145 Del' Aziz (Fulham) SW6 *(Max*)*
130 Cinnamon Kitchen EC2 *(Restaurant*)*
Del' Aziz (Bermondsey) SE1 *(Max*)*
Gate Street Barn GU5 *(Max*)*
King's Head Theatre N1 *(Max*)*
120 JuJu SW3 *(Max*)*
100 Balls Brothers SE1 *(Max*)*
Borscht & Tears SW3 *(Max*)*
Chuen Cheng Ku W1 *(Rm 2)*
JuJu SW3 *(Ground Floor)*
London Rowing Club SW15 *(Long Rm*)*
Paradise by Way of Kensal Green W10 *(Max*)*
95 Del' Aziz (Bankside) SE1 *(Max*)*
90 Del' Aziz (Westfield) W12 *(Max*)*
Ochre EC4 *(Max*)*
Shampers W1 *(Restaurant (Ground Floor & Basement)*)*
2 Amici SW1 *(Max*)*
85 Bar Soho W1 *(Max*)*
80 Chatham Hall SW11 *(Max*)*
Del' Aziz (Bankside) SE1 *(Downstairs)*
The Fellow N1 *(Max*)*
Garden Bar and Grill W10 *(Inside or Outside)*
Malabar Junction WC1 *(Max*)*
Mr Chow SW1 *(Room 1*)*
The October Gallery WC1 *(Max*)*
St Bride Foundation EC4 *(Bridewell Hall*)*
229 The Venue W1 *(Venue 2)*
229 W1 *(Gulbenkian Room or Venue 2)*
75 Del' Aziz (Fulham) SW6 *(Aziz)*
Earlsfield Library SW18 *(Max*)*
Vats WC1 *(Max*)*
70 Callooh Callay EC2 *(Max*)*
Cinnamon Kitchen EC2 *(Anise (bar))*
Crown & Greyhound SE21 *(Private Rm (large)*)*
Del' Aziz (Bermondsey) SE1 *(REstaurant)*
Del' Aziz (Fulham) SW6 *(Deli)*
St Moritz W1 *(Max*)*
65 The Lamb Tavern EC3 *(Max*)*
60 Alma SW18 *(Max*)*
Bistro 1 W1 *(Max*)*
Café Emm W1 *(Max*)*
Chuen Cheng Ku W1 *(Rm 3)*
Cinnamon Kitchen EC2 *(Terrace)*
Loft SW4 *(Max*)*
Mr Chow SW1 *(Room 2)*
Troxy E1 *(White Room)*
Zebrano (at the establishment) W1 *(Max*)*
50 Bar Kick E1 *(Max*)*
Cargo EC2 *(Restaurant*)*
Greenwich Park Bar & Grill SE10 *(Max*)*
JuJu SW3 *(JuJu Lounge)*
Newham City Farm E16 *(Max*)*
Patio W12 *(Max*)*
45 Del' Aziz (Bankside) SE1 *(Upstairs)*
Shampers W1 *(Downstairs Lounge)*
43 Clerkenwell House EC1 *(Upstairs*)*
40 The Atlas SW6 *(Max*)*
Captain Kidd E1 *(Max*)*
Chuen Cheng Ku W1 *(Rm 4)*
Patio W12 *(Basement)*
35 The Golden Lion SW1 *(Theatre Bar*)*
2 Amici SW1 *(Private Room)*
30 Cirque De Soir W1 *(VIP*)*
Del' Aziz (Bermondsey) SE1 *(Bar or Deli)*
JuJu SW3 *(VIP)*
London Rowing Club SW15 *(Balcony)*
Malabar Junction WC1 *(Private Room)*
Ochre EC4 *(Function Rm)*
St Bride Foundation EC4 *(Farringdon Rm or Parssmore Edwards Rm)*
Vincent Rooms SW1 *(Private Room*)*
25 North Pole SE10 *(VIP*)*
St Bride Foundation EC4 *(Layton)*
20 London Rowing Club SW15 *(Members Rm)*
St Bride Foundation EC4 *(Salisbury Rm)*
16 Michael Moore W1 *(Private Rooms*)*
12 Cinnamon Kitchen EC2 *(Private Dining Room)*
The Fellow N1 *(Private Room)*
Vats WC1 *(Private Dining Room)*
10 Clerkenwell House EC1 *(VIP Room)*
JuJu SW3 *(Booths)*
8 Gate Street Barn GU5 *(Meeting Room)*
St Bride Foundation EC4 *(Caxton)*

FUNCTION ROOMS LISTED BY CABARET CAPACITY

* largest entry for venue

£E

2500 Battersea Evolution SW11 *(Max*)*
300 Blenheim Palace OX20 *(Max*)*
250 Victoria and Albert Museum SW7 *(Dome*)*
200 Stoke Place SL2 *(Ballroom*)*
150 Chiswick House W4 *(Max*)*
Eltham Palace SE9 *(Great Hall*)*
120 Fishmongers' Hall EC4 *(Max*)*
Two Temple Place WC2 *(The Great Hall*)*
100 Blenheim Palace OX20 *(Orangery)*
80 Chiswick House W4 *(First Floor (6 Rms))*
Stoke Place SL2 *(Max)*
60 Stoke Place SL2 *(Howard Vyse Rm)*
Two Temple Place WC2 *(Max)*
50 Stoke Place SL2 *(Lakeside)*

£M-E

1600 The Grosvenor House Hotel W1 *(Great Rm*)*
1200 The Business Design Centre N1 *(Max*)*
Old Billingsgate EC3 *(Grand Hall, Mezzanine And Terrace*)*
Planit Finsbury Square EC2 *(Max*)*
1000 Hilton on Park Lane W1 *(Max*)*
Hurlingham Club SW6 *(Max*)*
Parkstead House SW15 *(Parkstead Lawns*)*
900 Hilton on Park Lane W1 *(Grand Ballroom)*
850 Roundhouse NW1 *(Max*)*
800 Old Trafford (Manchester United) M16 *(Manchester Suite*)*
Park Plaza Westminster SE1 *(Ballroom*)*
700 Chelsea Football Club SW6 *(Max*)*
Royal Armouries LS10 *(Royal Armouries Hall*)*
Royal Lancaster W2 *(Max*)*
650 Museum of Flight EH39 *(Concorde Experience*)*
Old Trafford (Manchester United) M16 *(Max)*
600 Millennium Gloucester Hotel SW7 *(Max*)*
500 St George's Hall L1 *(The Great Hall*)*
450 The Business Design Centre N1 *(Gallery Hall)*
Cardiff City Hall CF10 *(Max*)*
East Wintergarden E14 *(Hall*)*
The Grosvenor House Hotel W1 *(Ballroom)*
National Maritime Museum SE10 *(Neptune's Court*)*
Natural History Museum SW7 *(Central Hall*)*
Old Trafford (Manchester United) M16 *(International Suite)*
Somerset House WC2 *(Edmond J. Safra Fountain Court (with marquee)*)*
444 Royal Air Force Museum NW9 *(Historic Hangars*)*
430 Science Museum SW7 *(Max*)*
400 Cardiff City Hall CF10 *(Assembly Room)*
Dover Street Restaurant & Bar W1 *(Max*)*
Ham House & Garden TW10 *(Max*)*
Kew Gardens TW9 *(Marquee Site*)*
LABAN SE8 *(Outdoor Theatre*)*
Landmark NW1 *(Grand Ballroom*)*
Millennium Gloucester Hotel SW7 *(Orchard Suite)*
Millennium London Mayfair W1 *(Max*)*
Royal Opera House WC2 *(Paul Hamlyn Hall *)*
Science Museum SW7 *(Making The Modern World)*
390 The Park Lane Hotel W1 *(Ballroom*)*
375 Savoy WC2 *(Lancaster Rm*)*
350 Banqueting House SW1 *(Main Hall*)*
Forman's Fish Island E3 *(Max*)*
Imperial War Museum London SE1 *(Main Exhibits Gallery*)*
Madame Tussauds NW1 *(Max*)*
Science Museum SW7 *(Flight Gallery)*
320 The Conservatory at Painshill Park KT11 *(Max*)*
Guildhall EC2 *(Great Hall*)*
304 Grange St Paul's EC4 *(Max*)*
300 Circus Space N1 *(Max*)*
Cutty Sark SE10 *(Max*)*
The Hempel W2 *(Zen Garden*)*
Holiday Inn, Brentford Lock TW8 *(Max*)*
Madame Tussauds NW1 *(Tussauds - World Stage)*
One Mayfair W1 *(Grand Hall*)*
Southbank Centre SE1 *(Clore Ballroom*)*
294 LABAN SE8 *(Conference Room or Max)*
290 Millennium Gloucester Hotel SW7 *(Sentosa Suite)*
280 Hurlingham Club SW6 *(Boomhouse Suite or Quadrangle Suite)*
Manchester Town Hall M60 *(Great Hall*)*
Plaisterers' Hall EC2 *(Great Hall*)*
256 Grand Trafalgar Square WC2 *(Ballroom*)*
250 Hopetoun House EH30 *(Ballroom*)*
Inner Temple EC4 *(Max*)*
Jumeirah Carlton Tower SW1 *(Ballroom*)*
The Lowry M50 *(The Studio*)*
Mandarin Oriental Hyde Park SW1 *(Ballroom*)*
Merchant Taylors' Hall EC2 *(Max*)*
Old Royal Naval College SE10 *(Queen Mary Ante Rm*)*
Royal Opera House WC2 *(Linbury Theatre)*
240 London Zoo NW1 *(Max*)*
225 Middle Temple Hall EC4 *(Hall*)*
224 Grand Trafalgar Square WC2 *(Old Billiard Room)*
Renaissance London Chancery Court Hotel WC1 *(Max*)*
220 Assembly Rooms BA1 *(Max*)*
Sugar Quay EC3 *(Max*)*
210 Pestana Chelsea Bridge SW8 *(Max*)*
200 BMA House WC1 *(Max*)*

Hilton London Canary Wharf E14 *(Max*)*
Imperial War Museum North M17 *(Max*)*
Institute of Directors SW1 *(Nash*)*
InterContinental London W1 *(Max*)*
Kew Gardens TW9 *(Temperate House or The Orangery)*
One Mayfair W1 *(Mezzanine)*
Pacific Oriental EC2 *(Max*)*
Porte des Indes W1 *(Max*)*
Royal Opera House WC2 *(Ashton Studio)*
Somerset House WC2 *(River Terrace)*
192 Claridge's W1 *(Ballroom*)*
Merchant Taylors' Hall EC2 *(Great Hall)*
180 Il Bottaccio SW1 *(Max*)*
Café de Paris W1 *(Max*)*
The Collection SW3 *(Max*)*
London Aquarium SE1 *(Max*)*
LSO St Luke's EC1 *(Jerwood Hall*)*
Mary Ward House WC1 *(Mary Ward Hall*)*
Old Trafford (Manchester United) M16 *(Trafford Suite)*
One Whitehall Place SW1 *(Max*)*
Quaglino's SW1 *(Max*)*
Royal Air Force Museum NW9 *(Battle Of Britain Hall)*
Liverpool Town Hall L2 *(Max*)*
170 Andaz EC2 *(Great Eastern*)*
Cumberland Hotel W1 *(Max*)*
Skinners' Hall EC4 *(Max*)*
168 Royal Garden Hotel W8 *(Palace Suite*)*
160 The Berkeley SW1 *(Max*)*
BMA House WC1 *(Great Hall)*
Four Seasons Canary Wharf E14 *(Ballroom*)*
Haymarket Hotel SW1 *(Pool Area*)*
The Law Society WC2 *(The Common Room*)*
Pump Room and Roman Baths BA1 *(Max*)*
Liverpool Town Hall L2 *(Large Ballroom)*
156 Barbican Centre EC2 *(Garden Rm*)*
153 The London Art House N1 *(Manor Garden Hall*)*
150 Hilton on Park Lane W1 *(Wellington Ballroom)*
The Hospital Club WC2 *(TV Studio*)*
Kingsway Hall Hotel WC2 *(Max*)*
Millennium Gloucester Hotel SW7 *(Conservatory)*
1 Lombard Street Restaurant/Bar/Brasserie EC3 *(Max*)*
One Whitehall Place SW1 *(Gladstone Library or Whitehall Suite)*
The Park Lane Hotel W1 *(Tudor Rose Rm)*
Parkstead House SW15 *(Manresa Hall)*
Royal Armouries LS10 *(Nelson Bistro)*
Royal Hospital Chelsea SW3 *(State Apartments*)*
Royal Opera House WC2 *(Amphitheatre Bar)*
Savoy WC2 *(Abraham Lincoln & Manhattan Rms)*
Southbank Centre SE1 *(Queen Elizabeth Hall foyer)*
Surgeon's Hall Complex EH8 *(Quincentenary Main Hall*)*
Thistle Charing Cross Hotel WC2 *(Betjeman*)*
144 Royal Armouries LS10 *(Wellington Suite)*
140 America Square Conference Centre EC3 *(Ludgate Suite*)*
The Hospital Club WC2 *(The Gallery (North & South together))*
Roehampton Club SW15 *(Max*)*
Sartoria W1 *(Max*)*
Wallace Collection W1 *(Courtyard*)*
136 Bridgewater Hall M2 *(Barbirolli*)*
132 Landmark NW1 *(Drawing Rm)*
130 Mary Ward House WC1 *(Brewer & Smith)*
Smith's of Smithfield EC1 *(Max*)*
128 The Law Society WC2 *(Max)*
120 Arts Club W1 *(Dining Rm*)*
Forbes House SW1 *(Max*)*
The Grosvenor House Hotel W1 *(Court Suite)*
Guildhall BA1 *(Banqueting Room*)*
Imperial War Museum London SE1 *(Cinema)*
Landmark NW1 *(Empire Rm)*
The Lanesborough SW1 *(Belgravia*)*
London Marriott Hotel, County Hall SE1 *(County Hall Suite*)*
The Mayfair W1 *(Max*)*
No. 11 Cavendish Square W1 *(The Burdett Theatre*)*
Old Royal Naval College SE10 *(King William Restaurant)*
Orangery (Kensington Palace) W8 *(Max*)*
Prism EC3 *(Max*)*
The Queen's Club W14 *(The Presidents Room*)*
Savoy WC2 *(River Rm)*
Sketch W1 *(Gallery*)*
Southbank Centre SE1 *(Level 5 Function Room)*
Temple Island RG9 *(Max*)*
30 Pavilion Road SW1 *(Max*)*
110 The Caledonian Club SW1 *(Max*)*
Cardiff City Hall CF10 *(Marble Hall)*
The Imagination Gallery WC1 *(Gallery*)*
100 Assembly Rooms BA1 *(Tea Room)*
Cardiff City Hall CF10 *(Ferrier Hall)*
Churchill Museum and Cabinet War Rooms SW1 *(Max*)*
The Commonwealth Club WC2 *(Auditorium or Reception Area*)*
Haberdashers' Hall EC1 *(Max*)*
Hatfield House AL9 *(Max*)*
Hever Castle TN8 *(GuthriePavillion*)*
Hilton on Park Lane W1 *(Coronation Suite)*
Holiday Inn, Camden Lock NW1 *(The Glasshouse*)*
Hopetoun House EH30 *(Adam Stables)*
LABAN SE8 *(Studio Theatre)*
Legoland Windsor SL4 *(Max*)*
London Zoo NW1 *(Prince Albert Suite)*
Momo W1 *(Max*)*
Mosimann's Dining Club SW1 *(Max*)*
One Aldwych WC2 *(Max*)*
River & Rowing Museum RG9 *(Max*)*
Siobhan Davies Studios SE1 *(Max*)*
Tate Modern SE1 *(Cafe 2*)*
Tower Bridge SE1 *(Walkways*)*
Warwick Castle CV34 *(Great Hall*)*
Wollaton Hall NG8 *(Great Hall*)*
96 Cannizaro House SW19 *(Max*)*
Cumberland Hotel W1 *(Blue 3&4 Combined)*
90 Carlton Club SW1 *(Max*)*
The Casino at the Empire WC2 *(Face 2 Face*)*

The Hospital Club WC2 *(First Floor Bar & Restaurant)*
Inner Temple EC4 *(Parliament Chamber)*
Innholders' Hall EC4 *(Dining Hall*)*
London Zoo NW1 *(Raffles Suite)*
One Wimpole Street W1 *(Garden Rm*)*
Philharmonic Hall L1 *(Grand Foyer Bar* or Rodewald Suite)*
30 St Mary Axe EC3 *(39th & 40th Floor*)*
88 Stationers' Hall EC4 *(Livery Hall*)*
84 Claridge's W1 *(French Salon)*
Devonport House SE10 *(Max*)*
Grocers' Hall EC2 *(Max*)*
80 Assembly Rooms BA1 *(Octagon)*
Bermondsey Square SE1 *(Max*)*
BMA House WC1 *(Paget Room)*
The Caledonian Club SW1 *(Johnnie Walker Music Room)*
Churchill Museum and Cabinet War Rooms SW1 *(HCA Auditorium)*
Hotel Rafayel SW11 *(3rd Floor Event Space*)*
Kensington Palace W8 *(Orangery*)*
London Zoo NW1 *(Mappin Pavilion)*
Madame Tussauds NW1 *(Tussauds - whole attraction)*
The Merchants Hall EH2 *(The Hall*)*
Natural History Museum SW7 *(Earth Galleries)*
One Whitehall Place SW1 *(Reading And Writing Rms (Sold In Conjunction With Gla dstone Library))*
Roux at Parliament Square SW1 *(Max*)*
Royal Opera House WC2 *(Amphi Restaurant)*
Sadler's Wells Theatre EC1 *(Max*)*
Salters' Hall EC2 *(Max*)*
Savoy WC2 *(Beaufort Rm)*
Skinners' Hall EC4 *(Banqueting Hall)*
Smith's of Smithfield EC1 *(Top Floor)*
Somerset House WC2 *(Embankment East or Seamen's Hall)*
St. Mungo Museum of Religious Life and Art G4 *(Max*)*
Liverpool Town Hall L2 *(Small Ballroom)*
Waddesdon Manor, The Dairy HP18 *(Manor Restaurant or West Hall*)*
HQS Wellington WC2 *(Court Rm*)*
75 Arndale House WC2 *(Max*)*
72 28 Portland Place W1 *(Max*)*
70 Andaz EC2 *(Bishopsgate & Chancery)*
Aviator GU14 *(1 & 2* or Sky Lounge)*
Cannizaro House SW19 *(Viscount Melville Suite)*
Corrigan's Mayfair W1 *(Exclusive Use*)*
Grange Holborn WC1 *(Orion Suite*)*
Haymarket Hotel SW1 *(Shooting Gallery)*
Mandarin Oriental Hyde Park SW1 *(Carlyle Suite)*
Mary Ward House WC1 *(Lethaby Room)*
The Roof Gardens W8 *(Max*)*
Swissôtel The Howard, London WC2 *(Fitzalan Suite*)*
Thistle Charing Cross Hotel WC2 *(Regency Rm)*
64 BMA House WC1 *(Snow Room)*
Park Plaza County Hall SE1 *(Max*)*
60 Arts Club W1 *(Garden Rm)*
Bingham TW10 *(The Garden Room Exclusive*)*
Brocket Hall AL8 *(Ball Room*)*
The Carlton Mitre Hotel KT8 *(Max*)*
Chesterfield Mayfair W1 *(The Royal Suite*)*
Gray's Inn WC1 *(Max*)*
Hotel Rafayel SW11 *(Penthouse)*
Hurlingham Club SW6 *(Murgrave Theatre)*
Imperial War Museum London SE1 *(Conference Room)*
Institute of Directors SW1 *(Burton)*
The Law Society WC2 *(The Reading Room)*
The London Art House N1 *(Baroque Hall)*
Newstead Abbey NG15 *(The West Front Suite*)*
Parkstead House SW15 *(Loyola Room)*
Royal Opera House WC2 *(Crush Room)*
Sadler's Wells Theatre EC1 *(Lillian Bayliss Theatre)*
Southbank Centre SE1 *(St Paul's Roof Pavilion or Weston Roof Pavilion)*
56 Grand Trafalgar Square WC2 *(Annex)*
50 America Square Conference Centre EC3 *(Fleet Suite)*
Barnard's Inn Hall EC1 *(Max*)*
The Carlton Mitre Hotel KT8 *(Pavilion)*
Hampshire Hotel WC2 *(Penthouse*)*
Imperial War Museum London SE1 *(Upper Boardroom)*
Mary Ward House WC1 *(Voysey Room)*
Millennium London Mayfair W1 *(Mayfair Suite)*
One Whitehall Place SW1 *(Meston Suite or River Rm)*
The Park Lane Hotel W1 *(Oak Rm)*
Savoy WC2 *(Pinafore)*
Somerset House WC2 *(Terrace Rooms)*
Swissôtel The Howard, London WC2 *(Arundel Suite)*
48 BMA House WC1 *(Prince's Room)*
Cavendish SW1 *(Alto*)*
Guildhall BA1 *(Brunswick Room)*
Royal Garden Hotel W8 *(York Suite)*
45 Dukes Hotel SW1 *(Marlborough Suite*)*
Gray's Inn WC1 *(Large Pension Rm or Spy Room)*
Great Fosters TW20 *(Max*)*
42 Royal Garden Hotel W8 *(Kensington Suite)*
40 America Square Conference Centre EC3 *(Newgate Suite)*
The Caledonian Club SW1 *(Smoking Room)*
The Hospital Club WC2 *(Forest Room (Private Dining Room))*
Institute of Directors SW1 *(Waterloo)*
The Lanesborough SW1 *(Wellington Rm)*
Millennium London Mayfair W1 *(Waterloo Rm)*
Phyllis Court RG9 *(Grandstand Pavilion*)*
Sadler's Wells Theatre EC1 *(Cable & Wireless or Mezzanine Wood)*
Thistle Charing Cross Hotel WC2 *(Canterbury Rm)*
Tower Bridge SE1 *(Engine Rms)*
Liverpool Town Hall L2 *(Reception Rooms)*
38 Grand Trafalgar Square WC2 *(Victoria)*
36 Aviator GU14 *(Deli)*
35 Churchill Museum and Cabinet War Rooms SW1 *(Harmsworth Room)*
LABAN SE8 *(Meeting Room)*
32 The Caledonian Club SW1 *(Stuart Room)*
The Fox Club W1 *(Max*)*
Grand Trafalgar Square WC2 *(Entrance Hall)*
30 America Square Conference Centre EC3 *(Bishopsgate Suite or Walbrook Suite)*
Aviator GU14 *(1, 2 or 4 & 5)*
Bingham TW10 *(Garden Room 3)*

Grand Trafalgar Square WC2 *(Westminster)*
The Hempel W2 *(No 17)*
National Liberal Club SW1 *(Lady Violet*)*
Royal Exchange EC3 *(PDR*)*
Savoy WC2 *(Gondoliers)*
28 Portland Place W1 *(Sainsbury's Rm)*
27 Quaglino's SW1 *(Private Room 1)*
25 Cavendish SW1 *(Electra)*
Chesterfield Mayfair W1 *(The Conservatory)*
Philharmonic Hall L1 *(Green Room)*
24 Bingham TW10 *(Garden Room 1)*
Bridgewater Hall M2 *(Green Room)*
The Caledonian Club SW1 *(Library or Selkirk Room)*
Imperial War Museum London SE1 *(Lower Boardroom)*
The London Art House N1 *(Egyptian Room or Orangery)*
22 Sadler's Wells Theatre EC1 *(Fonteyn Rm)*
21 Grand Trafalgar Square WC2 *(Salon)*
20 America Square Conference Centre EC3 *(Aldgate Suite)*
28 Portland Place W1 *(Adam's Rm)*
18 Aviator GU14 *(Boardroom)*
Bingham TW10 *(Garden Room 2)*
The London Art House N1 *(Picasso Room)*
Savoy WC2 *(Mikado)*
16 Grand Trafalgar Square WC2 *(Smaller Meeting Rooms)*
Mary Ward House WC1 *(Boardroom)*
15 Grange Holborn WC1 *(Orion A-D)*
14 Quaglino's SW1 *(Private Room 2)*
12 Aviator GU14 *(3, 4 /5 or 6)*
Cavendish SW1 *(Stratus)*
The London Art House N1 *(Albert Moore Lounge or Bauhaus Room)*

£M

6000 Earls Court & Olympia SW5 *(Earl's Court 1*)*
5000 Alexandra Palace & Park N22 *(Great Hall*)*
4000 Earls Court & Olympia SW5 *(Earl's Court 2)*
3500 Earls Court & Olympia SW5 *(Olympia Grand)*
2500 Earls Court & Olympia SW5 *(Olympia National)*
2000 Alexandra Palace & Park N22 *(West Hall)*
Battersea Park SW11 *(Max*)*
1250 Earls Court & Olympia SW5 *(Brompton Hall)*
900 Ascot Racecourse SL5 *(Max*)*
850 Newbury Racecourse RG14 *(Max*)*
800 London Metropole W2 *(King's Suite or Monarch Suite*)*
Newbury Racecourse RG14 *(Grandstand Ground Floor)*
Twickenham Experience TW1 *(Max*)*
750 Addington Palace CR0 *(Max*)*
650 The Brewery EC1 *(Porter Tun*)*
600 Epsom Downs KT18 *(Max*)*
Newbury Racecourse RG14 *(Grandstand Second Floor)*
550 Royal Courts of Justice WC2 *(Max*)*
516 Aston Villa Hospitality and Events B6 *(Holte Suite*)*
500 Harrow School HA1 *(Max*)*
The Langley WD17 *(Ruby Suite*, Sapphire Suite or Topaz Suite)*
London Metropole W2 *(Palace Suite)*
Wyndham Grand London SW10 *(The Grand Room*)*
490 Riverbank Park Plaza SE1 *(Max*)*
466 The Decorium N22 *(Max*)*
450 The Guoman Tower E1 *(Max*)*
Vinopolis: The Venue SE1 *(Great Halls*)*
400 All Star Lanes (Brick Lane) E1 *(Max*)*
Central Hall Westminster SW1 *(Great Hall*)*
Conservatory at Chelsea SW3 *(Max*)*
Grand Connaught Rooms WC2 *(Grand Hall*)*
Kensington Conference & Events Centre W8 *(Max*)*
Thames Luxury Charters SW15 *(Dixie Queen (cruising) or Dixie Queen (static)*)*
380 The Oval SE11 *(Max*)*
Whipsnade Wild Animal Park LU6 *(Max*)*
370 Thorpe Park KT16 *(Lake View Events Zone*)*
360 Alexandra Palace & Park N22 *(Palace Restaurant)*
350 Epsom Downs KT18 *(Oaks Hall)*
Harrow School HA1 *(Shepherd Churchill Hall)*
Lord's Cricket Ground NW8 *(Thomas Lord Suite*)*
Waldorf Hotel WC2 *(Adelphi Suite*)*
308 London Marriott W1 *(Westminster Suite*)*
300 The Coronet SE1 *(Max*)*
Highgate School N6 *(Max*)*
St Mary's Church W1 *(Max*)*
Vinopolis: The Venue SE1 *(The Mezzanine)*
280 Twickenham Experience TW1 *(Spirit Of Rugby)*
270 Bank of England Sports Centre SW15 *(Terrace Room *)*
264 Church House SW1 *(Assembly Hall*)*
260 Delfina Galleries SE1 *(Max*)*
250 Aston Villa Hospitality and Events B6 *(1874)*
Beach Blanket Babylon E1 *(Max*)*
Blakemore House Conference and Wedding Venue SG4 *(Garden Room*)*
The Brewery EC1 *(King George III)*
Christ Church Spitalfields E1 *(Max*)*
Congress Centre WC1 *(Max*)*
Crown Moran Hotel NW2 *(Max*)*
Delfina Galleries SE1 *(Exhibition Gallery)*
Elstree Film Studio WD6 *(Max*)*
Guards Museum SW1 *(Marquee*)*
Newbury Racecourse RG14 *(Berkshire Stand Concourse or Hennessy Suite)*
The Regalia EC4 *(Max*)*
Swan at the Globe at Shakespeare's Globe SE1 *(Max*)*
220 One Great George Street SW1 *(Great Hall*)*
200 All Star Lanes (Brick Lane) E1 *(Main Hall)*
Aura SW1 *(Max*)*
Blackheath Concert Halls SE3 *(Max*)*
Bloomsbury Ballroom WC1 *(Max*)*
Central Hall Westminster SW1 *(Lecture Hall or Library)*
City Cruises SE16 *(Mayflower Garden*)*
Epsom Downs KT18 *(The Diomed Suit)*
Freemason's Hall WC2 *(Max*)*
Hard Rock Cafe W1 *(Max*)*

Hop Exchange SE1 *(Max*)*
Lloyd's of London EC3 *(Banqueting Suite*)*
One Marylebone Road NW1 *(Soane Hall*)*
One Moorgate Place EC2 *(Max*)*
Ronnie Scotts W1 *(Max*)*
Ruby Blue WC2 *(Max*)*
Savile Club W1 *(Max*)*
Simpsons-in-the-Strand WC2 *(Max*)*
Studio Valbonne W1 *(Max*)*
Tottenham Hotspur N17 *(Pat Jennings Lounge*)*

182 Gibson Hall EC2 *(Max*)*

180 Ambassadors Bloomsbury WC1 *(Max*)*
BAFTA, 195 Piccadilly W1 *(David Lean Room*)*
Lloyd's of London EC3 *(1688)*
Sound London WC2 *(Max*)*
Winchester House SW15 *(Max*)*

170 Glaziers' Hall SE1 *(Max*)*
Grand Connaught Rooms WC2 *(Edinburgh)*
No 4 Hamilton Place W1 *(Bill Boeing Rm*)*

162 Ambassadors Bloomsbury WC1 *(Enterprise)*

160 Forty Hall EN2 *(Max*)*

156 Alexandra Palace & Park N22 *(Londesborough Rm)*

150 Amadeus Centre W9 *(Max*)*
Aston Villa Hospitality and Events B6 *(Trinity and 82 Lounge)*
Blakemore House Conference and Wedding Venue SG4 *(Rosemary Room)*
Ealing Town Hall W5 *(Max*)*
Earls Court & Olympia SW5 *(Olympia Conference Centre)*
Epsom Downs KT18 *(The Blue Riband Room)*
Ham Polo Club TW10 *(Max*)*
RS Hispaniola WC2 *(Main Deck*)*
Jasmine Studios W6 *(Max*)*
Lansdowne Club W1 *(Ballroom*)*
Museum of Transport G3 *(Max*)*
Newbury Racecourse RG14 *(Long Room)*
Pacha SW1 *(Max*)*
Park Inn London Russell Square WC1 *(Max*)*
Queen's Eyot SL6 *(Marquee*)*
Regent's College NW1 *(Gardens*)*
Shadow Lounge W1 *(Max*)*
Simon Drake's House of Magic SE1 *(Max*)*
South London Gallery SE5 *(Max*)*
Syon Park TW8 *(Great Conservatory*)*
Thames Luxury Charters SW15 *(Erasmus)*

140 Aston Villa Hospitality and Events B6 *(McGregors Suite)*
Bank Restaurant & Zander Bar, Westminster SW1 *(Max*)*
Dartmouth House W1 *(Max*)*
SS Great Britain BS1 *(Dining Saloon*)*
Hellenic Centre W1 *(Great Hall*)*
London Metropole W2 *(Windsor Suite)*
The Private Rooms at Buckingham Gate SW1 *(Edwardian I*)*
Thames Luxury Charters SW15 *(Elizabethan)*
Tottenham Hotspur N17 *(Bill Nicholson Suite)*
Vinopolis: The Venue SE1 *(The Gallery)*

130 The Brewery EC1 *(Queen Charlotte Rm)*
City Inn Westminster SW1 *(Private Dining*)*
Painters' Hall EC4 *(Max*)*

120 Adam Street WC2 *(Max*)*
Church House SW1 *(Harvey Goodwin Suite or Hoare Memorial Hall)*
Common Ground Cafe & Bar SW18 *(Max*)*
Crypt EC1 *(Max*)*
Dominion Theatre W1 *(The Studio*)*
Epsom Downs KT18 *(Jockey Club Rm)*
Frederick's N1 *(Max*)*
Fulham Palace SW6 *(Max*)*
Goodenough College WC1 *(Great Hall*)*
Horniman Museum SE23 *(With Marquee*)*
London Canal Museum N1 *(1st Floor*)*
MIC Hotel & Conference Centre NW1 *(The Atrium*)*
One Marylebone Road NW1 *(Baccarat Room)*
Park Crescent Conference Centre W1 *(The Theatre*)*
Royal Air Force Club W1 *(Running Horse/Millennium Suite*)*
Royal Society of Arts WC2 *(Vaults*)*
Rubens SW1 *(Old Masters Restaurant*)*
76 Portland Place W1 *(Rutherford Suite*)*
Tiger Tiger SW1 *(Max*)*
Trinity House EC3 *(Max*)*
Washington W1 *(Max*)*
Winchester House SW15 *(River Rm)*

116 The CBI Conference Centre WC1 *(Concourse*)*

110 London Wetland Centre SW13 *(Waters Edge Rm*)*

105 IET London: Savoy Place WC2 *(Riverside Room*)*

100 Blackheath Concert Halls SE3 *(Recital Rm)*
The Brewery EC1 *(Sugar Rms)*
Browns WC2 *(Courtroom 1*)*
Central Hall Westminster SW1 *(Aldars Gate)*
Criterion Restaurant W1 *(Max*)*
Crown Moran Hotel NW2 *(Sala Rm)*
Crowne Plaza London - The City EC4 *(Bridewell Room*)*
Delfina Galleries SE1 *(Café Gallery)*
Dominion Theatre W1 *(The Gallery)*
The Garden Museum SE1 *(Max*)*
Greenwich Yacht Club SE10 *(Max*)*
House of St Barnabas W1 *(Max*)*
Kenwood House (Old Kitchen) NW3 *(The Brew House*)*
Newbury Racecourse RG14 *(Fred Winter or Paddoc View)*
St Stephen's Club SW1 *(Queensborough Room*)*
Theatre Royal, Drury Lane WC2 *(Max*)*
Tottenham Hotspur N17 *(Centenary Lounge, Gary Mabbutt Lounge or Steve Perryman Lounge)*

96 Barbican Art Gallery EC2 *(Max*)*
HMS Belfast SE1 *(Ship Co's Dining Hall*)*
City Inn Westminster SW1 *(Max)*

90 Ambassadors Bloomsbury WC1 *(Prosper)*
Butchers' Hall EC1 *(Max*)*
City of London Club EC2 *(Main Dining Rm*)*

Coin Street Neighbourhood Centre SE1 *(Max*)*
East Hampstead Park Conference Centre RG40 *(Max*)*
RS Hispaniola WC2 *(Upper Deck)*
National Army Museum SW3 *(Art Gallery*)*
Paramount WC1 *(Level 31*)*
Pinewood Studios SL0 *(Max*)*
Sofitel London St James SW1 *(Westminister*)*
St Thomas' Hospital SE1 *(Governor's Hall*)*
Tottenham Hotspur N17 *(Box Holders' West)*

85 Century W1 *(4th Floor*)*

80 Blakemore House Conference and Wedding Venue SG4 *(Thyme Room)*
Century W1 *(Rose Langton Room)*
The Cobden Club W10 *(Max*)*
Design Museum SE1 *(Riverside Hall*)*
Epsom Downs KT18 *(The Downs View Suit)*
Gallery Soho WC2 *(Max*)*
The Insurance Hall EC2 *(Max*)*
Lloyd's of London EC3 *(Captain's Rm)*
The Magic Circle Headquarters NW1 *(Max*)*
No 4 Hamilton Place W1 *(Argyll Rm & Terrace)*
SixtyOne Whitehall SW1 *(Duke of Wellington Rm*)*
Syon Park TW8 *(Syon Park House)*
V&A Museum of Childhood E2 *(Max*)*

75 ICA SW1 *(Nash & Brandon Rms*)*

72 Pewterers' Hall EC2 *(Max*)*

70 Aston Villa Hospitality and Events B6 *(Directors)*
Avenue House N3 *(Drawing Rm*)*
Central Hall Westminster SW1 *(George Thomas)*
Chutney Mary SW10 *(Max*)*
Courthouse Hotel Kempinski W1 *(Max*)*
Kensington Conference & Events Centre W8 *(Small Hall)*
Mandeville Hotel W1 *(deVille Restaurant*)*
The Old Sessions House EC1 *(Max*)*
Regent's College NW1 *(Herringham Hall)*
Royal Institute of British Architects W1 *(Florence Hall*)*
Thames Luxury Charters SW15 *(Golden Salamander)*
Vinopolis: The Venue SE1 *(Academia)*

64 Farmers' & Fletchers' Hall EC1 *(Max*)*

62 Washington W1 *(Richmond Suite)*

60 Avenue House N3 *(Max)*
HMS Belfast SE1 *(Gun Rm)*
Bentleys Oyster Bar and Grill W1 *(Jameson Room*)*
Bluebird SW3 *(Beaufort & Gallery Room or Gallery Room*)*
Crown Moran Hotel NW2 *(Barnet Rm)*
Crowne Plaza London - The City EC4 *(Bridewell 1)*
Epsom Downs KT18 *(Lammtarra Suit)*
Groucho Club W1 *(Max*)*
MIC Hotel & Conference Centre NW1 *(Hilda Porter)*
One Great George Street SW1 *(Smeaton Rm)*
Oxford & Cambridge Club SW1 *(Max*)*
Prenelle Gallery E14 *(Main Gallery*)*
Sofitel London St James SW1 *(Mayfair A&B)*
Thames Luxury Charters SW15 *(Edwardian)*

56 Broadway House SW1 *(Stevenson*)*
Goodenough College WC1 *(Large Common Room)*

55 Vanderbilt Hotel SW7 *(Max*)*

54 Ambassadors Bloomsbury WC1 *(Innovate)*

50 Addington Palace CR0 *(Winter Garden)*
Aston Villa Hospitality and Events B6 *(Sky Lounge or The Park Suite)*
belowzero restaurant + lounge & ICEBAR LONDON W1 *(Moose Dining Room*, Moose & Reindeer or Whole Venue)*
Blakemore House Conference and Wedding Venue SG4 *(Marjoram Room)*
Design Museum SE1 *(Design Museum Space)*
The Fashion and Textile Museum SE1 *(Max*)*
Horniman Museum SE23 *(Max)*
Newbury Racecourse RG14 *(Royal Box)*
Regent's College NW1 *(Tuke Common Rm)*
The Kingly Club W1 *(Max*)*
Vinopolis: The Venue SE1 *(The European Odysey)*

48 Bank of England Sports Centre SW15 *(Balcony Bar)*
Browns WC2 *(Courtroom 2)*
Butchers' Hall EC1 *(Taurus Suite)*
Chiswick Moran Hotel W4 *(Fairfax Room*)*
Dartmouth House W1 *(Churchill Rm)*

40 Amadeus Centre W9 *(Lower Hall)*
Browns WC2 *(Courtroom 3)*
Epsom Downs KT18 *(The Board Room)*
House of St Barnabas W1 *(Drawing Room)*
IET London: Savoy Place WC2 *(Faraday, Maxwell Suite or Thompson Room)*
The Old Sessions House EC1 *(London Rm)*
One Moorgate Place EC2 *(Main Reception Rm)*
Regent's College NW1 *(Knapp Gallery)*
Sixteen Park Crescent W1 *(Max*)*
Sofitel London St James SW1 *(Piccadilly/Bloomsbury)*
Tottenham Hotspur N17 *(Box Holders' North or Highlights)*
West Wycombe Caves HP14 *(Max*)*
The Zetter Hotel EC1 *(Max*)*

32 Bluebird SW3 *(Mezzanine)*

30 Central Hall Westminster SW1 *(Dinsdale Young)*
Epsom Downs KT18 *(The Gallops Suit)*
MIC Hotel & Conference Centre NW1 *(Epworth)*
76 Portland Place W1 *(Herschel Room)*
Vinopolis: The Venue SE1 *(The New World Odyssey)*

25 House of St Barnabas W1 *(Bazelgette Room)*
MIC Hotel & Conference Centre NW1 *(Alice)*

24 Blakemore House Conference and Wedding Venue SG4 *(Bay Room or Sage Room)*
Chiswick Moran Hotel W4 *(Fairfax East or Fairfax West)*
Dartmouth House W1 *(Small Drawing Rm)*

20 House of St Barnabas W1 *(Silk Room)*

18 Hoxton Hotel EC2 *(Room 3*)*
16 Broadway House SW1 *(Lawrence)*
Sofitel London St James SW1 *(Kensington)*
15 MIC Hotel & Conference Centre NW1 *(Exeter or Wesley)*
12 Crown Moran Hotel NW2 *(Brent/Camden Rm)*
MIC Hotel & Conference Centre NW1 *(Whitfield)*
9 Hoxton Hotel EC2 *(Room 2)*
5 Hoxton Hotel EC2 *(Room 1)*

£B-M

1379 The International Convention Centre B1 *(Hall 3*)*
800 ExCeL London E16 *(Platinum Suite*)*
Old Truman Brewery E1 *(Max*)*
750 The Royal Horticultural Halls SW1 *(Lawrence Hall*)*
640 ExCeL London E16 *(ICC Capital Suite)*
590 Debut London SE1 *(Max*)*
450 Whitechapel Art Gallery E1 *(Max*)*
440 Imperial College London SW7 *(Main Dining Hall*)*
413 The International Convention Centre B1 *(Hall 4)*
400 BAC SW11 *(Max*)*
Shoreditch Town Hall EC1 *(Max*)*
350 Hammersmith Town Hall W6 *(Max*)*
Lotus Chinese Floating Restaurant E14 *(Max*)*
The Royal Horticultural Halls SW1 *(Lindley Hall)*
300 Cecil Sharp House NW1 *(Max*)*
Royal College of Art SW7 *(Henry Moore Gallery*)*
250 The HAC EC1 *(Prince Consort Rooms*)*
Tamarai WC2 *(Max*)*
240 Proud Cabaret EC3 *(Max*)*
Victory Services Club W2 *(Carisbrooke Hall*)*
210 The International Convention Centre B1 *(Hall 11)*
HMS President EC4 *(Ball Rm*)*
200 Fulham Town Hall SW6 *(Max*)*
Imperial College London SW7 *(Senior Common Rm)*
Old Finsbury Town Hall EC1 *(Great Hall*)*
Rich Mix E1 *(Max*)*
7 Rifles Battalion W1 *(Max*)*
185 Conway Hall WC1 *(Max*)*
180 Balls Brothers Minster Pavement EC3 *(Minster Suite*)*
King's College School SW19 *(Great Hall*)*
Loose Cannon EC4 *(Max*)*
Trafalgar Tavern SE10 *(Nelson Rm*)*
175 The International Convention Centre B1 *(Hall 8)*
170 Mermaid Conference & Events Centre EC4 *(Blackfriars Rm*)*
160 Arts Depot N12 *(Main Auditorium*)*
Dickens Inn E1 *(Max*)*
St Martin In The Fields WC2 *(Max*)*
150 Bush Hall W12 *(Max*)*
King's College WC2 *(Great Hall*)*
London Scottish SW1 *(Max*)*
Proud Camden NW1 *(Max*)*
Trailfinders Sports Club W13 *(Olympic Pavilion*)*
Westminster Boating Base SW1 *(Max*)*
140 Chelsea Old Town Hall SW3 *(Main Hall*)*
City Hotel E1 *(Max*)*
Fabric EC1 *(Max*)*
Royal Over-Seas League SW1 *(Max*)*
130 Da Mario SW7 *(Max*)*
Docklands Sailing & Watersports Centre E14 *(Max*)*
120 BAC SW11 *(Lower Hall)*
Fulham House SW6 *(Max*)*
The HAC EC1 *(Long Rm)*
Levant W1 *(Max*)*
The Little Ship Club EC4 *(Max*)*
The Pavilion B6 *(Pearson Suite*)*
Tudor Barn Eltham SE9 *(Max*)*
110 The Irish Centre W6 *(Max*)*
100 Cecil Sharp House NW1 *(Trefusis Hall)*
Fulham Town Hall SW6 *(Concert Hall)*
Gow's Restaurant and Oyster Bar EC2 *(Restaurant*)*
Guy's Hospital SE1 *(Robens Suite*)*
Kings Place N1 *(Battlebridge Room*)*
Royal College of Art SW7 *(Gulbenkian Galleries)*
Shoreditch Town Hall EC1 *(Council Room)*
20th Century Theatre W11 *(Max*)*
Worx SW6 *(Max*)*
90 Space E14 *(Max*)*
84 Kings Place N1 *(Hall Two)*
80 The Battersea Barge SW8 *(Max*)*
Kingswood House SE21 *(Max*)*
74 Linden House W6 *(Max*)*
70 Chelsea Old Town Hall SW3 *(The Small Hall)*
60 Apartment 195 SW3 *(Max*)*
Balls Brothers Minster Pavement EC3 *(St Giles)*
Old Finsbury Town Hall EC1 *(Council Chamber)*
Royal Geographical Society SW7 *(The Hall*)*
55 Aragon House SW6 *(Max*)*
Vasco & Piero's Pavilion W1 *(Main Room*)*
50 Gow's Restaurant and Oyster Bar EC2 *(Oyster Bar)*
St Botolph's Hall EC2 *(Max*)*
48 ExCeL London E16 *(Gallery Meeting Rooms)*
Kings Place N1 *(St Pancras Room)*
40 Balls Brothers Minster Pavement EC3 *(St Claves or St Margaret's)*
Guy's Hospital SE1 *(Governor's Hall or Senior Staff Room)*
The HAC EC1 *(Queen's Rm)*
Kingswood House SE21 *(Charles Suite)*
30 Guy's Hospital SE1 *(Court Rm)*
18 Kings Place N1 *(Limehouse Room)*
12 Kings Place N1 *(Wenlock Room)*

£B

850 Troxy E1 *(Max*)*
630 Troxy E1 *(Grand Hall)*
460 Wandsworth Civic Suite SW18 *(Max*)*
380 229 The Venue W1 *(Max*)*
300 Lowiczanka Restaurant W6 *(Max*)*
229 The Venue W1 *(Venue 1)*
250 Queen Mary Students' Union E1 *(Max*)*
200 229 W1 *(Venue 1*)*

150 Bar Kick E1 *(Max*)*
The London Welsh Centre WC1 *(Max*)*
The Ministry of Sound SE1 *(Max*)*
Queen Mary College E1 *(The Octagon*)*
130 Gate Street Barn GU5 *(Max*)*
100 Balls Brothers SE1 *(Max*)*
Knightsbridge 145 SW1 *(Max*)*
90 St Bride Foundation EC4 *(Bridewell Hall*)*
80 Chatham Hall SW11 *(Max*)*
229 The Venue W1 *(Venue 2)*
229 W1 *(Venue 2)*
55 London Rowing Club SW15 *(Max*)*
50 229 W1 *(Gulbenkian Room)*
40 The Atlas SW6 *(Max*)*
36 Troxy E1 *(White Room)*

FUNCTION ROOMS LISTED BY THEATRE CAPACITY

* largest entry for venue

£E

323 British Museum WC1 *(BP Theatre*)*
200 Eltham Palace SE9 *(Great Hall*)*
Lancaster House SW1 *(Long Gallery*)*
Stoke Place SL2 *(Ballroom*)*
190 Tate Britain SW1 *(Clore Auditorium *)*
165 Two Temple Place WC2 *(The Great Hall*)*
150 National Portrait Gallery WC2 *(Ondaatje Wing Theatre*)*
Two Temple Place WC2 *(Lower Gallery)*
142 British Museum WC1 *(Stevenson Theatre)*
120 Blenheim Palace OX20 *(Marlborough*)*
100 Lancaster House SW1 *(The Music Rm)*
Tate Britain SW1 *(Gallery 9)*
80 British Museum WC1 *(Sackler Rooms combined)*
Eltham Palace SE9 *(Drawing Rm)*
Stoke Place SL2 *(Lakeside)*
72 Lancaster House SW1 *(State Dining Rm)*
70 Stoke Place SL2 *(Howard Vyse Rm)*
50 Chiswick House W4 *(Domed Saloon*)*
45 British Museum WC1 *(Sackler Room A or Sackler Room B)*
40 Cliveden SL6 *(Churchill Boardroom*)*
Tate Britain SW1 *(Duffield Room)*
35 British Museum WC1 *(Claus Moser Room or Studio)*
Liberty W1 *(Heritage Suite*)*
30 Stoke Place SL2 *(Thomas Gray)*

£M-E

9000 Manchester Central M2 *(Max*)*
8000 Manchester Central M2 *(Central 2)*
5200 Royal Albert Hall SW7 *(Max*)*
2500 The Business Design Centre N1 *(Max*)*
Southbank Centre SE1 *(Royal Festival Hall Auditorium*)*
1800 Bridgewater Hall M2 *(Max*)*
1770 The Grosvenor House Hotel W1 *(Great Rm*)*
1730 The Lowry M50 *(Max*)*
1650 Philharmonic Hall L1 *(Auditorium*)*
1600 IndigO2 SE10 *(Max*)*
Manchester Central M2 *(Central 1)*
1500 Saatchi Gallery SW3 *(Max*)*
Sadler's Wells Theatre EC1 *(Max*)*
1400 Park Plaza Westminster SE1 *(Ballroom*)*
Queen Elizabeth II Conference Centre SW1 *(Whittle & Fleming Rooms*)*
1200 Hilton on Park Lane W1 *(Grand Ballroom*)*
Edinburgh International Conference Centre EH3 *(Pentland Suite*)*
Old Trafford (Manchester United) M16 *(Manchester Suite*)*
Planit Finsbury Square EC2 *(Max*)*

Roundhouse NW1 *(Max*)*
1104 Old Trafford (Manchester United) M16 *(Max)*
1000 Grand Trafalgar Square WC2 *(Max*)*
Old Billingsgate EC3 *(Grand Hall, Mezzanine And Terrace*)*
Royal Lancaster W2 *(Max*)*
950 Chelsea Football Club SW6 *(Max*)*
900 Southbank Centre SE1 *(Queen Elizabeth Hall Auditorium)*
St George's Hall L1 *(The Great Hall*)*
804 Manchester Central M2 *(Exhange Auditorium)*
800 Grange St Paul's EC4 *(Max*)*
650 The Business Design Centre N1 *(Gallery Hall)*
630 London Studios SE1 *(Studio 1*)*
616 Royal Northen College of Music M13 *(Theatre*)*
600 Cardiff City Hall CF10 *(Assembly Room*)*
East Wintergarden E14 *(Hall*)*
Holiday Inn, Brentford Lock TW8 *(Waterfront Suite*)*
InterContinental London W1 *(Max*)*
Portman Hotel W1 *(Portman Ballroom*)*
550 The Grosvenor House Hotel W1 *(Ballroom)*
Royal Garden Hotel W8 *(Palace Suite*)*
518 Grand Trafalgar Square WC2 *(Ballroom)*
512 Landmark NW1 *(Grand Ballroom*)*
500 Assembly Rooms BA1 *(Max*)*
The Dorchester W1 *(Ballroom*)*
Hurlingham Club SW6 *(Boomhouse Suite*)*
Edinburgh International Conference Centre EH3 *(Cromdale Hall)*
Kew Gardens TW9 *(Marquee Site*)*
Manchester Town Hall M60 *(Great Hall*)*
Millennium Gloucester Hotel SW7 *(Orchard Suite*)*
Millennium London Mayfair W1 *(Ballroom*)*
The Park Lane Hotel W1 *(Ballroom*)*
480 Plaisterers' Hall EC2 *(Great Hall*)*
466 Royal Northen College of Music M13 *(Concert Hall)*
450 BFI IMAX SE1 *(Auditorium*)*
BFI Southbank SE1 *(NFT 1*)*
Hurlingham Club SW6 *(Quadrangle Suite)*
National Maritime Museum SE10 *(Max*)*
Old Trafford (Manchester United) M16 *(International Suite)*
Royal Opera House WC2 *(Paul Hamlyn Hall *)*
430 London Studios SE1 *(Studio 2)*
420 Pestana Chelsea Bridge SW8 *(Max*)*
416 Science Museum SW7 *(Imax Cinema*)*
404 Grand Trafalgar Square WC2 *(Old Billiard Room)*
400 Altitude 360 SW1 *(Altitude 360°*)*
Hilton London Canary Wharf E14 *(Max*)*
Jumeirah Carlton Tower SW1 *(Ballroom*)*
LABAN SE8 *(Foyer, Max*, Max or Outdoor Theatre)*
Merchant Taylors' Hall EC2 *(Great Hall*)*
Museum of Flight EH39 *(Concorde Experience*)*
One Mayfair W1 *(Grand Hall*)*
Science Museum SW7 *(Level 1)*
Southbank Centre SE1 *(Clore Ballroom)*
St George's Hall L1 *(Small Concert Room)*
394 Royal Opera House WC2 *(Linbury Theatre)*
365 Southbank Centre SE1 *(Purcell Room)*
360 Guildhall BA1 *(Banqueting Room*)*
350 Circus Space N1 *(Max*)*
Cumberland Hotel W1 *(Max*)*
Forman's Fish Island E3 *(Floor 2*)*
Hopetoun House EH30 *(Ballroom*)*
Liverpool FC L4 *(Champions Lounge*)*
The Lowry M50 *(The Studio)*
Mary Ward House WC1 *(Mary Ward Hall*)*
Middle Temple Hall EC4 *(Hall*)*
Millennium Gloucester Hotel SW7 *(Sentosa Suite)*
340 National Museum of Wales CF10 *(Reardon Smith Theatre*)*
320 The Conservatory at Painshill Park KT11 *(Max*)*
Drapers' Hall EC2 *(Max*)*
Saatchi Gallery SW3 *(Gallery 1, 5, 7, 8, 12)*
300 Altitude 360 SW1 *(Millbank Media Center or River Room)*
BMA House WC1 *(Great Hall*)*
Everton FC L4 *(The Marquee*)*
Forman's Fish Island E3 *(Max)*
Goldsmiths' Hall EC2 *(Livery Hall*)*
Grange Holborn WC1 *(Max*)*
Hatfield House AL9 *(Max*)*
Imperial War Museum North M17 *(Max*)*
Inner Temple EC4 *(Hall*)*
Institute of Directors SW1 *(Max*)*
Lincoln's Inn (Honourable Society of) WC2 *(Great Hall*)*
Madame Tussauds NW1 *(Tussauds Stardome 4D*)*
One Wimpole Street W1 *(Lecture Theatre*)*
Parkstead House SW15 *(Max*)*
Pump Room and Roman Baths BA1 *(Pump Room*)*
Royal College of Physicians NW1 *(Max*)*
Saatchi Gallery SW3 *(Gallery 3)*
Sugar Quay EC3 *(Max*)*
280 The Law Society WC2 *(The Common Room*)*
The London Art House N1 *(Manor Garden Hall*)*
Saatchi Gallery SW3 *(Gallery 2, 4, 6, 9, 11)*
270 Liverpool Town Hall L2 *(Large Ballroom*)*
262 Renaissance London Chancery Court Hotel WC1 *(Max*)*
260 Saatchi Gallery SW3 *(Gallery 10)*
254 FACT L1 *(Screen 1*)*
250 Andaz EC2 *(Great Eastern*)*
Assembly Rooms BA1 *(Tea Room)*
Il Bottaccio SW1 *(Max*)*
15 Hatfields SE1 *(Ground Floor*)*
Holiday Inn, Camden Lock NW1 *(The Glasshouse*)*
Institute of Directors SW1 *(Nash)*
Kingsway Hall Hotel WC2 *(Max*)*
Liverpool FC L4 *(European Lounge)*
London Zoo NW1 *(Max*)*
LSO St Luke's EC1 *(Jerwood Hall*)*
Le Meridien Piccadilly W1 *(Edwardian Suite*)*
Millennium Gloucester Hotel SW7 *(Conservatory)*
Nottingham Castle NG1 *(Long Gallery*)*

One Whitehall Place SW1 *(Gladstone Library* or Whitehall Suite)*
Phyllis Court RG9 *(Ballroom*)*
Royal Air Force Museum NW9 *(Cosford Rm (Dermot Boyle Wing)*)*
Royal Armouries LS10 *(Bury Theatre*)*
240 Bridgewater Hall M2 *(Barbirolli)*
Tate Modern SE1 *(Starr Auditorium*)*
230 America Square Conference Centre EC3 *(Ludgate Suite*)*
Le Meridien Piccadilly W1 *(Georgian Suites)*
Surgeon's Hall Complex EH8 *(Quincentenary Main Hall*)*
Liverpool Town Hall L2 *(Council Chamber)*
225 No. 11 Cavendish Square W1 *(The Burdett Theatre*)*
224 Royal Air Force Museum NW9 *(Lecture Theatre)*
220 The Commonwealth Club WC2 *(Auditorium*)*
Grange Holborn WC1 *(Orion Suite)*
Imperial War Museum London SE1 *(Max*)*
Landmark NW1 *(Empire Rm)*
London Film Museum SE1 *(Debating Chamber*)*
Old Trafford (Manchester United) M16 *(Trafford Suite)*
209 Natural History Museum SW7 *(Flett Events Theatre*)*
204 Landmark NW1 *(Drawing Rm)*
200 The Caledonian Club SW1 *(Johnnie Walker Music Room*)*
Cardiff City Hall CF10 *(Ferrier Hall or Marble Hall)*
Everton FC L4 *(The People's Club)*
15 Hatfields SE1 *(Boardroom)*
Four Seasons Canary Wharf E14 *(Ballroom*)*
Haberdashers' Hall EC1 *(Max*)*
Hatfield House AL9 *(Riding School)*
Hilton on Park Lane W1 *(Wellington Ballroom)*
Holborn Bars EC1 *(Holborn Suite*)*
Hopetoun House EH30 *(Adam Stables)*
The Imagination Gallery WC1 *(Gallery*)*
Imperial War Museum London SE1 *(Cinema)*
Kensington Palace W8 *(Orangery*)*
Liverpool FC L4 *(Reds Combined)*
London Zoo NW1 *(Huxley Theatre or Prince Albert Suite)*
Manchester Town Hall M60 *(Banqueting Hall)*
Mary Ward House WC1 *(Brewer & Smith)*
National Gallery of Scotland EH2 *(National Gallery*, Royal Scottish Academy or Weston Link)*
Old Billingsgate EC3 *(Gallery)*
Quaglino's SW1 *(Max*)*
Roehampton Club SW15 *(Max*)*
Royal Armouries LS10 *(Wellington Suite)*
Royal Opera House WC2 *(Ashton Studio)*
Sadler's Wells Theatre EC1 *(Lillian Bayliss Theatre)*
Southbank Centre SE1 *(Queen Elizabeth Hall foyer)*
Stationers' Hall EC4 *(Livery Hall*)*
Surgeon's Hall Complex EH8 *(Playfair Hall)*
180 Arndale House WC2 *(Max*)*
Burrell Collection G43 *(Lecture Theatre*)*
Café de Paris W1 *(Max*)*
The Grosvenor House Hotel W1 *(Court Suite)*
Holiday Inn, Camden Lock NW1 *(The Camden Suite)*
The Hospital Club WC2 *(TV Studio*)*
Hurlingham Club SW6 *(Murgrave Theatre)*
Le Meridien Piccadilly W1 *(The Oak Room)*
The Royal Pavilion BN1 *(Music Room*)*
Salters' Hall EC2 *(Mail Hall*)*
HQS Wellington WC2 *(Court Rm*)*
175 Cannon Bridge Roof Garden EC4 *(Max*)*
170 Hospital WC2 *(Max*)*
Kensington Palace W8 *(State Apartments)*
Royal Air Force Museum NW9 *(Locking Rm (Dermot Boyle Wing))*
160 Grocers' Hall EC2 *(Max*)*
Kent House Knightsbridge SW7 *(Sanctuary*)*
The Park Lane Hotel W1 *(Tudor Rose Rm)*
Royal Opera House WC2 *(Crush Room)*
Skinners' Hall EC4 *(Banqueting Hall*)*
Southbank Centre SE1 *(Level 5 Function Room)*
158 Surgeon's Hall Complex EH8 *(Auditorium)*
150 BMA House WC1 *(Black Suite or Paget Room)*
Brocket Hall AL8 *(Max*)*
Churchill Museum and Cabinet War Rooms SW1 *(HCA Auditorium*)*
Cumberland Hotel W1 *(Blue 3&4 Combined)*
The E Rejuvenation Centre E1 *(Max*)*
15 Hatfields SE1 *(Earth, Water, Air)*
Firepower - The Royal Artillery Museum SE18 *(Max*)*
Forbes House SW1 *(Max*)*
Great Fosters TW20 *(Max*)*
Hospital WC2 *(Studio)*
The Hospital Club WC2 *(The Gallery (North & South together))*
Inner Temple EC4 *(Parliament Chamber)*
The Law Society WC2 *(The Reading Room)*
The Merchants Hall EH2 *(The Hall*)*
One Mayfair W1 *(Mezzanine)*
One Wimpole Street W1 *(Max Rayne Auditorium)*
Portman Hotel W1 *(Berkley, Gloucester & Bryanston Suite)*
Royal Hospital Chelsea SW3 *(State Apartments*)*
Saddlers' Hall EC2 *(The Great Hall*)*
Siobhan Davies Studios SE1 *(Max*)*
Sketch W1 *(Gallery*)*
Skinners' Hall EC4 *(Max)*
Thistle Charing Cross Hotel WC2 *(Betjeman*)*
HM Tower of London EC3 *(New Armouries*)*
Wollaton Hall NG8 *(Great Hall*)*
147 BFI Southbank SE1 *(NFT2)*
140 Hilton on Park Lane W1 *(Coronation Suite)*
Imperial War Museum North M17 *(Watershard Cafe)*
Local Government House SW1 *(Bevan Hall*)*
National Liberal Club SW1 *(David Lloyd George*)*

One Whitehall Place SW1 *(Reading And Writing Rms (Sold In Conjunction With Gladstone Library))*
136 FACT L1 *(Screen 2)*
134 BFI Southbank SE1 *(NFT 3)*
130 Chesterfield Mayfair W1 *(The Royal Suite*)*
The Collection SW3 *(Mezzanine*)*
High Road House W4 *(Downstairs*)*
Lincoln's Inn (Honourable Society of) WC2 *(Old Hall)*
Museum of Science and Industry M3 *(Max*)*
St Martin's Lane Hotel WC2 *(Max*)*
Liverpool Town Hall L2 *(Small Ballroom)*
120 Assembly Rooms BA1 *(Octagon)*
BMA House WC1 *(Courtyard Suite)*
The Carlton Mitre Hotel KT8 *(Pavilion*)*
The Casino at the Empire WC2 *(Face 2 Face*)*
City Hall - London's Living Room SE1 *(Max*)*
Devonport House SE10 *(Max*)*
The Dorchester W1 *(Orchid)*
Gray's Inn WC1 *(Large Pension Rm*)*
Guildhall BA1 *(Brunswick Room)*
Hever Castle TN8 *(GuthriePavillion*)*
Hurlingham Club SW6 *(Napier Room or Rongelagh Room)*
Innholders' Hall EC4 *(Dining Hall*)*
Institute of Directors SW1 *(Burton)*
LABAN SE8 *(Studio Theatre)*
The Law Society WC2 *(Strand/Fleet/Bell Suites)*
Legoland Windsor SL4 *(Max*)*
Philharmonic Hall L1 *(Grand Foyer Bar or Rodewald Suite)*
The Queen's Club W14 *(The Presidents Room*)*
Royal Garden Hotel W8 *(Kensington Suite or York Suite)*
Royal Northen College of Music M13 *(Studio Theatre)*
Stationers' Hall EC4 *(Court Rm)*
Swissôtel The Howard, London WC2 *(Fitzalan Suite*)*
119 London Stock Exchange EC4 *(Theatre*)*
112 Thistle Charing Cross Hotel WC2 *(Regency Rm)*
110 Andaz EC2 *(Bishopsgate & Chancery)*
Bermondsey Square SE1 *(Max*)*
The Commonwealth Club WC2 *(Conference Room)*
London Stock Exchange EC4 *(Forum (whole))*
Mary Ward House WC1 *(Lethaby Room)*
Plaisterers' Hall EC2 *(Livery Hall)*
River & Rowing Museum RG9 *(Max*)*
Science Museum SW7 *(Dana Centre)*
Waddesdon Manor, The Dairy HP18 *(West Hall*)*
109 Dulwich Picture Gallery SE21 *(Linbury Rm*)*
107 Royal Northen College of Music M13 *(Lecture Theatre)*
105 Grand Trafalgar Square WC2 *(Annex)*
104 FACT L1 *(Screen 3)*
100 America Square Conference Centre EC3 *(Aldgate & Bishopsgate Suites)*
BMA House WC1 *(Harvey or Snow Room)*
Carlton Club SW1 *(Max*)*
Drapers' Hall EC2 *(Court Dining)*
The Foundling Museum WC1 *(Picture Gallery option 1*)*
Gray's Inn WC1 *(Spy Room)*
Grocers' Hall EC2 *(Piper Rm)*
Hampshire Hotel WC2 *(Max*)*
Hopetoun House EH30 *(Tapestry Room)*
Hospital WC2 *(Gallery)*
The Hospital Club WC2 *(First Floor Bar & Restaurant)*
Hotel Rafayel SW11 *(Max*)*
Imperial War Museum North M17 *(The Niveskind)*
Institute of Directors SW1 *(Waterloo)*
Kew Gardens TW9 *(Cambridge Cottage)*
The Lanesborough SW1 *(Belgravia*)*
The Law Society WC2 *(The Council Chamber)*
Manchester Town Hall M60 *(Conference Hall)*
Newstead Abbey NG15 *(The Great Hall*)*
Nottingham Castle NG1 *(Cafe)*
Park Plaza County Hall SE1 *(Max*)*
Roux at Parliament Square SW1 *(Max*)*
Royal Air Force Museum NW9 *(Halton Gallery)*
Royal Astronomical Society W1 *(Max*)*
Royal College of Pathologists SW1 *(Max*)*
Sadler's Wells Theatre EC1 *(Cable & Wireless)*
Science Museum SW7 *(Director's Suite)*
Soho Hotel W1 *(Max*)*
Somerset House WC2 *(Embankment East or Portico Rooms*)*
St. Mungo Museum of Religious Life and Art G4 *(Max*)*
Swissôtel The Howard, London WC2 *(Arundel Suite)*
Tate Modern SE1 *(East Room)*
28 Portland Place W1 *(Heggie Rm*)*
Wollaton Hall NG8 *(Willoby Room)*
97 BMA House WC1 *(Council Chamber)*
96 15 Hatfields SE1 *(Earth, Water)*
95 Canonbury Academy N1 *(Max*)*
94 Cardiff City Hall CF10 *(Council Chamber)*
90 America Square Conference Centre EC3 *(Fleet Suite)*
Aviator GU14 *(1 & 2*)*
Forman's Fish Island E3 *(Floor 1)*
The Foundling Museum WC1 *(Picture Gallery option 2)*
Haberdashers' Hall EC1 *(Court Rm)*
Merchant Taylors' Hall EC2 *(Drawing Rm or Parlour)*
Millennium London Mayfair W1 *(Mayfair Suite)*
National Museum of Wales CF10 *(Oriel Suite)*
The Park Lane Hotel W1 *(Oak Rm)*
Portman Hotel W1 *(Montagu Suite)*
Roundhouse NW1 *(Dr. Martens Free DM Studio)*
28 Portland Place W1 *(Adam Suite, Harben Suite or Sainsbury's Rm)*
85 Hampshire Hotel WC2 *(Penthouse)*
Royal Academy of Engineering SW1 *(F4*)*
80 America Square Conference Centre EC3 *(Newgate Suite)*
Apex City of London Hotel EC3 *(City Suite*)*
Arts Club W1 *(Garden Rm*)*

Baltic Exchange EC3 *(Max*)*
The Caledonian Club SW1 *(Smoking Room)*
Cavendish SW1 *(Alto*)*
Chandos House W1 *(Max*)*
The Commonwealth Club WC2 *(Seminar Room)*
Dukes Hotel SW1 *(Marlborough Suite*)*
Estorick Collection N1 *(Max*)*
The Foundling Museum WC1 *(Picture Gallery option 3)*
Goldsmiths' Hall EC2 *(Drawing Rm & Exhibition Rm or Exhibition Room)*
The Hempel W2 *(Max*)*
Imperial War Museum London SE1 *(Conference Room)*
London Capital Club EC4 *(The Oriental Room*)*
London Marriott Hotel, County Hall SE1 *(King George V*)*
London Studios SE1 *(Studio 3)*
Parkstead House SW15 *(Loyola Room or Manresa Hall)*
Phyllis Court RG9 *(Grandstand Pavilion)*
Royal Opera House WC2 *(Macmillan)*
Sheraton Park Tower SW1 *(Trianon Rm*)*
Skinners' Hall EC4 *(Old Court Rm)*
Southbank Centre SE1 *(St Paul's Roof Pavilion or Weston Roof Pavilion)*
Wax Chandlers' Hall EC2 *(Great Rm*)*

75 Four Seasons Canary Wharf E14 *(River Rm)*
Grand Trafalgar Square WC2 *(Salon)*
Millennium London Mayfair W1 *(Manhattan Suite)*
Sadler's Wells Theatre EC1 *(Kahn Theatre)*

74 Charlotte Street Hotel W1 *(Screening Rm*)*

72 Millennium London Mayfair W1 *(Waterloo Rm)*

70 The Bentley Hotel SW7 *(Max*)*
BMA House WC1 *(Prince's Room)*
Everton FC L4 *(Dixie Dean Suite)*
52-53 Russell Square WC1 *(Room 1*)*
Fortnum & Mason W1 *(Burlington Room*)*
The Foundling Museum WC1 *(Picture Gallery option 4)*
Inner Temple EC4 *(Luncheon Rm)*
The London Art House N1 *(Baroque Hall)*
London Zoo NW1 *(Mappin Pavilion)*
Middle Temple Hall EC4 *(Parliament Chamber)*
Newstead Abbey NG15 *(The West Front Suite)*
One Whitehall Place SW1 *(Meston Suite or River Rm)*
Royal Opera House WC2 *(Amphi Restaurant)*
Serpentine Gallery W2 *(Max*)*
St George's Hall L1 *(Cockerel Room)*
St Paul's Cathedral EC4 *(Wren Suite*)*
Warwick Castle CV34 *(Coach House*)*

65 Hurlingham Club SW6 *(Terrace Room)*
The Law Society WC2 *(Old Council Chamber)*
Mary Ward House WC1 *(Voysey Room)*

60 America Square Conference Centre EC3 *(Bishopsgate Suite)*
Andaz EC2 *(Fenchurch)*
Baglioni Hotel SW7 *(Max*)*
Chandos House W1 *(Duke Rm, First Floor)*
Chesterfield Mayfair W1 *(The Conservatory)*
The Commonwealth Club WC2 *(Craven Room)*
The Dorchester W1 *(Park Suite)*
The Foundling Museum WC1 *(Picture Gallery option 5)*
Geffrye Museum E2 *(Art rooms *)*
Ham House & Garden TW10 *(Gt Hall or Orangery *)*
Hayward Gallery SE1 *(Max*)*
Kent House Knightsbridge SW7 *(The Rutland Room)*
The Lanesborough SW1 *(Wellington Rm)*
London Zoo NW1 *(Bartlett Room)*
Mandarin Oriental Hyde Park SW1 *(Carlyle Suite* or Rosebery Rms)*
Merchant Taylors' Hall EC2 *(Courtroom)*
One Aldwych WC2 *(Private Rms 1&2*)*
One Wimpole Street W1 *(The Wimpole Rm)*
The Park Lane Hotel W1 *(Orchard Suite)*
Parkstead House SW15 *(Bessborough Room or Ponsonby Room)*
Phyllis Court RG9 *(Finlay or Thames Room)*
Roehampton Club SW15 *(Garden Rm)*
Royal Armouries LS10 *(Tower Gallery)*
Royal College of Radiologists W1 *(Lecture Theatre*)*
Salters' Hall EC2 *(Court Rm)*
Somerset House WC2 *(Navy Board Rooms or Screening Room)*
Stationers' Hall EC4 *(Stock Rm)*
Liverpool Town Hall L2 *(Reception Rooms)*

55 The Commonwealth Club WC2 *(Thorne Rm)*

50 America Square Conference Centre EC3 *(Walbrook Suite)*
Apex City of London Hotel EC3 *(Geneva)*
Aviator GU14 *(Sky Lounge)*
Bingham TW10 *(Garden Room 3*)*
Bridgewater Hall M2 *(Charles Halle)*
The Caledonian Club SW1 *(Stuart Room)*
Cavendish SW1 *(Electra)*
Churchill Museum and Cabinet War Rooms SW1 *(Harmsworth Room)*
FACT L1 *(The Box)*
The Foundling Museum WC1 *(Court Room option 1 or Picture Gallery option 6)*
Geffrye Museum E2 *(Lecture room)*
Grange Holborn WC1 *(Orion A-D)*
Guildhall BA1 *(Kaposvar Room)*
Hever Castle TN8 *(Castle Dining Hall or Tudor Suite)*
Hilton on Park Lane W1 *(Serpentine Suite)*
Hospital WC2 *(Forest Rm)*
The Hospital Club WC2 *(Forest Room (Private Dining Room))*
Imperial War Museum London SE1 *(Upper Boardroom)*
Institute of Directors SW1 *(St James's I or Trafalgar II/St James II)*
LABAN SE8 *(Meeting Room)*
Lincoln's Inn (Honourable Society of) WC2 *(Old Court Room)*
Local Government House SW1 *(Conference Rooms 1&2)*
London Stock Exchange EC4 *(Forum 1)*
Marble Hill House TW1 *(Great Room*)*
Le Meridien Piccadilly W1 *(Adams Suite)*
Middle Temple Hall EC4 *(Queen's Rm)*
National Liberal Club SW1 *(Lady Violet)*

National Museum of Wales CF10 *(Court Room)*
Old Trafford (Manchester United) M16 *(Lounge Bars)*
One Wimpole Street W1 *(Garden Rm or Lower Atrium Theatre)*
The Park Lane Hotel W1 *(Balcony Suite)*
The Queen's Club W14 *(Committee Room)*
Royal Opera House WC2 *(Lambert Studio)*
The Scotch Malt Whisky Society EH2 *(North View*)*
SS Robin E14 *(Max*)*
St Martin's Lane Hotel WC2 *(The Backroom)*
Thistle Charing Cross Hotel WC2 *(Canterbury Rm)*
Victoria Art Gallery BA2 *(Max*)*

48 Hampshire Hotel WC2 *(Digital Projection Suite)*
Liverpool FC L4 *(Directors Lounge)*

47 Covent Garden Hotel WC2 *(Screening Rm*)*

45 Aviator GU14 *(4 & 5)*
The Caledonian Club SW1 *(Library)*
Grand Trafalgar Square WC2 *(Victoria)*
The Lanesborough SW1 *(Westminster Rm)*
Mosimann's Academy SW11 *(Max*)*
St James's Club & Hotel SW1 *(Mayfair Suite*)*

43 Saddlers' Hall EC2 *(The Livery Room)*

42 The London Art House N1 *(Egyptian Room or Orangery)*

40 Apex City of London Hotel EC3 *(New York)*
Arndale House WC2 *(4th Floor Conference Rm)*
Bridgewater Hall M2 *(Green Room)*
The Caledonian Club SW1 *(Selkirk Room)*
Canonbury Academy N1 *(Queen Elizabeth)*
Carlton Club SW1 *(Cabinet Rm)*
Chandos House W1 *(Robert Adam Rm, Ground Floor)*
Churchill Museum and Cabinet War Rooms SW1 *(Learning Suite)*
The Dorchester W1 *(Crystal)*
Fan Museum SE10 *(Orangery*)*
52-53 Russell Square WC1 *(Room 2)*
The Foundling Museum WC1 *(Court Room option 2)*
Grand Trafalgar Square WC2 *(Entrance Hall)*
The Hempel W2 *(No 17)*
Holiday Inn, Camden Lock NW1 *(The Mezzanine Suite)*
The Hospital Club WC2 *(The Library & Terrace)*
Hotel Rafayel SW11 *(3rd Floor Event Space)*
Kent House Knightsbridge SW7 *(The Library)*
London Stock Exchange EC4 *(Forum 2)*
Mandarin Oriental Hyde Park SW1 *(Balfour Rm)*
The Merchants Hall EH2 *(The Court Room & Crush Hall)*
The Metropolitan W1 *(Met Space or White Room*)*
Miller's House E3 *(Max*)*
Portland Place Conference Centre W1 *(Tavistock/Grosvenor*)*
Pump Room and Roman Baths BA1 *(Kingston Room)*
Royal Opera House WC2 *(Conservatory or Trust Rooms)*
Sheraton Park Tower SW1 *(Venture Rm)*
Southbank Centre SE1 *(Level 3 Function Room or Sunley Pavilion)*
The Trafalgar SW1 *(Max*)*
28 Portland Place W1 *(Adam's Rm or Harben Rm)*
Waddesdon Manor, The Dairy HP18 *(Manor Restaurant or Terrace)*
HQS Wellington WC2 *(Model Rm)*

38 BFI Southbank SE1 *(Studio)*

36 Four Seasons Canary Wharf E14 *(City Rm)*
Tower Bridge SE1 *(Bridge Master's Dining Rm*)*

35 Aviator GU14 *(1 or 2)*
Grand Trafalgar Square WC2 *(Westminster)*
Haymarket Hotel SW1 *(Private Room 2*)*
Institute of Directors SW1 *(St James's II)*
The Law Society WC2 *(Six Clerks Room or The Old Bookshop)*
London Film Museum SE1 *(Jubilee)*
The Petersham TW10 *(River Rm* or Terrace Suite)*
Portland Place Conference Centre W1 *(Regent)*
Quaglino's SW1 *(Private Room 1)*
Royal Horseguards SW1 *(The Chelsea Suite or The Thames Suite*)*
The Trafalgar SW1 *(Boardroom)*

32 Chandos House W1 *(Duchess Rm, First Floor or James Adam Rm, Ground Floor)*
The London Art House N1 *(Picasso Room)*

30 The Academy WC1 *(Max*)*
America Square Conference Centre EC3 *(Aldgate Suite)*
Andaz EC2 *(Moorgate & Monument)*
Arts Club W1 *(Board Rm)*
Aviator GU14 *(Deli)*
Bingham TW10 *(Garden Room 1)*
The Carlton Mitre Hotel KT8 *(Cardinal Wolsey)*
Charlotte Street Hotel W1 *(Rm1)*
Chesterfield Mayfair W1 *(The Library)*
The Foundling Museum WC1 *(Court Room option 3)*
The Hospital Club WC2 *(The Rocket Meeting Room)*
Hotel Rafayel SW11 *(Penthouse)*
Innholders' Hall EC4 *(New Court Room)*
Institute of Directors SW1 *(Trafalgar I)*
Kew Gardens TW9 *(Orangery Conference Room)*
London Capital Club EC4 *(Boardroom)*
Merchant Taylors' Hall EC2 *(Kings Gallery)*
One Aldwych WC2 *(Private Rm 3 or Screen Room)*
One Wimpole Street W1 *(Marcus Beck Library)*
The Park Lane Hotel W1 *(Mirror Rm)*
The Petersham TW10 *(Meeting Rm)*
The Queen's Club W14 *(Board Room)*
Royal Exchange EC3 *(PDR*)*
Sadler's Wells Theatre EC1 *(Fonteyn Rm)*
The Trafalgar SW1 *(Strategy)*
Wax Chandlers' Hall EC2 *(Courtroom)*

28 London Marriott Hotel, County Hall SE1 *(Queen Mary)*

25 Bingham TW10 *(Garden Room 2)*
Merchant Taylors' Hall EC2 *(Library)*
Philharmonic Hall L1 *(Green Room)*
Sheraton Park Tower SW1 *(Inspiration Rm)*
St James's Club & Hotel SW1 *(Library)*
Victoria Art Gallery BA2 *(Upper Gallery)*
HQS Wellington WC2 *(Committee Rm)*
24 Cavendish SW1 *(Stratus)*
Plaisterers' Hall EC2 *(Humber Room)*
Portland Place Conference Centre W1 *(Chiswick)*
Quaglino's SW1 *(Private Room 2)*
22 Haymarket Hotel SW1 *(Private Room 1)*
The Park Lane Hotel W1 *(Smart Rms)*
20 Grand Trafalgar Square WC2 *(Smaller Meeting Rooms)*
Hilton on Park Lane W1 *(Argyll Suite)*
Imperial War Museum London SE1 *(Lower Boardroom)*
The London Art House N1 *(Albert Moore Lounge or Bauhaus Room)*
Mary Ward House WC1 *(Boardroom)*
Royal Horseguards SW1 *(The Terrace or The Waterloo)*
Sheraton Park Tower SW1 *(Discovery Rm)*
18 The Park Lane Hotel W1 *(Drawing Rm)*
16 Aviator GU14 *(3, 4 /5 or 6)*
Phyllis Court RG9 *(Kennet Room)*
15 Dukes Hotel SW1 *(Sheridan Rm)*
14 East Wintergarden E14 *(Promenade Room)*
One Wimpole Street W1 *(Cavendish Boardroom)*
12 Charlotte Street Hotel W1 *(Rm 2)*
The Hospital Club WC2 *(Games Room)*
The Queen's Club W14 *(Real Tennis Museum)*
The Scotch Malt Whisky Society EH2 *(Oval Room)*
Waddesdon Manor, The Dairy HP18 *(Dieppe)*
10 The House NW1 *(Max*)*

£M

17500 Earls Court & Olympia SW5 *(Earl's Court 1*)*
7250 Alexandra Palace & Park N22 *(Great Hall*)*
7000 Earls Court & Olympia SW5 *(Olympia Grand)*
6000 Earls Court & Olympia SW5 *(Earl's Court 2)*
4000 Earls Court & Olympia SW5 *(Olympia National)*
2500 Alexandra Palace & Park N22 *(West Hall)*
2400 The Coliseum WC2 *(Max*)*
2270 London Palladium W1 *(Max*)*
2196 Theatre Royal, Drury Lane WC2 *(Max*)*
2160 Central Hall Westminster SW1 *(Great Hall*)*
2100 Dominion Theatre W1 *(Max*)*
Lyceum Theatre WC2 *(Max*)*
2000 Barbican Art Gallery EC2 *(Max*)*
Earls Court & Olympia SW5 *(Brompton Hall)*
1600 London Metropole W2 *(King's Suite or Monarch Suite*)*
1400 Palace Theatre W1 *(Max*)*
1301 Shaftesbury Theatre WC2 *(Max*)*
1163 Aldwych Theatre WC2 *(Max*)*
1150 National Theatre SE1 *(Max*)*
1000 Newbury Racecourse RG14 *(Grandstand Ground Floor*)*
900 London Marriott W1 *(Westminster Suite*)*
895 Haymarket Theatre SW1 *(Max*)*
886 Noel Coward Theatre WC2 *(Max*)*
826 The Decorium N22 *(Max*)*
800 Aston Villa Hospitality and Events B6 *(Holte Suite*)*
Epsom Downs KT18 *(Oaks Hall*)*
Kensington Conference & Events Centre W8 *(Max*)*
London Metropole W2 *(Palace Suite)*
Wyndham Grand London SW10 *(The Grand Room*)*
790 Comedy Theatre SW1 *(Max*)*
750 Grand Connaught Rooms WC2 *(Grand Hall*)*
Harrow School HA1 *(Max*)*
The Langley WD17 *(Ruby Suite*, Sapphire Suite or Topaz Suite)*
700 Newbury Racecourse RG14 *(Grandstand Second Floor)*
Royal Courts of Justice WC2 *(Max*)*
664 Church House SW1 *(Assembly Hall*)*
650 Riverbank Park Plaza SE1 *(Max*)*
625 Twickenham Experience TW1 *(Max*)*
600 Addington Palace CR0 *(Marquee*)*
Blackheath Concert Halls SE3 *(Max*)*
Lord's Cricket Ground NW8 *(Nursery Pavilion*)*
St Mary's Church W1 *(Max*)*
570 The Coronet SE1 *(Max*)*
565 Whipsnade Wild Animal Park LU6 *(Max*)*
550 The Guoman Tower E1 *(Max*)*
500 Congress Centre WC1 *(Max*)*
Ealing Town Hall W5 *(Max*)*
Harrow School HA1 *(Speech Room)*
The Oval SE11 *(Max*)*
495 City Cruises SE16 *(Sightseeing on Riverliner*)*
470 Duchess Theatre WC2 *(Max*)*
462 IET London: Savoy Place WC2 *(Lecture Theatre*)*
450 Central Hall Westminster SW1 *(Lecture Hall or Library)*
Epsom Downs KT18 *(The Diomed Suit)*
Gibson Hall EC2 *(Max*)*
Jongleurs at Camden Lock NW1 *(Max*)*
432 Fortune Theatre WC2 *(Max*)*
403 Ambassadors Theatre WC2 *(Max*)*
400 Bank of England Sports Centre SW15 *(Terrace Room *)*
Bloomsbury Ballroom WC1 *(Max*)*
Chelsea Physic Garden SW3 *(Garden*)*
Christ Church Spitalfields E1 *(Max*)*
The Comedy Store SW1 *(Max*)*
Museum of London EC2 *(Sackler Hall *)*
One Great George Street SW1 *(Max*)*
Royal College of Music SW7 *(Concert Hall*)*
Vinopolis: The Venue SE1 *(The Mezzanine*)*
380 Royal Court Theatre SW1 *(Jerwood Theatre Downstairs*)*
360 Alexandra Palace & Park N22 *(Palace Restaurant)*
350 Royal College of Music SW7 *(Britten Theatre)*
Studio Valbonne W1 *(Max*)*
325 One Moorgate Place EC2 *(Great Hall*)*

300 Blakemore House Conference and Wedding Venue SG4 *(Garden Room*)*
Crown Moran Hotel NW2 *(Max*)*
Grand Connaught Rooms WC2 *(Edinburgh)*
Inmarsat EC1 *(Max*)*
London Marriott W1 *(Belgrave Rm)*
National Army Museum SW3 *(Max*)*
Newbury Racecourse RG14 *(Berkshire Stand Concourse or Hennessy Suite)*
One Great George Street SW1 *(Great Hall)*
Royal Institute of British Architects W1 *(Max*)*
St Andrew Holborn EC4 *(Max*)*
Swan at the Globe at Shakespeare's Globe SE1 *(Max*)*
Thames Luxury Charters SW15 *(Dixie Queen (cruising) or Dixie Queen (static)*)*
Thorpe Park KT16 *(Lake View Events Zone*)*
Waldorf Hotel WC2 *(Max*)*

280 Park Crescent Conference Centre W1 *(The Theatre*)*
Royal Institute of British Architects W1 *(Jarvis Auditorium)*

275 National Army Museum SW3 *(Art Gallery)*

260 Glaziers' Hall SE1 *(Max*)*

255 The British Library NW1 *(Max*)*

250 Ambassadors Bloomsbury WC1 *(Enterprise*)*
Aston Villa Hospitality and Events B6 *(1874 or Trinity and 82 Lounge)*
Bedford SW12 *(Theatre Room*)*
Central Hall Westminster SW1 *(Aldars Gate)*
Delfina Galleries SE1 *(Exhibition Gallery*)*
Earls Court & Olympia SW5 *(Olympia Conference Centre)*
Epsom Downs KT18 *(The Blue Riband Room)*
Goodenough College WC1 *(Great Hall*)*
London Metropole W2 *(Windsor Suite)*
Lord's Cricket Ground NW8 *(Thomas Lord Suite)*
No 4 Hamilton Place W1 *(Bill Boeing Rm*)*
Ronnie Scotts W1 *(Max*)*
Vinopolis: The Venue SE1 *(Great Halls)*
The Vinyl Factory W1 *(Max*)*

240 The Insurance Hall EC2 *(Max*)*
One Great George Street SW1 *(Telford Theatre)*

230 Carpenters' Hall EC2 *(Max*)*
Church House SW1 *(Hoare Memorial Hall)*
Pacha SW1 *(Main Rm*)*

227 BAFTA, 195 Piccadilly W1 *(Princess Anne Theatre*)*

225 Piccolino - Exchange Square EC2 *(Max*)*

220 Museum of London EC2 *(Weston Theatre)*

210 One Birdcage Walk SW1 *(Lecture Theatre*)*

202 Royal Society of Arts WC2 *(Great Rm*)*

200 BAFTA, 195 Piccadilly W1 *(David Lean Room)*
The CBI Conference Centre WC1 *(Methven*)*
Dominion Theatre W1 *(The Studio)*
Painters' Hall EC4 *(Max*)*
Park Inn London Russell Square WC1 *(Max*)*
Pinewood Studios SL0 *(Ballroom*)*
Royal Statistical Society EC1 *(Lecture Theatre*)*
Savile Club W1 *(Max*)*
St Andrew Holborn EC4 *(Church)*
St Thomas' Hospital SE1 *(Governor's Hall*)*
Twickenham Experience TW1 *(Spirit Of Rugby)*

190 Hellenic Centre W1 *(Great Hall*)*
Kensington Conference & Events Centre W8 *(Small Hall)*

185 ICA SW1 *(Cinema 1*)*

180 Butchers' Hall EC1 *(Max*)*
Church House SW1 *(Harvey Goodwin Suite)*
East Hampstead Park Conference Centre RG40 *(Max*)*
45 Millbank SW1 *(The Banqueting Hall*)*
Forty Hall EN2 *(Max*)*
The Old Sessions House EC1 *(Westminster*)*
The Private Rooms at Buckingham Gate SW1 *(Edwardian 1*)*
SixtyOne Whitehall SW1 *(Duke of Wellington Rm*)*
Sofitel London St James SW1 *(Westminister*)*

175 Ambassadors Bloomsbury WC1 *(Prosper)*
Jasmine Studios W6 *(Max*)*
Paramount WC1 *(Level 31*)*

172 The Geological Society of London W1 *(Lecture Theatre*)*

170 Alexandra Palace & Park N22 *(Londesborough Rm)*
Lansdowne Club W1 *(Ballroom*)*
76 Portland Place W1 *(Rutherford Suite*)*
Tiger Tiger SW1 *(Max*)*

168 ICA SW1 *(Theatre)*
International Coffee Organisation W1 *(Max*)*

166 Lainston House SO21 *(Barn*)*

162 The Magic Circle Headquarters NW1 *(Max*)*

160 Crowne Plaza London - The City EC4 *(Bridewell Room*)*
Highgate School N6 *(Max*)*
The Lincoln Centre WC2 *(Presentation 1*)*
Sofitel London St James SW1 *(Mayfair A&B)*
Tottenham Hotspur N17 *(Bill Nicholson Suite or Pat Jennings Lounge*)*

152 The Old Courtroom BN1 *(Max*)*

150 Addington Palace CR0 *(Great Hall)*
Barber-Surgeons' Hall EC2 *(Max*)*
Blakemore House Conference and Wedding Venue SG4 *(Rosemary Room)*
Browns WC2 *(Courtroom 1*)*
Central Hall Westminster SW1 *(George Thomas)*
City Inn Westminster SW1 *(Private Dining*)*
Coin Street Neighbourhood Centre SE1 *(Max Nasatyr Room* or Neighbourhood Room)*
Courthouse Hotel Kempinski W1 *(Max*)*
Design Museum SE1 *(Design Museum Space*)*
Epsom Downs KT18 *(The Downs View Suit)*
Gibson Hall EC2 *(Garden Rm)*
The Langley WD17 *(Conference Room)*
London Canal Museum N1 *(1st Floor*)*
London Wetland Centre SW13 *(Waters Edge Rm*)*

Menier Chocolate Factory SE1 *(Max*)*
Newbury Racecourse RG14 *(Paddoc View)*
One Great George Street SW1 *(Smeaton Rm)*
Pinewood Studios SL0 *(Pools Theatre)*
Syon Park TW8 *(Max*)*
Tottenham Hotspur N17 *(Steve Perryman Lounge)*
V&A Museum of Childhood E2 *(Max*)*
Vinopolis: The Venue SE1 *(The Gallery)*

144 IET London: Savoy Place WC2 *(Council Chamber)*

140 Aston Villa Hospitality and Events B6 *(McGregors Suite)*
Mayfair Conference Centre W2 *(Max*)*
Royal Air Force Club W1 *(Ballroom*)*
Winchester House SW15 *(River Rm*)*

130 Church House SW1 *(Bishop Partridge Hall)*
City Inn Westminster SW1 *(Max)*
The City Presentation Centre EC1 *(Max*)*
RS Hispaniola WC2 *(Main Deck*)*
Parliament Square (RICS) SW1 *(Max*)*

120 Century W1 *(Rose Langton Room*)*
The City Presentation Centre EC1 *(Theatre)*
Crown Moran Hotel NW2 *(Sala Rm)*
Dartmouth House W1 *(Max*)*
Farmers' & Fletchers' Hall EC1 *(Max*)*
Goodenough College WC1 *(Large Common Room)*
Greenwich Yacht Club SE10 *(Max*)*
Harrow School HA1 *(Old Harrovian Rm)*
Horniman Museum SE23 *(With Marquee*)*
London Transport Museum WC2 *(Cubic Theatre*)*
MIC Hotel & Conference Centre NW1 *(Hilda Porter*)*
National Army Museum SW3 *(Lecture Theatre)*
Syon Park TW8 *(Great Conservatory)*
Trinity House EC3 *(Library*)*

110 Aston Villa Hospitality and Events B6 *(Directors)*
Broadway House SW1 *(Council Chamber*)*
Pewterers' Hall EC2 *(Max*)*
Vanderbilt Hotel SW7 *(Max*)*
Washington W1 *(Richmond Suite*)*

100 Ambassadors Bloomsbury WC1 *(Innovate)*
AOP Gallery (The Association of Photographers) EC2 *(Max*)*
Blakemore House Conference and Wedding Venue SG4 *(Thyme Room)*
Bluebird SW3 *(Beaufort & Gallery Room or Gallery Room*)*
Broadway House SW1 *(Westminister Suite)*
Chelsea Physic Garden SW3 *(Reception Room)*
City of London Club EC2 *(Main Dining Rm*)*
The Cobden Club W10 *(Second Floor*)*
Dartmouth House W1 *(Churchill Rm)*
Delfina Galleries SE1 *(Café Gallery)*
Dominion Theatre W1 *(The Gallery)*
Epsom Downs KT18 *(Lammtarra Suit)*
The Frontline Club W2 *(Max*)*
SS Great Britain BS1 *(Lecture Theatre *)*
Horniman Museum SE23 *(Max)*
Kenwood House (Old Kitchen) NW3 *(Old Kitchen or The Brew House*)*
National Theatre SE1 *(The Deck)*
No 4 Hamilton Place W1 *(Argyll Rm & Terrace)*
One Great George Street SW1 *(Brunel Rm or Council Rm)*
Orangery (Holland Park) W8 *(Max*)*
Park Crescent Conference Centre W1 *(The Gulbekian Room)*
Parliament Square (RICS) SW1 *(Council Chamber or Lecture Hall)*
Pinewood Studios SL0 *(Hitchcock)*
Pitzhanger Manor W5 *(Max*)*
Regent's College NW1 *(Herringham Hall*)*
Royal Institute of British Architects W1 *(Wren)*
Royal Society of Arts WC2 *(Benjamin Franklin Rm)*
Sutton House E9 *(Wenlock Barn (including Café-Bar/Linenfold Parlour)*)*
Thames Luxury Charters SW15 *(Elizabethan)*
Tottenham Hotspur N17 *(Box Holders' West or Gary Mabbutt Lounge)*
Vanderbilt Hotel SW7 *(Victoria & Albert)*
Vinopolis: The Venue SE1 *(Academia)*

94 Courthouse Hotel Kempinski W1 *(Private Cinema)*

90 Addington Palace CR0 *(Winter Garden)*
The Fashion and Textile Museum SE1 *(Max*)*
Fulham Palace SW6 *(Great Hall*)*
RS Hispaniola WC2 *(Upper Deck)*
IET London: Savoy Place WC2 *(Maxwell Suite)*
Rubens SW1 *(Max*)*
76 Portland Place W1 *(Franklin Theatre)*
St Stephen's Club SW1 *(Queensborough Room*)*

84 Fulham Palace SW6 *(Max)*

80 Amadeus Centre W9 *(Lower Hall*)*
Avenue House N3 *(Drawing Rm*)*
Brewers' Hall EC2 *(Max*)*
Butchers' Hall EC1 *(Taurus Suite)*
The CBI Conference Centre WC1 *(Rms 1, 2 & 3)*
Chelsea Physic Garden SW3 *(Lecture Room)*
Chiswick Moran Hotel W4 *(Fairfax Room*)*
City of London Club EC2 *(Garden Rm)*
Crowne Plaza London - The City EC4 *(Bridewell 1)*
Ealing Town Hall W5 *(Nelson Rm)*
Founders' Hall EC1 *(Livery Hall*)*
Gallery Soho WC2 *(Max*)*
House of St Barnabas W1 *(Max*)*
ICA SW1 *(Nash & Brandon Rms)*
IET London: Savoy Place WC2 *(Faraday or Thompson Room)*
The Insurance Hall EC2 *(Court Room)*
London Wetland Centre SW13 *(Theatre)*
Museum of London EC2 *(Terrace Gallery)*
National Army Museum SW3 *(Templer Centre)*
The New Cavendish Club W1 *(Max*)*
Newbury Racecourse RG14 *(Fred Winter)*
Painters' Hall EC4 *(The Court Rm)*

Regent's College NW1 *(Tuke Common Rm)*
Royal Court Theatre SW1 *(Jerwood Theatre Upstairs)*
76 Portland Place W1 *(Hooke Room)*
Southwark Cathedral SE1 *(Garry Weston Library*)*
St Andrew Holborn EC4 *(Courtroom)*
Trinity House EC3 *(Court Rm)*
Vinopolis: The Venue SE1 *(The European Odysey)*

75 The Cobden Club W10 *(First Floor)*
House of St Barnabas W1 *(Chapel)*

70 Brown's Hotel W1 *(Clarendon*)*
Browns WC2 *(Courtroom 2)*
Chutney Mary SW10 *(Max*)*
The Cobden Club W10 *(Ground Floor)*
Groucho Club W1 *(Dining Rm*)*
House of St Barnabas W1 *(Drawing Room)*
Lord's Cricket Ground NW8 *(Media Centre)*
The Old Sessions House EC1 *(London Rm)*
One Birdcage Walk SW1 *(Council)*
One Moorgate Place EC2 *(Main Reception Rm)*
The Place WC1 *(Max*)*
Prenelle Gallery E14 *(Main Gallery*)*
River Lounge E1 *(Max*)*
Royal Institute of British Architects W1 *(Lutyens Rm)*
Ruby Blue WC2 *(Balcony Bar*)*
Sofitel London St James SW1 *(Piccadilly/Bloomsbury)*
Swan at the Globe at Shakespeare's Globe SE1 *(Balcony Rm)*
Tottenham Hotspur N17 *(Danny Blanchflower Suite)*
University Women's Club W1 *(Dining Room, Drawing Room* or Library)*
Watermen's Hall EC3 *(Freemen's Rm*)*

69 Avenue House N3 *(Stephens Rm)*

65 All Hallows EC3 *(Max*)*

64 Thames Luxury Charters SW15 *(Edwardian)*

60 Adam Street WC2 *(Gallery*)*
Aston Villa Hospitality and Events B6 *(Sky Lounge , The Corner Flag, The Park Suite or The Players Lounge)*
BAFTA, 195 Piccadilly W1 *(Run Run Shaw/Mezzanine)*
Bank of England Sports Centre SW15 *(Green Room)*
belowzero restaurant + lounge & ICEBAR LONDON W1 *(Moose Dining Room*, Moose & Reindeer or Whole Venue)*
Central Hall Westminster SW1 *(Dinsdale Young)*
Chartered Institute of Public Finance & Accountancy WC2 *(Conference Rm*, Council Chamber or Room 4)*
Crown Moran Hotel NW2 *(Barnet Rm)*
Epsom Downs KT18 *(The Board Room)*
Grand Connaught Rooms WC2 *(Durham)*
Lansdowne Club W1 *(Shelburne Rm)*
No 4 Hamilton Place W1 *(Council Rm & Foyer)*
The Old Sessions House EC1 *(Jailers Rm)*
One Birdcage Walk SW1 *(Hinton Rm)*
Queen's Eyot SL6 *(Clubhouse*)*
Rivington Place EC2 *(PS2*)*
Royal Institute of British Architects W1 *(Council Chamber)*
Royal Statistical Society EC1 *(Council Chamber)*
Sixteen Park Crescent W1 *(Max*)*
Tottenham Hotspur N17 *(Centenary Lounge or The Goalmouth)*
Waterstone's W1 *(Max*)*

55 Athenaeum Hotel W1 *(Max*)*
Barber-Surgeons' Hall EC2 *(Reception Rm)*
Women's Library E1 *(Clore Seminar Rm*)*

50 Adam Street WC2 *(Rehearsal Rm)*
Alexandra Palace & Park N22 *(Palm Court 5)*
All Star Lanes (Brick Lane) E1 *(Max*)*
Bank of England Sports Centre SW15 *(Balcony Bar)*
HMS Belfast SE1 *(Wardroom and Anteroom*)*
Blakemore House Conference and Wedding Venue SG4 *(Marjoram Room)*
Browns WC2 *(Courtroom 3)*
Dartmouth House W1 *(Small Drawing Rm)*
Dominion Theatre W1 *(The Chaplin Suite)*
Epsom Downs KT18 *(The Gallops Suit)*
Groucho Club W1 *(Gennaro Rm or Mary-Lou)*
Hellenic Centre W1 *(Boardroom)*
RS Hispaniola WC2 *(Board Rm)*
IET London: Savoy Place WC2 *(Common Room)*
MIC Hotel & Conference Centre NW1 *(Epworth)*
Newbury Racecourse RG14 *(Royal Box)*
One Birdcage Walk SW1 *(Napier)*
Park Crescent Conference Centre W1 *(The Club Room)*
The Private Rooms at Buckingham Gate SW1 *(Edwardian II)*
Royal Society of Arts WC2 *(Adelphi or Tavern Rm)*
Sutton House E9 *(Marriage Suite (Great and Little Chambers))*
Tottenham Hotspur N17 *(Box Holders' North)*
Vinopolis: The Venue SE1 *(The New World Odyssey or The Vineyard)*
Washington W1 *(Winchester)*
The Zetter Hotel EC1 *(Max*)*

45 ICA SW1 *(Cinema 2)*
Kew Bridge Steam Museum TW8 *(The Babcock Meeting Room*)*
The Lincoln Centre WC2 *(Presentation 2)*
MIC Hotel & Conference Centre NW1 *(Alice)*
76 Portland Place W1 *(Phillips Room)*

40 Addington Palace CR0 *(Dining Room or Robing Room)*
BAFTA, 195 Piccadilly W1 *(Run Run Shaw)*
Bluebird SW3 *(Beaufort Room)*
Broadway House SW1 *(Abbey Room)*
Chiswick Moran Hotel W4 *(Fairfax East or Fairfax West)*
Church House SW1 *(Westminster)*
Grand Connaught Rooms WC2 *(Penthouse)*
House of St Barnabas W1 *(Bazelgette Room, Monro Room or Silk Room)*
Mandeville Hotel W1 *(Red Room*)*
Namco Station SE1 *(Private Party Area*)*
No 4 Hamilton Place W1 *(Handley Page Rm or Sopwith Rm)*
The Old Sessions House EC1 *(Recorder Rm)*

One Birdcage Walk SW1 *(Courses Rm)*
One Moorgate Place EC2 *(Members' Rm)*
Pacha SW1 *(Funky Rm)*
Parliament Square (RICS) SW1 *(Brussels Room)*
The Private Rooms at Buckingham Gate SW1 *(Taj)*
Regent's College NW1 *(Knapp Gallery)*
Royal Institute of British Architects W1 *(Aston Webb)*
Sailing Barge Will E1 *(Max*)*
76 Portland Place W1 *(Ada Lovelace Room or Herschel Room)*
Sofitel London St James SW1 *(Kensington)*
Soho House W1 *(Roof Deck*)*
Southwark Cathedral SE1 *(The JTW Room)*
St Andrew Holborn EC4 *(Crypt)*
Twickenham Experience TW1 *(Council Rm)*
Vanderbilt Hotel SW7 *(Edwardian)*
Washington W1 *(Fairfax)*
Watermen's Hall EC3 *(Court Rm)*
Wyndham Grand London SW10 *(Albert Suite or Battersea)*

39 Ambassadors Bloomsbury WC1 *(Create or Think)*
38 The Cadogan SW1 *(Salon Lillie*)*
36 Ruby Blue WC2 *(Conference)*
35 Addington Palace CR0 *(Wellington Room)*
Ambassadors Bloomsbury WC1 *(Vision)*
Aston Villa Hospitality and Events B6 *(The Champions Lounge)*
Avenue House N3 *(Salon)*
Bluebird SW3 *(Mezzanine)*
Broadway House SW1 *(Lawrence)*
Coin Street Neighbourhood Centre SE1 *(Fred Miller 1&2)*
Radisson Edwardian Berkshire Hotel W1 *(Sonning Suite*)*
The Kingly Club W1 *(Max*)*
32 Broadway House SW1 *(The Whittle Room)*
30 Addington Palace CR0 *(Empire Room)*
Alexandra Palace & Park N22 *(Palm Court 2/3)*
BAFTA, 195 Piccadilly W1 *(Gallery)*
Bluebird SW3 *(Bluebird Room)*
City of London Club EC2 *(City Room)*
East Hampstead Park Conference Centre RG40 *(Windsor)*
The Guoman Tower E1 *(Mortimer Suite)*
House of St Barnabas W1 *(Garden Room)*
Hoxton Hotel EC2 *(Room 3*)*
Malmaison Hotel EC1 *(Mal 1*)*
Museum of London EC2 *(Garden Room)*
Museum of Transport G3 *(Cinema*)*
One Great George Street SW1 *(Stephenson Rm)*
Pinewood Studios SL0 *(Pine)*
The Place WC1 *(Theatre Bar)*
Royal Society of Arts WC2 *(Romney)*
Southwark Cathedral SE1 *(Chapter Room or The New Room)*
Thames Luxury Charters SW15 *(Golden Salamander)*
Waldorf Hotel WC2 *(Aldwych Suite)*
Winchester House SW15 *(Library)*
27 Soho House W1 *(Cinema)*
25 Alexandra Palace & Park N22 *(Palm Court 4)*
Avenue House N3 *(Dining Rm)*
Benjamin Franklin House WC2 *(Franklin's Parlour*)*
Coin Street Neighbourhood Centre SE1 *(Lil Patrick 1&2)*
Coopers' Hall EC2 *(Court Rm*)*
Founders' Hall EC1 *(Parlour)*
MIC Hotel & Conference Centre NW1 *(Wesley)*
The Private Rooms at Buckingham Gate SW1 *(Buckingham)*
Vanderbilt Hotel SW7 *(Harrington)*
20 Avenue House N3 *(Study Rm)*
belowzero restaurant + lounge & ICEBAR LONDON W1 *(Reindeer Lounge Bar)*
Benjamin Franklin House WC2 *(Mrs Stevenson's Parlour or Seminar Room)*
Blakemore House Conference and Wedding Venue SG4 *(Sage Room)*
Browns WC2 *(Courtroom 4)*
Church House SW1 *(Jubilee)*
Dominion Theatre W1 *(The Garland Suite)*
Farmers' & Fletchers' Hall EC1 *(Court Rm)*
Lansdowne Club W1 *(Findlay Rm)*
London Canal Museum N1 *(Meeting Rm)*
MIC Hotel & Conference Centre NW1 *(Exeter, Norfolk or Whitfield)*
The New Cavendish Club W1 *(Library)*
Rivington Place EC2 *(Meeting Room)*
Royal Statistical Society EC1 *(New Meeting Rm)*
Watermen's Hall EC3 *(The Silver Rm)*
Women's Library E1 *(Activties Rm)*
18 Hoxton Hotel EC2 *(Room 2)*
16 Sutton House E9 *(Linenfold Parlour)*
14 Malmaison Hotel EC1 *(Mal 2)*
Painters' Hall EC4 *(Painted Chamber)*
12 Chartered Institute of Public Finance & Accountancy WC2 *(Room 5)*
The Lincoln Centre WC2 *(Central Boardroom)*
Newbury Racecourse RG14 *(Private Boxes)*
The Scotch Malt Whisky Society EC1 *(Max*)*

£B-M

5000 ExCeL London E16 *(ICC Capital Hall*)*
3000 The International Convention Centre B1 *(Hall 3*)*
2000 The International Convention Centre B1 *(Symphony Hall)*
1190 ExCeL London E16 *(ICC Capital Suite)*
1125 ExCeL London E16 *(Platinum Suite)*
1000 London School of Economics WC2 *(Max*)*
The Royal Horticultural Halls SW1 *(Lawrence Hall*)*
900 Hammersmith Town Hall W6 *(Max*)*
825 The International Convention Centre B1 *(Hall 4)*
750 Imperial College London SW7 *(Great Hall*)*
Royal Geographical Society SW7 *(Theatre*)*
700 Old Truman Brewery E1 *(Max*)*
600 Mermaid Conference & Events Centre EC4 *(Auditorium*)*
550 BAC SW11 *(Max*)*
535 Bloomsbury Theatre WC1 *(Max*)*

500 City University EC1 *(Great Hall*)*
Streatham Ice Arena SW16 *(Max*)*
450 The HAC EC1 *(Prince Consort Rooms*)*
The Royal Horticultural Halls SW1 *(Lindley Hall)*
444 Riverside Studios W6 *(Max*)*
440 Chelsea Old Town Hall SW3 *(Main Hall*)*
Royal Institution of Great Britain W1 *(Max*)*
421 Greenwich Theatre SE10 *(Max*)*
420 Kings Place N1 *(Hall One*)*
400 Arts Depot N12 *(Main Auditorium*)*
Conway Hall WC1 *(Max*)*
Debut London SE1 *(Main*)*
Fulham Town Hall SW6 *(Max*)*
Riverside Studios W6 *(Studio 2)*
Royal Holloway College TW20 *(Windsor Auditorium*)*
Whitechapel Art Gallery E1 *(Max*)*
390 King's College WC2 *(Lecture Theatre*)*
St Paul's Church W1 *(Max*)*
380 Dulwich College SE21 *(Great Hall*)*
360 City University EC1 *(Oliver Thompson Lecture Theatre)*
350 Debut London SE1 *(Blue)*
Mall Galleries SW1 *(Main Gallery*)*
345 The International Convention Centre B1 *(Hall 11)*
320 Bishopsgate Institute EC2 *(Great Hall*)*
308 Cochrane Theatre WC1 *(Auditorium*)*
300 The International Convention Centre B1 *(Hall 8)*
Polka Theatre for Children SW19 *(Max*)*
Proud Camden NW1 *(Max*)*
St Paul's Church W1 *(Church Area)*
Tricycle Theatre NW6 *(Cinema*)*
University of London Union WC1 *(Max*)*
University of Westminster NW1 *(Hogg Lecture Theatre*)*
Victory Services Club W2 *(Carisbrooke Hall*)*
280 Bishopsgate Institute EC2 *(Max)*
278 Egg N7 *(Max*)*
275 New Players Theatre WC2 *(Max*)*
260 Bishopsgate Institute EC2 *(Upper Hall)*
250 Royal Over-Seas League SW1 *(Max*)*
239 Tricycle Theatre NW6 *(Theatre)*
230 Balls Brothers Minster Pavement EC3 *(Max*)*
224 London Scottish SW1 *(Max*)*
220 Balls Brothers Minster Pavement EC3 *(Minster Suite)*
Lotus Chinese Floating Restaurant E14 *(Max*)*
Music Room W1 *(Max*)*
Old Finsbury Town Hall EC1 *(Great Hall*)*
200 Bush Hall W12 *(Max*)*
Debut London SE1 *(Grey Arch or Red)*
Fabric EC1 *(Max*)*
Fulham Town Hall SW6 *(Concert Hall)*
Guy's Hospital SE1 *(Governor's Hall*)*
The Irish Centre W6 *(Max*)*
King's College WC2 *(Great Hall)*
Kings Place N1 *(Battlebridge Room or Hall Two)*
The Pavilion B6 *(Pearson Suite*)*
Proud Cabaret EC3 *(Max*)*
The Rag Factory E1 *(Max*)*
Royal Holloway College TW20 *(Founder's Dining Hall or Picture Gallery)*
Tudor Barn Eltham SE9 *(Max*)*
20th Century Theatre W11 *(Max*)*
Worx SW6 *(Studio 1* or Studio 2)*
196 School of Pharmacy WC1 *(John Hanbury Lecture Theatre*)*
University of Westminster NW1 *(Old Cinema)*
184 School of Pharmacy WC1 *(Maplethorpe Theatre)*
180 BAC SW11 *(Lower Hall)*
City University EC1 *(Cass main auditorium)*
Dulwich College SE21 *(Max)*
Rich Mix E1 *(Max*)*
156 Riverside Studios W6 *(Studio 4)*
150 Arts Depot N12 *(Studio Theatre)*
Chelsea Old Town Hall SW3 *(The Small Hall)*
Fulham House SW6 *(Max*)*
The HAC EC1 *(Long Rm)*
Old Truman Brewery E1 *(Bridge)*
Tab Centre E2 *(Main Hall*)*
Victory Services Club W2 *(El Alamein Rm)*
The Village Underground EC2 *(Max*)*
140 City Hotel E1 *(Max*)*
136 Royal College of Art SW7 *(Lecture Theatre 1*)*
130 Docklands Sailing & Watersports Centre E14 *(Max*)*
The Little Ship Club EC4 *(Max*)*
120 Canning House SW1 *(Max*)*
Dulwich College SE21 *(Lower Hall or Old Library)*
Hoxton Hall N1 *(Theatre*)*
The Mary Sumner House SW1 *(Conference Hall*)*
Mermaid Conference & Events Centre EC4 *(Clifford Rm or Studio)*
Oxford House E2 *(Max*)*
St Martin In The Fields WC2 *(St Martins Hall*)*
110 Guy's Hospital SE1 *(Robens Suite)*
100 Artworkers Guild, The WC1 *(Lecture Hall*)*
Kings Place N1 *(St Pancras Room)*
Linden House W6 *(Ballroom*)*
Mermaid Conference & Events Centre EC4 *(Miles Rm)*
Old Finsbury Town Hall EC1 *(Council Chamber)*
St Botolph's Hall EC2 *(Max*)*
90 Balls Brothers Minster Pavement EC3 *(St Giles)*
ExCeL London E16 *(Gallery Meeting Rooms)*
St Paul's Church W1 *(Blue Lounge)*
84 Greenwich Playhouse SE10 *(Max*)*
New End Theatre NW3 *(Max*)*
80 Bakers' Hall EC3 *(Max*)*
Photographers' Gallery W1 *(Max*)*
Polka Theatre for Children SW19 *(Studio Theatre)*
70 Canning House SW1 *(Library)*
Fitzroy Square W1 *(Max*)*
Victory Services Club W2 *(Trafalgar Rm)*
67 Imperial College London SW7 *(Council Rm)*
65 Theatre 503 at the Latchmere Pub SW11 *(Max*)*
60 Bakers' Hall EC3 *(Court Rm)*
Balls Brothers Minster Pavement EC3 *(St Claves or St Margaret's)*
Burgh House NW3 *(Max*)*
Canal Café Theatre W2 *(Max*)*
Fulham House SW6 *(Dining Rm)*

Hammersmith Town Hall W6 *(Marble Gallery)*
The Little Ship Club EC4 *(Library)*
Mall Galleries SW1 *(East Gallery)*
Royal Institution of Great Britain W1 *(Library)*
Trafalgar Events WC2 *(Orange Room, Purple Room* or Red Room)*
55 Apartment 195 SW3 *(Cellar*)*
50 Arts Depot N12 *(Dance Space)*
The Chapel Bar N1 *(Max*)*
Debut London SE1 *(Hide Out)*
The HAC EC1 *(Ante Room or Queen's Rm)*
Tamarai WC2 *(Max*)*
Tudor Barn Eltham SE9 *(Heritage Centre)*
Victory Services Club W2 *(Grill Rm)*
Worx SW6 *(Studio 4)*
45 Oxford House E2 *(Scott Rm)*
Tamarai WC2 *(Screening Room)*
40 Imperial College London SW7 *(Solar)*
The Mary Sumner House SW1 *(Mary Sumner Rm, Princess Elizabeth or Princess Victoria)*
Old Finsbury Town Hall EC1 *(Yellow Room)*
Trafalgar Events WC2 *(Blue Room)*
38 Guy's Hospital SE1 *(Court Rm)*
37 Kings Place N1 *(Limehouse Room)*
35 City Hotel E1 *(Lane Suite Rm 3)*
Victory Services Club W2 *(Allenby Rm)*
32 Kings Place N1 *(Wenlock Room)*
30 Artworkers Guild, The WC1 *(Gradidge Room)*
Bishopsgate Institute EC2 *(Elleyne Room)*
Linden House W6 *(Commodore's Rm)*
Madsen Restaurant SW7 *(Max*)*
The Mary Sumner House SW1 *(Princess Alexandra or Princess Beatrice)*
25 Guy's Hospital SE1 *(Senior Staff Room)*
The Mary Sumner House SW1 *(Princess Mary)*
The Research House W1 *(Studio 1* or Studio 2)*
24 Kings Place N1 *(Horsfall Room)*
Royal Holloway College TW20 *(Large Boardroom)*
Victory Services Club W2 *(Committee Rm)*
20 Linden House W6 *(Captain's Rm)*
Old Finsbury Town Hall EC1 *(Wedding Room)*
Oxford House E2 *(Classroom)*
Worx SW6 *(Studio 3)*
18 Bishopsgate Institute EC2 *(Boardroom)*
The Mary Sumner House SW1 *(Princess Helena)*
The Research House W1 *(Studio 3)*
16 Royal Holloway College TW20 *(Small Boardroom)*
Victory Services Club W2 *(Chetwode Rm)*
10 Madsen Restaurant SW7 *(Private Dining Room)*

£B

2000 Troxy E1 *(Grand Hall*)*
800 Queen Mary College E1 *(Great Hall*)*
748 Wandsworth Civic Suite SW18 *(Max*)*
400 Westminster Cathedral Hall SW1 *(Max*)*
300 Lowiczanka Restaurant W6 *(Max*)*
229 The Venue W1 *(Venue 1*)*
229 W1 *(Venue 1*)*
250 The Ministry of Sound SE1 *(Max*)*
Sway WC2 *(Max*)*
240 JuJu SW3 *(Max*)*
200 The London Welsh Centre WC1 *(Max*)*
163 Jacksons Lane N6 *(Theatre*)*
150 Gate Street Barn GU5 *(Max*)*
St Bride Foundation EC4 *(Bridewell Hall*)*
Sway WC2 *(Crystal Lounge)*
130 King's Head Theatre N1 *(Max*)*
100 London Rowing Club SW15 *(Long Rm*)*
Troxy E1 *(White Room)*
80 Chatham Hall SW11 *(Max*)*
60 St Bride Foundation EC4 *(Farringdon Rm)*
50 London Rowing Club SW15 *(Fairbairn Rm)*
St Bride Foundation EC4 *(Salisbury Rm)*
40 JuJu SW3 *(Ground Floor or JuJu Lounge)*
St Bride Foundation EC4 *(Layton)*
30 St Bride Foundation EC4 *(Parssmore Edwards Rm)*
25 London Rowing Club SW15 *(Members Rm)*

Alphabetical
Index of Services

Notes

Notes

Notes